C000265471

First published June 1991
Second edition published June 1993
Third edition published April 1995
Fourth edition published November 1997
Fifth edition published June 2000
Sixth edition published October 2002
Seventh edition published July 2005
Eighth edition published November 2008
© The Vegan Society

ISBN 978-0-907337-31-7

Design by Doughnut Design – www.doughnutdesign.co.uk

Printed on recycled paper by Westpoint Print

Published by
The Vegan Society
Donald Watson House, 21 Hylton Street, Hockley,
Birmingham B18 6HJ, United Kingdom
Local rate 0845 45 88244 Tel.0121 523 1730
Fax. 0121 523 1749
www.vegansociety.com
Registered Charity number 279228
Company Registration number 1468880
VAT Registration number 448 5973 95

CONTENTS

● Although, as far as is practical, the publisher has taken care to ensure the accuracy and reliability of information supplied to it, the reader should bear in mind that manufacturers may make alterations to the constituents, derivation and testing of their products *at any time*. The diligent animal free shopper always checks a product's ingredients listing (where one is provided!) before making a purchase.

● The absence of an (apparently) animal free product does not necessarily mean it does not meet the Society's **ANIMAL FREE CRITERIA** (page 42). Product categories that are obviously or typically animal-free (tinned fruit, tea, coffee, nuts, dried pulses, beans, peanut butter etc) have been excluded. Additionally, despite repeated approaches, some manufacturers/distributors (including a number whose products have appeared in previous editions) failed, or simply refused to supply the information requested.

● In order to make effective use of this guide, it is suggested that the new reader familiarises him/herself with the location of the **KEY** (page iii) and **CONTENTS** (page i) — and, at least initially, regularly consults the **PRODUCT INDEX** (page 414).

● The inclusion of a product should not be construed as constituting Vegan Society approval for the product, its intended use, or its manufacturer/distributor (see **OTHER ETHICAL CONSIDERATIONS**, page 50).

● The listing of products under 'Healthcare' is not intended to take the place of advice provided by health care professionals.

● The guide is also now online at ***www.animalfreeshopper.com*** and is updated frequently. All you have to do is register free of charge, log in and search under manufacturer, product type or product name.

KEY

The entire range of the company's products is animal-free
(see **ANIMAL FREE CRITERIA**, page 42) ☺

The company is an authorised user of the Vegan Society Trade Mark
(but not all its animal-free products may be registered)
(see **VEGAN SOCIETY TRADE MARK**, page 8) **TM**

The company has at least one vegan proprietor ❶

The company's entire product range is organic ☼

The company has a policy of ensuring that (as far as is possible and ⊘
practical) the production of its products has not involved the use of
genetically modified material
(see **GENETICALLY-MODIFIED ORGANISMS**, page 49)

The company has a policy of not 🐾
conducting nor commissioning animal testing

The company has signed up to the Humane Cosmetics Standard 👁
(see **ANIMAL TESTING CRITERIA**, page 48)

The company has a policy of using only ingredients which have not ✂
been tested on animals by, or at the initiative of, the company or its
suppliers since a specified date (Note: In the product listings, the year
follows this symbol — eg a1976 cut-off date appears as ✂1976)
(see **ANIMAL TESTING CRITERIA**, page 48)

Food and Drink products in **bold** are registered to use
The Vegan Society Trade Mark

w = with (product listings only)

SOCIETY

people ■ animals ■ environmen

WWW.VEGANSOCIETY.COM

Log on to the website of the world's premiere vegan organisation.

■ Shop securely online for Vegan Society goods
■ View listings of all Vegan registered products
■ Become a member
■ View Factsheets
■ Information
■ News and developments
■ 'Why Go Vegan' section
■ Links to other great vegan/veggie web pages

Return for updates and latest information

THE NO. 1 SITE FOR VEGAN SURFING

INTRODUCTION

Welcome to the eighth edition of the *Animal Free Shopper*, The Vegan Society's indispensable guide to each and every vegan product we are aware of on sale in the UK. The Vegan Society has now been established for more than 60 years, and animal-free products have never been easier to get hold of!

Veganism is increasingly mainstream, and no longer viewed as a bizarre 'fad' diet. Veganism is regularly featured in newspapers and magazines; the number of vegan guides, cookbooks and publications continues to grow. An increased awareness of the realities of animal exploitation has meant that many people are cutting down on their consumption of animal products and searching for cruelty-free alternatives.

With the release of the United Nations (UN) report *Livestock's Long Shadow,* environmental organisations are now starting to acknowledge that a reduction in the consumption of animal products would significantly benefit the environment and help to tackle climate change.

The UK's obesity crisis is of concern to many people, and studies have consistently found vegans to be less likely to be obese than meat-eaters. The consumption of greater quantities of fresh fruit, vegetables and whole grains is now widely encouraged by the UK government's 'five a day' programme, and increasingly lentils, beans and pulses are accepted into the mainstream as nutritious foods. Finally, the 'Meat Free' and 'Dairy Free' markets are among the fastest growing in today's food sector.

While the labelling of products is improving all the time, there are few things worse than scrutinising an ingredients list only to be confronted with obscure names, arrays of E numbers, or the dreaded unspecified 'flavourings'. By carrying this pocket-sized guide with you, it's easy and hassle-free to choose from thousands of animal-free products.

With the *Animal Free Shopper*, the hard work is already done for you. We've contacted hundreds of manufacturers - not just of food and drink, but also of toiletries, cosmetics, clothing and other products - to find out which of their products are vegan, and we have used that information to compile this easy-to-use guide.

The *Animal Free Shopper* includes products from supermarkets and independent retailers as well as guidance on additives and E numbers. In terms of background information on veganism, the *Animal Free Shopper* also includes a section on nutrition and some facts and figures about animal exploitation. There are so many reasons to go vegan, for the benefit of people, animals and the environment, that the question is no longer 'why vegan?', but rather 'why not?'.

MISSING, PRESUMED VEGAN

Although we've tried to make the *Animal Free Shopper* as comprehensive as possible, you may still come across products that are vegan but are not listed. There are a number of reasons for this, the main ones being:

- companies failing to respond to our requests for information
- lack of confidence on the part of the compilers that the manufacturers/suppliers really understand the ANIMAL-FREE CRITERIA (see page 42)
- companies supplying incomplete or inadequate product information.

PLAYING DETECTIVE

Though experienced in investigating the animal-free credentials of a product, there are limits to The Vegan Society's capabilities. Food processing technology is a vast, complex and rapidly changing subject. Unless we obtain evidence to the contrary - or the details provided are clearly suspect - The Vegan Society has to accept the information provided (normally in the form of a written declaration) in good faith.

However, playing detective isn't the sole province of The Vegan Society. Enquiries from members of the public are often more effective than those from an organisation, so please do contact companies if you would like to see changes in their formulations or labelling. Use the ANIMAL-FREE CRITERIA (see page 42) as the basis for your approach, and check ADDITIVES (see page 43) to identify E numbers that could be animal derived. You will quickly be able to determine whether the person responding to your enquiry is sufficiently knowledgeable to provide you with plausible product information.

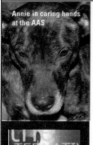

Confirming the animal-free status of a product can be thrilling, but be prepared for frustration and disappointment on occasion! That said, discovering that an apparently animal-free product is not suitable certainly isn't wasted effort. Manufacturers take note of consumer interest and will, sooner or later, act. An example of a company deciding to alter their product in response to demand for animal-free goods is Granovita developing a vegan Worcestershire sauce.

In addition to drawing the attention of manufacturers to the unmet needs of animal-free shoppers, it is equally important to tell them that you buy their products precisely because they are animal-free!

It is all too easy to complain and accuse companies of 'discriminating against vegans' or 'condoning animal suffering', but letters and phone calls of an encouraging nature are likely to elicit a receptive response and, ultimately, produce the desired outcome.

LOOKING AHEAD . . .

Research for the *Animal Free Shopper* never ceases, and The Vegan Society needs you to be part of this process! If you stumble across a new animal-free product, or discover that a manufacturer has introduced an animal ingredient into a product that was previously animal-free, please share your findings by contacting us at:

The Vegan Society
Donald Watson House
21 Hylton Street
Hockley
Birmingham
West Midlands
B18 6HJ

t 0121 523 1730
f 0121 523 1749
e info@vegansociety.com

A LITTLE BIT ABOUT THE VEGAN SOCIETY

The Vegan Society promotes ways of living free from animal products, for the benefit of people, animals and the environment.

Established in November 1944, the Society was founded by a group of vegetarians who had recognised the ethical compromises implicit in lacto-vegetarianism. Among the founding members was Donald Watson, who coined the word 'vegan' by taking the first three and last two letters of 'vegetarian'.

Today, The Vegan Society continues to highlight the problems caused by an unhealthy dependence on animal products. We are a registered educational charity, focused on the provision of information on all aspects of veganism. We publish a quarterly magazine, *The Vegan*, which is free to members and available to buy in some health food shops or directly from the Society. We also publish several books and a variety of leaflets, booklets and information sheets. The Society's

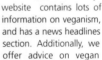

website contains lots of information on veganism, and has a news headlines section. Additionally, we offer advice on vegan pregnancy and parenting, have an interactive CD-ROM and run a school speakers programme. The message of The Vegan Society is simple: **go vegan - for people, animals and the environment.**

The Vegan Society needs funds to continue its work; if you would like to support the work please consider becoming a member so you can help us continue to promote compassionate vegan living. You can join the Society using the membership form at the back of this book, through our online shop at *www.vegansociety.com/shop*, or by calling 0121 523 1740. Thank you very much for your vital support.

LOCAL CONTACTS

In addition to our offices in Birmingham, The Vegan Society has a large network of local contacts throughout the UK. These are members who have offered to act as a point of contact for those interested in the Society's work. So if you are interested in becoming more involved in local campaigning, or if you need advice on being vegan in your area, they are the people to speak to.

Details of Vegan Society Local Contacts and Local Groups are published in *The Vegan* or are available on request. If you would like to become a local contact please contact the information department by calling 0121 523 1735/6 or emailing info@vegansociety.com.

OUR TRADEMARK

You will notice that some of the products listed in the *Animal Free Shopper* are highlighted in bold. These are the products that, at the time of going to press, were registered to use The Vegan Society's trademark sunflower logo.

The trademark was conceived as a way of helping people to shop for animal-free products. Only The Vegan Society registered products carry the trademark.

The trademark allows consumers to make easy, informed choices about the suitability of purchases, and enables us to work with companies who are willing to recognise their vegan customers. With thousands of items now bearing our familiar logo, and through international recognition of the trademark, our influence has never been greater. We have registered vegan alternatives to just about everything: vegan ice cream, margarine, cheese, fish fingers, wines, chocolate and even champagne. The trademark also covers household items such as cosmetics and bath products, cleaners and soaps, and has attracted a lot of interest from producers of remedies and supplements.

Have a flick through the guidebook to see the huge number and variety of animal-free products that are registered with us, and remember to ask the manufacturer of your favourite products whether they have registered with us yet!

VEGAN SOCIETY TRADEMARK STANDARD

The Vegan Society Trademark Criteria
Setting criteria for animal-free products is not as straightforward as it might at first appear. The standards that our Trademark holders are required to meet are as follows:

Animal Ingredients
The manufacture and/or development of the product, and where applicable its ingredients, must not involve, or have involved, the use of any animal product, by-product or derivative.

Animal Testing
The development and/or manufacture of the product, and where applicable its ingredients, must not involve, or have involved, testing of any sort on animals conducted at the initiative of the manufacturer or on its behalf, or by parties over whom the manufacturer has effective control. We do not accept products that have been developed using the 'five year rolling rule'.

Genetically Modified Organisms
The development and/or production of genetically modified organisms (GMO) must not have involved animal genes or animal-derived substances. Products put forward for registration which contain or may contain any GMOs must be labelled as such.

Animals
The Vegan Society understands the word "animal" to refer to the entire Animal Kingdom, that is all vertebrates and all multicellular invertebrates.

However we have to accept that some accidental contamination from animal substances is likely in many situations. Insect remains may occur in foods such as fruit, vegetables, flour and spices.

Even after thorough cleaning some cross-contamination may occur on production lines that are not dedicated to vegan products.

Chocolate production is a particular problem since production lines are not cleaned with detergent and water in between different products. Instead some of the next product is used to flush out the previous product and then discarded. This means that low levels of dairy contamination are likely if a vegan chocolate is manufactured after a milk chocolate. The only way to avoid this is to operate a completely vegan production area.

Even then manufacturers could not claim their product contains zero animal cross-contamination. To make such a claim would require the manufacturer to test every batch of every ingredient for animal contamination. A further problem is that the detection levels for the test methods do not go as low as zero. For example the detection limit for lactose is 70 parts per million (ppm) and so if this test produces a negative result a manufacturer can claim only that the product is known to contain less than 70 ppm of lactose.

Allergen labelling has caused confusion over whether some products can be classed as vegan.

There are currently fourteen allergens that must be labelled on foods and these include crustaceans, fish, milk, eggs and molluscs.

Under food-safety regulations companies are required to conduct a risk assessment to determine whether the foods they produce may contain any of the known allergens. If they establish that there is a risk and that risk cannot be eliminated then they must include a 'may contain...' label on the pack.

The ingredients list provides details of substances that have been deliberately added while the 'may contain' list gives details of allergens that could be present at a low level due to cross-contamination.

The Vegan Society does not claim that trademarked products are suitable for people with allergies; that will depend on the standards achieved by individual manufacturers.

To encourage manufacturers to give a serious commitment to avoiding animal cross-contamination the following statement has been added to the Trademark licence agreement:

I confirm that our company strives diligently to minimise cross-contamination from animal substances used in other (non-vegan) products as far as is reasonably practicable.

However we accept that some trademarked products may also carry warning labels such as 'may contain milk' because this refers to accidental low-level cross-contamination.

We live in an imperfect world and if we made the Trademark criteria any more stringent we could have very few products labelled vegan. We aim at encouraging manufacturers to produce more foods that do not contain deliberately added animal ingredients and so reduce the exploitation of animals. If our demands are unrealistic many manufacturers will ignore us.

As the demand for vegan products grows we will be in a stronger position to request dedicated vegan production lines and then purely vegan factories.

WHY ANIMAL-FREE?

Well, why not? By adopting a vegan diet you can:

- help stop animal exploitation and slaughter
- considerably reduce your environmental impact
- avoid contributing to the hunger of the world's poorest people
- start to feel good about the choices you make every day.

Let's start with the most common reason for going vegan...

FOR THE ANIMALS

Animals slaughtered for meat in the UK in 2007:

	Cattle	2,723,000
	Pigs	9,084,000
	Sheep	15,979,000
	Fowl	839,000,000
	Turkeys	15,000,000
	Ducks & Geese	17,000,000

Source: DEFRA website
http://statistics.defra.gov.uk/esg/publications/auk/2007/

The figures left do not include fish, male chicks that are killed as by-products of the poultry and egg industries, rabbits, or deer that are killed. So the true figure for animals killed in the UK each year exceeds one billion animals (one thousand million).

These animals all die unnecessarily, but it's how they lived that's the real tragedy. Despite free range farming being widely discussed in the media, the vast majority of farmed animals continue to be intensively reared. Over 95% of poultry meat is intensively farmed in England, while over 60% of eggs come from battery systems. All farming systems exploit animals, and farmed animals are slaughtered at a fraction of their natural lifespan.

POULTRY

Chickens raised for meat are known as 'broilers'. The majority of those reared each year in the UK are factory farmed. They are kept permanently indoors in huge windowless sheds so overcrowded that the floor can barely be seen.

A major welfare problem is that the birds have been selectively bred to reach their slaughter weight in 40-42 days, which is half the time taken 35 years ago. The lifespan of a natural chicken is 7-12 years.

While the muscle grows quickly enough, the supporting structure of legs, joints, heart and lungs fails to keep pace. As a result, every year millions of chickens suffer from painful, sometimes crippling leg disorders, while millions more die of heart failure. By the time they reach slaughter weight, many of them can barely walk to their feeding areas.

An investigation into broiler systems by Compassion in World Farming found crippled birds unable to reach food and drink, trampled carcasses, and piles of decomposing bodies left to rot.

Chickens may be subject to painful mutilations including debeaking, a process which removes the tip of the beak. Debeaking is carried out to reduce mortality as a result of the confined and frustrated birds fighting with each other. Debeaking can cause death from shock or loss of blood.

PIGS

Pigs raised for meat are often kept indoors in overcrowded, ill-lit, barren conditions. More than half of the fattening pigs raised in the UK are not provided with straw; instead they are forced to sleep on bare floors, leading to extreme discomfort and stress.

Sows kept for breeding normally give birth to their piglets in farrowing crates. These small cramped containers, in which sows are unable to turn around, and allow very little space in which to move or lie down comfortably. Sows remain locked in the farrowing crate for 3-4 weeks, until the piglets are weaned. Those justifying the use of farrowing crates say they are designed to reduce piglet mortality by preventing the mother from rolling onto and crushing her piglets. However, studies have shown that farrowing crate systems have similar mortality rates to higher-welfare outdoor systems. In reality, farrowing crate systems are more cost effective, and simplify the management of the animals.

Sow stalls are narrow stalls where pregnant sows are kept for the duration of their pregnancy. Sow stalls were banned in the UK in 1999, but their use will not be fully phased out in the rest of Europe until 2013.

Piglets would naturally be weaned at about four to five months, but they are often removed before four weeks, causing great stress to both mother and babies. But the piglets' traumatic existence has only just begun: in their short lives they will endure painful mutilations such as tail docking and teeth clipping to prevent the distressed animals from fighting and tail chewing. Males may be castrated. These procedures are often carried out by unqualified persons and without anaesthetic. The piglets are put into small pens or metal cages, and after about six weeks go to fattening pens where they have little room to move and no fresh air. Most pigs are slaughtered at six months of age. Pigs can live to an age of 15-20 years if left to live out their natural lifespan.

BEEF CATTLE

Cattle bred for beef may be kept in a variety of systems; frequently they are kept in windowless fattening sheds or in finishing yards before being rounded up and transported for slaughter.

They are often subjected to a range of painful procedures. Male calves are castrated surgically, through the use of tight rubber rings that restrict blood flow, or by crushing the spermatic cord of each testis. When the calves are four to six weeks old they may be 'disbudded' with a hot iron to prevent their horns from growing. This is done to stop closely-confined animals from injuring each other. If this is not done straight away, the cattle will often be de-horned later in life. This can involve the use of saws, horn shears or cutting wire. Horns contain blood and nerve endings so cauterisation is necessary to stem the bleeding that occurs after dehorning.

At the end of their short lives (a cow's natural lifespan is about 25 years; most beef cattle are allowed to live for fewer than three), they are loaded into lorries for their final journey. When they reach the slaughterhouse, they are herded along cramped corridors and into pens where their heads are restrained and a bolt is shot through their skull, destroying part of the brain. The cow is then 'stuck' and allowed to bleed to death. All too often the initial stunning is inadequate, and the animals may be conscious as they bleed to death.

DAIRY

If cattle raised for beef are to be pitied, the dairy cow deserves even more of our sympathy. To bring milk to the breakfast tables of the West, cows are kept in a constant cycle of pregnancy and lactation. This unnatural breeding regime results in painful udder infections such as mastitis, affecting up to 20% of the dairy herd. This condition is aggravated by insanitary living conditions: for at least six months of the year cows often have no choice but to stand and sleep in their own filth. Some herds never go out to pasture and are permanently confined to 'zero grazing' regimes. If they are lucky enough, zero grazed cows may have access to a covered 'loafing' yard. Cows in zero grazing regimes have been described as battery cows.

Frequent milking stimulates feed intake, increasing milk yields, so cows are often milked three times a day, usually by machines. The average dairy cow produces 6,770 litres of milk per year, more than three times the amount produced by her ancestors in the 1950s. With milk yields increasing all the time, the cow's body is forced to work harder and harder.

The amount of work done by the cow in peak lactation is immense...To achieve a comparably high work rate a human would have to jog for about 6 hours a day, every day.

(Professor AJF Webster, Dept of Animal Husbandry, Bristol University.)

The strain is such that after only a few years her fertility decreases, her milk levels drop, and she is quickly replaced with a more profitable animal. As with all other intensively farmed animals, she is destined for the dinner plate, usually as lower grade beef products such as minced beef: the white stuff is inseparable from the red stuff.

It is not only the cow that suffers. Male calves are of the wrong breed to be raised for beef, so their only economic worth is as veal. Because farmers want to sell the mother's milk to humans, little can be spared for the calf who is often taken from his mother after just a few hours, causing enormous distress to both mother and baby. In January 2008, veal crates became illegal across Europe nearly 20 years after the UK banned them. However veal crates are still used in other parts of the world, including the US. In Europe, veal crates have been replaced by group housing systems which are only marginally less cruel. Calves are confined to indoor pens with wooden slatted or concrete floors; there is no obligation for European veal farmers outside the UK to provide the calves with straw bedding.

EGGS

In the European Union over 200 million laying hens are kept in battery cages so small that they cannot stretch their wings, peck or scratch the ground, or perform most of their other natural behaviours. Up to 90,000 caged hens may be crammed into one windowless shed, with cages stacked up to four storeys high.

This close confinement not only causes major psychological stress, but can also cause physical damage to the birds. The lack of exercise and the unnatural diet can lead to brittle bones that are easily broken. The Institute of Food Research in Bristol found nearly 30% of caged birds had broken bones by the time they reached the slaughterhouse.

Battery systems are to be outlawed in Europe from 2012, but the so-called 'enriched cages' that will replace them are little better. Each hen will have roughly a postcard-sized piece of extra space. This may be an improvement of sorts, but evidence (and common sense) suggests that birds will continue to suffer both physical and psychological stress.

"But," says the ethical egg-lover, "I only buy free range eggs." The myth of free range continues to salve the consciences of many British consumers. But images of fat, feathery farmyard hens pecking and scratching in the dust couldn't be further from the reality of the majority of 'free range' systems. The birds are often kept in flocks of up to 16,000 to a shed. Birds in free range systems can be legally stocked at a density of 12 hens per square metre. Although there must be access to the outdoors, some free range chickens never make it outside during their lifetime. According to the Soil Association, hens may simply not be able to reach the exits, or the exits may be guarded by other birds who prevent them from leaving. Free range chickens may also be de-beaked.

When egg production decreases the hens are sent for slaughter; they end up in soups, pasties, pies, etc., where the pathetic condition of their bodies will not put consumers off their meal.

As with dairy calves, male chicks hatched from egg laying hens are of the wrong strain to be raised for meat. Male chicks are therefore completely worthless in both intensive and free range systems, and are killed when they are just one day old. Common slaughter methods include gassing, neck dislocation and the 'macerator', a device that shreds chicks alive. Defra describe macerators as humane, since the imechanical destruction of chicks is instantaneousi; the gassing of chicks can take 15 minutes before death occurs. Approximately 30 million male chicks are killed every year by the egg industry.

FISH

Fish farming is now the world's fastest growing sector of animal production. Up to 50,000 salmon can be crowded together in a single underwater cage, resulting in each 75cm long salmon having the equivalent of a bathtub of water to swim in. Trout are usually stocked at even higher densities (as many as 27 trout to one bathtub). The stress caused by these unnatural conditions (a wild salmon will swim thousands of miles to return to its spawning ground) leads to physical injuries and increased susceptibility to disease. Official figures show that disease-related death rates among farmed fish are as high as 10-30%.

Parasites and disease are other devastating problems for intensively farmed fish. The large concentrations of fish attract sea lice that feed on the host salmon, often causing such severe damage to the fish that the skull becomes visible, a condition that has become known as the 'death crown'.

Other diseases that affect farmed fish include bacterial kidney disease, furunculosis, infectious haematopoietic necrosis, and kudoa (soft-flesh syndrome). The highly toxic products used to treat these afflictions cause considerable environmental damage.

Fish may be starved for up to two weeks before slaughter to empty the gut and reduce the risk of the flesh becoming contaminated during the gutting process.

Slaughter methods include clubbing, suffocation in air or ice, or the use of a stunning tank that is saturated with carbon dioxide; whichever method is used their gills are then cut to enable the fish to 'bleed out'.

Today it is rarely disputed that fish feel pain. The European Food Safety Authority stated in their 2004 report that "many existing commercial killing methods expose fish to substantial suffering over a long period of time".

And it is not only the fish themselves that suffer. Every year hundreds of fish-eating species (notably seals, birds, mink and otters) are attracted to these vast stocks of fish, and are shot by fish farmers attempting to protect their stock.

Not only is the farming of fish cruel, it is also very inefficient, since wild fish are caught to feed farmed fish. It takes three tonnes of wild fish to produce one tonne of factory farmed salmon. In 2001, 139,000 tonnes of salmon and 16,000 tonnes of rainbow trout were produced in the UK.

Coastal environments are lost to large aquaculture operations. Tropical and subtropical mangrove systems, vital for healthy coral reef systems, are being lost at an alarming rate and converted to ponds for prawns and shrimps destined for the Western market.

HONEY

Non-vegans are often surprised to learn that honey and other bee products are unsuitable for vegans. It's the old storybook image that confuses us: we see honey bees flying around, gathering nectar and taking it back to their hives - what cruelty could possibly be involved?

In fact, bees are manipulated in similar ways to other farmed animals to provide a whole range of products, including honey, beeswax, propolis, bee pollen, royal jelly and venom.

A honeybee will, on average, fly about 800km in her working life, and produce half a teaspoon of honey.

The major welfare problems associated with bee keeping are centred around the egg-laying process. The queen is routinely artificially inseminated by sperm from decapitated male bees (they would normally mate in flight). She is usually killed after two years, when her egg-laying abilities begin to decline, and replaced by a new queen, often purchased by mail order from specialist breeding companies. The queens' wings are often clipped to force the hives to remain in a single location.

Honey, stored by the bees for the lean winter months, is removed for human use and replaced with nutrient-deficient glucose or corn syrup. Whole colonies of bees may be killed to save feeding them during the winter. Synthetic pesticides and antibiotics are also used as commercial bee colonies are prone to the rapid spread of disease, an example being the Varroa mite.

The farming of bees puts pressure on wild bees and other pollinating insects, and decreases biodiversity.

SHELLAC

Lac are insects (*Lacifer lacca*) living on lac trees, where the female secretes a protective resin over herself. It is this resin, along with encrusted live insects, that is scraped from the trees and manufactured into shellac. 300,000 lac insects are killed for 1kg of shellac. Global production is estimated to be approximately 20,000 tonnes a year.

Shellac is used as a glaze for fruit (such as those surprisingly shiny supermarket apples), and may be an ingredient in paint, varnish, tablets, cosmetics, confectionery, floor polish, and in hats as a stiffener. Whilst synthetic resin could easily replace shellac entirely, public demand for 'natural' products may actually be encouraging greater production.

COCHINEAL

Cochineal, also known as carmine (sometimes labelled as E120), is a red dye used in clothing and foodstuffs. It consists of the dried bodies of *Dactylopius coccus*, an insect indigenous to Central and South America. The female insects are picked by hand after mating and dried in the shade for 20-30 days. To produce 1 kg of raw cochineal requires about 100,000 to 150,000 insects. In 2005, Peru produced 200 tonnes of cochineal dye. Peru produces about 90% of the world's cochineal, with the rest coming from the Canary Islands.

SILK

The most common species of silkworm (moth larvae) used in commercial silk production, *Bombyx mori*, has been 'cultivated' over many centuries and no longer exists in the wild. The female annually lays 300-400 eggs on mulberry trees, secreting a sticky substance to fasten them to the surface. The eggs hatch into silkworms, which feed on the mulberry leaves and grow rapidly.

The fully grown silkworm secretes a fine thread to make a cocoon around itself consisting of about 300,000 figure-of-eight movements. The pupa stage would then be followed by the production of an alkaline substance which breaks the threads, allowing the moth to emerge. But as the industry requires the threads intact, the pupa is killed by immersion of the cocoon in boiling water, steaming, oven drying, or exposure to the hot sun. The cocoons are unwound onto reels in a continuous strand.

Only a tiny amount of usable silk is obtained from each cocoon: it takes around 200kg of cocoons and 11.25 tonnes of mulberry leaves to produce just 40kg of silk. The dead pupae are typically composted to feed the mulberry trees.

WOOL

The UK is the world's seventh largest producer of wool, producing approximately 60,000 tonnes a year. Around one third of this is exported. The majority of sheep are shorn for the first time at 14-15 months of age, and annually thereafter. Early season shearing in wet, windy and cold conditions can result in severe chilling and even death. Sheep farmed for wool are bred to have lambs for the meat trade. Lambs undergo ear punching for identification, tail docking, dipping, spraying and mulesing (see below). Rams are regarded as too difficult to handle, so the vast majority of male sheep are wethers (castrated rams).

Australia is the world's largest wool-producing country, with around 100 million sheep. 20-25% of Australian lambs die either at birth or before the age of eight weeks, from exposure to extreme weather conditions or starvation. An estimated one million Australian sheep die of exposure every year after shearing. The shearing of sheep can cause cuts and bruising. In some instances severe cuts have been caused to the faces of sheep, while males have had their penises shorn off.

Following cruel procedures such as castration, tail docking and mulesing - in which farmers carve strips of flesh (not wool) from around the anal and vaginal area of sheep without anaesthetic, or any training or qualification requirements - lambs are susceptible to shock, blood poisoning, tetanus, dislocated joints and arthritis.

Raw wool consists of 10-25% grease or lanolin, which is recovered during the scouring process. Lanolin consists of a highly complex mixture of esters, alcohols and fatty acids, and may be used in adhesive tape, printing inks, motor oils, and machine lubrication. It can also be refined for use in cosmetics and pharmaceuticals.

FUR

The trade in wild furs is responsible for the decline of many species, and the extinction of some. As the larger cats became commercially extinct or protected, the fur trade turned to the smaller ones. Thousands of lynx and bobcat are still being trapped each year in North America using steel leg-hold traps (now banned in Europe), which do not kill the animal outright and cause immeasurable suffering. Other wild animals trapped for their skins by today's fur industry include raccoons, opossums, red foxes, ermines, coyotes and beavers.

Worldwide, more than 30 million mink and foxes are imprisoned in row upon row of wire cages to produce fur. In the UK, long-term campaigning has led to the farming of animals exclusively for their fur being outlawed since 1st January 2003. Previously, the number of rabbits killed for fur was not included in fur industry figures, but recent investigations show that approximately 180 million rabbits are killed each year for the fur trade. This fur is not a by-product of the meat industry; rabbits bred for meat are killed while their flesh is still pale at 10-12 weeks of age, whereas those bred for their coats are killed some months later when their skin and coat is thicker.

Animals kept in fur factory farms can show signs of stereotypical behaviour such as rocking, self-mutilation and cannibalism. Fur-bearing animals are confined to small barren cages; cage sizes for mink, as recommended by the fur industry, are just 38cm wide, 30.5 cm high and 61cm long. They are killed by gassing, neck-breaking, lethal injection, or anal electrocution.

Sadly, fur is making a comeback mainly as fur trim; in 2001/2002, total fur sales worldwide equalled 10,905 million US dollars. Real fur trim can be found on inexpensive garments such as coats and jackets. Many consumers are unaware that they may be purchasing real fur, since there is no legal obligation to label real fur or label a garment as containing real fur.

LEATHER

Leather is simply fur with the hairs scraped off one side and the flesh scraped and chemically removed from the other side. The sale of leather makes a sizeable contribution to the viability of the meat industry: it is not a by-product of animal suffering, it is a contributing factor. (Also see tanneries section on the environmental damage of leather production.)

Synthetic alternatives such as Lorica, from which vegetarian shoes and jackets are made, are now widely available.

See the clothing section of the *Animal Free Shopper* for a range of vegan footwear suppliers.

VIVISECTION

Over three million animals are experimented on in the UK each year. Approximately 60% of all experiments are conducted without the use of anaesthetic. In addition to the above death toll, millions of animals are bred for vivisection and disposed of 'unused'. Despite also being victims of the vivisection trade, the deaths of these unused animals are not recorded among the figures.

There are three main areas of research in which these experiments are claimed to be useful: to increase scientific knowledge, to aid the development of new products, and to test the safety of new products and their ingredients.

Some of the most common animal experiments used globally are the LD_{50} test, the Draize test, and skin irritancy tests. LD_{50} (Lethal Dose 50%) involves giving animals increasing amounts of a chemical or drug to find the dosage required to kill 50% of the test group; doses may be administered orally or via inhalation and skin-application. The oral LD_{50} test was banned in the UK in 1999, only to be replaced by the Fixed Dose Procedure, which doses animals until they exhibit signs of toxicity.

However, the oral LD$_{50}$ test is still used by the Ministry of Defence and accounts for approximately one third of animal-based toxicity tests worldwide. The Draize test is most commonly performed on rabbits: substances such as laundry products, bleaches and washing-up liquids are dripped into their eyes, which are then examined for signs of damage such as ulcers, bleeding, swelling, or discharge; the animals are killed after the test. In skin irritancy tests, the skin of the rabbit or other rodent is shaved and the substance is applied to the area, which is then examined for adverse reactions.

Many people think there is a ban on cosmetic testing in the UK. This isn't strictly true: the government announced in 1998 that it would no longer issue licences for the testing of cosmetic products, but a ban is not enshrined in law. Many companies continue to test products and ingredients in mainland Europe and elsewhere.

A ban on cosmetic animal testing and the sale of cosmetics that have been animal tested may be phased in across the European Union from 2009. However, some members of the cosmetic industry have vigorously lobbied against the ban, or for generous concessions. The UK government has argued against banning the sale of animal tested cosmetics in the EU.

Most household products such as bleaches are still routinely tested on animals.

The vivisection of animals is an unreliable way of finding successful medical treatments for humans. Over 90% of pharmaceutical drugs successful in animal trials fail in clinical trials on humans. Put simply, animal models are poor models for human disease. Drugs that are unsafe for humans have come onto the market only to be withdrawn at a later date. An increasing number of scientists and medical professionals are publicly voicing their concerns over the continued use of animals in medical research.

HEALTH

HEART DISEASE AND CANCER

Replacing animal foods with plant foods, thus reducing intakes of saturated fat and cholesterol and increasing intakes of fibre, vitamin C, folate and carotenoids, promotes good health.

Dietary guidelines across the world, including the meat-guzzling USA, now acknowledge the validity of the vegan alternative. Fortified plant milks are accepted as an alternative to dairy products and as a source of calcium and vitamin B_{12}. Beans, nuts and pulses are accepted as alternatives to meat and fish as sources of protein. Recommended vegetable and fruit intakes continue to rise, with many experts replacing the familiar five-a-day advice with nine-a-day or more. Research strongly suggests that a diet rich in fruit and vegetables can decrease the risk of having a heart attack or stroke. It can protect against a variety of cancers, lower blood pressure, reduce risk of intestinal ailments, and guard against loss of vision in the elderly.

Compared with lacto-ovo-vegetarians and meat eaters, vegans usually have significantly higher intakes of nutrients associated with reduced risk of cardiovascular disease, including fibre, vitamin C, potassium, magnesium, and folate, as well as lower intakes of sodium. They also consume less total fat and less saturated fat, and have lower levels of total cholesterol, as well as a better ratio of total cholesterol to HDL cholesterol.

Research has confirmed a reduced risk of heart disease in vegans and other vegetarians. This is believed to be due to lower intakes of saturated fat and cholesterol, and higher intakes of fruit and vegetables. However, research has also indicated that some vegans are not getting the full potential benefit of their diet, due to less than optimal intakes of vitamin B_{12} and omega-3 fatty acids. This is easily remedied by getting at least 3 micrograms of B_{12} per day from fortified foods or supplements, and including some omega-3 rich foods such as rapeseed oil or flaxseed oil (see HEALTHY EATING FOR VEGANS page 34). We look forward to even better results from studies of vegan health once this advice becomes widely adopted.

Evidence is also growing to suggest that diets high in milk and dairy products increase the risk of prostate cancer, and that diets high in processed meats and low in fibre increase the risk of colon cancer. In this context, it is good news that plant protein sources are now almost universally accepted as providing all the protein we need: when it comes to health, there is nothing second rate about plant foods.

DAIRY ALLERGY AND INTOLERANCE

Dairy products are a common trigger for eczema in infants, and can also cause chronic constipation. Among those over the age of five, 90-95% of Afro-Caribbean individuals and 20-25% of Caucasians are lactose intolerant (source: *Milk Allergy and Lactose Intolerance*, Dr Harris Steinman, 2002): milk sugar causes digestive problems such as bloating and diarrhoea in such people because they lack the enzymes to break it down. It should therefore come as no surprise that in the UK many consumers are attempting to reduce their consumption of dairy products. Dairy alternatives are no longer confined to health food shops, but are found in most supermarkets. The dairy free sector is valued at approximately £86 million, and is growing at around 15% a year.

FOOD POISONING

Bovine, pig and chicken carcasses can become contaminated with *E coli* during the slaughter process. A 2002 study by the Food Standards Agency found that half of UK-bred chickens purchased from retail outlets contained *Campylobacter*. *Campylobacter* is the leading cause of food poisoning in the UK.

Over 14,000 cases of *Salmonella* infection in humans were confirmed in Defra's 2006 Zoonoses report. Food poisoning from eggs has become such a problem that current advice from the Government's Food Standards Agency is to cook both the egg white and yolk until it is solid. Diarrhoeic, paralytic and amnesic shellfish poisoning have also occurred in several areas of the UK (see also antibiotics for antibiotic-resistant bugs related to animal products).

CJD

Bovine Spongiform Encephalopathy (BSE) or 'mad cow disease' first appeared in the UK in 1986. The epidemic was caused by cattle being fed the processed remains of other animals, even though they are usually herbivores.

Animal feed regulations were changed to control the disease. However, a UK Government inquiry found that BSE continued to spread because the regulations were being broken.

Beef contaminated with BSE is linked to so-called 'variant CreutzfeldJacob Disease' (vCJD) in humans, which is fatal. More than 160 people have now died of vCJD in the UK. Due to the long incubation period of the disease, there is a real possibility that the final death toll will be over 10,000, but earlier estimates of millions of deaths now seem unlikely.

Prions - the 'rogue' proteins believed to be responsible for BSE and vCJD - have not been found in milk or milk products. However, the prion agent is contained in white blood cells ('pus') which are legally permitted in milk at levels of up to two million per teaspoon.

ANTIBIOTICS

Antibiotic-resistant bugs have resulted from the over-use of antibiotics in farm animals, not the over use of antibiotics in hospitals. 419 tonnes of antibiotics were administered to farmed animals in 2005.

Research in the Netherlands has shown that 21% of chicken, 20% of pork and 3% of beef is infected with MRSA. Farm-animal MRSA is transferred to farm workers and their families; all people living on cattle and pig farms in the Netherlands are now isolated when admitted to hospital. Patients with farm-animal MRSA have developed skin infection, endocarditis (heart infection), osteomyelitis (bone infection), blood poisoning and pneumonia. Farm-animal MRSA is unlikely to be confined to the Netherlands, yet neither DEFRA nor the Food Standards Agency routinely test for it in the UK.

Extended-Spectrum Beta-Lactamase (ESBL) is a recently discovered and almost untreatable type of E.coli that spreads to humans who consume infected animal products. ESBL has been found on a large number of UK farms. Those who contract this form of E.coli have a 30% risk of dying from the poisoning.

ECOLOGY

More and more people are becoming aware of the direct correlation between what they eat every day and the health of the planet. Environmentally conscious consumers are concerned not only with food miles, over-packaging, pesticide use and GM foods, but increasingly with the question of the environmental sustainability of foods.

The meat-intensive diets of the West contribute, among other things, to climate change, deforestation, desertification, water pollution and loss of biodiversity.

The 2006 UN report *Livestock's Long Shadow* states that "the livestock sector emerges as one of the top two or three most significant contributors to the most serious environmental problems, at every scale from local to global".

CLIMATE CHANGE

In relation to global climate change, *Livestock's Long Shadow* states, "The livestock sector is a major player, responsible for 18% of greenhouse gas emissions measured in CO_2 equivalent. This is a higher share than transport." (Transport causes 13.5% worldwide.)

Methane from farmed animals is produced by bacteria in the stomachs of ruminants such as sheep, cattle, and goats, and is farted and belched out. Studies at the Centre for Environmental Strategy at the University of Surrey calculated that beef cattle can produce up to 1,400kg CO_2 equivalent per animal per year, while dairy cows can produce up to 2,700kg CO_2 equivalent per animal per year. When manure is kept in anaerobic conditions (as in the liquid systems commonly used on intensive farms), even more methane is produced.

Animal farming contributes 65% of all human-caused nitrous oxide. Nitrous oxide has 296 times the global warming effect of carbon dioxide.

The evidence is now clear; diet has a major impact on climate change. The average vegan diet that includes imported foods has a lower impact on the environment than the average locally sourced diet that includes meat and dairy.

DEFORESTATION

We need forests. They store large quantities of carbon dioxide, release oxygen, protect soils, and harbour millions of plant and animal species. Yet they are being destroyed at an alarming rate. The United Nations Food and Agriculture Organisation estimated that the net loss of forests during the 1990s was 8.9 million hectares per year. Forests are being destroyed not only to provide wood, paper and fuel, but also to provide land for grazing cattle and for growing crops to feed to animals (see 'Resource Use' section).

DESERTIFICATION

The felling of forests and over-grazing contribute to soil loss and desertification. Thin layers of topsoil previously protected by a fine network of roots are extremely vulnerable when the forest cover is removed, and are often compacted and broken down by cattle or simply washed away.

The UN estimates that more than 250 million people are affected by desertification, and approximately two billion people, a third of the Earth's population, are potential victims. Desertification results in famine and malnutrition, as the fertility of the soil is lost and people are displaced from the land.

WATER POLLUTION

Every year farmers spread millions of tonnes of animal manures and other organic farm wastes onto the land as fertiliser. Slurry and silage effluent can pollute a nearby river or stream by encouraging algal blooms that block sunlight, and by encouraging bacteria that deplete the water of oxygen, in the worst cases killing all the fish and endangering the health of other animals in the area. This process is known as eutrophication, and farming is the major cause of the problem.

Slurry, which is made up of manure and urine, contains high levels of ammonia which encourages the bacteria that produce acid to thrive. This directly contributes to acid rain. Slurry can be up to 100 times more polluting than untreated domestic sewage. Silage effluent, the liquid produced when preserving crops for fodder, is up to 200 times more polluting.

TANNERIES

In its natural state as hide or skin, leather would be totally unsuitable for its current uses and would rot rapidly. To make it pliable and longer lasting, the removed animal skin is treated with a wide range of environmentally-damaging chemicals such as lime, sodium sulphate, sodium sulfhydrate, emulsifiers, degreasing agents, salt, aluminium, sulphuric acid, chromium sulphate, caustic soda, formic acid, aniline dyes, and various other chemicals.

Tannery effluent contains large amounts of solid pollutants such as proteins and hair, and can be toxic to aquatic life. Many tanneries have relocated their operations from developed to developing countries, where labour is cheaper and human safety laws and environmental regulations are less stringent. Hides may be exported from the UK to tanneries abroad for treatment only to be re-imported as leather goods, increasing the product's environmental impact.

Far from being a by-product of the meat industry, leather is a significantly profitable part of the slaughtered animal.

ENVIRONMENT EMERGENCY HOTLINE

The Environment Agency's emergency hotline number 0800 80 70 60 operates 24 hours a day, 365 days a year, for people to report pollution, fish in distress, illegal disposal of waste, poaching, and damage or danger to the natural environment.

RESOURCE USE

LAND

omnivorous diet

vegetarian diet

vegan diet

Meat and dairy production is a notoriously inefficient use of energy. All animals use the energy they get from food to move around, keep warm and perform their day-to-day bodily functions. This means that less than half of the plant protein eaten by farmed animals is converted to meat or dairy products.

Land availability is one of the main constraints on food production. In the UK, the average vegan requires just a third of the land needed to feed the average meat eater.

The World Resources Institute (WRI) stated that nearly 40% of all the world's agricultural land is seriously degraded. The United Nations Environment Programme found that overgrazing is responsible for 35% of this land degradation, deforestation for 30%, and agriculture for 27%. These main causes are all directly or indirectly related to the consumption of animal products.

In the case of the rainforests, 70% of previously forested land in the Amazon has been converted to pasture for livestock animals. 90% of soya protein grown and transported around the globe is used to feed livestock animals.

Switching to a vegan diet can help to prevent further deterioration of fertile land and protect the world's forested areas.

WATER

Although estimates vary, it takes over three times the amount of water to feed a meat eater in the UK compared with that used to feed a vegan. The United Nations Food and Agriculture Organisation report, *Livestock's Long Shadow,* states that "on average 990 litres of water are required to produce one litre of milk".

Slurry from cattle and other livestock pollutes groundwater, streams and rivers. The global figure for waste from industrial livestock systems is in the region of eight billion tonnes per year.

FEEDING A GROWING POPULATION

The United Nations Food and Agriculture Organisation (FAO) 2005 report stated that hunger causes the death of more then five million children a year. The world's population is expected to increase from six billion to nine billion by 2050. If we are to

avoid global food scarcity we must find a sustainable way of utilising our natural resources. A vegan diet is far more sustainable, using fewer resources and less land, meaning more food can be produced.

SPIRITUAL

Central to the beliefs of many of those following an animal-free lifestyle is the desire to strive to reduce harm and show reverence for life, embodied in the spirit of *ahimsa*, the Sanskrit word for non-killing and non-injury championed by Mahatma Gandhi.

Some animal-free shoppers are allied to a particular church, such as the Society of Friends (Quakers) or Seventh Day Adventists, or to a particular faith such as Buddhism, Hinduism, Jainism, Christianity or Paganism. Many consider that their animal-free lifestyle is a practical application of their faith, giving them a sense of inner peace.

Liberation of animals from human exploitation, health benefits for humans, resource use, and ecological and spiritual considerations, are five very good reasons for adopting an animal-free lifestyle. With the *Animal Free Shopper* in your pocket, it's never been easier or more fun to GO VEGAN!

For Updates to the Animal Free Shopper visit:
www.animalfreeshopper.com

HEALTHY EATING FOR VEGANS

Sandra Hood BSc(Hons) SRD

One of the most important ways to influence our health is through our diet and as vegans, we often feel that we have to prove that we can be healthy and that we are getting enough of this or that particular nutrient. However, it is all too easy to become obsessed with meeting the nutritional requirements of the general population and forget to look at the other side of the coin and how protective a vegan diet can be.

The mainstay of a healthy diet is plenty of unrefined carbohydrates, such as cereals, pulses and whole grains, plus the important vitamins, minerals and phytochemicals found in fruits and vegetables, and the essential fatty acids found in nuts, seeds and oils. This healthy eating diet has been shown not only to prevent illness but also to treat it. Compared with omnivores, vegetarians have been shown to be at lower risk for conditions such as constipation, diverticular disease, gallstones and appendicitis. Vegan diets have also been used to treat diseases such as angina, diabetes, high blood pressure, rheumatoid arthritis and kidney disease.

In recent years there has been a lot of emphasis on vegans adopting a more raw food oriented or fruitarian diet, and no doubt we should all be including more raw foods in our diet. However, it can also be very bulky and unsuitable for infants and children. Cooking may damage some plant nutrients, but in many cases it alters the structure of nutrients in a way that may actually increase the availability of phytochemicals, resulting in significant health effects. For instance, lycopene (a carotenoid and precursor of vitamin A) is far better absorbed from cooked tomatoes than from raw ones. To maximise benefit from the plant nutrients in the diet, therefore, it is best to include a variety of both raw and cooked foods.

The following paragraphs give a brief outline of nutrients that may be of particular interest to vegans. There are very few rules about what you should or should not eat, but it is important to ensure a reliable source of vitamin B12, and if sun exposure is limited vitamin D supplements or fortified foods should be used.

Aim to eat a variety of whole foods, including the following food groups on a daily basis:

- **Fruits** • **Vegetables** • **Nuts and seeds** • **Cereals** • **Pulses**

ENERGY

Carbohydrates

These are the main energy foods, and half your energy should come from carbohydrates. There are two types of carbohydrates: starchy foods and sugary foods. Try to choose mainly starchy foods such as whole grain bread, pasta, rice, potatoes and cereals. Vegans generally have a high fibre diet with less reliance on refined carbohydrates; in the refining process, essential nutrients are lost.

Fibre

This is the part of a plant that cannot be digested. All plant foods contain fibre. There are two categories of fibre, soluble and insoluble, and most plants contain a mixture of the two. Insoluble fibre adds bulk to stools and ensures that food passes quickly and easily through the intestinal tract. Soluble fibre, found in peas, beans, oats and lentils, has been shown to reduce blood cholesterol levels. Vegans have been shown to consume 40 to 50g of fibre per day compared with 30 to 40g per day for vegetarians and 10 to 20g per day for omnivores. Recommended minimum intakes are 18g per day and the World Health Organisation (WHO) recommends an upper limit of 54g per day. It has been suggested that intakes comparable with those of vegans would be beneficial for health.

It has been reported that excess fibre may reduce the absorption of certain minerals, but high fibre whole foods provide enough extra minerals to more than compensate for any losses incurred. When fibre does bind with minerals, they can be partly released during the fermentation of fibre by bacteria in the large bowel.

Fats

Fats provide vitamins and energy, are essential for the manufacture of hormones and are important for insulation and protection. Fat should provide approximately 30% of adult energy requirements while infants need a higher intake. Most people are confused about the type and quantity of fats. Whether a fat is solid or liquid at room temperature, it will contain the same amount of calories. The main constituents of all fats are fatty acids, which may be saturated, monounsaturated or polyunsaturated, depending on the number of double bonds between the carbon atoms in the molecule. As the number of double bonds increases, the fats become more unsaturated or oily. There are more than 40 fatty acids found in nature.

There is no physiological requirement for dietary fat, only for essential fatty acids.

These are the polyunsaturated fats:

- Linoleic – sunflower, corn, safflower and soya oils
- Alpha-linolenic – linseed, walnut and rapeseed oils

Humans and other mammals lack the enzyme to synthesise them, so they are essential in the diet.

Saturated fats
Saturated fat has been linked with heart disease; it raises cholesterol levels in the blood, and the higher your cholesterol level the greater the risk of suffering a stroke or heart attack. Meat and saturated fat go hand in hand, and animal products are the greatest sources of saturated fat in the Western diet. Milk fat is more than 60% saturated fat, compared with 6 to 25% for plant fats, most being in the 10-15% range. The exceptions are tropical oils such as coconut and palm oil.

Monounsaturated fat
Studies have shown that monounsaturated fats (MUFAs) can reduce the risk of heart disease. Vegan dietary sources include olives and olive oil, rapeseed oil, nuts (such as almonds, cashews, hazelnuts, macadamias) and avocados. MUFAs should provide the main source of fat intake.

Polyunsaturated fat
The main dietary sources are vegetable oils, seeds, nuts, grains, legumes and other plant foods. Studies regarding their health effects are inconsistent, but when they replace saturated fats and trans fatty acids in the diet there is no doubt that they are beneficial. The two essential fatty acids are linoleic and alpha-linolenic acid. Linoleic acid is found in vegetable seeds and oils such as soya, corn, sunflower, safflower, walnuts and grains. Alpha-linolenic acid is found in linseed, rapeseed and walnuts. A high ratio of linoleic to alpha-linolenic acid inhibits the production of eicosapentaeonic acid (EPA) and docosahexaenoic acid (DHA), so it is important that vegans achieve a good balance of polyunsaturated fatty acids to ensure adequate levels of EPA and DHA.

Trans fatty acids (hydrogenated oils)
People believe that they are making healthier choices by changing from butter to margarine, but trans fatty acids produced in the manufacture of margarine have been shown to be as harmful as saturated fat. Therefore, choose margarines which do not contain hydrogenated oils and avoid processed foods such as crackers, chips, biscuits, pastries and crisps.

PROTEIN

Protein provides the building blocks for new tissue and is vital for the growth and repair of all cells. It can also be used for energy production, if needed, or stored as fat. Protein is made up of 22 amino acids, the building blocks of protein; 8 of these are essential amino acids because the human body cannot make them, but they are easily supplied by plants. Plant sources can provide adequate amounts of essential and non-essential amino acids. Good sources of protein include nuts, seeds, grains (wheat, oats, rice, barley, buckwheat, millet, pasta, bread) and pulses (peas, beans, lentils).

Many people erroneously believe that animal protein is necessary for human health and that plant protein is inferior. Omnivores tend to have protein intakes above recommendations while vegan intakes meet the recommendations. Combining amino acids is unnecessary as they are stored in protein pools which can be drawn upon as needed.

Summary

- Use whole grains in preference to refined grains.
- Ensure a good balance of polyunsaturated fatty acids.
- Monounsaturated fatty acids should provide the main source of fat intake.
- Avoid hydrogenated oils.

VITAMINS

Vitamins are found in small quantities and are essential for normal body functioning. Fat soluble vitamins are A, D, E and K. Water soluble vitamins are B and C. With few exceptions, vitamins cannot be synthesised by the body and must be obtained from the diet. A vegan diet can provide all the vitamins necessary for good health. The following are of particular interest to vegans:

Vitamin C
Vitamin C is a powerful water soluble antioxidant, neutralising harmful reactions in the blood and the fluid inside the surrounding cells. Vegans and vegetarians are at a distinct advantage here and need to lead the way in the health revolution.

Vitamin D

Vitamin D3 is normally obtained from lanolin, which is derived from sheep's wool and not acceptable to vegans. However, most people get sufficient vitamin D through the action of sunlight on the skin. Spending time outside reduces your need for foods fortified with vitamin D. When sun exposure is limited, a vitamin D supplement may be necessary. Vitamin D promotes the absorption of calcium and is essential for bones and teeth. Foods fortified with a vegan source of vitamin D (vitamin D2, ergocalciferol) include margarine, fortified cereals and some fortified non-dairy milks.

Vitamin B12

This vitamin is essential for the formation of red blood cells and a healthy nervous system. Some plant foods may contain vitamin B12 on their surface from soil residues, but this is not a reliable source. Much of the vitamin B12 present in spirulina, sea vegetables, tempeh and miso has been shown to be an inactive form rather than the active vitamin. So if you are not taking foods fortified with vitamin B12, ensure that you take a supplement. The UK government recommends 1.5 micrograms per day as sufficient to reliably prevent clinical deficiency, but higher intakes are required to avoid elevated homocysteine and associated increased mortality. The Vegan Society therefore recommends that all vegans get at least 3 micrograms of B12 every day to maximise the health benefits of their diet. (For further details, see www.vegansociety.com or contact The Vegan Society for a B12 information sheet.)

Summary

- Ensure regular exposure to sunlight for adequate vitamin D.
- Ensure a daily source of vitamin B12.

MINERALS

There are a number of minerals essential for health, but most are only needed in small amounts which come from a varied diet of whole grains, fruits, vegetables, nuts and seeds. The two main minerals needed in larger amounts which are of some interest to vegans are iron and calcium.

Calcium

Studies have found that vegan diets may be below current recommendations for calcium. Claims are commonly made that vegans require less calcium than omnivores, based on the lower acid production resulting from metabolism of plant proteins. This has not been resolved. Although oxalates, phytates and fibre in plant foods decrease calcium availability, research shows that absorption of calcium from many plant foods is excellent. Calcium absorption from low oxalate vegetables such as broccoli and kale is better than for cow's milk while absorption from beans, nuts and seeds is lower. Good vegan sources of calcium include dark green leafy vegetables such as spring greens and kale, calcium-set tofu, baked beans and fortified foods.

Iron

Vegan diets are higher in total iron content than omnivorous diets, but iron stores are lower in vegans because the iron from plant foods, known as non-haem iron, is less well absorbed than the haem iron found in meat. However, iron deficiency anaemia is no more common in vegans than in omnivores. Vitamin C and other organic acids commonly found in vegetables strongly enhance the absorption of non-haem iron. Vitamin C intakes of vegans are frequently high and this, in conjunction with generous levels of dietary iron, may compensate for the lower bioavailability of non-haem iron. Good iron sources include whole or enriched grains and grain products, iron-fortified cereals, legumes, green leafy vegetables and dried fruits.

Zinc

Diets of vegans and non-vegans often contain similar amounts of zinc. However, zinc from plant foods is less well absorbed as some plant foods contain phytate which interferes with zinc absorption. However, no reports of zinc deficiency in vegans have been found. Zinc is an essential component of a number of enzyme systems within the body and is widely distributed in plant foods. Good sources include nuts, seeds, beans and cereals.

Iodine

Iodine is needed by the thyroid gland to produce the thyroid hormone which regulates physical and mental development, including growth, reproduction and other essential functions. Iodine deficiency is rare in the UK. The main source of iodine in the UK is cow's milk, due to iodine supplemented cattle feed and the contamination of milk from teat dips containing iodophors as sterilising agents. Sea foods are rich sources of iodine, with dried seaweed being a popular choice for vegans.

Two kelp tablets (with a declared iodine content between 150 and 250 micrograms) per week will ensure sufficient iodine; more than this is not desirable.

Summary

- Calcium absorption from low oxalate vegetables such as broccoli and kale is good.
- Vitamin C aids iron absorption.
- Good sources of zinc are nuts, seeds, beans and cereals.
- Seaweed is rich in iodine.

PHYTOCHEMICALS

It has been known for a long time that fruits and vegetables, grains, seeds, nuts and pulses are good for you, being rich in vitamins, minerals and fibre, but in the past few years there has also been interest in the phytochemicals, which have been shown to have many health benefits.

Some phytochemicals are strong antioxidants which mop up free radicals (active harmful molecules circulating in the body).

A special group of phytochemicals are the plant oestrogens, which block the deleterious action of the potent form of oestrogen either by competing with it for receptor sites or by reducing production of the potent form while increasing production of the less potent form, possibly reducing the risk of osteoporosis and certain types of hormone-dependent cancers. Concerns have been raised regarding the potential adverse effects of phytoestrogens in soya infant formulas, and the best food for babies is certainly breast milk. Nevertheless, where breast feeding is not possible there is a role for soya infant formulas, which have been used for many years without any reports of adverse effects other than occasional allergy. For children and adults, soya should be regarded as another healthy food to be added to the diet in moderation.

Another important group are the plant sterols - a type of fat which has been shown to protect against heart disease. There are no dietary recommendations for sterols, but plant sterols have been shown to be beneficial in lowering cholesterol; high levels of cholesterol in the blood can cause heart disease. The average Western diet contains 180 to 400mg plant sterols per day while the vegan diet contains 600 to 800mg per day.

Useful references

Davis B, Melina V (2000) *Becoming Vegan: the complete guide to adopting a healthy plant-based diet,* Book Publishing Co. Summertown.

Key TJ, Davey GK, Appleby PN (2001) *Health benefits of a vegetarian diet,* Proc Nutr Soc 58 271-275.

Walsh S (2003) *Plant Based Nutrition and Health*, The Vegan Society.

Sandra Hood is a State Registered Dietitian and author of The Vegan Society's Raising your Vegan Infant - With Confidence. *For more information, or to order your copy, go to www.vegansociety.com/shop or call 0121 523 1731.*

ANIMAL-FREE CRITERIA

To qualify for inclusion in the Animal-Free Shopper, products must, as far as is possible and practical, be entirely free of animal involvement.

NO ANIMAL INGREDIENTS

The manufacture and/or development of the product, and where applicable its ingredients, must not involve, or have involved, the use of any animal product, by-product or derivative.

SUCH AS:

• **animal-derived additives** — (see below) • **animal fibres** — angora, astrakhan, cashmere, mohair, silk, wool • **animal milks** – cow's, goat's etc • **animal milk derivatives** — casein, caseinates, lactates, lactic acid, lactose • **bee products** — bee pollen, bee venom, beeswax, honey, propolis, royal jelly • **dairy products and by-products** — butter, cheese, cream, ice-cream, margarine, whey, yoghurt • **eggs and their derivatives** (eg albumen, lecithin, lutein) • **items obtained directly from the slaughter of animals** — fish (including anchovies), game and their derivatives (eg meat/fish extracts and stocks), poultry, meat • **marine animal products** — ambergris, capiz, caviar(e), chitin, coral, fish scales, fishmeal, isinglass, marine oils and extracts (eg fish oils, shark oil (squalene or squalane), seal oil, whale oil), natural sponge, pearl, roe, seal meat, shellfish, sperm oil, spermaceti wax, whale meat • **miscellaneous** — amniotic fluids, animal and fish glues, catgut, chamois, cochineal/carmine/carminic acid (E120), crushed snails or insects, fixatives (eg musk, civet, castoreum), hormones (eg oestrogen, progesterone, testosterone), ivory, lanolin(e), oil of mink, parchment, placenta, silk, shellac, snake venom, some vitamins (eg D3), urea, vellum, and any carriers, processing aids or release agents containing/comprising substances of animal origin • **slaughter by-products** — animal fats (eg dripping, lard, suet, tallow), amino acids, aspic, bone, bone charcoal, bone meal, bristles, collagen, down, dried blood, fatty acid derivatives, feathers, fur, gelatin(e), glycerin(e)/glycerol, hair, hides (leather, suede etc), hoof & horn meal, oleic acid, oleoic oil, oleostearin, pepsin, proteins (eg elastin, keratin, reticulin), rennet, skins, stearates, stearic acid, stearin(e)

Vegetable, mineral or plant/mineral-derived synthetic forms of the substances above are acceptable, as are microbiologically-fermented substances of plant origin.

NO ANIMAL TESTING

The development and/or manufacture of the product, and where applicable its ingredients, must not involve, or have involved, testing of any sort on animals conducted at the initiative of the manufacturer or on its behalf, or by parties over whom the manufacturer has effective control.

ADDITIVES

A food additive alters the properties of a basic foodstuff or mixture of foodstuffs for the purpose of achieving one, or a combination, of the following: aiding the production process, preserving, modifying consumer perception. The majority of additives possess no nutritional value.

All the countries of the European Union have a common list of additives. They are preceded with an 'E' to show they have been approved for use within the Union and must be displayed on the labels of all foods containing them. Some additives have no E-numbers and therefore do not have to be declared. These include solvents used to dilute other additives such as colourings and to extract flavours. Flavourings constitute the largest group of non-E additives.

Colourings and dyes that are approved for use in the cosmetics industry within the EU are also allocated a Colour Index ('CI') number.

The addition of substances to modify food is by no means a new phenomenon. Salt, for example, has been used as a preservative since about 3000 BCE. However the sheer number of additives available for use today, the routine and insidious use of animal-derived substances, the known or suspected health problems associated with some additives (including hyperactivity, allergies and migraine) and the totally unnecessary and morally objectionable requirement to test new additives on animals all provide the animal free shopper with an incentive to avoid additive-containing products where alternatives are available.

ANIMAL-DERIVED ADDITIVES

- **E120 (CI75470)** carmine/cochineal • **E542** edible bone phosphate • **E901** beeswax
- **E904** shellac • **E913** Lanolin • **E996** Lactitol • **E1000** Cholic Acid • **E1105** Lysozyme
- **calcium mesoinositol hexaphosphate** • **lactose** • **sperm oil** • **spermaceti**

POSSIBLY ANIMAL-DERIVED

• **E101** riboflavin, lactoflavin, vitamin B₂ • **E101a** riboflavin 5'-phosphate • **E153** (believed animal-free version only may be used in food) carbon black, vegetable carbon • **E161(b)** lutein • **E161(g)** canthaxanthin • **E236** formic acid • **E237** sodium formate • **E238** calcium formate • **E270** lactic acid • **E304** Fatty acid esters of ascorbic acid, ascorbyl palmitate and ascorbyl stearate • **E322** lecithin • **E325** sodium lactate • **E326** potassium lactate • **E327** calcium lactate • **E304** fatty acid esters of ascorbic acid, ascorbyl palmitate and ascorbyl stearate • **E422** glycerol (glycerine) • **E430** (believed to be no longer permitted in food) polyoxyethylene (8) stearate, polyoxyl (8) stearate • **E431** polyoxyethylene (40) stearate, polyoxyl (40) stearate • **E432** polyoxyethylene sorbitan monolaurate, polysorbate 20, tween 20 • **E433** polyoxyethylene sorbitan mono-oleate, polysorbate 80, tween 80 • **E434** polyoxyethylene sorbitan monopalmitate, polysorbate 40, tween 40 • **E435** polyoxyethylene sorbitan monostearate, polysorbate 60, tween 60 • **E436** polyoxyethylene sorbitan tristearate, polysorbate 65, tween 65 • **E442** glycerol • **E470(a)** sodium, potassium and calcium salts of fatty acids • **E470(b)** magnesium salts of fatty acids • **E471** glycerides of fatty acids, glyceryl monostearate, glyceryl distearate • **E472(a)** acetic acid esters of glycerides of fatty acids, acetoglycerides, glycerol esters • **E472(b)** lactic acid esters of glycerides of fatty acids, lactylated glycerides, lactoglycerides • **E472(c)** citric acid esters of glycerides of fatty acids • **E472(d)** tartaric acid esters of glycerides of fatty acids • **E472(e)** mono and diacetyltartaric acid esters of glycerides of fatty acids **E472(f)** mixed acetic and tartaric acid esters of mono- and di-glycerides of fatty acids • **E473** sucrose esters of fatty acids • **E474** sucroglycerides • **E475** polyglycerol esters of fatty acids • **E476** polyglycerol esters of polycondensed fatty acids of castor oil, polyglycerol polyricinoleate; polyglycerol esters of dimerised fatty acids of soya bean oil • **E477** propylene glycol esters of fatty acids; propane-1,2-diol esters of fatty acids • **E478** lactylated fatty acid esters of glycerol and propane-1,2-diol • **E479(b)** thermally oxidised soya bean oil interacted with mono- and di-glycerides of fatty acids • **E481** sodium stearoyl-2-lactylate • **E482** calcium stearoyl-2-lactylate • **E483** stearyl tartrate • **E491** sorbitan monostearate • **E492** sorbitan tristearate, span 65 • **E493** sorbitan monolaurate, span 20 • **E494** sorbitan mono-oleate, span 80 • **E495** sorbitan monopalmitate, span 40 • **E570** fatty acids (including myristic, stearic, palmitic and oleic), butyl stearate • **E572** magnesium salts of fatty acids (including magnesium stearate); calcium stearate • **E585** ferrous lactate • **E626** guanylic acid • **E627** guanosine 5'-disodium phosphate, sodium guanylate, disodium guanylate • **E628** dipotassium guanylate • **E628** calcium guanylate • **E631** inosine 5'-disodium phosphate, sodium 5'-inosinate • **E632** dipotassium inosinate • **E633** calcium inosinate • **E634** calcium 5'-ribonucleotides • **E635** disodium 5'-ribonucleotides

• **E635** sodium 5'-ribonucleotide • **E640** glycine and its sodium salt • **E631** disodium 5'-inosinate (IMP) • **E920** L-cysteine hydrochloride • **E921** L-cystine • **E1518** glyceryl mono-, di- and tri-acetate (triacetin) • **calcium heptonate** • **calcium phytate** • **diacetin** • **glyceryl** • **leucine** • **monoacetin** • **oxystearin** • and **any unspecified flavourings.**

ANIMAL-DERIVED CARRIERS

Some additives that are not animal derived may involve the use of gelatine as a carrier. These include E104 quinoline yellow, E160a(i) mixed carotenes and E160a(ii) ,-carotene.

GLOSSARY OF ANIMAL SUBSTANCES

* indicates that non-animal (synthetic, vegetable or plant/mineral-derived) versions/sources by the same name are known to exist.

• **albumen/albumin** egg white Use/s: food binder • **alpha hydroxy acids (AHAs)*** naturally occurring chemicals derived from fruit or milk Use/s: cosmetics • **ambergris** morbid concretion obtained from the intestine of the sperm whale Use/s: perfumes • **amino acids*** 'building blocks' of proteins • **amniotic fluid** fluid surrounding the foetus within the placenta Use/s: cosmetics • **amylase*** enzyme in saliva and pancreatic juice • **anchovy** small fish of the herring family, often an ingredient of Worcester sauce and pizza toppings Use/s: flavour enhancer • **angora** fibre obtained from rabbits or goats Use/s: clothing • **aspic** savoury jelly derived from meat and fish Use/s: glazing agent • **astrakhan** skin of stillborn or very young lambs from a breed originating in Astrakhan, Russia Use/s: clothing • **beeswax* (E901)** secreted by bees to produce combs Use/s: furniture- and floor-polishes, candles, cosmetics • **bone/bonemeal** animal bone Use/s: horticultural fertiliser, bone-china ornaments, crockery, supplements • **brawn** boiled meat, ears and tongue of pig Use/s: foodstuff • **bristle*** stiff animal hair, usually from pigs Use/s: brushes • **calcium mesoinositol hexaphosphate** Use/s: baked goods, soft drinks, processed vegetables • **capiz** shell Use/s: lampshades • **carmine/carminic acid (E120)** red pigment obtained from cochineal Use/s: food and drink dyes • **casein** milk protein Use/s: cheese • **cashmere** fine wool from the cashmere goat and wild goat of Tibet Use/s: clothing • **castoreum** obtained from the anal sex gland of the beaver Use/s: fixative in perfumes • **catgut** dried and twisted intestines of the sheep or horse Use/s: stringed musical instruments, surgical stitching • **caviar(e)** roe of the sturgeon and other fish Use/s: a relish

• **charcoal*** charred bone or wood Uses: clarifying agent • **chitin** organic base of the hard parts of insects and crustacea e.g. shrimps, crabs Use/s: conditioners and skin-care products, thickener and moisturiser in shampoos • **chamois** soft leather from the skin of the chamois antelope, sheep, goats, deer etc. Use/s: cleaning cloth • **cholecalciferol** see vitamin **D3** • **cholic acid (E1000)** extracted from the bile of cows Use/s: emulsifier • **civet** substance scraped from glands in the anal pouch of the civet cat Use/s: fixative in perfumes • **cochineal (E120)** dye-stuff consisting of the dried bodies of scale insects, used for making carmine Use/s: red food and drink colouring • **cod-liver oil** oil extracted from the liver of cod and related fish Use/s: food supplement • **collagen** constituent of connective tissue which yields gelatin(e) on boiling Use/s: cosmetics, sausage skins, supplements • **coral** hard calcareous substance consisting of the continuous skeleton secreted by coelenterate polyps for their support and habitation Use/s: jewellery, ornaments • **deoxyribonucleic acid (DNA)*** controls protein synthesis/stores genetic information. Found in all animal and plant cells Use/s: cosmetics, genetically modified organisms, shampoos • **down** underplumage of fowls (especially duck and goose) Use/s: filling quilts, pillows, sleeping bags, padded clothing • **dripping** melted animal fat Use/s: frying • **eider down** small, soft feathers from the breast of the eider duck Use/s: filling quilts • **elastin** protein uniting muscle fibres in meat Use/s: moisturiser in cosmetics • **fatty acids*** organic compounds: saturated, polyunsaturated and unsaturated • **feather** epidermal appendage of a bird Use/s: fashion accessory, feather dusters • **felt*** cloth made of wool, or of wool and fur or hair Use/s: clothing • **gelatin(e)** jelly obtained by boiling animal tissues (skin, tendons, ligaments etc.) or bones Use/s: confectionery, biscuits, capsules, jellies, photographic film, match heads • **glycerin(e)/glycerol (E422)*** clear, colourless liquid which may be derived from animal fats, synthesised from propylene or from fermentation of sugars Use/s: solvent for flavours, texture improver, humectant • **hide** animal skin (raw or tanned) Use/s: clothing and footwear, clothing accessories, upholstery • **insulin*** pancreas of cattle, sheep or pigs Uses: managing diabetes • **isinglass** very pure form of gelatin(e) obtained from the air bladders of some freshwater fish, especially the sturgeon Use/s: clarifying alcoholic drinks, jellies • **keratin** protein found in hair, horns, hooves and feathers Use/s: shampoos and conditioners, fertiliser • **L'cysteine hydrochloride (E920)*** manufactured from animal hair and poultry feathers or synthetically from coal tar Use/s: shampoo, improving agent for white flour • **lactic acid (E270)*** acid produced by the fermentation of milk sugar but also by fermentation in pickles, cocoa and tobacco Use/s: acidulant in confectionery, soft drinks, pickles and sauces • **lactitol (E966)** produced from milk sugar Use/s: sweetener • **lactose** milk sugar Use/s: tablet filler, sweetener, carrier for flavouring agents, especially in crisps • **lanolin(e)*** fat extracted from sheep's wool and hide Use/s: cleaning products, an emollient and emulsifier used in cosmetics, especially lipsticks • **lard** fat surrounding the stomach and kidneys of pigs, sheep and cattle Use/s: culinary • **leather** tanned hide (mostly from cattle but also sheep, pigs, goats etc.) Use/s: clothing and footwear, clothing accessories, upholstery • **lecithin (E322)*** fatty substance found in nerve tissues, egg yolk, blood and other tissues, mainly obtained commercially from soya bean, peanut and corn Use/s: emulsifier in baked goods and confectionery • **lutein (E161(b))*** deep-yellow substance found in egg yolk, obtained commercially from marigold Use/s: food colouring • **lysozyme (E1105)*** enzyme which may be derived from eggs Use/s: preservative • **mohair** cloth or yarn made from the hair of the angora goat Use/s: clothing • **musk*** substance secreted by glands of the male musk deer Use/s: perfume • **oleic acid*** fatty acid occurring in animal and vegetable fats Use/s: soaps, cosmetics, ointments • **oleic oil** liquid obtained from pressed tallow Use/s: margarines • **oleostearin** solid obtained from pressed tallow Use/s: soap and candles • **oestrogen*** female sex hormone from cow ovaries or pregnant mares' urine Use/s: cosmetics, body-building supplements, hormone creams • **parchment*** skin of the calf, sheep or goat, dressed and prepared for writing etc. • **pearl** ('Mother of', or 'cultured') concretion of layers of pain-dulling nacre formed around a foreign particle within the shell of various bivalve molluscs, principally the oyster Use/s: jewellery and decorative • **pepsin** enzyme found in gastric juices Use/s: cheese making • **placenta** organ by which the foetus is attached to the umbilical cord Use/s: cosmetics • **progesterone*** sex hormone Use/s: hormone creams • **propolis** bee glue, used by bees to stop up crevices and fix combs to the hive Use/s: toiletries and cosmetics • **rennet*** extract of calf stomach containing the enzyme rennin which clots milk Use/s: cheese, junkets • **reticulin** one of the structural elements (together with elastin and collagen) of skeletal muscle • **ribonucleic acid (RNA) *** see **deoxyribonucleic acid (DNA)** • **roe** eggs obtained from the abdomen of female fish Use/s: a relish • **royal jelly** food on which bee larvae are fed and which causes them to develop into queen bees Use/s: food supplement • **sable** fur from the sable marten, a small carnivorous mammal Use/s: clothing, artists' brushes • **shellac (E904)** insect secretion Use/s: hair spray, lip sealer, polishes, glazing agent • **silk** cloth made from the fibre produced by the larvae (silk worm) of certain bombycine moths, the harvesting of which entails killing the insect Use/s: clothing, cosmetics • **sodium 5'-inosinate** occurs naturally in muscle, prepared from fish waste Use/s: flavour enhancer • **sperm oil** oil found in the head of various species of whale Use/s: candles • **spermaceti wax** fatty substance found mainly in the head of whales and dolphins Use/s: medicines, candles, cosmetics • **sponge*** aquatic animal or colony of animals, characterised by a tough elastic skeleton of interlaced fibres Use/s. bathing aid • **squalene/squalane*** found in the liver of the shark (and rats) Use/s: toiletries and cosmetics • **stearate*** salt of stearic acid Use/s: body-building supplements • **stearic acid (E570)*** organic acid prepared from stearin • **stearin(e)*** general name for the three glycerides (monostearin, distearin, tristearin), formed by the combination of stearic acid and glycerin; chiefly applied to tristearin, which is the main constituent of tallow and suet Use/s: medicines, skin softener in toiletries and cosmetics • **suede*** kid-, pig- or calfskin, tanned Use/s: clothing and footwear • **suet*** solid fat prepared from the kidneys of cattle and sheep Use/s: cooking • **tallow** hard animal fat, especially that obtained from the parts around the kidneys of ruminants Use/s: soap, candles • **taurine*** amino acid • **testosterone*** male hormone Use/s: body-building supplements • **urea*** nitrogenous waste formed in the liver and excreted by the kidneys Use/s: toiletries and cosmetics • **vellum*** fine parchment prepared from the skins of calves, lambs or kids Use/s: writing material • **vitamin A*** (retinol) derived from fish-liver oil or egg yolk Use/s: cosmetics, food supplement • vitamin **D3 (cholecalciferol)** vitamin derived from lanolin or fish oil Use/s: vitamin and food supplements • **velvet*** fabric made of silk, cotton, rayon or nylon Use/s: clothing • **volaise** ostrich meat • **whey** residue from milk after the removal of the casein and most of the fat, by-product of cheese making Use/s: margarines, biscuits, crisps, cleaning products • **wool** hair forming the fleecy coat of the domesticated sheep and similar animals Use/s: clothing, mattresses.

ANIMAL TESTING CRITERIA

It remains the case that different animal protection groups and manufacturers promote a number of variations on the 'not tested on animals' theme. Depending on one's perspective or strategy, all have their strengths and weaknesses.

The criterion used to complete the Animal Free Shopper recognises that most substances have been, and some may continue to be, animal tested and simply requires that a product's manufacturer has not initiated testing on either the finished product or, where applicable, the ingredients.

For those who prefer companies using either a fixed cut-off date or the Humane Cosmetics Standard (see below), an appropriate symbol (see **KEY**, see page iii) appears in the product listings after the company name.

FIXED CUT-OFF DATE

A company that has adopted a fixed cut-off date (FCOD) has a policy of using only ingredients that have not been tested on animals since a specified date. In addition, the company will not initiate animal tests on its finished products. Fixed cut of dates have been described as the gold standard in terms of "not animal tested" criteria

The Cosmetics Industry Coalition for Animal Welfare (CICAW) encourages cosmetic companies to adopt an animal testing fixed cut-off date — preferably 1976 (the year the EU required all new ingredients to be safety(animal)-tested).

See 'Vivisection' (page 23) for more details on animal testing.

HUMANE COSMETICS STANDARD

In response to pressure from animal protection groups and consumers across Europe, the European Parliament proposed a ban on the marketing of animal tested cosmetics (Directive 93/35). However, early in 1997, to widespread dismay, the European Union (EU) postponed its 1 January 1998 target date until into the new century. An international coalition of animal protection groups from across the EU and North America drew up an international Humane Cosmetics Standard and launched a major campaign calling on all manufacturers and retailers to adopt it.

Co-ordinated (in the UK) by the British Union for the Abolition of Vivisection (BUAV), the standard requires companies not to conduct, commission, nor be party to any animal testing either now or in the future, and to adopt a fixed cut-off date for ingredients testing. The cut-off date is chosen by the company, but must be before the date that it applies to join the standard.

GENETICALLY MODIFIED ORGANISMS

Of concern to the consumer wishing to avoid genetically modified organisms (GMOs), because of possible effects on health or the implications of their release into the environment, is the presence in the UK food supply of GM foods, including soya.

Genetically modified foods are foods produced from genetically modified organisms. The insertion of foreign genes into foods may have many unexpected effects: for instance the insertion of a Brazil nut gene into soya results in a reaction in people allergic to nuts. There is also a risk of increasing resistance to antibiotics. Critics warn of unexpected and irreversible effects on agriculture and biodiversity. They condemn the immorality of the 'patenting of life' — transgenic animals, plants and seeds. From a vegan perspective, even if no animal gene is used during the modification process, it is likely that animal-derived enzymes are employed.

GM material can cross species barriers to other crops and to weeds, and once it has been released it is impossible to counteract any unforeseen consequences. Plants designed to kill 'pests' can kill beneficial insects as well and stimulate the development of resistance in the pests.

The Soil Association believes that genetic modification has no place in the production of safe and healthy food. Organic farming systems aim at producing food with care for human health, the environment and animal welfare.

In keeping with its vegan ethic, The Vegan Society is totally against the use of animal genes and animal substances in the development and production of GMOs. The Vegan Society believes that all foods that contain, may contain or have involved GMOs should be clearly labelled and has signed up to the Five-Year Freeze campaign for a moratorium on genetic engineering and patenting in food and farming.

OTHER ETHICAL CONSIDERATIONS

To qualify for inclusion in the Animal-Free Shopper a product need only be free of animal ingredients and animal testing. However, whilst avoiding products that have direct animal involvement is a very positive and far-reaching ethical stance, many animal-free shoppers choose to make purchases on a range of additional ethical considerations for the sake of humans, animals and the environment — such as:

- **vegan ownership** Some shoppers prefer to support those companies which are wholly or partly owned by vegans (see **KEY**, page iii)
- **product range** Many companies manufacture or distribute both animal and non-animal products. Given the choice, many animal-free shoppers prefer to buy from those companies whose entire range is animal-free (see **KEY**, page iii)
- **company activities** A number of companies manufacturing or distributing animal-free (and animal) products are involved directly in animal abuse — such as the meat and dairy industries.
- **company connections** Some seemingly innocuous companies have parent, sister or subsidiary companies which are involved directly in animal abuse such as animal testing or the dairy and meat industry. See company details (page 396) for parent companies of listed brands.
- **company affiliations** Possible animal abuse affiliations include: The British Industrial Biological Research Association (BIBRA), Research Defence Society (RDS), Countryside Alliance, Game Conservancy.

- **company sponsorships & donations** Companies producing animal free products may donate to medical research charities involved in vivisection or may sponsor sporting events that involve animals.
- **organised boycotts** Even large multi-national companies have ceased an objectionable activity when threatened with, or subjected to, a boycott campaign. In some instances boycotts can result in a significant financial loss. Though not always successful, it is argued that boycotts are a useful means by which to heighten public awareness.
- **pesticide use** The excessive use of chemical pesticides and fertilisers damages the environment and kills wildlife. Many animal-free shoppers prefer to avoid contributing to the destruction of our countryside and instead chose organic products, we have printed organic products in bold and highlighted those companies whose entire product range is organic (see KEY page iii).
- **vegan organic farming** While organic farming is kinder to the environment and it's animal inhabitants compared to chemical farming, an increasing number of animal free shoppers are seeking fruits and vegetables that have been produced through vegan farming methods. Stock free organic systems avoid all chemical inputs, animal manure and slaughterhouse by-products such as blood powder, bone meal and fish meal etc
- **genetically-modified organisms** See **GENETICALLY-MODIFIED ORGANISMS**, (page 49 and **KEY**, page iii).
- **fair trade** As humans are animals too many animal free shoppers are choosing to by fairly traded products. The Fairtrade Foundation's Fairtrade mark ensure minimum standards related to pay, working conditions, and local and environmental sustainability are met

Recognising that human and animal rights are inextricably linked and that all life is dependent upon the well-being of the planet, the animal-free shopper might also wish to avoid companies involved in or with: cash crops, environmentally damaging practices, irresponsible marketing, land rights, low wages and poor conditions, and oppressive regimes.

As well as boycotting certain goods, many shoppers actively seek out products that promote a cleaner environment or seek to improve workers' rights. Organic and fair trade products are now available almost everywhere in the UK, with the number and variety of products increasing all the time. You can find contact details for organisations promoting these aspects of food production in the USEFUL ADDRESSES section, page 59.

FURTHER INFORMATION

The Ethical Consumer Research Association Unit 21, 41 Old Birley St, Manchester M15 5RF **t** 0161 226 2929 **w** www.ethicalconsumer.org **e** mail@ethicalconsumer.org

Publishes The Ethical Consumer: a magazine providing information on companies behind brand names across a range of ethical issues — including animal testing, factory farming, fair trade and environmental impact.

CONTACT NETWORKS

BUSINESS

- **Vegan Business Connection** 245 Gladstone St, Nottingham, NG7 6HX, 0845 458 9595, vbc@veggies.org.uk, www.veggies.org.uk/vbc.htm
- **Vegan Chamber of Commerce** info@VeganChamber.org, www.veganchamber.org
- **Vegan Village** postie@veganvillage.co.uk, www.veganvillage.co.uk

FAMILIES

- **Vegan Family House** www.veganfamily.co.uk
- **VegParent NW** 01257 793550, tankiegirlie@aol.com, www.ukveggie.com/vegparentsnw
- **VegParent SE** lesley@vegan4life.org.uk, http://groups.yahoo.com/group/VegParentsSE
- **Vegan Society Families' List** Donald Watson House, 21 Hylton St, Birmingham, B18 6HJ, 0121 523 1730, info@vegansociety.com, www.vegansociety.com
- **Vegetarian and Vegan Families** Lesley Dove, 35 Rectory Gr, Hampton, TW12 1AH, 0208 941 8075, lesley@vegan4life.org.uk
- **York Vegan Families** 01759 380400, georgia.n@tinyworld.com

INTERNATIONAL

- **International Vegetarian Union** www.ivu.org
- **European Vegetarian Union** www.europeanvegetarian.org
- **Happy Cow** www.happycow.org
- **World Animal Net** www.worldanimalnet.org
- **VegDining** info@vegdining.com, www.vegdining.com
- **Veggies' Animal Contacts Directory** Sumac Centre, 245 Gladstone St, Nottingham, NG7 6HX, 0845 458 9595, acd@veggies.org.uk, www.veggies.org.uk/acd

- **Africa** Vegans in South Africa, gailjoslin@hotmail.com, http://home.intekom.com/animals/orgs/visa/
- **Australia** Vegan Society of Australia info@veganaustralia.org, www.veganaustralia.net
- **Austria** Vegane Gesellschaft Österreich, Waidhausenstr. 13/1, A 1140 Wien, Austria, info@vegan.at, www.vegan.at
- **Chile** Corporación Vegetariana Vegana Chilena, HomoVegetus-owner@gruposyahoo.com, http://www.homovegetus.cl/web2.htm
- **Czech Republic** âeská Vegetariánská Spoleânost, PO Box 23, Praha 011, 11801, Czech Republic, veg@vegspol.cz, www.vegspol.cz
- **Denmark** Danmarks Veganerforening, c/o Kirsten Jungsberg, Rådmand Steins Allé 45, 7, DK-2000 Frederiksberg, Denmark, kjungsberg@hotmail.com, www.vegana.dk
- **Finland** Vegaaniliitto Ry, Hämeentie 48, 00500 Helsinki, Finland, www.vegaaniliitto.fi
- **France** France Veg, vegorg02@yahoo.com, www.geocities.com/vegorg02
- **Ghana** Vegan Society of Ghana, PO Box 200, Arts Centre, Accra, Ghana, veghana@ivu.org, www.ivu.org/veghana
- **Hong Kong** Hong Kong Vegan Society, annie@hongkongvegan.com, www.ivu.org/hkvegan
- **India** Indian Vegan Society, indianvegansociety@rediffmail.com, www.indianvegansociety.com
- **Indonesia** The Indonesian Vegan Society, info@i-v-s.org, www.i-v-s.org
- **Iran** Iranian Vegan Forum, www.vegan.ir
- **Italy** Associazione per l'Informazione sul Veganismo in Italia, www.veganitalia.com
- **Japan** The Tokyo Vegan Meetup Group, www.vegan.meetup.com/389
- **Luxembourg** De Vegabond, Dr Claude Pasquini, PB 44, L-3107, Rumelange, Luxembourg, devegabond@hotmail.com
- **Netherlands** Vereniging Voor Veganisme, Herenweg 59, 3513 CC Utrecht, Netherlands, +31 30-2400824, www.veganisme.org

- **New Zealand** Vegan Christchurch, john@goddess.gen.nz, www.vegan.org.nz
- **New Zealand** VEGANZ, PO Box 4309, Shortland St, Auckland, New Zealand, veganz@pl.net, www.veganz.pl.net
- **Norway** Norsk Vegetarforening, Postboks 101 Blindern, 0314 Oslo, Norway, kontakt@vegetar.com, www.vegansiden.com
- **Puerto Rico** Carivegan, www.myspace.com/carivegan
- **Spain** Asociación Vegana Española (AVE), Apartado Postal 478, 29740 Torre del Mar (Málaga), Spain, +34-5-2513981, ave@ivu.org, www.ivu.org/ave
- **USA** American Vegan Society, 56 Dinshah Lane, PO Box 369, Malaga, NJ 08328, USA, +1 856-694-2887, www.americanvegan.org

LOCAL – ENGLAND

BERKSHIRE
- **Reading University Veg*ans** 07740 902060, jadeeastley@yahoo.com

BRISTOL
- **Bristol Vegans** 0117 377 7901, ellenhoward@blueyonder.co.uk, www.veganbristol.makessense.co.uk

BUCKINGHAMSHIRE
- **MKVEGAR** 01908 503919, mkvegar475@talktalk.net, www.mkvegar.makessense.co.uk

CAMBRIDGESHIRE
- **Cambridge Vegans** 01223 520311, adam@gimp.org, www.camvegans.xonline.org.uk/

CHESHIRE
- **Stockport Veg*ans** Flat 1, 22 Derby Rd, Withington, M14 6UW, 0161 718 9909, jehanine@ntlworld.com, www.groups.yahoo.com/group/stockveg

CORNWALL
- **Cornish Vegans** 81 Pendarves St, Tuckingmill, Camborne, TR14 8NP, 07988 542479 , kmedlyn@hotmail.com

DORSET
- **Bournemouth/Dorset Veg*ans** jjnanaz@yahoo.co.uk, uk.groups.yahoo.com/group/VegansWorldWide

ESSEX
- **North-East Essex Vegans** nesxvegans@hotmail.co.uk, www.nesxvegans.makessense.co.uk
- **Southend Animal Aid Vegans** PO BOX 11, Southend on Sea, SS1 1AA, southendanimalaid@hotmail.com, www.southendanimalaid.org.uk www.myspace.com/southendanimalaid

- **Vegan Essex** 4 Tyrells Rd, Gt Burstead, Billericay, CM11 2QE, 01277 653603, www.veggie-events.co.uk

GLOUCESTERSHIRE

- **Gloucestershire Vegans** 1 Hambutts Cotts, Edge Rd, Painswick, Stroud, GL6 6UP, mcxg46@dial.pipex.com

HAMPSHIRE

- **Solent Vegetarians and Vegans** 50a Macnaghten Rd, Bitterne Pk, Southampton, SO18 1GJ, 07790 461937, ziggwoo@googlemail.com, www.solentveg.org.uk

HEREFORDSHIRE

- **Three Counties Vegans** 01684 541808, info@vegan3counties.org.uk, www.vegan3counties.org.uk

HERTFORDSHIRE

- **North Herts Veg*ans** 01462 643424, rachel@veganhouse.co.uk, www.nhvegetariansandvegans.org.uk

KENT

- **Kent Vegans** 59 Chapel Rd, Ramsgate, CT11 0BS, 01843 589027
- **Medway Veg*ans** 7 Masefield Dr, Cliffe Woods, Rochester, ME3 8JW, 01634 220027, sheilamccrossan@hotmail.com
- **Sevenoaks Veg*ans** 01732 841790, sevenoaksvegansandveggies@blueyonder.co.uk
- **Tunbridge Wells Veg*ans** Fletcher's Cott, Knowle La, Halland, BN8 6PR, 01825 841104, mark.hanna@virgin.net, www.hypnotherapy-southeast.com

LANCASHIRE

- **Blackpool Vegans** blackpoolvegans@yahoo.co.uk, www.blackpoolvegans.makessense.co.uk
- **Manchester Veg*ans** 0161 304 8350, 07808 929556, chrissie@mvvg.co.uk, www.groups.yahoo.com/group/mvvg
- **Manchester Vegan Society** 07980 161025, sarahalliez@yahoo.co.uk, www.manchestervegans.veggroup.org

LEICESTERSHIRE

- **Leicestershire Veg*ans** 07786 175445, info@leicesterveggies.org.uk, www.leicesterveggies.org.uk

LINCOLNSHIRE

- **Lincoln Veg*ans** 01522 720526, christine.east@btinternet.com

LONDON

- **London Vegans** 5 Great Bushey Dr, N20 8QN, 0208 446 3480, vegans@veganlondon.co.uk, www.londonvegans.org.uk
- **Vegan Campaigns** BM2300, WC1N 3XX, 07980 739190, info@vegancampaigns.org.uk, www.vegancampaigns.org.uk

MERSEYSIDE
- **Scouseveg** 0151 933 1338, jane@vegsoc.org, www.scouseveg.co.uk

MIDDLESEX
- **Twickenham & Surrey Veg*ans** 35 Rectory Gr, Hampton, TW12 1AH, 0208 941 8075, Lesley@vegan4life.org.uk

NORFOLK
- **Norfolk Veg*ans** 15 Station Rd, Attlebridge, NR9 5AA, vegerose@hotmail.com, vegfolk.co.uk

NORTHAMPTONSHIRE
- **Northants Vegans** 07929 017088

NOTTINGHAMSHIRE
- **NottsVeg** notts.veg@googlemail.com, www.nottingham.vegangroup.co.uk
- **Nottingham University Veg*ans** 07846 739197, aeyaac@nottingham.ac.uk, www.nottsveg.co.uk

OXFORDSHIRE
- **OxVeg** 01235 769425, www.ivu.org/oxveg

SHROPSHIRE
- **Shropshire Veg*ans** 01952 432874, malc@C3173.freeserve.co.uk, www.shropveg.org.uk

STAFFORDSHIRE
- **Wolverhampton Veg*ans** 34 White Oak Dr, Wolverhampton, WV3 9AW, 07766 826534, dean_bracher@yahoo.co.uk, www.wolverhamptonvegansandveggies.makessense.co.uk

SURREY
- **GuildfordVeg** 01483 425040, guildfordveg@yahoo.co.uk
- **Twickenham & Surrey Veg*ans** 35 Rectory Gr, Hampton, TW12 1AH, 0208 941 8075, Lesley@vegan4life.org.uk

SUSSEX
- **Eastbourne Vegans** 01323 723855, eviesier@o2.co.uk
- **Hastings & Rye Bay Veg*ans** Stream Cott, Chapel La, Guestling, TN35 4HN, 01424 814895, richie@oldschool.ruralinternet.co.uk, www.herb.veggroup.org
- **Vegan Lewes** 19 Hillman Cl, Lewes, BN7 2FA, 01273 483110, godsend.eleisha@gmail.com, www.veganlewes.makessense.co.uk
- **Brighton Veg*ans** 83 Sutton Rd, Seaford, BN25 4QH, 01323 896244, 07794 108494, angie@angiewright.co.uk

TEESSIDE
- **TeesVeg** 07950 017928, tees_veg@yahoo.co.uk, groups.google.com/group/tees_veg/about

TYNE & WEAR
- **Northumbria Veg*ans** 9 Seymour St, N. Shields, NE29 6SN, 0191 258 6793, gmforrest@tiscali.co.uk

- **VegNE** 0191 236 8519, 079410 79999, mark@vegne.co.uk, www.vegne.co.uk

WARWICKSHIRE
- **Rugby Vegans** 4 Keyes Dr, Rugby, CV22 7ST, 01788 810805, andrea_elson@yahoo.com

WEST MIDLANDS
- **Birmingham Veg*ans** 0121 243 2337, hello@ecraftsmen.co.uk, www.bvv.org.uk
- **Redditch Veg*ans** PO Box 10202, Redditch, B98 8YT, 01527 458395, reddiveggie@lycos.com, www.redditchveggies.org.uk
- **Midlands Vegan Campaigns** info@veganmidlands.org.uk, www.veganmidlands.org.uk

WILTSHIRE
- **Vegan Wiltshire** 07973 517029, veganwiltshire@fastmail.fm, www.wiltshire.vegangroup.co.uk
- **Swindon Veg*ans and Animal Concern** 90 Beaulieu Cl, Toothill, Swindon, SN5 8AJ, 01793 644796, denisvegan01@tiscali.co.uk

WORCESTERSHIRE
- **Three Counties Vegans** 01684 541808, info@vegan3counties.org.uk, www.vegan3counties.org.uk

YORKSHIRE
- **N. Riding Veg*ans** 3 Arrathorne, Bedale, DL8 1NA, 01677 450176 (after 8 pm), vegan@phonecoop.coop
- **East Riding Vegans** 140 Victoria Ave, Hull, HU5 3DT, 01482 471119, ervegans@merrydowncontrolware.co.uk, www.merrydowncontrolware.co.uk/ervegans
- **Leeds Veg*ans** 20 Berkeley Mt, Leeds, LS8 3RN, 0113 248 4044, natalie@tharraleos.freeserve.co.uk, www.leedsveg.co.uk
- **Sheffield Animal Friends & Vegans** sheffieldanimalfriends@gmail.com, www.myspace.com/sheffieldaf
- **York Action for Animals & Veganism** swain4micklegate@yahoo.co.uk, www.yafa.co.uk

LOCAL – SCOTLAND

- **Aberdeen Vegans and Friends** 01224 573034, 07713 848663, george_rodger1940@yahoo.co.uk
- **Arbroath Veg*ans** 07751 335591, lizbegg@btinternet.com
- **Scottish Vegans** 08454 082385, scottishvegans@gmail.com, http://groups.yahoo.com/group/scottishvegans

- **Scottish Vegans Yahoo Group** Barravourich, Ramoyle, Dunblane, FK15 0BD, 01786 825171, 07871 570283, pv47@live.co.uk, scottishvegans@yahoogroups.com
- **University of Glasgow Vegan Society** vegan-info@glasgow.ac.uk, www.glasgow.ac.uk/clubs/vegan/

LOCAL – WALES

- **Chester and Clwyd Veg*ans** Nant yr Hafod Cott, Llandegla, Wrexham, LL11 3BG, 01798 790442, indesigneko@aol.com
- **Swansea Vegans** 01639 844992, Cmpalfrey@tiscali.co.uk
- **Wrexham Veg*ans** 07904 375178, info@wrexhamveg.org, www.wrexhamveg.org

LOCAL – IRELAND

- **Belfast Vegans** 07749 438079, donna.black@gmail.com

SOCIAL

- **London Lesbian Vegans** japope_1982@hotmail.co.uk, www.groups.yahoo.com/group/lvegangroup
- **Vegan Camp** c/o 9 Seymour St, North Shields, NE29 6SN, gmforrest@tiscali.co.uk, www.veggies.org.uk/vegancamp
- **Vegan Runners** 07900 160829, mfregan@tgwu.org.uk, www.veganrunners.makessense.co.uk
- **Vegan Summer Gathering** vegancom@btinternet.com, www.veganviews.org.uk/vsg
- **Vegetarian Matchmakers** www.groups.yahoo.com/group/lvegangroup
- **Veggie Romance** 0207 354 5399, info@veggieromance.com, www.veggieromance.com
- **Veggie Snow** 0118 946 4858, veggiesnow@makessense.co.uk, www.veggiesnow.org
- **Vegi Ventures** Castle Cott, Castle Sq, Castle Acre, King's Lynn, Norfolk, PE32 2AJ, 01760 755888, holidays@vegiventures.com, www.vegiventures.com
- **Vegans Worldwide uk** www.groups.yahoo.com/group/vegansWorldWide
- **Young Indian Veg*ans** 0208 686 6931, animalahimsa@yahoo.co.uk, www.youngindianvegetarians.co.uk

USEFUL ADDRESSES

Many of the groups listed below have limited funds and would therefore probably appreciate receiving an SAE with your enquiry.

ANIMAL EXPERIMENTS & ALTERNATIVES

- **British Union for the Abolition of Vivisection**, 16a Crane Grove, Islington, London, N7 8LB **tel.** 0207 700 4888 **e-mail** info@buav.org **website** www.buav.org
- **Doctors & Lawyers for Responsible Medicine**, PO Box 302, London, N8 9HD **tel.** 0208 340 2482 **e-mail** dlrm@gn.apc.org **website** www.dlrm.org
- **Dr Hadwen Trust for Humane Research**, 84a Tilehouse St, Hitchin, SG5 2DY **tel.** 01462 436819 **e-mail** info@drhadwentrust.org.uk **website** www.drhadwentrust.org.uk
- **Safer Medicines Campaign**, PO Box 62720, London, SW2 9FQ **tel.** 0208 265 2880 **e-mail** info@safermedicines.org **website** www.curedisease.net
- **FRAME**, 96-98 North Sherwood St, Nottingham, NG1 4EE **tel.** 0115 958 4740 **e-mail** education@frame.org.uk **website** www.frame.org.uk
- **Gateway to Hell**, BCM Box 8231, London, WC1N 3XX **tel.** 0845 458 3528 **e-mail** info@gatewaytohell.net **website** www.gatewaytohell.net
- **Humane Research Trust**, 29 Bramhall Lane S, Bramhall, Stockport, SK7 2DN **tel.** 0161 439 8041 **e-mail** info@humaneresearch.org.uk **website** www.humaneresearch.org.uk
- **Lord Dowding Fund for Humane Research** see National Anti-Vivisection Society
- **National Anti-Vivisection Society**, Millbank Tower, Millbank, London, SW1P 4QP **tel.** 0207 630 3340 **website** www.navs.org.uk
- **Physicians' Committee for Responsible Medicine**, 5100 Wisconsin Ave, NW, Suite 400, Washington, DC 20016, USA **e-mail** pcrm@pcrm.org **website** www.pcrm.org
- **Speak**, PO Box 6712, Northampton, NN2 6XR **tel.** 0845 330 7985 **e-mail** info@speakcampaigns.org **website** www.speakcampaigns.org
- **Uncaged**, 9 Leopold St, Sheffield, S1 2GY **tel.** 0114 272 2220 **e-mail** info@uncaged.co.uk **website** www.uncaged.co.uk

BLOODSPORTS

- **Hunt Saboteurs' Association**, BM HSA, London, WC1N 3XX **tel.** 0845 458 0727
  e-mail info@huntsabs.org.uk **website** www.huntsabs.org.uk
- **League Against Cruel Sports**, 83-87 Union St, London, SE1 1SG
  tel. 0845 330 8486 **website** www.league.uk.com

CIRCUSES & ZOOS

- **Captive Animals Protection Society**, PO Box 4186, Manchester, M60 3ZA
  tel. 0845 330 3911 **e-mail** info@captiveanimals.org
  website www.captiveanimals.org

'DEVELOPING WORLD'

- **Help International Plant Protein Organisation** (HIPPO), The Old Vicarage,
  Llangynog, Carmarthen, SA33 5BS **tel.** 01267 241547
  e-mail hippocharity@aol.com **website** www.ivu.org/articles/net/hippo.html
- **Vegfam**, Cwm Cott, Cwmynys, Cilycwm, Llandovery, SA20 0EU
  tel. 01550 721197 **website** www.vegfamcharity.org.uk

DIET/LIFESTYLE

- **Penny Brohn Cancer Care**, Grove Ho, Cornwallis Gr, Clifton, Bristol, BS8 4PG
  tel. 0117 980 9500 **e-mail** info@bristolcancerhelp.org
  website www.pennybrohncancercare.org
- **Compassionate Cooks**, **e-mail** info@compassionatecooks.com
  website www.compassionatecooks.com
- **Fresh Network**, 9 Stratton Rd, Hainford, Norwich, CB7 5TU **tel.** 0845 833 7017
  website www.fresh-network.com
- **Institute for Plant Based Nutrition**, 333 Bryn Mawr Ave, Bala Cynwyd,
  Pennsylvania 19004-2606, USA **e-mail** info@plantbased.org
  website www.plantbased.org
- **International Vegetarian Union**, **e-mail** manager@ivu.org
  website www.ivu.org
- **Movement for Compassionate Living**, 105 Cyfyng Rd, Ystalyfera, Swansea,
  SA9 2BT **website** www.mcl.unisonplus.net

- **Raw Times, website** www.rawtimes.com
- **Realfood, website** www.realfood.org.uk
- **Vegan Views, e-mail** editor@veganviews.org.uk
  website www.veganviews.org.uk
- **Vegan Village, e-mail** postie@veganvillage.co.uk
  website www.veganvillage.co.uk
- **Vegetarian Society**, Parkdale, Dunham Rd, Altrincham, WA14 4QG
  tel. 0161 925 2000 **e-mail** info@vegsoc.org **website** www.vegsoc.org
- **Vegetarian & Vegan Foundation**, 8 York Ct, Wilder St, Bristol, BS2 8QH
  tel. 0117 970 5190 **e-mail** info@vegetarian.org.uk **website** www.vegetarian.org.uk
- **World Vegan Day, website** www.worldveganday.org
- **Young Indian Vegetarians**, 226 London Rd, W Croydon, CR0 2TF
  tel. 0208 681 8884 **e-mail** animalahimsa@yahoo.co.uk
  website www.youngindianvegetarians.co.uk

FARMING & GROWING

- **Compassion in World Farming**, River Ct, Mill La, Godalming, GU7 1EZ
  tel. 01483 521950 **website** www.ciwf.org.uk
- **Farm & Food Society, e-mail** enquiries@fafs.org **website** www.fafs.org
- **Farm Animal Welfare Network (FAWN)**, PO Box 40, Holmfirth, Huddersfield,
  HD7 1QY **tel.** 01484 688650 **website** www.fawn.me.uk
- **Garden Organic**, Ryton Organic Gardens, Coventry, CV8 3LG
  tel. 02476 303517 **e-mail** enquiry@gardenorganic.org.uk
  website www.gardenorganic.org.uk
- **Kent Against Live Exports**, PO Box 363 Folkestone, CT30 3GJ,
  tel. 01304 204688 **e-mail** kale@globalnet.co.uk
  website www.users.globalnet.co.uk/~kale
- **Plants for a Future, website** www.pfaf.org
- **Soil Association**, South Plaza, Marlborough St, Bristol, BS1 3NX
  tel.0117 314 5000 **website** www.soilassociation.org
- **Vegan Organic Network**, 58 High La, Chorlton, Manchester, M21 9DZ
  website www.veganorganic.net

FUR & LEATHER

- **Campaign Against Leather & Fur** (CALF), BM 8889, London, WC1N 3XX
- **Coalition to Abolish the Fur Trade** (CAFT), PO Box 38, Manchester, M60 1NX
  tel. 0845 330 7955 **e-mail** caft@caft.org.uk **website** www.caft.org.uk

GENERAL

- **Advocates for Animals**, 10 Queensferry St, Edinburgh, EH2 4PG
  tel. 0131 225 6039 **website** www.advocatesforanimals.org.uk
- **Animal Aid**, The Old Chapel, Bradford St, Tonbridge, TN9 1AW
  tel. 01732 364546 **e-mail** info@animalaid.org.uk
  website www.animalaid.org.uk
- **Animal Cruelty Investigation Group**, PO Box 8, Halesworth, IP19 0JL
  tel. 01986 782280 **e-mail** mike@acigawis.freeserve.co.uk
  website www.acigawis.co.uk
- **Animal Defenders** see National Anti-Vivisection Society
- **Campaign for the Abolition of Animal Slavery**,
  e-mail campaign_abolition_animal_slavery@live.co.uk
  website www.animalslavery.net
- **Chickens' Lib** see Farm Animal Welfare Network (FAWN)
- **IFAW**, 87-90 Albert Embankment, London, SE1 9UD **tel.** 0207 587 6700
  e-mail info-uk@ifaw.org **website** www.ifaw.org
- **People for the Ethical Treatment of Animals** (Europe), PO Box 36668,
  London, SE1 1WA **tel.** 0207 357 9229 **e-mail** info@peta.org.uk
  website www.peta.org.uk
- **Petsearch** (register of animals lost & found), **tel.** 01225 705175
  e-mail petsearch.steele@ukonline.co.uk **website** www.petsearchuk.org.uk
- **Respect for Animals**, PO Box 6500, Nottingham, NG4 3GB **tel.** 0115 952 5440
  e-mail info@respectforanimals.org **website** www.respectforanimals.co.uk
- **RSPB**, The Lodge, Sandy, SG19 2BR **tel.** 01767 680551 **website** www.rspb.org.uk
- **RSPCA**, Wilberforce Way, Southwater, Horsham, RH13 9RS **tel.** 0300 1234 555
  e-mail Enqserv@rspca.org.uk **website** www.rspca.org.uk
- **Viva!**, 8 York Ct, Wilder St, Bristol, BS2 8QH **tel.** 0117 944 1000
  e-mail info@viva.org.uk **website** www.viva.org.uk
- **World Society for the Protection of Animals**, **tel.** 0207 587 5000
  e-mail info@wspa.org.uk **website** www.wspa.org.uk
- **WWF UK**, Panda House, Weyside Pk, Godalming, GU7 1XR **tel.** 01483 426444
  website www.wwf.org.uk

MARINE ANIMALS

- **British Divers Marine Life Rescue**, Lime Ho, Regency Cl, Uckfield, TN22 1DS
  tel. 01825 765546 **e-mail** info@bdmlr.org.uk **website** www.bdmlr.org.uk
- **Cetacea Defence**, **e-mail** CetDef@hotmail.co.uk **website** www.cetaceadefence.net

- **Marine Conservation Society**, Unit 3, Wolf Business Pk, Alton Rd, Ross-on-Wye, HR9 5NB **tel.** 01989 566017 **website** www.mcsuk.org
- **Shellfish Network**, 16 East Gdns, Woking, GU22 8DP **tel.** 01483 766291 **website** www.shellfishnetwork.org.uk
- **Whale & Dolphin Conservation Society**, 38 St Paul St, Chippenham, SN15 1LJ **tel.** 01249 449500 **email** info@wdcs.org **website** www.wdcs.org

MISCELLANEOUS

- **Vegetarian For Life** (for Elderly Vegetarians), 182 Higher Bebington Rd, Bebington, Wirral, CH63 2PT **tel.** 0151 608 1595 **website** www.vegetarianforlife.org.uk

PRISONERS' SUPPORT (FOR ANIMAL RIGHTS/VEGAN PRISONERS)

- **Vegan Prisoners' Support Group**, BM 2107, London, WC1N 3XX **tel.** 0208 292 8325 **e-mail** info@vpsg.org **website** www.vpsg.org

RELIGIOUS

- **Anglican Society for the Welfare of Animals**, PO Box 7193, Hook, RG27 8GT **tel.** 01252 843093 **e-mail** feedback@aswa.org.uk **website** www.aswa.org.uk
- **Catholic Concern for Animals**, 36 Broad Oak Pk, St John's, Colchester, CO4 4JY **e-mail** deborahjark@aol.com **website** www.all-creatures.org/ca
- **Christian Ecology Link**, 3 Bond St, Lancaster, LA1 3ER **tel.** 01524 36241 **email** info@christian-ecology.org.uk **website** www.christian-ecology.org.uk
- **Christian Vegetarian Association UK**, Foresta, Pines Rd, Liphook, GU30 7PL **tel.** 01428 723747 **e-mail** dongwil@uk2.net **website** www.christianvegetarian.co.uk
- **The Fellowship of Life**, 43 Braichmelyn, Bethesda, Bangor, LL57 3RD **e-mail** fol@fol-online.org **website** www.all-creatures.org/fol
- **Humanist Vegetarian Group**, **tel.** 01803 858576 **website** www.humanist.veggroup.org
- **Islamic Concern**, **e-mail** info@islamicconcern.com **website** www.islamicconcerns.com
- **Jewish Vegetarian and Ecological Society**, **email** ijvs@yahoo.com **website** www.ivu.org/jvs
- **Kindness Unlimited**, The Old Vicarage, Llangynog, Carmarthen, SA33 5BS **website** www.ivu.org/ku

- **Latter Day Saints Vegetarian/Vegan Support**, **e-mail** LDSVeg@LDSveg.org **website** www.ldsveg.org
- **The Mary T and Frank L Hoffman Family Foundation**, **e-mail** flh@all-creatures.org **website** www.all-creatures.org/ff
- **The Methodist Animal Welfare Group**, 32 Balderton Bldgs, Balderton St, London, W1Y 1TA **website** www.christianecology.org.uk/mawg.htm
- **Muslim Vegan/Vegetarian Society**, 59 Brey Towers, 136 Adelaide Towers, London, NW3 3JU **tel.** 0207 483 1742
- **Quaker Concern for Animals**, 29 Blair Pk, Knaresborough, HG5 0TH **tel.** 0845 458 4168 **website** www.all-creatures.org/qa
- **Spiritual Vegans**, Kent Ho, Kent Pl, Lechlade, GL7 3AW **e-mail** spiritualvegans@yahoo.co.uk **website** www.geocities.com/spiritualvegans
- **Vegan Pagans**, **website** http://veganpagans.tribe.net/

SPORTS

- **Vegan Bodybuilding**, **e-mail** info@veganbodybuilding.org **website** www.veganbodybuilding.org
- **Vegetarian Cycling & Athletic Club**, **website** www.vcac.vegfolk.co.uk
- **Vegan Fitness Forum**, **website** www.veganfitness.net
- **Vegan Runners**, 13 Peers La, Shenley, Church End, Milton Keynes, MK5 6BG **tel.** 01908 503919 **e-mail** veganrunners@talktalk.net **website** www.veganrunners.makessense.co.uk

THEORY OF ANIMAL RIGHTS

- **Animal Rights FAQs**, **website** www.speciesism.com
- **Animal Rights: The Abolitionist Approach** (blog of Prof. Gary Francione), **website** www.abolitionistapproach.com
- **Culture and Animals Foundation**, **website** www.cultureandanimals.org

WILD ANIMALS

- **Born Free Foundation**, 3 Grove Ho, Foundry La, Horsham, RH13 5PL **tel.** 01403 240170 **e-mail** info@bornfree.org.uk **website** www.bornfree.org.uk
- **British Hedgehog Preservation Society**, Hedgehog Ho, Dhustone, Ludlow, SY8 3PL **tel.** 01584 890801 **e-mail** info@ britishhedgehogs.org.uk **website** www.britishhedgehogs.org.uk

- **Care for the Wild International**, The Granary, Tickfold Farm, Kingsfold, RH12 3SE **tel.** 01306 627900 **e-mail** info@careforthewild.com **website** www.careforthewild.com
- **Fox Project**, The Lodge, King's Toll Rd, Pembury, TN2 4BE **tel.** 01892 826222 **e-mail** fox@foxproject.org.uk **website** www.foxproject.org.uk
- **Jenita Fox Rescue**, Oak Tree Cattery, Main Rd, Colden Common, Winchester, SO21 1TL **tel.** 02380 692309
- **The Wildlife Trusts**, The Kiln, Waterside, Mather Road, Newark, NG24 1WT **tel.** 01636 677711 **e-mail** enquiries@wildlifetrusts.org **website** www.wildlifetrusts.org
- **Badger Trust**, PO Box 708, East Grinstead, RH19 2WN **tel.** 0845 828 7878 **e-mail** enquiries@badgertrust.org.uk **website** www.nfbg.org.uk
- **Seal Sanctuary**, Gweek, Helston, TR12 6UG **tel.** 01326 221361 **e-mail** seals@sealsanctuary.co.uk **website** www.sealsanctuary.co.uk
- **St Tiggywinkle's** (Wildlife Hospital), Aston Rd, Haddenham, Aylesbury, HP17 8AF **tel.** 01844 292292 **e-mail** mail@sttiggywinkles.org.uk **website** www.sttiggywinkles.org.uk

YOUTH GROUPS

- **Animal Action Club** see RSPCA (General)
- **Animal Aid Youth Group**, The Old Chapel, Bradford St, Tonbridge, TN9 1AW **tel.** 01732 364546 **e-mail** info@youth4animals.com **website** www.youth4animals.com
- **Go Wild Club** (WWF Youth Group), Panda Ho, Weyside Pk, Godalming, GU7 1XR **tel.** 01483 426444 **e-mail** www.wwf.org.uk **website** gowild@wwf.org.uk
- **Students Against Animal Cruelty**, PO Box 211, Short St, Southend, SS1 1AA **e-mail** info@saac.org.uk **website** www.saac.org.uk
- **Vegan Society YOUth**, Donald Watson House, 21 Hylton Street, Birmingham, B18 6HJ **tel.** 0121 523 1738 **e-mail** youth@vegansociety.com **website** www.vegansociety.com/youth_pages
- **Viva! Activists**, 8 York Ct, Wilder St, Bristol, BS2 8QH **tel.** 0117 944 1000 **e-mail** info@viva.org.uk **website** www.vivaactivists.org.uk
- **Wild Crew** (Born Free Foundation Youth Group), Grove Ho, Foundry La, Horsham, RH13 5PL **tel.** 01403 240170 **e-mail** info@bornfree.org.uk **website** www.bornfree.org.uk/kids-go-wild
- **Young Veggie** (Vegetarian Society Youth Group), Parkdale, Dunham Rd, Altrincham, WA14 4QG **tel.** 0161 925 2000 **e-mail** education@vegsoc.org **website** www.youngveggie.org

SUGGESTED READING

There is now a wide range of literature related to vegan food and cookery, nutrition, vegan living, animal rights, activism and ethics. One of the roles of the Vegan Society is to provide resources to make vegan living as easy as possible. The Society provides free fact sheets and booklets including information on nutrition, vegan parenting and activism and also catering packs for restaurants, hospitals and care homes. For a full list contact the Vegan Society by e-mail or phone (details below).

BOOKS

Some of the titles below are available from the Vegan Society. You can visit our online shop at www.vegansociety.com/shop. Books can be paid for online or over the phone by calling 0121 523 1740. For a current list of books and merchandise contact the Vegan Society at Donald Watson House, 21 Hylton Street, Hockley, Birmingham, B18 6HJ, telephone 0121 523 1730, e-mail: info@vegansociety.com.

Note: The titles listed below may not have been written from an entirely animal-free viewpoint but are included on the basis of their educational or practical value.

ACTIVISM

Campaign Against Cruelty Alex Bourke and Ronny Worsey, Scamp Media (2001)
Striking at the Roots: A Practical Guide to Animal Activism Mark Hawthorne, O Books (2008)
The Lifelong Activist: *How to Change the World Without Losing Your Way* Hillary Rettig, Lantern Books (2006)
You Can Save the Animals Ingrid Newkirk, Prima (1999)

ADDITIVES

A Consumer's Dictionary of Food Additives Ruth Winter, Three Rivers Press (2004)
Animal Ingredients A-Z The EG Smith Collective, AK Distribution (2004)
Not on the Label: *What Really Goes into the Food on Your Plate* Felicity Lawrence, Penguin Book Ltd (2004)

ANIMAL CARE

Vegetarian Cats and Dogs James Peden, Harbingers of a New Age (1995)

ANIMAL EXPERIMENTS & ALTERNATIVES

Caught in the Act: Feldberg Investigation Melody MacDonald, Jon Carpenter (1994)

Sacred Cows and Golden Geese Jane Goodall & Dr C R Greek & J S Greek, Continuum International Publishing Group (2002)

Slaughter of the Innocent Hans Ruesch, Slingshot (2003)

Specious Science C Ray Greek & Jean Swingle Greek, Continuum (2003)

Vivisection or Science: An Investigation into Testing Drugs and Safeguarding Health Pietro Croce, Zed Books (2000)

Vivisection Unveiled: An Exposé of the Medical Futility of Animal Experimentation Dr Tony Page, Jon Carpenter (1997)

What Will We Do If We Don't Experiment On Animals? Medical Research for the Twenty-first Century Jean Swingle Greek, C. Ray Greek, Trafford Publishing (2006)

ANIMAL LIBERATION

Capers in the Churchyard: Animal Rights Advocacy in the Age of Terror Lee Hall, Nectar Bat Press (2006)

Free the Animals: The Story of the Animal Liberation Front Ingrid Newkirk, Lantern Books (2000)

From Dusk 'til Dawn: An Insider's View of the Growth of the Animal Liberation Movement Keith Mann, Puppy Pincher Press (2007)

Terrorists or Freedom Fighters?: Reflection on the Liberation of Animals Steven Best, Lantern Books (2004)

ANIMAL RIGHTS/ETHICS

Animal Century: A Celebration of Changing Attitudes to Animals Mark Gold, Jon Carpenter (1999)

Animal Liberation Peter Singer, Ecco (2001)

Animal Rights: A Very Short Introduction David DeGrazia, Oxford University Press (2002)

Animal Welfare: Limping Towards Eden John Webster, Wiley Blackwell (2005)

Animals as Persons: Essays on the Abolition of Animal Exploitation Gary L Francione, Columbia University Press (2008)

Animals, Politics & Morality: Second Edition Robert Garner, Manchester University Press (2005)

Animals, Property, and the Law Gary L. Francione, Temple University Press (1995)

Born to be Wild Juliet Gellatley, The Women's Press (2001)

Empty Cages: Facing the Challenge of Animal Rights Tom Regan, Rowman & Littlefield Publishers (2005)

Eternal Treblinka: Our Treatment of Animals and the Holocaust Charles Patterson, Lantern Books (2002)

Introduction to Animal Rights: Your Child or the Dog Gary L. Francione, Temple University Press (2000)

Making a Killing: The Political Economy of Animal Rights Bob Torres, AK Press (2008)

Rain Without Thunder: The Ideology of the Animal Rights Movement Gary L. Francione, Temple University Press (1996)

The Case for Animal Rights Tom Regan, University of California Press (2004)

The Dreaded Comparison: Human and Animal Slavery Marjorie Spiegel, Mirror Books (1997)

The Pig Who Sang to the Moon: The Emotional World of Farm Animals Jeffrey Moussaieff Masson, Ballantine Books (2003)

The Savour of Salt: A Henry Salt Anthology George and Willene Hendrick, Open Gate Press (1989)

The Silent Ark Juliet Gellatley, HarperCollins (1996)

BABIES & CHILDREN

Benji Bean Sprout Doesn't Eat Meat! Sarah Rudy, Sun King Pub and Graphics (2004)

Compassionate Kids: Raising Children the Vegan Way Helen Hewitt & Jacqulyn Edwards, Magpie House (2005)

Go Vegan Go! Seamus Brough, Magpie House (2006).

Happy, Caring, Healthy & Sharing – a book for young green vegans Graham Burnett, Land & Liberty (1991)

Raising Vegan Children in a Non-Vegan World Erin Pavlina, VegFamily (2003)

Raising Vegetarian Children Joanne Stepaniak & Vesanto Melina, Contemporary Books (2003)

Raising your Vegan Infant – With Confidence Sandra Hood, The Vegan Society (2005)

The Amazing Adventures of Wonderpig Phil Tutton, Wonderpig Publishing (2007)
Vegetarian and Vegan Mother and Baby Guide Rose Elliot, Viva! (2003)

CATERING

Profit From Emerging Dietary Trends John Hartley, Go Publish (2000)
Vegan Catering For All The Vegan Society (2008)

CIRCUSES AND ZOOS

Animals in Circuses and Zoos – Chiron's World? Marthe Kiley-Worthington, Aardvark Publishing (1997)
Rattling the Cages: 50 Years of Campaigning for Animals Captive Animals Protection Society (2007)
The Rose-Tinted Menagerie William Johnson, Heretic Books (1994)

COOKERY BOOKS

Alternative Vegan: International Vegan Fare Straight from the Product Aisle Dino Sarma, Tofu Hound Press (2007)
Another Dinner is Possible Isy Morgenmuffel, Mike Home Brew, Anarchist Teapot & Active Distribution (2007)
A Vegan Taste of France Linda Majzlik, Jon Carpenter (2003)
A Vegan Taste of Greece Linda Majzlik, Jon Carpenter (2003)
A Vegan Taste of India Linda Majzlik, Jon Carpenter (2002)
A Vegan Taste of Italy Linda Majzlik, Jon Carpenter (2001)
A Vegan Taste of Mexico Linda Majzlik, Jon Carpenter (2002)
A Vegan Taste of North Africa Linda Majzlik, Jon Carpenter (2003)
A Vegan Taste of Thailand Linda Majzlik, Jon Carpenter (2004)
A Vegan Taste of the Caribbean Linda Majzlik, Jon Carpenter (2001)
A Vegan Taste of the Middle East Linda Majzlik, Jon Carpenter (2002)
Authentic Chinese Cuisine Bryanna Clark Grogan, Book Publishing Company (2000)
Cook Vegan Richard Youngs, Ashgrove Publishing (2001)
Easy Vegan Cooking: Over 350 Delicious Recipes for Every Occasion Leah Leneman, Thorsons (1998)
Fat-Free & Easy Jennifer Raymond, Heart & Soul Publications (1997)
Green Gastronomy Colin Spencer, Bloomsbury (1996)

Healing Foods Cookbook: The Vegan Way to Wellness Jane Sen, HarperCollins (2000)

Incredibly Delicious: Recipes for a New Paradigm M. Katz, Gentle World (2003)

Japanese Cooking Miyoko Nishimoto Schinner, Book Publishing Company (1999)

Kitchen Doctor – Vegan Cooking for Health Nicola Graimes, Southwater (2003)

La Dolce Vegan!: Vegan Livin' Made Easy Sarah Kramer, Arsenal Pulp Press (2007)

More Fabulous Beans Barb Bloomfield, Book Publishing Company (2003)

Nonna's Italian Kitchen Bryanna Clark Grogan, Book Publishing Company (1998)

PETA Celebrity Cookbook PETALantern Books (2002)

Simple Treats Ellen Abraham, Book Publishing Company (2003)

Simply Vegan Debra Wasserman & Reed Mangels, Vegetarian Resource Group (US) (1999)

Skinny Bitch in the Kitch: Kick-ass Solutions for Hungry Girls who want to Stop Cooking Crap (and Start Looking Hot!) Rory Freedman, Kim Barnouin, Running Press (2007)

So What Do You Eat? Liz Cook (1999)

The Absolutely Animal-Free Cookbook Wendy Turner, The Book Guild (1997)

The Anglelica Home Kitchen Leslie McEachern, Ten Speed Press (2003)

The Artful Vegan Eric Tucker with Bruce Enloe/desserts by Amy Pearce, Ten Speed Press (2003)

The Cake Scoffer Ronny, Vegan International Cake Engineers (2000)

The Everyday Vegan Dreena Burton, Arsenal Pulp Press (2003)

The Health Promoting Cookbook Alan Goldhamer, Book Publishing Company (1997)

The Joy of Vegan Baking: The Compassionate Cooks' Traditional Treats and Sinful Sweets Colleen Patrick-Goudreau, Fair Winds Press (2007)

The Joy of Vegan Cookery Amanda Grant, Metro Publishing Ltd (2002)

The Uncheese Cookbook Joanne Stepaniak, Book Publishing Company (2003)

The Vegan Cookbook Alan Wakeman and Gordon Baskerville, Faber & Faber (1996)

The Vegan Gourmet: Full Flavor and Variety with over 100 Delicious Recipes Susann Geiskopf-Hadler & Mindy Toomay, Prima Publishing (1999)

The Whole Foods Diabetic Cookbook Patricia Stevenson, Michael Cook & Patricia Bertron RD, Book Publishing Company (2003)

Vegan Tony Weston and Yvonne Bishop, Hamlin (2004)

Vegan Baking Linda Majzlik, Jon Carpenter (2000)

Vegan Barbecues & Buffets Linda Majzlik, Jon Carpenter (1999)

Vegan Cooking: Recipes for Beginners Eva Batt, Thorsons (2002)

Vegan Cooking for Everyone Leah Leneman, HarperCollins (2003)

Vegan Cooking for One Leah Leneman, Thorsons (2000)
Vegan Cupcakes take Over the World: 75 Dairy-free Recipes for Cupcakes that Rule Isa Chandra Moskowitz & Terry Hope Romero, Da Capo Lifelong (2008)
Vegan Dinner Parties Linda Majzlik, Jon Carpenter (1998)
Vegan Feasts Rose Elliot, Thorsons (2000)
Vegan Rustic Cooking for all Seasons Diana White, Vegan Organic Trust (2002)
Vegan Vittles: Second Helping: Down-Home Cooking for Everyone Joanne Stepaniak, Book Publishing Company (2007)
Vegan with a Vengeance: Over 150 Delicious, Cheap, Animal-free Recipes Isa Chandra Moskowitz, Grub Street (2007)
Veganomicon: The Ultimate Vegan Cookbook Isa Chandra Moskowitz & Terry Hope Romero, Da Capo Lifelong (2008)
Vice Cream: Gourmet Vegan Desserts Jeff Rogers, Celestial Arts (2004)

FEMINISM & ANIMAL RIGHTS

Animals & Women: Feminist Theoretical Explorations CJ Adams & J Donovan, Duke University Press (1995)
Feminist Care Tradition in Animal Ethics: A Reader Josephine Donovan & Carol Adams, Columbia University Press (2007)
Neither Man Nor Beast: Feminism and the Defence of Animals Carol Adams, Continuum International Publishing Group Ltd (2003)
The Pornography of Meat Carol Adams, Continuum International Publishing Group Ltd (2003)
The Sexual Politics of Meat: A Feminist-vegetarian Critical Theory: Tenth Anniversary Edition, Carol Adams, Continuum International Publishing Group Ltd (2000)

FOOD

Food For Free Richard Mabey, Collins (2004)
Food Wars: The Global Battle for Mouths, Minds and Markets Tim Lang & Michael Heasman, Earthscan (2004)
Poison on a Plate: Dangers in the Food we Eat and How to Avoid them Richard Lacey, Metro Books (1998)
The Atlas of Food Erik Millstone & Tim Lang, Earthscan (2003)

GARDENING

All New Square Foot Gardening: Grow More in Less Space! Mel
Bartholomew, Cool Springs Press (2006)
Forest Gardening Robert A de J Hart, Green Earth (1996)
***How to Grow More Vegetables: And Fruits, Nuts, Berries, Grains, and Other
Crops Than You Can Imagine*** John Jeavons, Ten Speed Press (2006)
Permaculture: A Beginners' Guide Graham Burnett, Land & Liberty (2000)
Plants for a Future Ken Fern, Permanent Publications (1997)
Sprout Garden Mark M Braunstein, Book Publishing Company (1999)
***The Earth Care Manual: A Permaculture Handbook for Britain and Other
Temperate Countries*** Patrick Whitefield, Permanent Publications (2004)
The Gaia Natural Garden: Gardening in Harmony with Nature Peter Harper,
Jeremy Light & Chris Madsen, Gaia Books (2005)

GMOs

Animal Genetic Engineering: of Pigs, Oncomice and Men Peter Wheale &
Ruth McNally (eds), Pluto Press (1995)
Eat Your Genes: How Genetically Modified Food is Entering our Diet
Stephen Nottingham, Zed Books Ltd (2003)
Genetic Engineering, Food and our Environment Luke Anderson, Green Books
(1999)
Seeds of Deception Jeffrey M. Smith, Green Books (2004)
Unnatural Harvest: How Genetic Engineering is Altering Our Food Ingeborg
Boyens, Doubleday Canada (2001)

MEAT/DAIRY INDUSTRIES

***Animal Pharm: One Man's Struggle to Discover the Truth about Mad Cow
Disease and Variant CJD*** Mark Purdey, Clairview Books (2007)
Cannibals, Cows and the CJD Catastrophe Jennifer Cooke, Random House USA
Inc (2000)
Chew on This: Everything You Don't Want to Know About Fast Food Eric
Schlosser, Puffin Books (2006)
***Don't Worry (It's Safe to Eat): The True Story of GM Food, BSE and Foot
and Mouth*** Andrew Rowell, Earthscan Publications (2003)
Fast Food Nation: What the All-American Meal is doing to the World Eric
Schlosser, Penguin Books Ltd (2002)

Meat Market: Animals, Ethics, & Money Erik Marcus, Brio Press (2005)
Milk: The Deadly Poison Robert Cohen, BookWorld Press (1998)
Slaughterhouse: The Shocking Story of Greed, Neglect and Inhumane Treatment Inside the U.S. Meat Industry Gail A. Eisnitz, Prometheus Books (2006)
The Meat Business – Devouring A Hungry Planet Geoff Tansey & Joyce D'Silva (eds) Earthscan (1999)

NUTRITION & HEALTH

10 Days to Better Health Kirsten Hartvig & Dr Nic Rowley, Piatkus Books (2003)
Becoming Vegan Brenda Davis & Vesanto Melina, Book Publishing Company (2000)
Diet, Life Expectancy and Chronic Disease: Studies of Seventh-day Adventists and other Vegetarians Gary E Fraser, OUP (2003)
Dr Neal Barnard's Program to Reverse Diabetes Now MD Neal Barnard, Rodale (2007)
Feel-Good Food Susie Miller & Karen Knowler, The Women's Press (2000)
Foods That Fight Pain Neal Barnard, Bantam Books (1999)
Love Yourself, So Hate the Weight! Brother Craig, Woodbridge Press (1996)
Plant Based Nutrition and Health Stephen Walsh PhD, The Vegan Society (2003)
The Dietitian's Guide to Vegetarian Diets Virginia Messina, Reed Mangels and Mark Messina, Jones & Bartlett Publishers (2004)
The Vegan Diet as Chronic Disease Prevention: Evidence Supporting the New Four Food Groups Kerrie Saunders, Lo Scarabeo (2004)
Vegan Nutrition: Pure & Simple Michael Klaper MD, Book Publishing Company (1987)
Vegan + Sports: Vegan Nutrition and Endurance Sports Arnold Wiegand, (2006)

QUOTATIONS

The Extended Circle: A Dictionary of Humane Thought Jon Wynne-Tyson, Open Gate Press (1990)

RAW FOOD

Detox Your World Shazzie, Raw Creation Limited? (2003)
Eat Smart Eat Raw: Detox Recipes for a High-Energy Diet Kate Wood, Grub Street (2002)
Naked Chocolate: Uncovering the Astonishing Truth About the World's

Greatest Food Shazzie, Raw Creation Limited (2005)
Raw Food Made Easy Jennifer Cornbleet, Book Publishing Company (2005)
Raw Living: Detox Your Life and Eat the High Energy Way Kate Wood, Grub Street Publishing (2007)
Warming Up to Living Foods Elysa Markowitz, Book Publishing Company (1998)

REFERENCE

Animals' Contacts Directory Veggies
The Good Shopping Guide Charlotte Mulvey, (2007)

TRAVEL

The New Spain – Vegan & Vegetarian Restaurants Jean-Claude Juston, available from www.vegetarianguides.co.uk
The Vegan Passport George Rodger (ed.), The Vegan Society (2006)
Vegan Guide to New York Rynn Berry, Chris Suzuki & Barry Litsky, Ethical Living (2005)
Vegetarian Britain Alex Bourke, Vegetarian Guides (2006)
Vegetarian Europe Alex Bourke, Vegetarian Guides (2000)
Vegetarian Guide to the Lake District Angie Greenaway, Viva! (2008)
Vegetarian Journal's Guide to Natural Foods Restaurants: In the U.S. and Canada Vegetarian Resource Group (2005)
Vegetarian London Alex Bourke, Vegetarian Guides (2008)
Vegetarian Visitor Annemarie Weitzel (2008)

VEGANISM & VEGETARIANISM

Abundant Living in the Coming Age of the Tree Kathleen Jannaway, MCL (1999)
Being Vegan Joanne Stepaniak, McGraw-Hill (2003)
Diet for a New America: How your Choices Affect your Health, Happiness & the Future of Life on Earth, John Robbins, H J Kramer (1998)
Making Kind Choices Ingrid Newkirk, St Martin's Griffin (2005)
Skinny Bitch Rory Freedman and Kim Barnouin, Running Press (2007)
The Food Revolution: How your Diet can Help Save your Life and our World John Robbins, Conari Press (2001)

The Livewire Guide to Going, Being and Staying Veggie Juliet Gellatley, Trafalgar Square Publishing (1997)

The Vegan Sourcebook Joanne Stepaniak, McGraw-Hill Companies (2001)

Vegan Freak: Being Vegan in a Non-Vegan World Bob Torres & Jenna Torres, Tofu Hound Press (2005)

Vegan Stories Julie H Rosenfield (ed.), The Vegan Society (2002)

Vegan: The New Ethics of Eating Erik Marcus, McBooks Press (2003)

Why Vegan? Kath Clements, Heretic (1995)

VERSE

Explicit Vegan Lyrics: The Little Book of Vegan Poems Benjamin Zephaniah, AK Distribution (2001)

No Room, Save in the Heart: Poetry and Prose on Reverence for Life-Animals, Nature and Human-kind Ann C. Free, Flying Fox Printing (1986)

Talking Turkeys Benjamin Zephaniah, Puffin Books (1995)

MAGAZINES

Animal Action (youth magazine) and Animal Life RSPCA, Wilberforce Way, Southwater, Horsham, RH13 9RS, www.rspca.org.uk

Animal Times PETA, PO Box 36668, London, SE1 1WA www.peta.org.uk

Animals Defender & Campaigner Animal Defender International, Millbank Tower, Millbank, London, SW1P 4QP, www.ad-international.org

ArcNews (online magazine) PO Box 330, Wolverhampton, WV10 7BZ, arcnews.redblackandgreen.net

Arkangel BCM 9240, London, WC1N 3XX, www.arkangelweb.org

Ethical Consumer ECRA Publishing, Unit 21, 41 Old Birley St, Manchester, M15 5RF, www.ethicalconsumer.org

Farm Animal Voice Compassion in World Farming, Godalming, GU7 1EZ, www.ciwf.org.uk

Get Fresh The Fresh Network, 9 Stratton Rd, Hainford, Norwich, NR10 3AZ

Green Futures 13-17 Sturton St, Cambridge, CB1 2SN, www.forumforthefuture.org.uk

HOWL Hunt Saboteurs Association, BM HSA, London, WC1N 3XX, www.hsa.enviroweb.org

New Consumer 5 Rose St, Edinburgh, EH2 2PR, www.newconsumer.com

Outrage Animal Aid, The Old Chapel, Bradford St, Tonbridge, TN9 1AW, www.animalaid.org.uk

Realfood (online magazine) PO Box 330, Wolverhampton, WV10 7BZ, www.realfood.org.uk

Resurgence Rocksea Farmhouse, St Mabyn, Bodmin, PL30 3BR, www.resurgence.org

The Ecologist 102 B Lana House Studios, 116-118 Commercial St, London, E1 6NF, www.theecologist.org

The Vegan The Vegan Society, Donald Watson House, 21 Hylton St, Hockley, Birmingham, B18 6HJ, www.vegansociety.com

The Vegetarian VSUK, Parkdale, Dunham Rd, Altrincham, WA14 4QG, www.vegsoc.org

Vegan Views (online magazine) www.veganviews.org.uk

Veggie Health Vegetarian and Vegan Foundation, 8 York Court, Wilder St, Bristol, BS2 8QH, www.vegetarian.org.uk

Viva! Life Viva!, 8 York Court, Wilder St, Bristol, BS2 8QH, www.viva.org.uk

Wales Vegan Bron yr Ysgol, Montpellier Park, Llandrindod, LD1 5LW

Wildlife Guardian League Against Cruel Sports, 83-87 Union St, London SE1 1S, www.league.org.uk

VEGAN COMPANIES

Ahimsa Cosmetics
All Seasons Health
Alpro Soya
Alternative Stores
Alvin Connor Limited
Ambrosian Vegetarian Foods
Anglesey Natural Foods
Animal Aid
Ann Elise Skincare
Aqua Natural Ltd
Aquados Ltd
Aroma Comforts
Aromafoods
Beanie's Health Foods
Bio-D Co Ltd
Biofun bvba
Blue Lotus Products Ltd
Bourgeois Boheme
Brackencraft
Bute Island Foods Ltd
Calder Valley Soap
Cruelty Free Wholesale T/A The Cruelty
Free Shop
Daivita
Daniel Field Laboratory Ltd
DEVA Nutrition
Dipak Foods Ltd
Dipl - Kfm (FH) Wolfgang Schiller
Dolma
Eat Me Ltd
Conscious Chocolate
Essentially Yours Ltd
Floraroma Ltd
Fox Hall
Freerangers
Fry Group Foods

Funk Bubble
Georgette bvba
Green Garden Café
Green Valley Trading Co
Green Wych
Happy And Healthy Foods
Harlow Lubricants Ltd
Healthy Herbs
Hedgecraft
Herbsgo Limited T/A Clive Foot
Honesty Cosmetics Ltd
Innocent Oils
International Investments & Trade Ltd
T/A Babyboo Organic
International Partnership Ltd (Seagreens
Division)
Jingando
K Creations
Kobashi
Leeora Vegetarian Food
Live Native
Majik Blankit Skin Care
Mandala Aroma Ltd
Mediterranean Foods (London) Ltd
MIAMO World Foundation for
Wellbeing
MJ Health New Zealand Ltd
Mood Foods Limited
Mooncup Ltd
Mulu Chocolate Ltd
Munchy Seeds
Natural by Nature Oils
Natural Eco Trading Ltd
Natural House Products Ltd
Naturally ME Inc
Nature Complete Ltd

NOHARM
Orange Burst Ltd
Oreganum Health Ltd
Organatural
Organic Soap Company
Patisserie Organic
Pinks Boutique
Pitfield Brewery
Plamil Foods Ltd
Polar Sun Products Ltd
Premier Lifestyles Ltd
Pure Gaisha
QianNa Agricultural Products Ind & Trading Co Ltd
R & R Tofu
Ragazzi Vegan
Rare Natural Care, Inc
Raw Gaia
Red Star Natural Liquid Soaps
Redwood Co.
Roar Chocolate
Rosie's Gourmet Products (UK) Ltd
Safe 2Eat Ltd
Sanbera GmbH
Sant'Or
Scottish Herbal Supplies
Sedlescombe Organic Vineyard
SheaCare
Skinvac
Skincare Cafe Ltd
Supernutrients
Tanjero
The Barn
The Booja-Booja Company Ltd
The Food Doctor Ltd
The Lodge
The Natural Spa Company Ltd
The Raw Chocolate Company Ltd
Tisserand Aromatherapy
TOPAS Klaus Gaiser GmbH

Total Raw Food Ltd
Treasured Earth Skin Care
Truelove Organics Limited
Truthful Co Ltd (Purely Skincare)
Vegan Perfection
Veganline.com
Veganstore.co.uk
Veggierose
Vegetarian Shoes And Bags
Veggies Catering Campaign
Vindotco (UK) Ltd
Visionary Soap Company
X35 Energy Ltd
Yagga SRL

ANIMAL FREE SHOPS

The outlets listed below are run by vegans and only stock vegan products

- **Bristol** *Vegetarian Shoes* 12 Gardner Street, Brighton, East Sussex, BN1 1UP
  t 01273 685685 **e** shop@vegetarian-shoes.co.uk **w** www.vegetarian-shoes.co.uk
- **Derby** *Soundbites* 11 Morledge, Derby, DE1 2AW **t** 01332 291369
  e info@soundbitesderby.org.uk **w** www.soundbitesderby.org.uk
- **Gwynedd** *Vegonia Wholefoods* 49 High Street, Port Madoc, Gwynedd, LL49 9LR
  t 01766 515195
- **London** *Bourgeois Boheme* Hydrex House, Garden Road, Richmond,TW9 4NR
  t 0208 8788 388 **w** www.bboheme.com
- **Manchester** *Unicorn* 89 Albany Rd, Chorlton, Manchester, M21 0BN
  t 0161 861 7675 **e** office@unicorn-grocery.co.uk **w** www.unicorn-grocery.co.uk
- **Nottingham** *The Screaming Carrot* 42 Foxhall Road, Forest Fields, Nottingham,
  NG7 6LJ **t** 0115 910 3013 **w** www.screamingcarrot.co.uk
- **West Midlands** *One Earth Shop* 54 Allison Street, Digbeth, Birmingham, B5 5TH
  t 0121 632 6909
- **York** *Kyi-po* 9 Goodramgate, York, YO1 7LW **e** shop@kyi-po.com
  w www.kyi-po.com

ONLINE SHOPS

- **Animal-Aid** www.animalaidshop.org.uk
- **Alternative Stores** www.alternativestores.com
- **Baby Cakes Direct** www.babycakesdirect.co.uk
- **Bourgeois Boheme** www.bboheme.com
- **Ethical Wares** www.ethicalwares.co.uk
- **Freerangers** www.freerangers.co.uk
- **Honesty Cosmetics** www.honestycosmetics.co.uk
- **Redwood Wholefood Company** www.redwoodfoods.co.uk
- **Vegan Society** www.vegansociety.co.uk
- **Veganstore.co.uk** www.veganstore.co.uk
- **Veganline** www.veganline.com
- **Vegan Health and Beauty** www.veganhealthandbeauty.com
- **Vegetarian Shoes** www.vegetarian-shoes.co.uk
- **Viva!** www.viva.org.uk/shop
- **Yagga** www.yagga.co.uk

FOOD

BISCUITS

BIOFAIR
Spelt Brazil Nut Cantuccini Cookies

BIONA
Spelt Fruit Hearts; Sunflower Cookies

BLACKFRIARS BAKERY
Flapjacks: Apple & Raspberry, Apple &
Sultana, Apricot, Date & Walnut, Fruit,
Original

BURTON'S FOODS LTD
Coconut Rings; Country Snapjacks;
Fruit Shortcake; Fruit Snapjacks; Rich
Tea; Water Biscuits

CLIVE'S PIES ⊘
Flapjacks: Almond & Apple, Chocolate
Chip, Original, Sultana & Apple

DOVES FARM FOODS LTD ⊘
Fairtrade: Organic Apple & Sultana
Flapjack; *Organic:* Apple & Sultana
Flapjack - Individual Bars, Digestives,
Fruity Oat Biscuits, Hazelnut Cookies,
Lemon Zest Cookies

**ESSENTIAL TRADING
CO-OPERATIVE LTD** ™❶⊘ ✔
Organic Flapjacks: **Almond Fruit,
Chocolate Chip & Brazil Nut, Date &
Apricot, Vine Fruit**

FIRST QUALITY FOODS ⊘ ✔
Al'fez: Apricot & chilli chutney 200g;

Ma baker: Limited edition bars-
pomegranate 90g, Mixed fruit range-
apple, apricot, cherry, banana 90g,
Mixed nut range-peanut, hazelnut,
almond, walnut 90g, Mixed seed
range-pumpkin, sunflower, multi-seed,
sesame 90g, Mixed tropical range-pecan,
pistachio, mango, coconut 90g,
Traditional flapjack 90g; *Obars:* Apple &
cranberry 55g, Blueberry & vanilla 55g,
Pomegranate & raspberry, Strawberry &
peach 55g; *Sammy's:* Organic pesto 200g

GLUTEN FREE FOODS LTD
Barkat: Ice Cream Cones, Waffle Ice
Cream Cones

GRANOVITA UK LTD ⊘ ✔
Organic Flapjack with LinuSprout:
Apricot, Chocolate Chip, Cranberry,
Ginger, Linseed & Raisin, Pumpkin &
Sunflower Seed, Raisin, Apple &
Cinnamon, Traditional Oat

HANDMADE FLAPJACK COMPANY LTD
Flapjack: Apricot, Brazil Nut Cluster,
Cherry & Coconut, Date & Walnut,
Fruit, Plain, Raspberry

IL MANGIAR SANO S.P.A. ™⊘ ✔
Conventional Bakery Products: **Milk
and Egg Free Biscuits**

KALLO FOODS ⊘
Thin Slice Slightly Salted Rice Cakes
with Sesame

L'AGE VERT LINXIS ™
Organic chlorella biscuits

MCVITIES
Butter Puffs; Fruit Shortcake; Ginger
Nuts; Lincoln; *Hob Nobs:* Original

ORGANICO ⊘ ✿
Break & Bil: Spelt Tea Biscuits

ORGRAN ☺
Biscotti: Amaretti, Choc Chip, Lemon &
Poppy Seed; *Cookies:* Apricot & Coconut,
Sultana & Cinnamon

PETER RABBIT ORGANICS ⊘ ✿
Organic Cookies: Appley, Orange & Raisin

QUINUA REAL BRASIL LTDA ™⊘
**Cookie Flavour Cocoa; Cookie
Flavour Vanilla; Granola Traditional**

R J FOODS LIMITED ™⊘
Flapjacks: **Apple & Apricot, Cherry &
Coconut, Cherry & Sultana, Date &
Walnut, Fig, Fruit and Nut, Fruit Bar,
Plain, Raspberry, Rum & Raisin**

THE FOOD DOCTOR LTD ™☺
Food Bar: **Apple & Walnut, Apricot &
Almond, Fig & Mango, Pineapple &
Banana, Tomato & Chilli**

TRAIDCRAFT PLC ⊘

TRIALIA FOODS AUSTRALIA ™
Eskal Noble Choice: **Scottish Chocolate
Chip Shortbread, Scottish Shortbread**

UNITED BISCUITS LTD ⊘
Crawford's: Ginger Nuts, Morning Coffee

WHOLEBAKE LTD ⊘
Hemp Flapjack; Mixed Crisp Bars;
Flapjack Bites: Cherry, Sultana & Apple;
Organic Flapjack: Mixed, Original;
Wholebake Flapjacks: Almond, Apple,
Apricot, Banana, Berry, Cherry,
Cranberry, Hazelnut, Mixed Fruit, Mixed
Nut, Pecan, Pistachio, Premium Mixed,
Sesame, Walnut

BREADS, ROLLS, PIZZA BASES ETC

ALLIED BAKERIES
Burgen: Soya & Linseed Bread; *Country
Maid:* White Bread; *Dayofresh:* Brown
Rolls, White Bread, White Rolls;
Pennysave: White Bread

ALLINSON
Bread: Hibran, Oatmeal White, Sunflower
Multigrain Batch, Wholemeal Batch

ALNAVIT GMBH ™
Knusperbrot aus Reis und Mais

AMISA
Hildegard Whole Spelt Bread; Hildegard
Wholegrain Spelt Melba Toasts;
Crispbread: Buckwheat Wholegrain,
Corn & Rice

BIONA
Biodiet Gluten-Free Bread: Corn/Lupin,
Four Grain Pizza Base, Millet, Rice, Rice
& Sunflower Seed, Rice/Buckwheat

Seed; *Long Life Bread:* Pumpernickel, Rye, Rye & Hempseed, Rye & Pumpkin Seed, Rye Amaranth, Rye Omega 3, Rye w Sunflower Seed; *Pizza Base:* Mini, Original, w Spelt Flour

COOPLANDS
Breads: All

CUISINE DE FRANCE
12" Thin Crust Pizza Base; *Bagel:* Blueberry, Cinnamon & Raisin, Everything, Healthier Option, Multigrain, Plain, Poppy, Sesame; *Baguette:* Classic Demi, Demi, Granary Demi, Half, Malted Grain Demi, Plain, Poppy Seeds Half, Rusticata, Sourdough, Triple Grain, Triple Grain Demi; *Baps:* Granary, Kara Floured; *Batard:* Cross Cut, Small White; *Bloomer:* Granary, Malted Brown, Organic White, Plain, Poppy, White; *Bread:* 5 Grain Loaf, Almond/Apricot Loaf, Bouchon, Ciabattina Olive Bread, Country White Sourdough Oval, Cranberry, Cranberry & Rosemary, Golden Grain Seeded Tin Loaf, Granary Sandwich, Grand Rustique, Green Olive Focaccia, Harvester, Healthier Option White, Large Sun Dried Tomato Plait, L'Art Du Pain Parisienne, Longuet Rustic, Malted Brown, Malted Grain Petit Pain, Malted Grain Rusticata, Multigrain Shamrock, Olive Oval, Onion & Herb Loaf, Pain Complet, Pain du Couronne, Pain Rustique, Panini, Parisien, Pecan Raisin Oval, Petit Pain, Petit Pain Sandwich, Petite Parisienne, Plain Rusticata, Premium White Tin Loaf, Provencale

Herbs Focaccia, Roasted Garlic Loaf, Rosemary Olive Oil Round, Rustic Flatbread, Rustic Sandwich Bread, Rustic Square, Seeded Rye Loaf, Seeded Tin Loaf, Small Bocata, Soft Grain, Split Tin Malted Brown, Split Tin White, Square Artic Flatbread, Stencilled Organic White Bread, Sundried Tomato Boutarde, Tear & Share, Triple Grain Loaf, Value French Stick, White Iced Fingers, White Loaf, White Petit Batard, Wholemeal Farmhouse Loaf, Wholemeal Tin; *Buns:* Plain Burger, Seeded Burger; *Ciabatta:* Mini, Plain, Rustica, Sandwich Roll, w Extra Virgin Olive Oil; *Doughnut:* Jam, Ring; *Rolls:* Brown, Classic Dinner, Cranberry & Rosemary Gourmet Rolls, Crusty Brown, Crusty White, Harvester Batched Crusty, Onion & Herb Gourmet Rolls, Rectangular Rustique, Rustic, Rustic Dinner, Sandwich, Seeded Classic Dinner Roll, Sun Dried Tomato Rolls, Triple Grain Roll, White Continental; *Wraps:* Plain, Tomato

DEES CARIBBEAN IMPORTS
HTB Jamaican Spiced Bun

DISCOVERY FOODS
Tortillas: Bakery, Garlic & Coriander, Gluten Free Corn, Plain Wheatflour

FRY GROUP FOODS ™☺
Fry's Special Vegetarian Frozen Foods:
Veg Express Sausage Rolls

G. COSTA & CO ⊘
Granforno Breadsticks: Garlic Breadsticks, Plain Breadsticks, Sesame Breadsticks

RAW CHOCOLATE
altered the face of Shazzie
when she discovered it in 2003

The **raw cacao bean** is one of the most complex and uplifting gifts nature has to offer. The **cacao gods** have invited everyone to become part of **The Raw Chocolate Revolution**. Let's eat some today and beam love ecstatically across the universe.

GENERAL DIETARY
Pizza Bases; *Bread:* Brown Rice, Low-Protein Rice, Tapioca, White Rice; *Loaf:* Flax, Gluten-Free, High Fibre White, Raisin, Seattle Brown, Six Flour, Yeast-Free Rice; *Rolls:* Dinner, White Long, White Round

GLUTEN FREE FOODS LTD
Glutano: Wholemeal Sliced Bread, WM Sliced Bread Snack Pack

GR WRIGHT & SONS LTD ☺◌
Bread Mixes: Ciabatta, Garlic & Rosemary Focaccia, Malty, Mixed Grain, Organic Stoneground Wholemeal, Premium White, Sunflower, Wholemeal

HOVIS
Best of Both; Classic Cut; Granary; Original Wheatgerm; Seeded Granary; White Farmhouse; White Half; White Square Cut; Wholemeal; Wholemeal Farmhouse

KINGSMILL
Plain White Bread; *50 50:* Bread, Rolls; *Crusts Away:* 50 50 Bread, White Bread; *Good As Gold:* Golden Wholemeal Bread, Malted Grain Bread, Soft White Bread; *Great Everyday:* Big Soft White Rolls, Sliced White Rolls, Soft White Bread, Soft White Rolls, Tasty Wholemeal Bread, Tasty Wholemeal Rolls; *Love to Toast:* Crumpets, Muffins, Orange Marmalade Fruit Bread, White Thick Bread

MOTHERS PRIDE
Brown; White; White Danish

NEW YORK BAGEL CO. LTD STARBURST ◌
Cinnamon & Raisin; Multiseed; Onion and Poppyseed; Plain; Sesame

NIMBLE
White; Wholemeal

ORGANICO ◌ ✿
Rustic Classic Breadstick; Rustic Sesame Breadstick; Rustic Spelt Breadstick; Rustic Wholewheat Breadstick

ORGRAN ☺
Bread Mix; Pizza & Pastry Mix

PATAKS FOODS ◌
Chapattis: Garlic and Herb, Plain; *Wrap:* Chilli, Garlic & Herb, Plain, Tikka; *Wraps:* Chilli, Garlic and Herb, Tikka

PAUL'S TOFU ™◌ 🖊 ✿
Breads: **Focaccia, Four Seed, Fruit Rye, Gluten Free Number One Sourdough, Gluten Free Number Three Sourdough, Gluten Free Number Two Sourdough, Light Rye, Melton Loaf, Olive Bread, Organic Herb Bread, Organic Individual Baguette, Organic Melton Loaf, Organic Rolls, Organic Sesame Rolls, Organic Tea Cakes, Organic Unbleached White, Organic Yeast Free Wheat Free Rye Bread, Organic Yeasted Bread, Organic Yeasted Malthouse, Organic Yeasted Mixed Seed, Organic Yeasted Spelt Bread, Organic Yeasted Stoneground Wholemeal, Pain de Campagne,**

Pane Basilicum, Rye & Sweetcorn Sourdough, Sechskorn, Sourdough 4 Seed Bread, Sourdough Bread Yeast Free, Sourdough Rice, Spelt Sourdough, Tsampa Sourdough, Unbleached White Bread, White Rolls

SUNBLEST
Crumpets; Currant Buns; Hot Cross Buns; Muffins; *Bread:* Brown, Danish White, Longlife White, Scottish Plain Batch Bread, White, Wholemeal; *Rolls:* Brown, Scottish Morning Rolls, White

WARBURTONS ⊘
6 Crumpets; 6 Round Potato Cakes; Brown Danish; Malted Danish; White Danish; Wholemeal Toast; *400g:* Crusty, Half Loaf Stoneground Wholemeal Batch, Healthy Inside, Healthy Inside Oats, Medium White, Seeded Batch, Soft White Farmhouse, Toastie White, Wholemeal Medium; *800g:* All in One Medium, All in One Toastie, Medium White, Our Thickest Slice White, Premium White Batch, Seeded Batch, Soft White Farmhouse, Stoneground Wholemeal Batch, Toastie White, Wholegrain Goodness, Wholemeal Medium, Wholemeal Toastie; *Fruit Breads:* Fruit Loaf with Orange, Raisin Loaf with Cinnamon; *Organic 400g:* Organic White, Organic Wholemeal; *Rolls:* 12 Large Sandwich Rolls, 12 Sliced Fruity Teacakes, 12 Sliced Sandwich Rolls, 3 Seeded Sandwich Rolls, 3 Wholemeal Soft Sandwich Rolls, 4 Fruity Teacakes, 4 Large

Sandwich Rolls, 4 Oven Bottom Muffins, 4 Sandwich Rolls, 6 Sliced Sandwich Rolls, 6 Wholemeal Rolls

BREAKFAST FOODS

ALARA WHOLEFOODS LTD ⊘
Coconut Crunch; *Gluten-Free Muesli:* Active, Goji & Yacon, Luxury; *Muesli:* Branberry, Date with Cacao, Fruit, Seeds & Spice w Spelt, Goji & Yacon, Prime, Rich, Tropical, Very Berry; *Porridge:* OT Chocolate, OT Strawberry, OT Vanilla

AMISA
Hildegard Spelt Pops

BACHELDRE WATERMILL ORGANIC FLOWERS
Stoneground Fine Bran Flakes

BIOFAIR
Andean Muesli; Quinoa Pops

BIONA
Amaranth Fruit Muesli; Amaranth Popcorn

CARRIE'S COOKIES ™
Muesli Mad: **Gluten Free, Standard, Tropical**

DOVES FARM FOODS LTD ⊘
Organic: Bio-Biz Breakfast Biscuits, Chocolate Stars Wheat and Gluten Free, Cornflakes, Low Fat Cereal Bar,

FOX HALL VEGAN B&B
@ PRIZET STABLES,
Helsington, Kendal,
Cumbria, LA8 8AB

Tel:- Sylvia or Chris on 015395 61241
Email:- fox.hall@btinternet.com
Website:- www.fox.hall.btinternet.co.uk

*We are 2 miles south of Kendal, South Lakes, 10 mins by car from
M6 junction 36, 20 mins from Windermere on the A591 & 10 mins
from Oxenholme railway station.*

Π *4 Guest Rooms, all en-suite*

Π *Children very welcome*

Π *Special Diets catered for*

Π *Evening Meals available*

Π *Organic food*

Π *Vegan Cookery Courses*

**Our nearest tourist attractions are Levens Hall
& Sizergh Castle. There are good local walks
along the Lancaster to Kendal Canal towpath,
River Kent and into Levens Park as well as
Scout Scar & The Helm.**

Registered by the Vegan Society

"A no-smoking, vegan family home with organic food
where children are always welcome"

*Please visit our website for more up-to-date information on
accommodation, availability, location, menus,*

Q. Looking for a dairy free option?

A. Try _pure_ Soya goodness.

At Pure, we know you care about what you eat but don't want to compromise on taste. That's why when we created Pure spreads, we left out the dairy, artificial additives and hydrogenated oils, leaving them full of goodness. Pure tastes great on bread or toast, and is perfect in cooking and baking too.
So, even if you suffer from food allergies or intolerances, with Pure you can still enjoy your favourite foods.

Visit us at puredairyfree.co.uk for advice on dairy free living, including recipe ideas.
Or call us on 0800 028 4499 for more information on Pure.

Vegan

Tropical Fruit And Nut Bar; *Organic Tasty Cereal:* Chewy Rice Pop & Chocolate Cakes - Individual Bars

ESSENTIAL TRADING CO-OPERATIVE LTD ™❶⊘*i*
Essential Brand- Muesli (Organic & Conventional): **Cereal Base, Date & Apricot, Deluxe, Fine Organic, Fruit & Nut, Harvest, Organic, Organic Apple & Cinnamon Cereal, Organic Cereal Base, Organic Deluxe, Organic Fruit Crunch, Organic Strawberry & Cashew Crisp, Sultana Crunch, Sunflower, Super Hi-fibre, Tropical;** *Essential Brand-Muesli (Organic & Conventional):* **Organic Date & Apricot**

GLUTEN FREE FOODS LTD
Barkat: Organic Chocolate Cornflakes, Organic Chocolate Rice Crunchies, Organic Muesli, Organic Porridge Flakes; *Glutano:* Cornflakes

GRANOVITA UK LTD ⊘*i*
Classic Flakes

GREENCITY WHOLEFOODS ❶⊘
Crunchy Muesli; De Luxe Muesli; Deluxe Muesli; Five Star Muesli; Gluten-Free Muesli; High Fibre Muesli; Highland Bramble Crunch; Muesli Base; No Coconut Muesli; Paradise Muesli; Super Muesli; Super Muesli No Coconut

JORDANS ⊘
DUO Strawberry; Multigrain Porridge; Natural Country Bran; Natural

Wheatgerm; Organic Flakes & Berries; Organic Fruit & Fibre; Porridge: Raisin & Apple; Porridge: Sultana & Apricot; Superfoods Breakfast Flakes; Superfoods Porridge; *Country Crisp:* Chocolate (Export), Chocolate (France), Four Nut Combo, Luxury Raisin, Real Strawberries, Whole Raspberries, Wild about Berries; *Country Crisp & Flakes:* Berries, Raisin & Hazel; *Crunchy:* Luxury Maple & Pecan, New Fruits Recipe, Raisin & Coconut; *Morning Crisp:* Maple & Pecan; *Muesli:* Light & Crispy, Ligne, Natural, Organic, Special, Special Fruit, Special Nut, Special Recipe Export, Superfoods Muesli

KALLO FOODS ⊘
Whole Earth: Cornflakes, Flakes with South Asian Exotic Fruit, Fruit & Fibre, Maple Frosted Flakes, North American Flakes with Blosson Berries, Puffed Rice Cereal Original, Swiss Style Muesli

KELLOGGS
Cornflakes; Just Right; Raisin Wheats; Special K Medley; *Coco Pops:* Mega Muncher, Original; *Frosties:* Original, Reduced Sugar; *Rice Krispies:* Multi-Grain Shapes, Original

NATURE'S PATH FOODS INC
Crispy Rice; Mesa Sunrise; Millet Rice Flakes; Oaty Bites; Optimum Power; *Envirokidz:* Gorilla Munch, Koala Crisp

ORGAN ☺
Breakfast Cereals: Muesli Gluten Free, Rice Porridge

PERTWOOD ORGANIC
CEREAL COMPANY ⊘ ✿
Maple Flakes; Muesli Delicious Fruits; Muesli Fruit and Seeds; *Organic barley crisp:* Barley Flakes

PETER RABBIT ORGANICS ⊘ ✿
Organic Cornflakes

PORTER FOODS CO LTD
Lovedean Larder Granola: No.1, No.1 Lite, No.2 with Cranberries, No.3 Date and Apple

QUAKER OATS LTD ⊘
Quaker Oat Crisp; Quaker Oat Crunch; Quaker Oat Hoops; Quaker Oats Simple Baked Apple Flavour; Quaker Oats Simple Blackberry & Apple Flavour; Quaker Oats Simple Fruit Muesli Flavour; Quaker Oats Simple Golden Syrup Flavour; Quaker Oats Simple Original; Quaker Puffed Wheat; Scott's Porage Oats Original; Scotts Old Fashioned Porage Oats; Scotts So Easy - Original

REBECCA'S CAKES ™
Vegan croissants

RYVITA ⊘
Corn Cakes; *Crackerbread:* High Fibre, Original; *Rice cakes:* High Fibre; *Ryvita Minis:* Apple, Caramel, Garlic & Herb, Mature Cheddar & Onion, Salt and vinegar, Sweet Chilli, Worcester Source; *Snack Bar:* Apple & Sultana, Cherry, Cranberry & Raisin, Mixed Berry

SANITARIUM HEALTH FOOD CO ⊘
Granola; Lite-Bix; Puffed Wheat; Weet-Bix; Weet-Bix Kids; Weet-Bix Organic

SUMA WHOLEFOODS
™❶⊘ 🖌 ☜ 🏃 1985
Branflakes; Bransticks; *Crunch:* **Cranberry;** *Muesli:* **Base, Gluten Free, Luxury Tropical, Roast Hazelnut, Super;** *Organic Muesli:* **Base, De Luxe, Standard**

THE FOOD DOCTOR LTD ™☺
Breakfast Cereals: **Cereal Mix, Muesli Mix, Porridge Mix**

TRAIDCRAFT PLC ⊘
Fruit & Nut Muesli

TROPICAL WHOLEFOODS
Tropical 5 Fruit Salad; Tropical Fruit Mix

WEETABIX LTD
Alpen: Crunchy Bran, Wheat Flakes; *Natures Own Organic:* Malt Wheat Squares; *Oatibix:* Bitesize, Original; *Ready Brek:* Original; *Weetabix:* Mini Crunch Fruit & Nut, Organic, Original

'BURGERS', 'SAUSAGES', 'MEAT' SLICES ETC

ALICER ☺
Mexican Burgers; Tandoori Burgers; Thai Burgers; Vegetable Burgers

ALPRO UK LTD ™☺⊘
Provamel Meat Free: **Organic tofu burgers with vegetables**

AMBROSIAN VEGETARIAN FOODS ™☺❶⊘ ✿
Organic burgers: **Chilli Bean, Savoury, Sesame & Sunflower Seed Vegetable;** *Organic Dry Mixes:* **Organic Savoury Burger Mix, Sesame & Sunflower Seed Vegetable, Sosage;** *Organic Sausages:* **Plain, Savoury Herb, Tomato & Garlic**

BEANIE'S HEALTH FOODS ™☺❶⊘
Alicer Gluten-Free Burgers: **Mexican Veggie Burgers, Tandoori Veggie Burgers, Thai Veggie Burgers, Vegetable Veggie Burgers;** *Fry's Special Vegetarian Frozen Foods:* **Schnitzels, Spiced Burgers, Traditional Burgers, Traditional Sausages;** *Fry's Special Vegetarian Frozen Foods:* **Braai (BBQ) Sausages, Cutlets, Hot Dogs, Nuggets, Polony Slicing Sausage, Vegetarian Mince, Wok and Stew Chunky Strips**

BIONA
Schnitzels in Crispy Breadcrumbs

DIXIE DINERS CLUB
Chicken NOT fillets; Tuna NOT Salad

DRAGONFLY FOODS ⊘ ✿
Organic Soysage; *Beany Burgers:* Baked, Curry, Fennel, Fruity, Mushroom, Natural, Nut, Olive, Smoky, Spicy, Tomato, Vegetable

FIVE STAR FOODIES ™☺
Artichoke Burgers; Gourmet Grillers; Sloppy Joe

FRY GROUP FOODS ™☺
Fry's Special Vegetarian Frozen Foods: **Braai Flavour Sausages, Chunky Strips, Golden Crumbled Cutlets, Golden Crumbled Schnitzels, Golden Nuggets, Mince, Original Hot Dogs, Polony, Spiced Burgers, Traditional Burgers, Traditional Sausages, Vegetarian chicken-style burgers, Vegetarian Chicken-Style Strips**

GOBBLIN WHOLEFOODS
Lentil Burger; Millet Burger

GOODLIFE FOODS ⊘
Nut Cutlet; Spicy Bean Burger

JUST WHOLEFOODS ☺⊘
Organic Mixes: Banger, Burger

LINDA MCCARTNEY
Vegetarian Sausages

PAUL'S TOFU ™⊘ ✔ ✿
Savouries: **Five Grain Tofu & Herb Burgers, Five Grain Tofu & Nut Burgers, Ganmodoki Tofu Mock Goose, Organic Five Grain Tofu Bengal Burger, Organic Five Grain Tofu Mexican Chilli Burger**

REDWOOD WHOLEFOOD COMPANY ™☺❶⊘
Bio Curry Wurst; Fishless Steaks; Organic Coated Nuggets; Organic

Coated Schnitzels; Organic Frankfurter Sausage; Organic Gyros Sausage; Organic Merguez Sausage; Scampi; Vegetarian Breaded Fish-Style Fingers; Vegetarian Style Mince; *Cheatin':* Chorizo Chunks; *Cheatin' Bites:* Chicken Style, Chicken Style Barbeque, Chicken Style Tikka, Chicken w 5-spice; *Cheatin' Chicken:* Chicken Style Pieces; *Cheatin' Roasts:* Beef, Celebration, Turkey; *Cheatin' Slices:* Beef, Chicken, Garlic Sausage, Ham, Pepperoni, Sage & Onion, Turkey; *Organic:* Frankfurter Style Sausages; *Rashers:* Streaky-Style, Tempeh; *Vegi-Deli:* Oregano & Basil Sausages, Ready to Eat Lincolnshire Sausage, Sage & Marjoram Sausages (Not Ready to Eat), Sage & Marjoram Sausages (Ready to Eat), Thai Fish Style Cakes; *Vegideli Organic Range:* Organic Beef Style Slices, Organic Chicken style pieces, Organic Chicken Style Slices, Organic Ham Style Slices, Organic Pepperoni Style Slices, Organic Ready to Eat Lincoln Sausages, Organic Ready to Eat Pork Style Sausages, Organic Southern Fried Chicken Style Nuggets, Organic Vegetarian Rashers

SANITARIUM HEALTH FOOD CO ⊘
Lime and Ginger Sausages; Roast with Mint and Rosemary Glaze; *Classic:* Hot Dogs; *Deli:* Chicken Style Slices, Ham Style Slices, Hencheon Luncheon, Smoked Luncheon; *Traditional:* BBQ Soya Sausages, Curried Sausages, Homestyle Soya Sausages, Original Soya Sausages, Soya Sausages, Vegie Soya Sausages

SUMA WHOLEFOODS
™❶⊘ ✓ ☞⊱1985
Burger Mix; Sausage Mix; *Pre-Packs:* TVP Chunks, TVP Flavoured Chunks, TVP Flavoured Mince, TVP Mince

TAIFUN ☺⊘
Tofu Sausages: Grill Sausages, Herb Sausages, Mini Wiener, Puszta-Wiener, Rostbrääterle, Sombreros, Tofu-Bratgriller, Wiener

THE CRUELTY FREE SHOP ™☺❶
All products are vegan

TOPAS KLAUS GAISER GMBH ™☺✲
Gran Chorizo; Sausage Frankenberger; Sausage Hot Dog; Toro; Wheaty Kebab Doener; Wheaty Steaklets; *Wheaty:* Vegan Organic Rolls "Cevapwheaty", Vegan Organic Steak "Pizza"; *Wheaty Big Blocks For Slicing:* Vegan Organic Seitan Block, Vegan Organic Seitan With Herbs Block, Vegan Organic Slices "Salami" Bar, Vegan Smoked Organic Seitan Block; *Wheaty Convenience:* Vegan Organic "Chilli con Wheaty", Vegan Organic Wheaty "Stroganoff"; *Wheaty Kebabs (Big Packs):* Vegan Organic "Hamburger Medallions", Vegan Organic "Minced Meat" 2.5 kg, Vegan Organic "Vegoulash" 2.5 kg, Vegan Organic Greek Style "Gyros" 2.5 kg, Vegan Organic

Kebab "Plain" 2.5 kg, Vegan Organic Mexican Style Kebab "Acapulco" 2.5 kg; *Wheaty Roast:* **Vegan Organic Roast With Mushrooms;** *Wheaty Sausages:* **Vegan Organic "Dwarf Wienies", Vegan Organic Seitan Sausages "Country Style", Vegan Organic Seitan Sausages "La Rossa", Vegan Organic Seitan Sausages With Herbs "Thuringen";** *Wheaty Sausages & Snacks (Big Packs):* **Vegan Organic Seitan Sausages "Country Style", Vegan Organic Seitan Sausages With Herbs "Thuringen", Vegan Organic Spacebar "Hemp", Vegan Organic Spacebar "Hemp" Maxi Display, Vegan Organic Spacebar "Pyrossi" Maxi Display, Vegan Organic Spacebar "Red Hot Chilli Peppers" Maxi Display;** *Wheaty Slices For Frying:* **Vegan Smoked Organic Seitan Steak, Vegan Thick Organic Slices For Frying;** *Wheaty Slices For Frying (Big Packs):* **Vegan Organic "Hamburger Medallions Piquant" Bar, Vegan Organic "Hamburger Medallions" Bar, Vegan Organic Seitan Slices Block, Vegan Organic Smoked Seitan Steak Block;** *Wheaty Thin Slices:* **Vegan Organic Seitan Slices, Vegan Organic Seitan Slices With Hemp, Vegan Organic Seitan Slices With Herbs, Vegan Organic Slices "Red Bell Pepper", Vegan Organic Slices "Salami", Vegan Smoked Organic Seitan Slices;** *Wheaty Vegan Kebabs:* **Vegan Organic Greek Style Kebab "Gyros", Vegan**

Organic Indian Style Kebab "Jaipur", Vegan Organic Mexican Style Kebab "Acapulco", Vegan Organic Turkish Style Kebab, Vegan Organic Vegoulash; *Wheaty Vegetarian Salads:* **Mixed Pack of Vegan Organic Salads: 2 x Meaty, Galina, KOsaken, Vegan Organic "Meat Salad" Meaty, Vegan Organic Salad "Galina", Vegan Organic Salad "Kosaken"**

TURTLE ISLAND FOODS ☺

'Giblet' Gravy, Feast; Wild Rice & Mushroom Stuffing; *Deli Slices:* "Philly Style" Steak, Cranberry and Stuffing, Hickory Smoked, Peppered; *Franks:* Breakfast Links, Chipotle Franks, Franks; *Holiday Products:* Cranberry Apple Potato Dumplings, Giblet and Mushroom Gravy, Roast and Gravy, Vegetarain Feast, Wild Rice and Mushroom Stuffing; *Jurky:* Peppered; *Sausages:* Foot Long Veggie Dogs; *SuperBurgers:* Original, Tex Mex; *Tofurky Deli Slices:* Oven Roasted; *Tofurky Jerky:* Original; *Tofurky Sausages:* Beer Brats, Italian, Kielbasa

VEGAN PERFECTION ™☺
All products are vegan

VEGAN STORE ™☺❶◌ⓙ
All products are vegan including tuna (not) salad, chicken (not) fillets, veggie ribs and seitan quick mix

VEGEFARM CORP ™
VeggieMaster -Vegan: **Chicken-free Tender Chunks, Fish-free Steak, Hot Dog, Nuggets, Poultry-free Breast**

VEGETARIANS CHOICE ™☺❶⊘
Vegetable Protein: **Burgers, Sausage Mix (400g tube), Sausages**

VEGGIES CATERING CAMPAIGN ™☺❶⊘
Burger Mix: **Hemp-Seed, Veggies;** *Burgers:* **Chilli, Hemp, Veggies;** *Sosage Mix:* **Veggies;** *Sosages:* **Savoury, Tomato, Veggies**

VEG-OUT ™
Store Cupboard: **Cheatin' chicken nuggets / dips**

WICKEN FEN ⊘
Burger: Mexicana; *Sausages:* Apple and Sage, Carrot and Coriander, Carrot and Coriander Gluten Free, Country Herb, Cumberland Style, Mediterranean Roasted Vegetable, Mushroom & Tarragon, Tasty Mexicana, Tomato & Garlic

YAGGA SRL ™
Bresaolo Coldcuts; Florentine Steak; Roasted Coldcuts; Vegetable Burger; Vegetarian Bresaola slices; Vegetarian fillet; Vegetarian roast; Vegetarian roasted slices; Vegetarian steak; Vegetarian stew; Vegetarian strips

ZEDZFOODS ⊘✔
Herb & aubergine 'burger'; Sage & onion 'burger'; Tofu & Ginger Burger

CAKES & CAKE MIXES

AMANDA TRADING LTD T/A AFRICAN DELIGHTS ☺
Banana Rice Cake

AROMAFOODS ™☺✔
Carrot & Orange Cake; Fabulush Bread Pudding

BABYCAKES DIRECT ™☺❶
Apple Cake; Banana and coconut cake; Carrot and Cinnamon Cake; Carrot and raisin cake; Chocolate Cake; Chocolate Chip Muffins; Coffee Cake; Cranberry and Almond Cake; Date and Walnut Cake; Ginger and Pineapple Cake; Gluten- and Wheat-Free Carrot and Cinnamon Cake; Gluten- and Wheat-Free Chocolate Cake; Gluten- and Wheat-Free Spicy Apple Cake; Gluten free Banana, Coconut & Lime Cake; Gluten free carrot and raisin cake; Gluten free cranberry and almond cake; No added sugar carrot and raisin cake; No added sugar coconut, date and banana cake; No Added Sugar Fruit Cake; Rich Fruit Cake; Victoria Sponge

BLUE LOTUS PRODUCTS LTD ™☺
'No Added Sugar' Fruit Cake; Apple Cake; Apricot & Cashew Nut Cake; Banana, Coconut & Lime Cake; Carrot & Cinnamon Cake; Carrot & Raisin

Cake; Coffee Cake; Cranberry & Almond Cake; Date & Walnut Cake; Gluten Free Apple Cake; Gluten Free Banana, Coconut & Lime; Gluten Free Carrot & Cinnamon Cake; Gluten Free Carrot & Raisin Cake; Gluten Free Chocolate Cake; Gluten Free Cranberry & Almond Cake; No Added Sugar Banana Cake; No Added Sugar Carrot Cake; Orange and Lemon Cake; Pineapple & Ginger Cake; Regal Iced Celebration Cake - All; Rich Fruit Cake; Victoria Sponge Cake; *Scones:* **Cheese & Spring Onion, Cherry & Almond, Chocolate Chip, Cranberry & Almond, Original Sweet, Raisin;** *Vegan:* **Chocolate Cake**

DIXIE DINERS CLUB
Brownie Mix; Choc Chip Cookie Mix; Fudge Mix

DOLMIO
Chunky Sauces for Bolognese: Mushroom & Courgette

ESSENTIAL TRADING CO-OPERATIVE LTD ™❶⊘✦
Midnight mix; Paradise Mix

FAYSNZ LTD ™
Apple sultana and cinnamon bake

GOBBLIN WHOLEFOODS
Apricot & Cinnamon Flapjack; Apricot Slice; Banbury Cake; Barmbrack; Black Cherry Slice; Coconut Flapjack; Date Slice; Eccles Slice; Fig Slice; Fruit & Nut Sesame Slice; Seville Coconut Slice;

Organic: Apricot Slice, Coconut Flapjack, Date Slice

HAPPY AND HEALTHY FOODS ™☺❶
Cherrybrook Kitchen: **Chocolate Cake, Chocolate Chip Cookies, Chocolate Frosting, Sugar Cookies, Vanilla Frosting, Yellow Cake**

K CREATIONS ™☺✿
The Cake

MRS CRIMBLE'S ⊘
Dutch Apple Cake; Dutch Fruit Loaf; Stem Ginger Cake

NATASHA'S LIVING FOOD ☺⊘
Mixed Nut Cashew Cream Cake; Raw Chocolate Mousse Cake

NATURALLY ME INC ☺
Apple Muffins; Blueberry Muffins; Cherry Muffins

ORGRAN ☺
Gluten-free Pancake Mixes: Apple & Cinnamon, Buckwheat

PATISSERIE ORGANIC ™⊘✿
Banana Pecan 'Cheesecake'; Banana, Orange and Hazelnut Cake; Chocolate Cake; Ginger Cake; Passion Cake/Loaf; Pear & Nut Cake/Loaf; Spiced Date and Walnut Cake

PAUL'S TOFU ™⊘✦✿
Cakes: **Apple Strudel, Fruit Pie with Kuzu**

REBECCA'S CAKES ™

Apple cinnamon pancakes; Banana blueberry muffins; Banana cupcakes; Banana loaf cake; Banana pecan pancakes; Banana Raspberry Layer Cake; Banana split cupcakes; Banoffee Cake Layer Cake; Black and White Cupcakes; Blackberry almond loaf cake; Blueberry cupcakes; Blueberry Waffles; Brownie; Butterfly cupcakes; Capuccino Cupcakes; Carrot cupcakes; Cherry almond loaf cake; Chocolate "Honey" Cupcakes; Chocolate cherry cupcakes; Chocolate chunk cookies; Chocolate fudge cupcakes; Chocolate orange cupcakes; Chocolate Sponge Layer Cake; Chocolate syrup loaf cake; Chocolate syrup muffins; Cinnamon apple muffins; Coconut Cake Layer Cake; Coconut cupcakes; Coconut lime cupcakes; Coconut pancakes; Coffee cupcakes; Coffee Layer Cake; Coffee walnut loaf cake; Cola float cupcakes; Flapjack; Fruit Cake Cupcakes; Fruit Loaf Cake; Ginger ginger ginger cupcakes; Half and half cupcakes; Hummingbird cupcakes; Jaffa orange drizzle loaf cake; Kids Birthday Cake Layer Cake; Lemon almond loaf cake; Lemon Cheesecake; Lemon cranberry muffins; Lemon drizzle loaf cake; Lemon kiss cupcakes; Lemon pistachio cupcakes; Lemon poppyseed loaf cake; Lemon Sponge Layer Cake; Lemon Victoria Sponge Layer cake; Lime drizzle loaf cake; Lime poppyseed loaf cake; Mango passion cupcakes; Maple pecan cupcakes; Maple streusel muffins; Marshmallow rice crispy squares; Mini bakes doughnuts; Mint chocolate chip cupcakes; Orange drizzle loaf cake; Orange poppyseed loaf cake; PB&J cupcakes; Peach pecan muffins; Peanut butter loaf cake; Pineapple allspice loaf cake; Pink vanilla cupcakes; Plum and almond loaf cake; Pumpkin cupcakes; Raspberry almond loaf cake; Raspberry cupcakes; Red velvet cupcakes; Rocky Road Cupcakes; Rum and raisin cupcakes; Sour cherry yogurt loaf cake; Sticky ginger loaf cake; Sticky toffee cupcakes; Sticky Toffee Pudding; Strawberries and cream cupcakes; The Black Velvet Cupcake; Vanilla Cheesecake Brownie; Vanilla Layer Cake; Vanilla loaf cake; Vegan cheese and chive muffins; Vegan chocolate cake mix; Vegan Flapjack; Vegan Gingerbread Squares; Vegan Marble Cake Squares; Victoria Sponge Layer Cake

VEGAN STORE ™☺❶⊘𝑖

All Products are vegan including brownie, pancake, muffin, cake and cookie mix

ZEDZFOODS ⊘𝑖

Apple & Cinnamon; Apricot & Ginger;

Apricot & ginger muffin; Banana, coconut & Date muffin; Carrot & raison muffin; Cherry & coconut muffin; Chocolate & orange muffin; Chocolate muffin; Chocolate, banana, coconut & date muffin; Coffee & Walnut Muffin; Mincemeat & brandy muffin; Olive & oregano muffin; Parsnip, date & walnut muffin; Poppy Seed & Lemon muffin; Rich fruit cake; Rich fruit cake with apricots & brandy; Rum & plum pudding; Sundried Tomato & Oregano muffin

'CHEESE' & 'CHEESE' SPREADS

ANGLESEY NATURAL FOODS ™☺🌙ɾ
Vegerella: **Cheddar, Italian, Mexican**

BIOFUN BVBA ™☼
Blocks- olivio; Blocks- original; Blocks- pomodori; Blocks-greek style; Fleur de Soja; Spread- basil; Spread- chive; Spread- fine herbs; Spread- horseradish; Spread- original; Spread- provencale; Young Ripened-herbs; Young Ripened- original

BUTE ISLAND FOODS LTD ™☺🌙⊘
Creamy Sheese: **Cheddar Flavour Creamy Sheese, Chives Flavour Creamy Sheese, Garlic and Herb Flavour Creamy Sheese, Mexican Flavour Creamy Sheese, Original Flavour Creamy Sheese;** *Scheese:*

Blue Flavour, Cheddar Style, Cheddar w Chives, Cheshire Style, Edam Style, Emmental Flavour, Gouda Style, Hicory Smoked Style, Mozzarella Style

DIXIE DINERS CLUB
Cheese NOT Sauce Mix

HAPPY AND HEALTHY FOODS ™☺🌙
Road's End Organics: **Alfredo Style Gluten Free Chreese Mix, Cheddar Style Chreese Mix, Cheddar Style Gluten Free Chreese Mix, Mozzarella Style Chreese Mix, Nacho Chreese - Mild Dip, Nacho Chreese - Spicy Dip**

MH FOODS LTD ™⊘ɾ
Florentino: **Parmazano;** *Life Free From:* **Cheddareese**

REDWOOD WHOLEFOOD COMPANY ™☺🌙⊘
Cheezly: **Feta Style, Garlic & Herb Flavoured, Greek Style, Mature Cheddar Style, Mature Cheddar Style w Cranberries, Nacho Style, Red Cheddar Style, Smokey Style w Added Bacon Style Pieces;** *Cheezly Melting:* **Cheddar Blocks, Cheddar Slices, Edam Blocks, Gouda Blocks, Mozzarella Blocks, Mozzarella Slices**

TOFUTTI ☺🌙⊘
Creamy Smooth Slices: Cheddar, Mozzarella; *Soft Cheese:* Creamy Smooth Country Vegetable, French Onion, Garlic & Herb, Herb & Chives, Original

VEG-OUT ™
Store Cupboard- Cheese substitutes:
Redwoods Cheezly; silken tofu; Tofutti; Parmazano

CHOCOLATE

ALTERNATIVE STORES ™☺❶
All products are vegan

ANIMAL AID SOCIETY ™☺❶⊘✍⅍1976
Boxed Chocolates: **Coffee Creams 120g, Marzipan Assortments, Orange Cremes, Pecan Parfaits, Peppermint Fondant Cremes, Stem Ginger, Vegan Selection Boxes**

BENDICKS OF MAYFAIR
Bittermints

BIONA
Dark Chocolate Bar; Dark Chocolate Cranberry Bar; Plain Chocolate Covered Brazils

CELTIC CHOCOLATES LTD ⊘
Freefrom: Dairy Free Choclate Selection, Dairy Free Chocolate Bar, Dairy Free Easter Egg, Dairy Free Mint Crisps

CHOCOLALA LIMITED ™
Chocolate Almond (Dark); Chocolate Brazil (Dark); Chocolate Walnut (Dark); Dark Chocolate Bars; Dark Chocolate Squares; Dark Chocolate Truffle; Dark Praline Stick; Ginger Lala; Mango Stick

D & D CHOCOLATES ☺☺
Dark Couverture: Animal Shapes, Bar, Dinosaur Shapes, Flower Shapes, Lemon Fondant Creams, Peppermint Fondant Creams, Plain Chocolate Chips for Cooking/Eating, Praline Hearts, Strawberry Fondant Creams

DARK SECRETS CHOCOLATE ☺
Easter Eggs; Kentucky Orange Truffles; Mint & Rosemary Truffles; Noir Tuffles; Peanut Butter Truffles; Vanilla Truffles

DIETARY NEEDS DIRECT ™
Advent Calendar Inserts; Santa Lollies; Santa Lollies with No Added Sugar; Snowmen Lollies with No Added Sugar; Animal Faces; Bite Size Mr & Mrs Santa; Chocolate Money; Christmas Shapes; Christmas Tree Baubles; Easter Eggs; Farm Animals; Hearts; Hollow Easter Egg; Snowmen Lollies; Stars; Turtles; *Chocolate / Mint Choclate / Orange Chocolate:* **Easter Eggs on Lolly Sticks, Easter Shapes, Mini Eggs, Rabbits on Lolly Sticks;** *Mint Chocolate:* **Mint Chocolate Christmas Shapes, Mint Mr & Mrs Santa, Mint Presents, Mint Santa Lollies, Mint Stars, Mint Swirls, Mint Turtles, Rudolf Mint Lollies;** *Orange Chocolate:* **Orange Christmas Shapes, Orange Santa Lollies, Orange Stars, Orange Turtles**

DIVINE CHOCOLATE ⊘
Divine After Dinner Mints; Divine Dark; Divine Dark Easter Egg; Divine Dark Mini Eggs; Divine Dark Mint; *Divine Delights:* Apricot, Brazil Nuts, Mango

EJS CONSCIOUS CHOCOLATE ™☺
All varieties

HOTEL CHOCOLAT
72% Dark Chocolate Engraved Easter Egg; Chocolate for Anything 72% Dark; Serious Dark Fix Egg

HUMDINGER LTD ™
Dairy Free Rice Crackle Bar; Dairy Free Tangerine Bar; Dairy-Free Chocolate Buttons; Dairy-Free Chocolate Spread

KINNERTON LTD
Luxury Dark Chocolate bar

LINDT & SPRUNGLI ⊘
Excellence: 70% Cocoa, 85% Cocoa, 99% Cocoa; *Excellence Origins:* Cuba, Ecuador, Madagascar

LYME REGIS FINE FOODS LTD ⊘
Kidz Break: Chocolate; *Marzipan Bar:* Organic Orange Marzipan, Organic Plain Choc Coated Original, Plain Chocolate Coated

MALAGASY
Moia Moia: 73% Cocoa Fine Chocolate Par; *Sambirano Grand Cru:* 75% Cocoa Fine Chocolate Par

MCKEITH ☺
Cacao Bean Bar; Cacao Nibs; Cacao Powder

MISS BELLASIS ☺❶✦
Amour de Tita Chocolate

MONTEZUMAS CHOCOLATES
Dark Chocolate Tubby Teddy; Giant Dark Buttons; *3175 Series:* Box; *Bar:* Dark with Chilli, Very Dark Foundation; *Bars:* Orange & Geranium, Vera - Dark Chocolate with Pistachio; *Choco-Block:* Cocoa Nibs, Dark Brazil, Date, Walnut & Pecan; *Dainty Dollops:* Bergamot, Mandarin, Peppermint; *Emperor Bar:* Chilli, Orange & Geranium; *Fruit and Nuts:* Dark Chocolate Ginger, Dark Chocolate Mango, Dark Chocolate Orange, Dark Dusted Dates, Grand Marnier Apricots, Kirsch Cherries, Madeira Prunes; *Single Origin:* Ecuador, Papua New Guinea, Peru; *Speciality Bar:* Gourmet Gorilla, Orangutang, Spice it Up; *Truffles:* Cheers III, Famous Five, Nut Case, Quick Fix, Scurvy, Sunrise; *Turtles:* Turtlely Nuts

MOOD FOODS LIMITED ™☺
Alchemy Raw Chocolate Bar; Goji Berry Bar; Organic Banana & Hempseed Raw Chocolate Bar; Relax Kids Chocolate Bar

MULU CHOCOLATE LTD ™☺⊘✿
Dark Bar; Dark Individual Chocolates; Dark with Cacao Nibs Bar; Dark with Cacao Nibs individual chocolates; Silk Bar; Silk Individual Chocolates

NATASHA'S LIVING FOOD ☺⊘
Raw Chocolates: Almonds, Cacao Nibs, Chilli, Ginger, Nutmeg, Orange, Walnuts

PLAMIL FOODS LTD ™☺❶⊘

Chocolate Drop Snack Pots: **Dairy Free Chocolate Drops;** *Dairy Free & No Added Sugar Chocolate Bars:* **Dairy Free Alternative to Milk Chocolate, Dairy Free Chocolate, Dairy Free Mint Chocolate, Dairy Free Orange Chocolate;** *Fairtrade Chocolate:* **Organic Dairy Free Alternative To Milk Chocolate;** *No Added Sugar Chocolate:* **No Added Sugar Chocolate 72% Cocoa, No Added Sugar Chocolate with Shelled Hemp;** *Organic Chocolate (Dairy Free):* **Organic Orange Chocolate;** *Organic Chocolate (Dairy Free):* **Organic Cayenne Chocolate (70% Cocoa), Organic Chocolate, Organic Ginger Chocolate, Organic Mint Chocolate;** *Organic Dairy Free Chocolate:* **Organic Dark Chocolate 87% Cocoa;** *Premium Impulse and No Added Sugar Chocolate Bars:* **Dark Chocolate 87% Cocoa, No Added Sugar Chocolate 72% Cocoa, No Added Sugar Mint Chocolate, Organic Dark and White Mint Chocolate, Organic Orange Chocolate with Cranberries**

RAW LIVING ™
Bullet Ride Power Bar

RAWCREATION LTD ™☺
Christmas Love Bar; Desire Chocolate Bar; Empress; Feaster; Goddess Chocolate Bar; I Love u; Intacta Chocolate bar; Raw Cacao Liquor; Raw Organic Cacao Butter; Raw organic chocolate powder; Raw Shelled Cacao Beans; Raw Whole Cacao Beans; Temptress Chocolate Bar; The Siren Chocolate Bar

RITTER SPORT ⊘
Dark Chocolate 71%; Marzipan; Peppermint; Plain 50%

ROAR CHOCOLATE ™☺⊘ ✿
Bar/pods Orange; Bar/Pods Signature 81%; Chilli Orange Bar; Cool Mint Crisp Bar; Pecan & Cranberry Bar

ROCOCO CHOCOLATES ⊘
Ciociolato Nocciole Piemonte (Dark Chocolate with Crunchy Hazelnuts); Cocoa Dusted Scorched Almonds; Cocoa Powder; *Dark Chocolate Bars:* Chocolate Amer 70%, Extra Brut 85%, Grenada Chocolate 60%, Grenada Chocolate 71%, Organic Dark 65%, Plus Noir Que Noir 100%, Sugar Free 56%, Valrhona 64%, Valrhona 66%, Valrhona 70%; *Dark Chocolate Flavoured Bars:* Arabic Spices, Basil & Lime, Black Pepper, Caramelized Almond, Cardamom, Chilli, Cocoa Nibs, Crystallised Ginger, Earl Grey, Fine Mocha, Geranium, Lavender, Morello Cherry, Orange & Geranium, Peppered Mint, Pink Peppercorn; *Dark Chocolate Mini Bars "Bee Bars":* 65%, Chilli, Earl Grey, Ginger, Lavender, Orange & Geranium; *Hot Chocolate:* Plain, Spiced with Cardamom Nutmeg & Cinnamon; *Loose English Creams:* Brazil Nut,

Coffee, Dark Banana, Dark Raspberry, Dark Strawberry, Geranium, Lavender, Lemon, Marzipan, Orange, Passion Fruit, Rose, Stem Ginger, Violet; *Loose House Selection:* Cherry in Cognac, Dark Nut Cluster, Dipped Apricot, Dipped Orange Slices, Dipped Orange Sticks, Ginger Slices, Ginger Sticks, Lubecker Almond Marzipan

SJAAK'S ORGANIC CHOCOLATES
Almond Butter Bites; Dark Chocolate Bar; Dark Chocolate with Almonds; Dark Chocolate with Creamy Caramel; Dark Chocolate with Espresso Bar; Dark Chocolate with Raspberry Bar; Extra Dark 70% Chocolate Bar; Extra Dark Bites; Peanut Butter Bites; Vegan European Assortment; Vegan Nuts & Chews Assortment; Vegan Truffle Assortment

SUMA WHOLEFOODS
™ ❶ ⊘ 𝗶 ☞ ⅍ 1985
Dark Chocolate Coated: **Ginger, Peanuts, Raisins**

SUPERNUTRIENTS ™☺⊘ 𝗶
Organic cacao nibs

THE BOOJA-BOOJA COMPANY LTD ™☺⊘ ✿
Toffee Apple Crumble Truffle; *Truffles:* **Around Midnight Espresso Truffle, Champagne Truffle, Cognac Flambed Banana Truffle, Ginger Wine Truffle, Hazelnut Crunch Truffle, Toffee Apple Crumble Truffles**

THE CHOCOLATE ALCHEMIST ⊘ ✿
Choc Chunks with Brazilnuts & Sultanas; Choc Chunks with Ginger; Choc Chunks with Walnuts & Dates; Chunky Bar with Brazilnuts & Sultanas; Chunky Bar with Walnuts & Apricots; Dark Chocolate Big Buttons; Dark Chocolate Fruity Bar with Blackcurrant; Dark Chocolate Nutty Slab; Dark Chocolate Spicy Bar with Chilli; Dark Chocolate Spicy Bar with Nutmeg; Plain Dark Chocolate Bar; *Fruit Spice & All Things Nice:* Mango in Dark Chocolate with Orange & Nutmeg; *Wo Wo's Favourite Food:* Dark Chocolate Alphabets, Dark Chocolate Big Buttons

THE FAMOUS CHOCOLATE HOUSE 1657 ⊘ 𝗶
Loose Chocolates: Coffee and Pecan (Plain), Coffee Creme with Bean (Plain), Firm Bittermint (Plain), Stem Ginger (Plain), Strawberry Creme (Plain)

THE RAW CHOCOLATE COMPANY LIMITED ™☺
Chocolad; Mid Winter; Pitch Dark; Raw GO!; Twilight; Vanoffe

TRAIDCRAFT PLC ⊘
After Dinner Mints; Swiss Plain Chocolate

TRIALIA FOODS AUSTRALIA ™
Eskal Noble Choice: **Mint Crunch Dark Chocolate, Raspberry Dark Chocolate, Rice Crisp Dark Chocolate, Rich Dark Chocolate, Semi Sweet Choc Chip, Toasted Almond Dark Chocolate**

TRUELOVE ORGANICS LIMITED ™☺
Mini gift bags petits fours- several flavours; Mixed gift tray- petits fours; Potion Box; Potion Heart; **Potion Large Box;** *chocolate hearts:* **Coconut, Goji and orange, Goji berry, Goji, fruit and nut, Lemon flavour, Mega chocolate heart, Mint flavour, Orange flavour**

VEGETALIA LIMITED
Organic Dark Chocolate with Candied Ginger

VEG-OUT ™
Store Cupboard: **Chocolate truffles**

VENTURE FOODS UK LTD ™⊘
Swiss Chocolate couverture with Raisins & Almonds; Swiss Chocolate Marrakesh; Swiss Chocolate Tangiers; Swiss Couverture; Swiss Dark Chcolate with Hazelnut; Swiss Dark Chcolate with Cranberries; Swiss Food of the Gods; Swiss Plain Chocolate; Swiss Plain Chocolate with Mint; Swiss Vegan Diets White Bar

VIVA! ☺❶⊘ ✦
Coffee Cremes; Giant Buttons; Handmade Vegan Chocolate Selection; Orange Cremes; Viva!'s Moondance Praline Truffles

CONFECTIONERY & SWEET SNACKS

ALNAVIT GMBH ™
Apfel Zimt Riegel

AUSTRALIAN NOUGAT COMPANY ™⊘
Macadamia Bliss Nougat with Pistachio

BIONA
Bio Smarties; Cola Bottles; Fruit Lollies; Peppermints; Pineapple Chews; Tutti Frutti Wine Gums; *Jelly Bears:* Licorice, Tutti Frutti

BLACK OPAL INTERNATIONAL AUSTRALIA
Soft-Eating Liqorice: Black, Raspberry

CADBURY TREBOR BASSETT
Bassett's: Mint Creams, Pear Drops; *Clorets:* Original; *Trebor - Extra Cool:* Peppermint, Spearmint; *Trebor - Soft Mints:* Peppermint, Spearmint; *Trident - Soft:* Peppermint, Tropical Twist

CARRIE'S COOKIES ™
Brownies: **Chocolate Brownie;** *Flapjacks:* **Apricot & Almond, Apricot&Hazel, Bird Seed Pie, Blackberry, Blackberry gluten free, Blackcurrant, Blackcurrant gluten free, Blueberry & Poppy, Blueberry Berry, Carob & Sesame, Carob and ginger, Cherry & Almond, Cherry**

FOOD

Gluten Free, Chocolate and ginger, Chocolate Forest, Cranberry & Pecan, Date & Seed, Date and Seeds gluten free, Funky Fig, Hazel, Hazel & Carob, Hazel & Chocolate, Orange & Carob, Orange & Chocolate, Raspberry & Almond, Seeded, Vanilla Blueberry, Walnut & Plum, Warming Ginger

CEDAR HEALTH LTD
Castus Fruit Bars: Apricot, Banana, Fig, Stawbery; *Panda Licorice:* Bar, Bear, Comfits, Cuts, Raspberry Bar

CLEARSPRING ™☺❶🚫🍴👁
Ginger Rice Malt Sweets; Lotus Rice Malt Sweets; Peppermint Rice Malt Sweets; Sour Plum Rice Malt Sweets; Vanilla Rice Malt Sweets; *Organic Snack Bars:* Almond, Sesame, Sesame and Raisin

D & D CHOCOLATES ☺🚫
Siesta: Carob Animal Shapes, Carob Bar (Original/Orange/Mint), Carob Dinosaur Shapes, Carob Drops, Carob Flakes for Cooking, Carob Flower Shapes (Original/Orange/Mint), Carob Orange Fondants, Carob Peppermint Fondants, Carob Strawberry Fondants

DIETARY NEEDS DIRECT ™
Pineapple Chunks; Pineapple Pear Drops; *Fudge:* Chocolate Fudge, Vanilla Fudge; *Sweets:* Carob Mixed Christmas Shapes, Carob Santas, Carob Snowmen, Mint Humbugs, Strawberry & Peach Delights,

Strawberry & Peach Fruit Pear Drop, Strawberry Humbugs, Treacle Toffee

FAYSNZ LTD ™
Fudgilicious coconut; Tipsy mincey; Treacle Toffee; Yummycomb

GRANOVITA UK LTD 🚫🍴
Castus Date & Apricot Fruit Bar; *Coconut Bars:* Almond, Cherry, Mango, Original, Pineapple, Strawberry; *Organic Oskri Snack Bar:* Quinoa, Sesame with Date Syrup, Sesame with Date Syrup & Black Cumin, Sesame with Date Syrup & Fennel; *Taste of Nature Organic Snack Bars:* Argentina Peanut Bar, Brazilian Raisin & Nut Bar, California Sesame, Almond & Raisin Bar, Niagara Oat, Apple & Cinnamon Bar

GUARANA COMPANY ™
Blueberries; Cranberries; Goji Berries; Sun Dried Inca Berries; Sun Dried Mango Strips

HOTEL CHOCOLAT
Turkish Delight

JORDANS 🚫
Multigrain bar: Cranberry & Raspberry; *Frusli:* All Fruit bar: Apple & Passionfruit, All Fruit bar: Apple & Strawberry

JUST WHOLEFOODS ☺🚫
VegeBears: Frooty Fruits, Fruit Jellies

FOOD

K CREATIONS ™☺☼
Airo Bar; Blonde With Vanilla; Choshi; Dark Orange; Darkly Ginger; Jungle Bar; Lavender with Vanilla; Lemon&Rose; Lovely Dark with Lemon; Minted Rare; Nutty Dreams; Oat & Date Biscuit Bar; Rare With Nibs; Spice Island; The Dark Bar; The Super Bar; Walk on the Wild Side

KALLO FOODS ◌
Flapjacks; Raisin Flapjacks

KELLOGGS
Strawberry Fruit Winders

LARABAR ☺
Apple Pie; Banana Cookie; Cashew Cookie; Cherry Pie; Chocolate Coconut Chew; Cinnamon Roll; Cocoa Mole; Ginger Snap; Key Lime Pie; Lemon Bar; Pecan Pie; Pistachio

LIFEFOOD CZECH REPUBLIC S.R.O. ™
Cashew and Date Balls; Jakonella Bio; Organic Apple Cinnamon Flax Rolls; Organic Cacao and Date Flax Rolls; Organic Coconut Balls; Organic Ginger Lemon Flax Rolls; Organic Raw Cacao Buckwheaties; Organic Raw Cacao Dream Deluxe; Organic Vanilla Buckwheaties

LYME REGIS FINE FOODS LTD ◌
Fruit 4 U: Apple, Cherry, Raspberry; *Fruit Break:* Banana, Date & Fig, Plum & Apricot; *Kidz Break:* Blackcurrant, Raisin; *Kidz Organic Fruit Bars:* Apple, Blackcurrant, Strawberry; *La Fruit:* Apricot, Blackcurrant, Raspberry; *Organic Fruitus Bars:* Apple, Apricot, Mixed Berry, Sultana & Hazelnut; *Organic Seven Seeds & Nut Bar:* Cranberry, Orginal

MARS
Starburst: Fruity Chews, Sour Chews, Strawberry Mix

MASTERFOODS ◌
Blackcurrant; Strawberry; *Aquadrops:* Apple; *Tunes:* Cherry

MCKEITH ☺
Goji Berry Bar; Goji Berry Bar Bites; Living Food Energy Cookie Bites; Living Food Energy Love Bites; Raw Hemp Seed Bar; *Living Food Bar:* Energy, Love, Vitamin C

MUNCHY SEEDS ™☺
Vanilla Pumpkin

NATASHA'S LIVING FOOD ☺◌
Raw Superfood Sprouted Sunflower Crunch

NATURKRAFTWERKE ™
Energy 1 bar with Spirulina & Banana; Energy 2 bar with Chlorella; Energy 3 bar with Weizengras; Energy 4 bar with Gruentee & Zitrone; Energy 5 bar with Guarana & Kakao; Energy 6 bar with Acerola

NESTLÉ
Jelly Tots; *Polo:* Original, Spearmint, Sugar Free, Xtra Strong

ORGANICO ⊘ ☼
Break & Bil: Spelt Apricot Delizia Bars, Spelt Blueberry Delizia Bars

ORGANIX BRANDS PLC ⊘ ☼
Cereal Bars: Apple & Orange, Blackcurrant, Carrot Cake, Cocoa & Raisin, Munch Bar, Raspberry & Apple

ORGRAN ☺
Gluten-free Fruit Bars: Apricot, Blueberry-Filled, Choc Cherry, Chocolate Hazel Bars

PATISSERIE ORGANIC ™⊘ ☼
Chocolate Flapjacks; Date Slice; Flapjacks; Fruity Flapjacks; Millet Munchies

PETER RABBIT ORGANICS ⊘ ☼
Organic 100% Fruit Bar; Organic Fruit & Oat Bar

PLAMIL FOODS LTD ™☺❶⊘
Carob Bars: **Carob No Added Sugar or Hydrogenated Fat, Carob No Hydrogenated Fat**

PREMIER LIFESTYLES LTD ™☺
Fruits and Fruits Products: **Yoconut, Yocoslice**

PROBIOS
Almond Finger Snacks; Hazelnut-Choc Finger Snacks

RAW LIVING ™
Be The Change; Bullet Ride

REBECCA'S CAKES ™
Vegan Flapjack Fruit crumble Squares

RENK'S INDUSTRIAL LTDA ™☺⊘ ☼
eBar Organic Fruit Bar Flavor Acai; eBar Organic Fruit Bar Flavor Acerola; eBar Organic Fruit Bar Flavor Guava; eBar Organic Fruit Bar Flavour Cupuacu

RJ'S
Natural Licorice: Soft Eating Raspberry; *Natural Licorice Logs:* Chocolate Orange, Raspberry

SCIENCE IN SPORT
SMART1 Gel; *GO Bars:* All Flavours; *GO Gels:* All Flavours

SUMA WHOLEFOODS
™❶⊘ ⛏ ☞⚓1985
Carob Drops: **No Sugar**

SUPERNUTRIENTS ™☺⊘ ⛏
Organic goji berries

SWIZZELS MATLOW LTD ⊘ ⛏
Climpies; Mr Fruits; Rainbow Drops; Refresher bar lemon mega; *Deposited Crystal:* Barley Sugar, Crystal Fruits, Licorice; *Lolly:* Fruity Pops, Fruity Pops Sour, Ice Cream Pops, Swizz Kid Fruity

THE BOOJA-BOOJA COMPANY LTD
™☺⊘ ☼
Organic, Raw Cacao Beans 50g & 200g; Organic, Raw Cacao Nibs 50g & 200g; *Organic:* **Raw cacao beans 50g & 200g, Raw Cacao Nibs 50g & 200g**

THE CRUELTY FREE SHOP ™☺❶
All products are vegan

THORNTONS ⊘
Fruit Jellies; Single Ice Cream Cone

TRAIDCRAFT PLC ⊘
Mixed Fruit Sweets

TROPICAL WHOLEFOODS
Tropical Fruit Bar

VEGAN PERFECTION ™☺
All products are vegan

VEGAN STORE ™☺❶⊘ ✔
All products are vegan including fudge, marshmallows, golden crunch, boxed chocolates and after dinner chocolates

VEGETALIA LIMITED
Lemon Spelt Biscuits Coated in Chocolate; Orange Biscuits

VENTURE FOODS UK LTD ™⊘
Vegan Dark Chocolate & Coconut; Vegan Dark Chocolate & Hazelnut Nougat

VIMTO
Fizzy Centred Lollipops

WILLIAM SANTUS & CO. LTD ™⊘
Uncle Joe's: **Mintballs**

WINNING WAYS
FINE FOODS LIMITED ™
Coconut Ice; Cranberry Fudge; Vanilla Fudge

WRIGLEY CO LTD ☺⊘ ✔
Doublemint; Juicy Fruit; Spearmint; York Fruits; *Airwaves:* Black Mint, Cherry Menthol, Menthol & Eucalyptus; *Extra:* Cool Breeze, Fire, Ice, Ice Liquid Filled Peppermint, Ice Liquid Filled Spearmint, Peppermint, Spearmint; *Extra Fusion:* Orange Pineapple & Banana, Peppermint Berry, Raspberry Blackcurrant & Grapefruit, Spearmint Melon; *Extra Mints:* Cool Mints, Ice, Peppermint; *Hubba Bubba:* Atomic Apple, Cool Cola, Seriously Strawberry, Snappy Strawberry Bubble Tape; *Juicy Fruit:* Strappleberry; *Orbit:* Completer Freshmint; *Orbit Complete:* Peppermint, Spearmint, Strong Mint

ZEDZFOODS ⊘ ✔
Date & ginger flapjack

COOKING AIDS - SAVOURY

A. VOGEL
Herbamare: All Varieties

AMISA
Bouillon

BETTY CROCKER
Bac-Os: Bits, Chips

BIONA
Gluten-Free Breadcrumbs; Gomasio

BLUE DRAGON
Panko Breadcrumb Mix; Rice Flour
Pancakes; Spring Roll Wrappers;
Tamarind Paste; Tempura Batter Mix;
Sushi Ingredients: Wasabi Paste

CLEARSPRING ™☺❶◌♦️👁
Johsen Shoyu; Kuzu; Shiso
Condiment; Tamari Soya Sauce;
Ume Puree; *Organic:* Sesame Sea
Salt - Gomasio, Shoyu Soya Sauce,
Soya Sauce, Sushi Rice Seasoning,
Sushi Sauce, Teriyaki Sauce

DOVES FARM FOODS LTD ◌
Quick Yeast

**ESSENTIAL TRADING
CO-OPERATIVE LTD** ™❶◌♦️
Organic Yeast Extract; Yeast Extract;
Essential Brand- Flours: All (Organic &
Conventional); *Essential Brand- Herbs:*
All (Organic & Conventional); *Soya
Sauce:* Organic Shoyu, Organic
Tamari, Shoyu, Tamari

GILCHESTERS ORGANICS LTD ™◌✿
Stoneground Organic 100% Spelt;
Stoneground Organic 100%
Wholemeal Flour; Stoneground
Organic Farmhouse Flour;
Stoneground Organic Pizza Ciabatta
Flour; Stoneground Organic
Unbleached White

GLUTEN FREE FOODS LTD
Barkat: Baking Powder

GREEN'S
Dumpling Mix

HIGHER NATURE PLC ™◌♦️
Omega Excellence: Organic Cold
Milled Flax Seeds, Organic Sprouted
Flax Seeds

HOLISTIX ™❶
Dried Herbs: All

**INTERNATIONAL PARTNERSHIP LTD
(SEAGREENS DIVISION)** ™☺
Seagreens- Ascophyllum Pieces: Table
Condiment Grinder; *Seagreens-
Medium Granules:* Catering
Ingredient, Culinary Ingredient;
Seagreens-Medium Granules: Culinary
Ingredient Shaker

JUST WHOLEFOODS ☺◌
Organic Sprouting Mix; Organic
Wholemeal Breadcrumbs; VegeRen;
Organic Stuffing Mixes: Apple & Sage,
Cranberry & Orange, Sage & Onion

KITCHEN GARDEN
Curry Flavour TVP

KNORR
Paste Bouillon: Mediterranean
Vegetable, Rich Vegetable, Vegetable

MARIGOLD ❶◌
Engevita: Nutritional Yeast Flakes

MCKEITH ☺
Hemp Sauce

FOOD

NATURE'S OWN LTD ™
Cytoplan- Nutritional Support:
Linseeds; *Nutritional Support:*
Linseeds NO VAT

NATURKRAFTWERKE ™
Zhug

ODYSEA
Tomato Perasti; Vine Leaves

ORGRAN ☺
All Purpose Gluten-Free Crumbs

POLAR SUN PRODUCTS LTD ™☺⊘
Soya flour

QIANNA AGRICULTURAL PRODUCTS IND & TRADING CO. LTD ™☺
Roasted Black Bean; Roasted Green Soybean; Roasted Soybean

QUINUA REAL BRASIL LTDA ™⊘
Quinoa Flour

RAW LIVING ™
Barleygrass

RAWCREATION LTD ™☺
Crushed Purple Corn; Organic Hemp Powder from Canada; Purple Corn Flour; Purple Corn Powder; Raw Pink Himalayan Fine-Ground Salt; Raw Pink Himalayan Rock Salt

SACLA
Artichokes Antipasto; Char-Grilled Borretane Onions; Char-Grilled Peppers Antipasto; Italian Oven Roasted Tomatoes with Chilli; Italian Oven Roasted Tomatoes with Garlic; Italian Oven Roasted Tomatoes with Olives; Mixed Beans; Peperonata Antipasto; Sun-Dried Tomato Paste; Sun-Dried Tomatoes Antipasto; Wild Mushroom Antipasto; *Bread Toppings:* Red Pepper, Onion & Chilli, Tomato & Olive

SUPERCOOK
Bread Crumbs: Golden; *Breadcrumbs:* Savoury

UNCLE BEN'S
Dinner Kits: Hoi Sin Kit, Sizzling Fajita Kit

VEGETALIA LIMITED
Himalayan Cooking Salt

VENTURE FOODS UK LTD ™⊘
Essential: **Coarse Sea Salt, Fine Sea Salt;** *Geo Organics:* **Atlantic Sea Salt, Atlantic Sea Salt Shaker, Bagged Sea Salt, Balti Curry Paste, Cranberry Sauce, Korma Curry Paste, Madras Curry Paste, Thai Green Curry Paste, Thai Pine Nut Satay Paste, Thai Red Curry Paste, Thai Yellow Curry Paste, Tikka Masala Curry Paste, Tomato Relish, Tomato Sauce;** *The Raintree:* **Fleur de Sel**

WHITWORTHS LTD ⊘
Sage & Onion Stuffing

COOKING AIDS - SWEET

CLEARSPRING ™☺❶⊘◑☜👁
Japanese Brown Rice Malt Syrup;
Organic: **Barley Malt Syrup, Corn and
Barley Malt Syrup, Rice Malt Syrup**

CUISINE DE FRANCE
Assorted Sugar Strands

**ESSENTIAL TRADING
CO-OPERATIVE LTD** ™❶⊘☜
Coconut milk

G. COSTA & CO ⊘
Royal ascot: Stem ginger in syrup

GENERAL DIETARY
Xanthan Gum

GREEN'S
Lemon Pie Filling; Quick Gel

HIGHER NATURE PLC ™⊘☜
ZyloSweet

JIF
Lemon Juice: Bottled, Squeezy; *Lime
Juice:* Bottled

JUST WHOLEFOODS ☺☺
All Natural Custard Powder

KALLO FOODS ⊘
Multigrain Rice Cakes; Traditional
Grissini Breadsticks; *Rice Cakes:* Corn
Cakes

MAXIM MARKETING COMPANY ™
Weikfield - Jelly Crystals: **Banana,
Cherry;** *Weikfield- Jelly Crystals:*
**Mango, Orange, Pineapple,
Raspberry, Strawberry**

MERIDIAN FOODS ⊘
Malt Extract; Mince Pie Filling; *Natural
Sweeteners:* Malt Extract, Mince Pie
Filling

NESTLÉ
Dessert Sauce: Caramel, Chocolate

NIELSEN-MASSEY VANILLAS INC.
Extract: Almond, Chocolate, Coffee,
Lemon, Vanilla; *Pure Vanilla Extracts:* All

RAW LIVING ™
Acai Powder; Agave Nectar; Cacao
Butter; Chocolate Powder; He Shon
Wu; Lucuma powder; Mesquite
powder; Yacon flour

RAWCREATION LTD ™☺
Agave Syrup; Dark Agave Syrup;
Organic Goji Berries; Organic Lucuma;
Organic Yacon Slices; Raw Apricot
Kernels; Raw Carob Nectar; Raw Incan
Berries; Raw Whole Carob Pods; Raw
Wild Mesquite Meal; Yacon Syrup

RYVITA ⊘
Crackerbread: Rice

SAUCES OF CHOICE
Belgian Chocolate Sauce; Passion Fruit
& Mango Sauce; Raspberry Sauce;
Strawberry Sauce

SUMA WHOLEFOODS
™❶⊘ⓘ☜↦1985
Cherries: **All**

SUPERCOOK
Angelica; Baking Powder; Bicarbonate of Soda; Chocolate Flavour Strands; Cream of Tartar; Extract of Vanilla; Glucose; Glycerine; Ground Arrowroot; Hundreds and thousands; Liquid Glucose; Ready to Roll Icings; Ready to Roll Regalice; Sugar strands; Vanilla Flavouring; *Bread Crumbs:* Golden, Wholemeal; *Buttercream Easyice:* Chocolate; *Colours and Flavours:* All, Except Natural Red; *Easyice:* Chocolate, Vanilla; *Marzipan:* Golden, Natural; *Natural Colours:* Natural Yellow; *Ready to Roll Marzipan:* Golden, Natural; *Select Vanilla Pods:* Extract, Powder; *Standard Colourings:* All suitable

SWEETBIRD ⊘
Syrups: English Toffee, Hazelnut, Vanilla

VEG-OUT ™
Store Cupboard Sweeteners: **Maple Syrup;** *Store Cupboard- Sweeteners:* **Fruit Juice**

CRACKERS, CRISPBREADS ETC

ARTISAN BISCUITS
Bread: 3 Seed; *Millers:* Damsels Wheat Wafers, Organic Damsels Wheat Wafers; *Mondovino Crackers:* Black Olive, Spicy Seed & Nut; *Wheat Wafers:* Charcoal, Oat, Organic 3 Seed, Organic Spelt, Organic Wheat, Rye, Sour Dough, Spelt, Wheat

BIONA
Corn Cakes; *Rice Cakes:* Dark Chocolate Coated, No Salt, With Amaranth, With Quinoa, With Salt

BURTON'S FOODS LTD
Cream Cracker

CLEARSPRING ™☺❶⊘ⓘ☜
Brown Rice Wafers - Sesame; Japanese Rice Cakes - Black Sesame; Japanese Rice Cakes - Miso; Japanese Rice Cakes - Tamari Garlic; Japanese Rice Cakes - Teriyaki; Japanese Rice Cakes- Sea Vegetable; Rice Snacks - Black Sesame; Rice Snacks - Quinoa; Rice Snacks - Sea Vegetable; Rice Snacks - Whole Sesame; *Organic:* **Puffed Rice Cakes - Plain, Puffed Rice Cakes - Multigrain with Spelt, Puffed Rice Cakes - Salted, Rice Cracker - Olive Oil and Salt, Rice Crackers - Tamari**

DEES CARIBBEAN IMPORTS
Homemade Special Cream Water Crackers; HTB Crackers

G. COSTA & CO ⊘
Pagen Krisprolls: Cranberry & Blueberry Krisprolls, Golden Krisprolls, Wholegrain Krisprolls; *Pop pan:* Spring Onion crackers

GEO ORGANICS ⊘
Toasted Croutons

GLUTEN FREE FOODS LTD
Glutano: Crispbread

KALLO FOODS ⊘
High Fibre Oat and Rice Cakes; Low Fat
Lightly Salted Rice Cakes; No Added Salt
Rice Cakes; No Added Salt Rice Cakes
with Sesame; Original Breadsticks; Rice
Cake Bites With Sea Salt; Rice Cake Bites
With Yeast Extract; Rosemary Crackers;
Savoury Rice Cakes; Slightly Salted Rice
Cakes with Sesame; Thin Slice No Added
Salt Rice Cakes; Thin Slice Slightly Salted
Rice Cakes with Sesame; Wholemeal
Rye Crispbread; *Grains and Seeds:*
Khorasan and Sorghum Corn Cakes,
Quinoa and Amaranth Corn Cakes,
Quinoa and Amaranth Rice Cakes;
Primo D'Oro Torinesi: Original Breadsticks,
Pepper Breadsticks

LIFEFOOD CZECH REPUBLIC S.R.O. ™
Organic Flax Onion Crackers; Organic
Garlic Marjoram Flax Crackers;
Organic Tomato Chilli Flax Crackers

MARMITE
Breadsticks; Ricecakes

NATASHA'S LIVING FOOD ☺⊘
Raw Carrot & Thyme Crackers; Raw
Indian Spice Crackers

ORGRAN ☺
Gluten-Free Corn Cakes; *Gluten-free*
Crispbreads: Corn, Rice, Rice & Cracked

Pepper, Rice & Garden Herb, Salsa
Corn; *Organic Rice Cakes:* Salted,
Sesame Salted, Sesame Unsalted,
Sunsalted; *Rice Cake Thins:* Salted,
Unsalted

PROBIOS
Rice Crackers

RYVITA ⊘
Crispbreads: Dark Rye, Multigrain,
Original, Pumpkin and Oat, Sesame,
Sunflower and Oat; *Rice cakes:*
Multigrain, Original, Sesame

SUMA WHOLEFOODS
™❶⊘ ℹ ⌾⅍ 1985
Japanese Rice Crackers

THE FOOD DOCTOR LTD ™☺
Organic Spelt Crackers

UNILEVER
Pappadum: Mini Mixed, Plain

UNITED BISCUITS LTD ⊘
Carr's - Table Water: Cracked Black
Pepper, Large, Small, Toasted Sesame
Seed; *Hovis:* Cracker; *Jacob's:* Cornish
Wafer, Table Cracker; *Jacob's - Cream*
Cracker: High Fibre, Light, Original;
Jacob's - Thins: Rosemary & Sea Salt,
Sesame & Roasted Onion; *Jacob's -*
Water Biscuit: High Bake

VENTURE FOODS UK LTD ™⊘
Geo Organics: **Toasted Salted**
Croutons; *The Raintree:* **Garlic Soup**
Croutons

CREAM REPLACERS

ALPRO UK LTD ™☺⊘
Chilled Dairy Free Alternative to single cream 250ml; Soya Dream

FIRST FOODS LTD ☺⊘
Oat Supreme: Oat Cream

GRANOVITA UK LTD ⊘♦
Organic Cremo Vita - alternative to dairy whipping cream

DESSERTS

ALPRO UK LTD ™☺⊘
Dairy Free Custard; Fruits of the Orchard; *Pot Desserts:* **Caramel Dessert Calcium and Vitamins 4X125g, Chocolate, Dark chocolate, Vanilla;** *Pot Desserts Provamel:* **Organic mocha 4x125g;** *Provamel:* **Organic chocolate custard, Organic vanilla custard;** *Provamel Pot Desserts:* **Organic caramel 4x125g, Organic Chocolate 4x125g, Organic Vanilla 4x125g**

BRITISH SUGAR PLC
Silver Spoon - Treat Toppings: Dark Chocolate, Monster Crackin'

CLEARSPRING ™☺❶⊘♦☞
Organic: **Brown Rice Amazake, Fruit Puree - Apple, Fruit Puree - Apple and Pineapple, Fruit Puree -** Apple/Apricot, Fruit Puree - Apple/Blueberry, Fruit puree - Apple/Pineapple, Fruit Puree - Apple/Plum, Fruit Puree - Pear, Fruit Puree - Pear/Banana, Millet Amazake, Oat Amazake

CUISINE DE FRANCE
7" Plate Rhubarb Pie; 7/" Plate Apple Pie; Apple & Blackberry Lattice; Apple & Blackberry Pie; Apple & Cinnamon Strudel; Apple & Cranberry Lattice; Apple Lattice; Apple Puff; Apple Tart; Apple Turnover; Deep Fill Apple Pie; Delicious Apple & Blackberry Pie; Delicous Apple Pie; Delicous Rhubarb Pie; Everyday Apple & Blackberry Tart; Everyday Bramley Apple Tart; Everyday Rhubarb Tart; Hero Apple Pie; Hero Premium Apple Tart; Lattice Rhubarb Tart; Mini Apple Pie; Rhubarb Tart

ESSENTIAL TRADING CO-OPERATIVE LTD ™❶⊘♦
Canned mango chunks; Canned pineapple chunks; Canned tropical fruit mix; *Essential Brand- Canned Fruit:* **Organic Canned Papaya in Juice**

FAYSNZ LTD ™
Fruiticous

JUST WHOLEFOODS ☺⊘
Jelly Crystals: Lemon, Raspberry, Strawberry, Tropical

NATASHA'S LIVING FOOD ☺⊘
Cacao Ganach Tart(ginger/mint/orange/almond)

NATURALLY ME INC ☺
Cherry Pie; Chocolate Mousse Pie; Gourmet Apple Cranberry Pie; Gourmet Apple Struesel Pie; Gourmet Blueberry Struesel Pie; Pie Shells; Pumpkin Pie

NATURGREEN
Almond Dessert; Hazelnut and Chocolate Dessert; Hazelnut Dessert

ORGANICO ◌ ✧
Coteaux Nantais: Apple and Blueberry Desserts, Apple and Cherry Desserts, Apple and Rhubarb Desserts, Apple and Strawberry Desserts, Magic Apricot Compote, Magic Nectarine Compote, Magic Plum Compote

PREMIER FOODS
Lyons: Lattice Treacle Tart, Treacle Tart

PROBIOS
Rice Cocoa Dessert; Rice Vanilla Dessert; Spelt Apricot Crostatina; Spelt Blueberry Crostatina

REBECCA'S CAKES ™
Apple and Blackberry Crumble; Banoffee Trifle; Fruit Pies; *Mini Desserts/Petit Fours:* **Caramel Trifle Shots with Kahlua, Cherry Gallettes, Chocolate and Nut Dipped Frozen Bananas, Chocolate Brownie Squares with Raspberries, Chocolate Dipped Seasonal Fruit, Cocoa Dusted Truffles, Fruit Patisserie Tarts, Mini Chocolate Cupcakes, Mini Vanilla Cupcakes with Pink Icing and White Piped Initials:, Peanut Butter and Chocolate**

Squares, Pecan Pies, Rocky Roads, Scones with Cream and Strawberries, Victoria Sponges with Cream and Berries

UNILEVER
Carte D'Or - Coulis: Blackcurrant, Mango, Raspberry

DIPS & DRESSINGS

ANGLESEY NATURAL FOODS ™☺◌ ♦
Alavon Egg-Free Mayonnaise: **Cajun, Garlic, Plain**

DISCOVERY FOODS
Ranch Style Salsa: Hot, Medium

FIRST QUALITY FOODS ◌ ♦
Al'fez: Baharat dressing 200ml, Falafel mix 150g, Roasted pepper & pine nut dip, Tahini dressing 200ml

G. COSTA & CO ◌
Casa fiesta: Guacamole flavour dip

GOBBLIN WHOLEFOODS
Houmous; *Organic:* Houmous

GRANOVITA UK LTD ◌ ♦
Mayola! Egg Free Mayonnaise: Garlic, Lemon, Original

HEINZ ™◌
Dips: Mild Salsa Dip

HELLMANNS
Fat Free Vinaigrette

FOOD

JETHROS
'Spirits of Summer' Vinaigrettes:
Cranberry Pepper & Vodka, Irish Whiskey
& Grain Mustard, Orange & Bourbon

KITCHEN GARDEN
Salad Oil: Oregano, Piri Piri

LEEORA VEGETARIAN FOOD ™☺⊘
Mediterranean Cuisine: **Babaganush,
Chilli sauce, Greek Aubergine Dip,
Lebanese Style Humous, Tunisian
Style Harissa**

MH FOODS LTD ™⊘ ✔
Life: **Mayonnaise Style Sunflower
Oil Dressing - Egg Free**

ODYSEA
Meze: Aubergine, Roasted Red Pepper,
Sun-Dried Tomato

**PATCHWORK TRADITIONAL
FOOD COMPANY**
Pate: Brown Lentil with Hazelnuts,
Brown Lentil with Mushrooms

PHILEAS FOGG
Barbecue Dip; Chunky Salsa Dip; Sweet
Chilli Dip

PLAMIL FOODS LTD ™☺❶⊘
Egg-Free Mayonnaise: **Chilli, Garlic,
Plain with Cold Pressed Flax Oil,
Tarragon;** *Organic Egg-Free
Mayonnaise:* **Plain, with Lemongrass**

SOURCE FOODS ☺✿
Organic Miso Mustard

THE ENGLISH PROVENDER CO. ⊘
Hot Chilli Marinade; Smokey Barbecue
Marinade; Thai Lime & Coriander Dressing

UNILEVER
Hellmann's Dehydrated Dressing: Dry
Vinaigrette Classic, Dry Vinaigrette
Raspberry, Dry Vinaigrette Sun Dried
Tomato; *Hellmann's Dressing:* Classic
Vinaigrette, Garlic & Herbs, Olive Oil &
Balsamic Vinegar, Raspberry Flavour
Vinegar & Mustard

EGG REPLACERS

GENERAL DIETARY
Egg Replacer

ORGRAN ☺
No Egg - Egg Replacer (Gluten-Free)

VEG-OUT ™
Store Cupboard- Egg substitutes:
**Ackee; egg replacer; gram flour;
soya flour**

GRAVIES & STOCKS

A. VOGEL
Kelpamare; Plantaforce

BISTO
Favourite Gravy Granules; Favourite
Gravy Granules (Reduced Salt); Onion
Gravy Granules; Original Gravy Powder

FIVE STAR FOODIES ™☺
Grandma's Gourmet Gravy

HAPPY AND HEALTHY FOODS ™☺❶
Golden Gravy Mix; Savoury Herb
Gravy Mix; Shiitake Mushroom
Gravy Mix

KALLO FOODS ⊘
French Onion Stock Cubes; Garlic &
Herbs Stock Cubes; Low Salt Vegetable
Stock Cubes; Mushroom Stock Cubes;
Tomato & Herb Stock Cubes; Vegetable
Stock Cubes; Vegetable Stock Powder;
Yeast Free Vegetable Stock Cubes; *Just
Bouillon:* Vegetable Concentrate; *Just
Bouillon:* Vegetable Gravy Granules,
Vegetable Stock Cubes

KNORR
Simply Stock; Simply Stock - Vegetable;
Touch of Taste - Vegetable; Vegetable
Stock Cubes

MARIGOLD ❶⊘
Gravy Mix; Marigold Liquid Aminos;
Bouillon Cubes: Low Salt, Regular, Yeast
Free; *Instant Miso Bouillon Powder:*
Organic; *Swiss Vegetable Bouillon
Powder:* Organic, Organic Reduced Salt,
Reduced Salt

ORGRAN ☺
Gluten-Free Gravy Mix

REDWOOD WHOLEFOOD COMPANY
™☺❶⊘
Cheatin': **Vegan Gravy Powder**

VEG-OUT ™
Store Cupboard- Stocks: **Marigold
vegan boullion; marmite; vecon;
kallo organic veg stock cubes**

'ICE CREAMS', SORBETS ETC

BEANIE'S HEALTH FOODS ™☺❶⊘
B'Nice: **Non Dairy Rice Cream
Chocolate, Non Dairy Rice Cream
Strawberry, Non Dairy Rice Cream
Vanilla**

B'NICE ™☺
**Non Dairy Rice Cream Chocolate;
Non Dairy Rice Cream Strawberry;
Non Dairy Rice Cream Vanilla**

**ESSENTIAL TRADING
CO-OPERATIVE LTD** ™❶⊘⚭
Organic Fruit Lollies

FANTASY ICE CREAMS LTD
3 Sorbets Cup

FIRST FOODS LTD ☺⊘
*Oat Supreme- Low Fat Sugar Free
Diabetic Oat Ice:* Lite; *Oat Supreme-
Non-Dairy Choc Ice's on a Stick:* Supreme;
Oat Supreme- Oatbased Ice Cream:
Chocolate Supreme, Classic Vanilla,
Strawberry, Vanilla Chocolate Fudge Swirl

SANITARIUM HEALTH FOOD CO ⊘
So Good Bliss Ice Cream: All Flavours

SWEDISH GLACE ☺
Smooth Vanilla Lollies with Chocolate Flavoured Coating; Smooth Vanilla with Strawberry Ripple Cornets; *Non Dairy Frozen Dessert:* Juicy Raspberry, Neapolitan, Rich Chocolate, Smooth Vanilla, Wild Blueberry

THE BOOJA-BOOJA COMPANY LTD ™☺⊘☼
Stuff In A Tub: **Coconut Hullabaloo, Feisty Winjin Ginger, Hunky Punky Chocolate, Keep Smiling Vanilla M' Gorilla, Keep Smiling Vanilla M'Gorilla, Pompompous Maple Pecan**

TOFUTTI ☺❶⊘
Non Dairy Dessert: Strawberry, Vanilla; *Non Dairy Frozen Soya Organic Desserts:* Chocolate, Mango & Passionfruit; *Rock & Roll:* Cakes, Cones; *Sour Supreme:* Soya Alternative to Sour Cream

MARGARINES, FATS, OILS ETC

AZIZ CHAIR ™
Argan Oil Classic; Argan Oil Light

BIONA
Omega 3 Oil Enriched Spread; Organic Vegetable Margarine; *Olive Extra:* Extra Virgin Olive Oil Margarine, Reduced Fat Extra Virgin Olive Oil Spread

BRAHAM & MURRAY LTD ™📔
Good Oil Mild&Light; Good Oil Original

CLEARSPRING ™☺❶⊘📔👁
Toasted Sesame Oil; *Organic:* **Hazelnut Oil, Italian Extra Virgin Oil, Olive Flax Oil, Omega Oil, Rapeseed Oil, Safflower Oil, Sesame Oil, Soya oil, Styrian toasted pumpkin seed oil, Sunflower frying oil, Sunflower oil, Toasted sesame oil, Walnut oil**

ESSENTIAL TRADING CO-OPERATIVE LTD ™❶⊘📔
Essential Brand- Organic Oils: **All**

FAUSER VITAQUELLWERK KG ™
Vitaquell Extra Margarine: **Extra Omega 3 Organic 250g;** *Vitaquell Margarine:* **Organic 500g**

HEALTHY AND ESSENTIAL ™
Lignan Flax Oil

HIGHER NATURE PLC ™⊘📔
Omega Excellence: **Organic Coconut Butter, Organic Flax Seed Oil, Organic Hemp Seed Oil, Organic Omega 3:6:9 Balance Oil, Organic Virgin Coconut Butter**

KERRY FOODS LTD ™⊘
PURE: **Organic Spread, Soya Spread, Sunflower Spread**

KOBASHI ™☺⊘📔👁⚖1976
Misc: **Hempseed Oil**

LIFEPLAN PRODUCTS LTD ™⊘ ✓
Flaxseed Oil

MH FOODS LTD ™⊘ ✓
Fry Light- Cooking Non-Stick Spray:
Extra Virgin Olive Oil, Sunflower Oil

MUNCHY SEEDS ™☺
Roasted Sunflower & Pumpkin Seed Oil

NATURE'S OWN LTD ™
Organic Linseed (Flaxseed) Oil 200ml; *Cytoplan:* **Organic Flax Oil 300ml, Organic Flaxseed Oil 200ml;** *Dentavital:* **Flaxseed Oil;** *Nutritional Support:* **Organic Linseed (Flaxseed) Oil**

PANACEA APS ™
Udo's Choice- Ultimate Oil Blend:
Coconut Oil, Flax Seed Oil, Oat Bran Oil, Oat Germ Oil, Rice Bean Oil, Sesame Seed Oil, Soy Lecithin, Sunflower Seed Oil; *Udo's Choice-Ultimate Oil Blend:* **Toco Trienols**

RAKUSEN'S ™⊘
Tomor: **250g Block Margarine, 250g Sunflower Tub**

ROSIE'S GOURMET PRODUCTS (UK) LIMITED ™☺
Extra Virgin Olive Oil; Extra Virgin Olive Oil with Basil and Rosemary; Extra Virgin Olive Oil with Lemon; Extra Virgin Olive Oil with Red Chilli

SMILDE ™⊘
Sunflower Spread

SUMA WHOLEFOODS
™❶⊘ ✓ ☜⊱1985
Suma Spreads: **100% Sunflower – 2kg/1Kg/500g, Low Fat – 500g, Organic Sunflower 500g, Soya – 2kg & 500g**

THE FOOD DOCTOR LTD ™☺
Salad Oil: **Omega Oil;** *Spreads:* **Omega Nut Butter, Omega Seed Butter**

UNILEVER
Margarine: Phase Dawn; *Solid Vegetable Fat:* Cookeen, Flora White

VEG-OUT ™
Store Cupboard -Fats and spreads:
Tomor; Vitaquell; Pure; oils

YAOH ™☺❶⊘ ✓
Hemp Oil 250ml; Hemp Oil 500ml

PASTRY

AMBROSIAN VEGETARIAN FOODS
™☺❶⊘ ✿
Organic Pastries: **Cheez'n'Chive, Cheezy Bean, Savory Herb Sosage Rolls, Tomato & Garlic Sosage Rolls**

BABYCAKES DIRECT ™☺❶
Cheeseley and chive scones; Choc chip scones; Original scones; Sun dried tomato and olive scones

CUISINE DE FRANCE
Medium Vol Au Vent Cases; Puff Pastry Sheets

FAYSNZ LTD ™
Flapjacks

JUS-ROL
Frozen: Filo Pastry Sheets, King Size Puff Pastry Cases, Medium Size Puff Pastry Cases, Party Size Puff Pastry Cases, Puff Pastry Blocks, Puff Pastry Sheets, Shortcrust Pastry Blocks, Shortcrust Pastry Sheets

REBECCA'S CAKES ™
Maple pecan Danish pastries

ZEDZFOODS ⊘ ◖
Spiced apple mirabel

PICKLES, SAUCES, VINEGARS ETC

ANILA'S AUTHENTIC SAUCES LTD ™☺
Aubergine Pickle; Carrot & Date Pickle; Chilli Chutney; Chilli Dipping Sauce; Fruity Mild Korma Curry Sauce; Goan Green Curry Sauce; Hot Lime Pickle; Hot Mango Pickle; Hot Methi Curry Sauce; Lemon Pickle; Mild Korma Curry Sauce; Shredded Mango Chutney; Spicy Apple Chutney; Spicy Hot Curry Sauce; Spicy Korma Curry Sauce; Spicy Medium Curry Sauce; Spicy Mild Curry Sauce; Sweet Lime Pickle; Sweet Mango Chutney; Sweet Mango Pickle; Tamarind & Date Chutney; Tindori (Mini Gherkin) Pickle

ASPALL ⊘ ◖
Vinegar: All

BAXTERS ⊘
Albert's Victorian Chutney; Apple Sauce; Apple, Cider & Fig Chutney; Baby Beetroot; Beetroot in Redcurrant Jelly; Beetroot Pickle; Beetroot Wedges; Cranberry Jelly; Cranberry Sauce; Crinkle Cut Beetroot; Crushed Pineapple& Sweet Pepper Chutney; Fire Roasted Pepper Chutney; Mango with Ginger Chutney; Mint Jelly; Mint Sauce; Redcurrant Jelly; Rosebud Beets; Sliced Beetroot; Spanish Tomato&Black Olive Chutney; Spiced Fruit Chutney; Sweet Cherry Tomato & Piquante Chutney; Tomato & Red Pepper Chutney

BERTOLLI
Pasta Sauces: Basil Family Pasta Sauce, Chilli & Peppers, Garlic Family Pasta Sauce, Grilled Vegetable, Mushroom and Roasted Garlic, Original Family Pasta Sauce, Red Wine and Shallots, Spicy Family Pasta Sauce, Sundried Tomato & Oregano, Tomato and Basil; *Rustico Sauces:* Mediterranean Vegetables, Mushroom Garlic & Oregano, Sweet Chilli & Red Onion, Sweet Red & Yellow Pepper

BIONA
Hot Pepper Sauce; Tomato Ketchup; Worcestershire Sauce; *Anti Pasti:* Black Olive Pate, Capers in Extra Virgin Olive Oil, Pesto; *Mustard:* Dijon, Horseradish, Wholegrain; *Passata:* Original, Rustica, With Basil; *Pasta Sauce:* Arrabbiata Hot & Spicy, Basilico Tomato & Basil, Peperona Tomato & Sweet Pepper, Toscana Tuscan Style; *Relish:* Harrissa Chilli, Horseradish; *Vinegar:* Balsamic, Cider, Red Wine, White Wine

BLUE DRAGON
Chilli Sauces: Chilli & Garlic Sauce, Hot Chilli Sauce, Sweet & Sour Chilli Sauce, Sweet Chilli Sauce; *Condiment Sauces:* Mirin; *Cooking Sauces:* Plum, Spring Roll, Teriyaki Marinade; *Dips:* Hot Chilli Dipping Sauce, Sweet Chilli & Pineapple Dipping Sauce, Sweet Chilli Dipping Sauce, Sweet Chilli with Kaffir Lime; *Pastes:* Thai Magic Paste; *Pesto's:* Coriander & Kaffir Lime, Satay & Sweet Chilli; *Premium Cooking Sauces:* Chinese Dynasty Bang Bang Stir Fry Sauce, Chinese Dynasty Capital Stir Fry Sauce, Chinese Dynasty Kung Po Stir Fry Sauce; *Premium Stir Fry Sauces:* Black Bean with Roasted Garlic & Chilli, Chinese Mushroom & Garlic, Sticky Plum, Sweet Soy & Roasted Red Chilli, Tangy Lemon with Ginger & Cracked Black Pepper; *Soy Sauces:* Dark Soy, Garlic Infused Soy, Japanese Soy, Light Soy, Mushroom Infused Soy, Premium Soy Sauce; *Stir Fry Sachets:* Black Bean, Hoi Sin & Garlic, Peking Lemon, Sweet & Sour, Sweet Chilli & Garlic, Szechuan Tomato; *Stir Fry Sauces:* Black Bean, Hoi Sin, Plum, Sweet & Sour, Sweet Chilli, Szechuan Tomato, Teriyaki; *Vinegar:* Japanese Rice, Rice, Sushi Su Rice

BUITONI ☺
Sauces: All

CALEDONIAN CURRY CO. ™⊘
Beetroot & Chilli Relish; Hot Rhubarb & Chilli Relish; Red Pepper & Chilli Relish; Tomato & Chilli Relish

CLEARSPRING ™☺❶⊘ ✔ ◉
Brown Rice Vinegar; Miso relish; Sushi Cucumber Pickle; Sushi Daikon Pickle; Sushi ginger pickle; Takuan (Pickled Daikon Radish); Tsuyu; Ume concentrate; Umeboshi puree; Wasabi; *Organic:* Apple balsamic vinegar, Balsamic vinegar, Balsamic vinegar - Vintage Red, Brown Rice Vinegar, Chuno Dipping Sauce, Mikawa mirin, Miso Dipping Sauce, Red wine vinegar, Umeboshi plums, White wine vinegar

COLMANS
Mustards: American Mild Squeezy, Dijon, DSF Mustard, English, English Mustard Powder, English Mustard Tube, English Squeezy, Mild, Wholegrain; *Packet Sauces:* Bread Sauce Mix, Cottage Pie, Lasagne, Rich Sausage and Onion, Shepherds Pie, Spaghetti Bolognese, Swedish Style Meatball, Sweet and Sour; *Sauces:* Apple, Classic Mint, Fresh Mint

CUISINE DE FRANCE
Chilli Sauce; Red Onion Relish; Red Pepper Dressing; Sweet Chilli & Garlic Sauce

DISCOVERY FOODS
Sliced Jalapenos; *2-Step:* Chilli Con Carne, Texan Fajita Sauce; *Sauce:* Buffalo Wings, Enchilada, Hot & Smoky BBQ, Mexican, New Orleans Creole

DOLMIO
Chunky Sauces for Bolognese: Mediterranean Vegetable, Roasted Garlic & Onion, Sweet Pepper; *Lasagne Sauce:* Red Lasagne Sauce; *Microwaveable Sauce Pouches:* Spicy Itallian Chilli, Sun Ripened Tomato & Basil; *Pasta Bake:* Roasted Mediterranean Vegetable; *Sauce for Bolognese:* Extra Mushroom, Extra Onion & Garlic, Extra Spicy, Original, Original Light; *Stir in Sauce:* Sun Dried Tomato Light

ESSENTIAL TRADING CO-OPERATIVE LTD ™❶⊘✔
Wholegrain mustard; *Essential Brand-Bottled, Jarred, Canned:* Organic Dijon Mustard

FIRST QUALITY FOODS ⊘✔
Al'fez: Hot chilli sauce 150g, Spice & sauce garlic & ginger 142g, Spice & sauce sweet pepper & coriander 142g

G. COSTA & CO ⊘
Curry club: Madras sauce, Mild curry paste, Sweet mango chutney, Tandoori paste; *Elsenham:* Apple & Pear Sauce with Calvados, Country Mint Sauce, Cumberland Berry Sauce, Fresh Mint & Rosemary Jelly, Hot English Horseradish Sauce, Luxury Cranberry Sauce, Spiced Orchard Chutney, Three Apple Sauce, Wild Cranberry Sauce; *Elsenham Mustard:* English Ale Mustard, Hot English Mustard, Irish Whiskey Mustard, Tewkesbury Mustard; *Frenchs:* Deli Mustard, Frenchs American Mustard, Frenchs American Mustard Squeezy; *Go tan:* Java's spicy indonesian crackers, Ketjap manis, Nasi goreng meal kit, Sambal oelek, Satay kit, Satay manis; *Grey Poupon:* Dijon Mustard, Wholegrain Mustard (A l'ancienne); *Ken Holm sauces:* Black bean with orange and lime, Chilli and garlic with jalapeno peppers, Sweet and sour with Passion fruit; *La Favorite:* Coarsegrain Mustard, Dijon Mustard, Hot English Mustard; *Maille:* Bearnaise, Dijon Mustard Dressing, Dijon Original Mustard, Dijonnaise, Hollandaise, Wholegrain Mustard; *Old Ranch House:* Bar-B-Bar Caribbean Calypso BBQ Sauce, Caribbean Calypso BBQ Sauce, Coln Valley Dill Sauce, Geo Watkins Mushroom Ketchup, OK Fruity Sauce; *Old Ranch House Cattlemen's BBQ Sauces:* Classic BBQ Sauce, Smokehouse BBQ Sauce; *Old Ranch House Lorenz Snack World:* Crunchips X Cut Paprika Crisps, Crunchips X Cut Salted Crisps, Saltletts Classic Sticks; *Rajah:* Balti sauce, Vindaloo sauce; *S & B:* Wasabi paste; *S& B:* Wasabi powder; *Tabasco:* Chipolata Sauce, Green Sauce, Habanero Sauce, Red Sauce, Red Sauce

Minis, Red Travel Pack, Spicy Manzanilla Olives, Spicy Pepper Jelly, Spicy Stuffed Olives; *Vincotto:* Aceto di vincotto, Mild pepper sauce, Vincotto originale; *Zest:* Coriander,Basil & hazelnut pesto sauce, Hot & spicy pasta sauce, Mexican chilli sauce, Mushroom & green garlic sauce, Organic tomato & herb pasta sauce, Sundried tomato paste, Vegan pesto

GEETA'S FOODS LIMITED ᵀᴹ
Aubergine Pickle; Chilli Pickle; Dhansak Spice & Stir; Garlic Pickle; Goan Cooking Sauce; Hara Masala Curry Creation; Jalfrezi Spice & Stir; Karai Bhuna Spice & Stir; Kashmiri Curry Creation; Lime & Chilli Chutney; Madras Spice & Stir; Mumbai Cooking Sauce; Onion Chutney; Papaya & Orange Chutney; Pineapple Chutney; Premium Mango Chutney; Tamarind Chutney; Tandoori Curry Creation

GEO ORGANICS ⊘
Apple, Apricot & Ginger Chutney; Balti Curry Paste; Black Bean Cooking Sauce; Brinjal Pickle; Brown Sauce; Fairtrade Mango Chutney; Garlic Pickle; Korma Curry Paste; Lime Pickle; Madras Curry Paste 180g; Mango Chutney in Apple Juice; Mexican BBQ Sauce; Mexican Salsa; Mexican Tomato Fajita Sauce; Picalilli; Spicy Tomato Chutney; Sweet & Sour Cooking Sauce; Sweet Chilli Sauce; Sweet Pickle; Szechuan Stir Fry Sauce; Thai Green Curry Paste; Thai Red Curry Paste; Thai Satay Paste with Pine Kernels; Thai Yellow Curry Paste;

Tikka Masala Curry Paste; Tomato & Apple Chutney; Tomato Sauce; Veggie Relish; Worcestershire Sauce; *Pasta Sauce:* Tomato & Basil, Tomato Mushroom, Tomato Pepper

GRANOVITA UK LTD ⊘ ⓲
Organic Brown Sauce

HEINZ ᵀᴹ⊘
Pickles: Mild Mustard, Piccalilli, Ploughmans, Tangy Sandwich, Tangy Tomato, Tomato Relish; *Relish:* Right Fruit, Sweet Chilli, Sweet Onion, Tomato; *Sauces:* Chilli Ketchup, Curry Ketchup, Exotic Sweet and Sour Sauce, Extra Hot Salsa Sauce, Hot 'n' Sizzling TK, Hot Ketchup, Mango Curry, Mustard, Organic Tomato Ketchup, Original Barbecue Sauce, Reduced Sugar and Salt Tomato Ketchup, Spiced Plum, Sundried Tomato Sauce, Tomato Ketchup, Tomato Ketchup with a Twist of Chilli, Tomato Ketchup with a Twist of Garlic, Tomato Ketchup with a Twist of Sweet Onion

HENDERSONS ☺
Hendersons Relish

HIGHER NATURE PLC ᵀᴹ⊘ ⓲
Omega Excellence: **Organic Apple Cider Vinegar**

JEREMY'S SOUPS ⊘ ⓲
Sauce: BBQ, Tomato & Chilli, Tomato & Garlic

JETHROS

Glazes - for Roast & Grill: Balsamic Ginger, Blackcurrant Chilli; *Marinades:* Amadou Barbecue Sauce, Cajun Lime & Jalapeno, Lemon Bay & Rosemary, Lemon Chilli & Coriander, Lime Chilli & Oregano, Orange Chilli & Cumin, Pineapple Chilli & Basil; *Sauces - for Dipping & Basting:* 12 Days of Christmas, Ginger & Orange, Ginger Chilli, Ginger Lime, Green Chilli & Coriander, Red Chilli & Garlic

KALLO FOODS ⊘

Whole Earth: Tomato Sauce

KITCHEN GARDEN PRESERVES ✐

Chutney: Autumn Apple, Beetroot, Christmas, Hot Mango, Ploughmans Pickle, Plum & Cranberry, Red Pepper & Chilli Relish, Spiced Apple with Mint, Spiced Apricot & Orange, Spiced Tomato & Apple, Sweet Mustard Pickle, Sweet Onion Relish, Sweet Plum & Date, Tomato; *Cranberry Sauce:* Non-organic, Organic; *Jelly:* Apple with Mint, Organic Redcurrant, Redcurrant; *Organic Chutney:* Spiced Apricot & Orange

KNOBBLY CARROT FOOD COMPANY

Pasta Sauce: Luxury Vegetable, Spicy Tomato w ithPepper & Ginger, Sun Dried Tomato & Pesto

KNORR

Curry Granulated Sauce; Provencale Sauce; *Beef Tonight Sauces:* Ale & Mushroom, Goulash; *Chicken Tonight Sauces:* Chasseur, Spanish Chicken, Strir Fry Tomato and Vodka; *Indian Collection Pastes:* Biryani, Jalfrezi, Madras, Masala, Rogan Josh, Tandoori, Tikka, Tikka Masala, Vindaloo; *Indian Collection Sauces:* Jalfrezi, Madras, Paltia, Rogan Josh, Vindaloo; *Mediterranean Range - Sauces:* Bolognese, Cacciatora, Napoli Tomato & Basil, Spicy Arrabbiata, Tuscan Bean, Vegetale; *Oriental Collection - Pastes:* Black Bean, Hoi Sin, Szechuan, Thai Green; *Oriental Collection - Sauces:* Beijing Five Spice, Cantonese Sweet & Sour, Shanghai Black Bean, Spicy Szechuan, Sweet & Sour, Sweet Vietnamese Chilli; *Ragu Sauces:* Basil & Oregano, Bolognese Original Sauce, Onion & Roasted Garlic, Red Lasagne Sauce, Red Wine & Herb, Spicy, Sweet Red Pepper, Traditional; *Sausage Tonight Sauces:* Cumberland, Ranch BBQ, Red Wine & Onion; *Sizzle & Stir Sauces:* Balti, Chilli Con Carne, Stir Tikka Bhuna, Sweet & Sour; *Standard Sauce Mix:* Chasseur, Curry, Demi Glace, Sweet & Sour; *Stir It Up Pastes:* Bejing 5 Spice, Chinese 5 Spice, Fajita, Jamaican, Jamaican Jerk, Mexican Fajita; *Taste of Americas - Pastes:* Cajun, Hickory Smoked BBQ, Jamaican Jerk, Salsa; *Taste of Americas - Sauces:* Cajun, Chilli, Salsa, Sweet Hickory BBQ

LEEORA VEGETARIAN FOOD ™☺⊘

Sauces: **Vegetarian Thai Style Curry**

LYME BAY WINERY

Cider Vinegar

MERIDIAN FOODS ⊘
Cool Salsa; French Dressing; *Free From:* Creamy Mushroom and White Wine Sauce, Creamy Sundried Tomato Sauce, Garlic & Herb Sauce, Hot Salsa, Korma Sauce, Tikka Masala Sauce, Tomato Ketchup; *Free From Range:* Creamy Tomato & Herb, Dopiaza Sauce, Garlic and Herb, Green Thai Sauce, Madras Sauce; *Pasta Sauces:* Mushroom, Red Chilli & Pepper, Spanish Olive, Sundried Tomato, Tomato & Basil, Tomato & Chilli, Tomato & Herb; *Salad Dressing - Organic:* French; *Soya Sauces:* Shoyu, Tamari

MH FOODS LTD ™⊘ 🦺
Life: **Fish Free Worcestershire Sauce**

**NOTHING BUT
GOODNESS LIMITED** ™⊘
Sugar free balsamic onion chutney

ODYSEA
Aged Corinthian Vinegar

ORGANICO ⊘ ✿
Mushroom & Red Wine Pasta Sauce; Olives, Capers & Chilli Sauce; Red Pepper and Balsamic Vinegar Sauce; Tomato & Aubergine Sauce; Tomato & Basil Sauce; Tomato & Zucchini Sauce; Veggie Bolognese Pasta Sauce; *Danival:* Bolognese Sauce with Seitan, Bolognese Sauce with Tofu, Chilli with Seitan, Ketchup Squeezy Bottle, Ratatouille, Ravioli Stuffed Seitan

PASTA KING (UK) LTD ™
Arrabiata; Arriba Arriba; Basilico; Cajun Quinoa; Hoisin Sauce; Kari Veg; Mediterranean Vegetables; Mushroom Thyme; Peperonata; Pomodoro; Ratatouille; Tuscan Bean; Veg Sweet and Sour; Vegetable Chilli; Veggie-Bol; Zingy Peppers

PATAKS FOODS ⊘
Canned Cooking Sauces: Madras, Medium Balti, Mild Balti, Rogan Josh, Vindaloo; *Chutneys:* Hot Mango, Major Grey, Sweet Mango; *Cooking Sauces in Jars:* Balti, Jalfrezi, Madras, Rogan Josh, Vindaloo; *Pickles:* Brinjal, Chilli, Garlic, Hot Lime, Hot Mango, Lime Pickle Medium/Hot, Mango Pickle Medium, Mixed Pickle

PETER RABBIT ORGANICS ⊘ ✿
Organic Garden Vegetable Sauce; Organic Ketchup; Organic Roast Courgette Sauce

PORTER FOODS CO LTD
Classic Thai Sauces: Peanut Satay, Sriracha, Sweet and Sour, Sweet Chilli; *Dress Italian Pesto:* Artichoke & Almond, Aubergine & Black Olive, Pistachio & Fennel, Red Pepper & Walnut, Sun Ripened Tomato; *Italian Pasta Sauces:* Basil & Onion, Red Hot Chilli, Sun Dried Tomato, Sweet Cherry Tomato; *PET Range:* Red Hot Chilli Sauce

REAL ORGANIC FOODS ◌

Organic Barbeque Sauce: Spicy Mexican; *Organic Indian Sauce:* Jalfrezi, Rogan Josh; *Organic Pasta Sauce:* Arrabbiata, Sicilian Tomato & Olive, Tomato, Pepper & Herb; *Organic Thai Sauce:* Green Curry, Red Curry, Yellow Curry

ROSIE'S GOURMET PRODUCTS (UK) LIMITED ™☺

Artichoke Paste; Basil Pesto; Black Olive Tapenade; Fresh Tomato Bruschetta Topping; Hot Red Chilli Relish; Mushroom Bruschetta Topping; Olive Bruschetta Topping; Roasted Pepper Bruschetta Topping; Spicy Sundried Tomatoes; Spicy Sundried Tomatoes With Herbs; Sun Dried Tomato Pesto; *Pasta Sauce:* **Basil Sauce, Courgettes Sauce, Neopolitan Sauce, Olive Sauce, Torcini Sauce, Wild Rocket Sauce**

SACLA

Salsa Rossa; *Stir-Through Sauces for Pasta:* Olive & Tomato, Roasted Vegetable & Tomato, Sun-Dried Tomato & Garic, Tomato & Artichoke, Vine-Ripened Tomato and Chilli Pepper; *Whole Cherry Tomato Sauces:* Tomato & Basil, Tomato & Chilli, Tomato & Roasted Vegetables

SAFE 2EAT LTD ☺

Chutney: Mulled Wine, North African, Spicy Fig; *Sauce:* Apple and Brandy, Bolognese, Korma Curry, Moroccan Seven Vegetable, Pear and White Wine, Peking Lemon, Red Pepper and Tequila, Red Wine and Garlic, Roast Vegetable Pasta, Rogan Josh, Sweet and Sour, Szechuan Spicy, Thai Red Curry, Tikka Massala, Tomato and Basil Pasta

SANCHI ◌

Ume Su plum Vinegar; *Sauces:* Mirin, Organic Shoyu, Organic Tamari, Shoyu Soy Sauce, Tamari Reduced Sugar, Tamari Soy Sauce, Teriyaki; *Vinegar:* Organic Brown Rice, Ume Su Plum

SAUCES OF CHOICE

Apricot & Orange Chutney; Balsamic & Garlic Sauce; Caramelised Onion Chutney; Lemon & Dill Vinaigerette; Mango Chutney; Spicy BBQ Sauce; Spicy Fruit Chutney; Sweet Chilli Sauce; Tomato & Red Pepper Chutney; Tomato Sauce; *Cook in Sauces:* Bolognese Sauce, Chilli Con Carne, Coconut Lime & Coriander, Creamy Peppercorn, Red Pepper & Sun Dried Tomato, Sweet 'n' Sour; *Curry Sauces:* Balti, Green Thai, Jalfrezi, Korma, Madras, Red Thai, Rogan Josh, Tikka Masala; *Kids Sauces:* BBQ, Bolognese, Mild Chilli, Sweet and Sour, Tomato and Herb

SEEDS OF CHANGE

Pasta Sauces: Bolognese, Cherry Tomato & Olive, Mediterranean Vegetable, Roast Pepper, Slow Roasted Garlic & Chilli, Tomato & Basil; *Sauces:* Balti, Chilli, Jalfrezi, Madras, Sweet & Sour; *Stir in Pasta Sauces:* Roasted Red Peppers, Sun Dried Tomato

SHARWOODS ⊘
Green Label Mango Chutney

SIMPLY ORGANIC ⊘ ✿
Soup: Chunky Tomato

SOMA ORGANIC ☺☺ ⸜ ✿
Nomato: Chilli, Ketchup, Pasta Sauce

SUMA WHOLEFOODS
™❶⊘ ⸜ ✇⤙1985
Pasta Sauces: **Affumicata, Arrosta, Romana, Rustica**

THE ENGLISH PROVENDER CO. ⊘
Cumberland Sauce; Dill Mustard Sauce; Hot Chilli Relish; Hot Horseradish; Mint Sauce with Balsamic Vinegar; Moroccan Spiced Chutney; Organic Spicy Onion Chutney; Organic Sweet Tomato & Chilli Chutney; Organic Wild Cranberry Sauce; Ploughmans Plum Chutney; Sweet Pickle; Wild Cranberry Sauce

TINY DEOL (CURRY SLIM)
Curry Slim Cooking Sauces: Jalfrezi

UNCLE BEN'S
Express Rice: Mexican Rice; *Sauces:* Black Bean, Cajun, Cantonese, Hoi Sin, Lemon Chicken, Medium Curry, Sweet & Sour Extra Pineapple, Sweet & Sour Light, Sweet & Sour Original, Szechuan Chilli, Thai Sweet Chilli

VEGEFARM CORP ™
VeggieMaster- Vegan: **Beijing Spicy Orange Sauce, Original Black Bean Sauce, Original Sweet & Sour Sauce;**

VeggieMaster -Vegan: **Black Pepper Sauce;** *VeggieMaster-Vegan:* **Sweet Lemon Sauce, Teriyaki BBQ Sauce**

VEG-OUT ™
Store Cupboard: **Vegan mayo**

VENTURE FOODS UK LTD ™⊘
Geo Organics: **Brown Sauce, Faitrade Mango Chutney, Mango & Apple Juice Chutney, Sweet Chilli Sauce, Veggie Relish, Worcestershire Sauce**

PIES & PASTIES

AMBROSIAN VEGETARIAN FOODS
™☺❶⊘ ✿
Cheeze 'n' Onion Pie; Porkless Pie

BABYCAKES DIRECT ™☺❶
Broccoli, mushroom and tofu tart; Butterbean, sun dried tomato and cashew nut tart; Pizza tart

BEANIE'S HEALTH FOODS ™☺❶⊘
Special Vegetarian Frozen Foods: **Veg Express Cottage Pie**

CLIVE'S PIES ⊘
Vegetable Chilli Pasty; *Organic Gluten Free Pies:* Aloo Gobi, French Cassoulet, Lentil & Olive, Minty Chickpea, Vegetable Chilli; *Organic Pies:* Aloo Matar, Arabian Chickpea, Chestnut Cassoulet, Creamy Mushroom, Greek Olive & Lentil, Hungarian Goulash, Mexican Chilli

FRY GROUP FOODS ™☺
Fry's Special Vegetarian Frozen Foods:
Veg Express Cottage Pie

IL MANGIAR SANO S.P.A. ™⊘ 🦮
Gaia Organic Bakery Products: **Apricot Tart, Blueberry Tart, Strawberry-Raspberry Tart;** *Germinal Organic Bakery no added sugar:* **Apple & Raisins Puff-Pastry, Apricot Stuffed Bar, Apricot Tart, Blueberry Stuffed Bar, Blueberry Tart, Snacks with Apple and Puffed Rice, Snacks with Wild Fruits and Puffed Rice, Wild Fruit Tart**

LINDA MCCARTNEY
Cornish Pasties; Country Pie; Sausage Rolls

PAUL'S TOFU ™⊘ 🦮 ♺
Savouries: **Mushroom & Nut Parcels, Organic Mushroom & Tofu Pie, Tofu Arame Pasty, Tofu Vegetable Pasty**

REBECCA'S CAKES ™
Vegan Cornish Pasties; Vegan Pies; Vegan Pizza; Vegan Vegetable Pasties

VEG-OUT ™
Store Cupboard: **Red pepper and broccoli quiche**

ZEDZFOODS ⊘ 🦮
'cheese' & onion pasty-vegan; 'pizza' pasty-vegan; Bolog-No-No - Soya Mince & Tomato Filling; Coconut Curry Pasty; Mexican bean & 'cheese' pasty-vegan; Vegetable & Split Pea pasty

SAVOURIES - CANNED/BOTTLED

BIONA
Baked Beans in Tomato Sauce; Plain Tofu in Jars; Sauerkraut

DISCOVERY FOODS
Refried Beans; Spicy Refried Beans

ESSENTIAL TRADING CO-OPERATIVE LTD ™❶⊘ 🦮
Borlotti beans; Cannellini Beans; Green soya edamame beans; *Essential Brand- Bottled, Jarred, Canned:* **Organic Apples, Organic Apricots, Organic Baby Carrots, Organic Blackberries, Organic Blackeye Beans, Organic Button Mushrooms, Organic Cherries, Organic Chickpeas, Organic Chopped Peeled Tomatoes, Organic Chopped Tomatoes, Organic Cranberries, Organic Forest Fruits, Organic French Beans, Organic Gherkins - Sour, Organic Grapefruit Segments, Organic Green Peas, Organic Green Peas & Carrots, Organic Green Peas & Mint, Organic Haricot Beans, Organic Mango Chunks, Organic Mixed Beans, Organic Passata, Organic Peach Slices, Organic Pineapple, Organic Plums, Organic Prunes, Organic Puy Lentils, Organic Raspberries, Organic Red Kidney Beans, Organic Sauerkraut, Organic Spinach,**

Organic Strawberries, Organic
Sweetcorn, Organic Tomato Puree,
Organic Tropical Fruits, Organic
Whole Tomatoes

GRANOSE
Lentil & Vegetable Casserole; Meatless
Mince & Onion; Mock Duck; Nuttolene

GRANOVITA UK LTD ◎ ✦
Nut Luncheon; Vegetable Hotpot

HEINZ ™◎
Baked Beans: Barbecue, Curried, In
Tomato Sauce, Italian Beanz, Organic in
Tomato Sauce, Reduced Sugar and Salt,
Smoky Barbeque, Sweet Chilli Beanz;
Farmers Market Chilled Soups: Autumn
Three Bean and Tomato Soup; *HP -
Baked Beans:* In Tomato Sauce; *Pasta
Shapes in Tomato Sauce:* Thomas the
Tank Engine; *Spaghetti:* In Tomato
Sauce; *Weight Watchers from Heinz:*
Baked Beans in Tomato Sauce,
Spaghetti in Tomato Sauce with Parsley

KALLO FOODS ◎
Whole Earth: Baked Beans

ODYSEA
Karyatis: Artichokes, Atlas Green Olives,
Baked Gigantes Beans, Bruschetta
Meze, Colossal Green Olives, Garlic
Stuffed Olives, Green Olive Meze,
Green Organic Olives, Jumbo Kalamata
Olives, Jumbo Natural Black Olives,
Kalamata Olive with Capers, Kalamata
Olives, Kalamata Organic Olives, Mixed
Hot Chillies, Mixed Olives, Roasted Red

Peppers, Stuffed Vine Leaves; *Olives:*
Green Cracked with Lemon, Hot Spiced
Natural Black, Kalamata & Green; *Olives
Relish:* Sweet Kalamata; *Rovies:* Almond
Stuffed Green Olives, Almond Stuffed
Green Organic Olives, Garlic Stuffed
Green Olives, Green Olives, Green
Organic Olive Paste, Green Organic
Olives, Kalamata Olives, Kalamata
Organic Olive Paste, Kalamata Organic
Olives, Lemon Stuffed Green Olives,
Mixed Olives, Natural Black Olives,
Pimento Stuffed Green Olives, Pimento
Stuffed Green Organic Olives; *Stuffed
Green Olives:* Almond, Chilli, Garlic,
Jalapeno, Pimento

ORGANICO ◎ ✿
Danival: Lentils Meal with Tofu

ORGRAN ☺
Gluten-Free Tinned Spaghetti

PATAKS FOODS ◎
Canned Vegetable Curries: Lemon Dhal

SOMA ORGANIC ☺◎ ✦ ✿
Nomato: Baked Beans

SUMA WHOLEFOODS
™❶◎ ✦ ◉ ☀ 1985
Cannellini Beans

UNILEVER
Bean, Celery & Coriander Chilli

WESTLER FOODS LTD ◎
Chesswood: Chilli No Carne, Organic
Baked Beans, Organic Vegetable Chilli,

Organic Vegetable Hot Pot, Vegetable Chilli, Vegetable Curry; *Wayfarer:* Spicy Vegetable Rigatoni; *Westlers BIGMEX:* Chips & Dips Box, Salsa Pots

SAVOURIES - CHILLED/FRESH

AROMAFOODS ™☺✔

Aromatic Braised Red Cabbage; Greek Spinach Falafel; Japanese Pulse Salad; Lemon & Coriander Falafel; Lime and Coriander Aloo; Masala Veget-Apple Pakora; Mexican Bean Burger; Sesame Samosa; Spinach & Onion Bhajia; Sweetcorn & Pineapple Bhajia

BIONA

Energy Mini Burgers; Lucky Stars with Pumpkin Tofu & Ginger; Provancale Style Ballini; Spelt & Almond Cutlets; *Fresh Filled Pasta:* Fresh Gnocci, Spelt Tortellini with Green Spelt and Vegetables, Tortellini Tri Colore with Tofu & Spice; *Spring Rolls:* Mini, Original, Spicy Mexicana, Thai

BLUE DRAGON

Quick Wok Noodles: Chilli Infused, Coriander Infused, Medium Wheat, Medium Wholewheat, Wide Wheat

CAULDRON FOODS LTD ⊘

Organic: Falafel

CHIMANS ™⊘

Cauliflower & Spinach Bhaji;
Organic: **Cauliflower & Spinach Bhaji**

CLEARSPRING ™☺❶⊘✔👁

Rice Mirin

CLIVE'S PIES ⊘

Soya Roll

CUISINE DE FRANCE

Battered Onion Rings; Chilled Chips; Croquettes; Fruity Rice Salad; Mediterranean Vegetable Salad; Mild Curry Fries; Mini Vegetable Spring Rolls; Pierres Spicy Wedges; Savoury Rice; Seasoned Wedges; Spanish Style Salad; Stealth Fries; Sweet Chilli Potato; Traditional Roast Potatoes; Vegetable & Salsa Burritos; Vegetable Samosa; Vegetable Spring Rolls

DIPAK FOODS LTD ™☺❶⊘✔

Dal Kachori; Mixed Vegetable Spring Rolls; Onion Bhaji; Peas Kachori; Peas Petis; Soya Chunks Curry; Soya Mince Curry; Spinach Bhaji; Spinach Pakora; Sunder Curry Sauce; Vegetable Curry Sauce;
Samosas: **Mixed Vegetable, Soya**

DOLMIO

Microwaveable Pasta Pouches: Conchigle

FAYSNZ LTD ™

Caribbean; Tropicana; *Sandwiches / Rolls:* **Cheese and Onion Roll, Falafel with Mango and Peach Chutney**

FIRST QUALITY FOODS ⊘ ✦
Al'fez: Kofta kebab 42g, Sumac 38g, Zahtar 38g

FIVE STAR FOODIES ™☺
Eggless Egg Salad; Vegetarian Turkey Rolls

GOBBLIN WHOLEFOODS
Aduki Shepherds Pie; Curry Pastie; Onion Bhaji; Pinto Pie; Samosa; Savory Roll; Savory Vegetable Pastie; Spiced Pastie; Spicy Nutburger; Spinach Pakora; Spring Roll; Vegetable Tofu Pie; *Organic:* Lentil Samosa, Pinto Pie, Vegetable Tofu Pie

LEEORA VEGETARIAN FOOD ™☺⊘
Meal Centres: **10 Koobbe, 12 Swedish Style Veggie Balls;** *Mediterranean Cuisine:* **Falafel;** *Ready Meals:* **3 Koobbe with Pasta & Sundried Tomato, 3 Koobbe with Rice, Vegetarian Thai Style Curry with Mejadra Rice, Veggie Balls with Mushroom Rice**

LOVE FOODS ™
Black Bean; Green Thai Curry; Madras; Red Thai Curry; Sweet And Sour

MACSWEEN OF EDINBURGH ⊘
Haggis: Vegetarian

MEDITERRANEAN FOODS (LONDON) LTD ™☺
Aubergine Salad; Couscous Salad; Dolma (Stuffed Vine Leaves); Teboula

NATASHA'S LIVING FOOD ☺☺⊘
Raw Super Sprouted Salad

NOTHING BUT GOODNESS LIMITED ™⊘
Balsamic onion soya bean dip; Lemon and parsley soya bean dip; Red chilli ginger soya bean dip; Tomato and basil soya bean dips

PATAKS FOODS ⊘
Microwaveable Rice: Basmati, Garlic & Coriander, Pilau, Saffron, Vegetable Biryani

PAUL'S TOFU ™⊘ ✦ ✿
Savouries: **Tofu & Vegetable Samosa**

QIANNA AGRICULTURAL PRODUCTS IND & TRADING CO. LTD ™☺
Soba Instant Noodle

RAWCREATION LTD ™☺
Peruvian Olives; Sicilian Olives

REDWOOD WHOLEFOOD COMPANY ™☺❶⊘
Vegi-Deli: **Falafel**

SIMPLY ORGANIC ⊘ ✿
Pure & Pronto: Lentil & Vegetable Stew, Moroccan Vegetable Tagine, Roasted Vegetable with Quinoa, Thai Vegetable Curry with Green Lentils, Vegetable & Bean Casserole

TAIFUN ☺⊘
Falafel; Mexico-Sticks; Pizza-Pizza Tofu Filets; Thai-Sticks; *Pan Ready Tofu:*

Spelt-Sunflower Cutlets, Tofu Filets Japanese style, Tofu-Hazelnut Cutlets, Tofu-Rice Cutlets Corn-Pepper, Tofu-Rice Cutlets Curry-Pineapple

UNCLE BEN'S
Express Rice: Chicken Flavour, Garlic & Coriander Rice, Golden Vegetable, Tomato & Basil

VEG-OUT ™
Store Cupboard: **Quinoa salad**

YAGGA SRL ™
Stracetti; Vegetable Fillet; Vegetable Roast; Vegetable Stew

SAVOURIES - DRIED

ALNAVIT GMBH ™
Spaghetti; Spirelli

BLUE DRAGON
Dry Noodles: Dried Soba Noodles, Dried Udon Noodles, Express Instant Noodle Multi Pack, Fine Brown Rice Noodles, Fine Rice Noodles, Green Tea Rice Noodles, Medium Rice Noodles, Wholewheat Noodles; *Lunchbox Noodles:* Beef Noodles, Chicken Noodles; *Noodle Town:* Beef & Black Pepper, Chicken & Chilli, Chow Mein, Crispy Duck, Mushroom, Won Ton; *Noodle Wok:* Oriental Chicken, Spicy Thai, Sweet Chilli Chicken; *Rice Noodle Bowl:* Garlic Chicken Rice Noodle Bowl; *Wheat Noodle Bowl:* Beef & Black

Pepper Snack Noodles, Chicken & Spring Onion Snack Noodles, Won Ton Snack Noodles

CLEARSPRING ™☺❶⊘☾☞
Bifun Rice Noodles; Lotus root slices; Maitake mushrooms; Shiitake mushrooms; Shredded Daikon; Sushi Rice; *Organic:* **Brown rice udon noodles, Lomein noodles(wheat), Mochi -Brown Rice, Mochi -Mugwort, Soba Noodles - 100% Buckwheat (Salt Free), Soba Noodles - Jinenjo (Mountain Yam), Soba noodles(with wheat), Soba noodles-Jinenjo(Mountain yam), Sushi Brown Rice, Sushi rice, Udon noodles(with wheat)**

DISCOVERY FOODS
Traditional Tacos Shells; *Kit:* Cajun Fajita, Chinese Dinner, Gluten Free, Mexican Fajita, Nachos; *Wrap & Roll:* Healthy 'n' White, Original, Wholemeal

ESSENTIAL TRADING CO-OPERATIVE LTD ™❶⊘☾
Essential Brand- Pastas: **Organic Fusilli, Organic Lumache, Organic Penne, Organic Spaghetti, Organic Stoneground Fusilli, Organic Stoneground Penne, Organic Stoneground Spaghetti, Organic Tortiglioni;** *Essential Brand- Pre Packs (Organic & Conventional):* **Apple Rings, Apricots, Cereals Flakes & Grain Meals, Cranberries, Crystallised Ginger, Currants, Dates, Figs, Flours (All), Fruit Salad, Grains**

(All), Herbs & Spices (All), Mango
Slices, Mixed Fruit, Nuts, Papaya,
Pear Halves, Pineapple Rings,
Prunes, Pulses & Beans, Raisins, Rice
(All), Seeds (All), Sugars (All),
Sultanas, Tomatoes (All); *Essential
Brand-Pre Packs (Organic &
Conventional):* **Textured Vegetable
Protein - Plain**

FIRST QUALITY FOODS ⊘ ◢

Wholegrain plain 375g; *Sammy's:*
Falafel 150g, Moroccan spice 200g,
Organic French Provencale 200g,
Organic mediterranean tomato & herb
200g, Organic plain, Salad mix with
lemon mint & parsley 200g, Sundried
tomato & italian herb 200g,
Wholegrain Moroccan 220g,
Wholegrain mushroom 220g,
Wholegrain mushroom 220g, Wild
mushroom garlic & herb 200g, Zesty
lemon & coriander 200g

G. COSTA & CO ⊘

Casa fiesta: Ambient flour tortillas,
Green sliced jalapeno, Natural tortilla
crisps, Refried beans, Taco shells

GENERAL DIETARY

Pasta: Lasagna, Macaroni, Small Shells,
Spaghetti, Vermicelli

GLUTEN FREE FOODS LTD

Barkat: Buckwheat Pasta Penne,
Buckwheat Pasta Spirals

GREENCITY WHOLEFOODS ❶ ⊘

Broth Mix; Chickpea Noodles

HAPPY AND
HEALTHY FOODS ™☺❶

Road's End Organics: **123'z and Chreese,
Mac & Chreese - Brown Rice Alfredo
Style, Mac & Chreese - Whole
Wheat Elbow Macaroni Style, Penne
& Chreese, Shells & Chreese**

HEINZ ™⊘

Weight Watchers from Heinz: Beef
Flavoured Noodles, Chicken Noodles,
Spicy Thai Flavour Noodles; *Weight
Watchers Pasta:* Mild Curry Flavour
Noodles

JUST WHOLEFOODS ☺⊘

Organic World Mixes: Biryani, Chow
Mein, Cous Cous with Lentils, Falafel,
Hummus

NATURKRAFTWERKE ™

**Blinis; Falafel with black cumin oil;
Latkes; Tabouleh**

ORGANICO ⊘ ✿

Serrra Rica: Mediterranean Chestnut
Stuffing with Couscous, Traditional
Chestnut Stuffing with Breadcrumbs

ORGRAN ☺

Falafel Mix; *Biscotti:* Pasta & Sauce

PAUL'S TOFU ™⊘ ◢ ✿

Savouries: **Organic Nut Roast**

POLAR SUN PRODUCTS LTD ™☺⊘

**Soya Bolognese; Soya Burger Mix;
Soya Chunks; Soya Flakes; Soya
Goulash; Soya mince brown; Soya**

Mince Neutral; Soya Strips; Soya Tex-Mex Mix

PREMIER FOODS

Paxo: Sage & Onion Stuffing

QIANNA AGRICULTURAL PRODUCTS IND & TRADING CO. LTD ™☺

Black Bean Spaghetti; Brown Rice Noodle; Carrot Ginger Instant Noodle; Corn Noodle; Garlic & Pepper Instant Noodle; Green Tea Noodle; Mung Bean Noodle; Rice Noodle; Soba; Soba (Buckwheat Noodle); Soyabean Chicken; Soybean Fish; Soybean Noodle; Soybean Sausage; Soybean Spaghetti; Spinach Instant Noodle; Tomato Instant Noodle; Udon; Vegetable Instant Noodle; Whole Wheat Noodle

QUINUA REAL BRASIL LTDA ™⊘

Organic Quinoa; Quinoa Flakes; Spaghetti

ROSIE'S GOURMET PRODUCTS (UK) LIMITED ™☺

Dried Porcini Mushrooms

SANCHI ⊘

Noodles: Organic 40% Soba, Organic Brown Rice Udon, Organic Cup, Organic Green Tea, Organic Thai Rice, Organic Udon, Somen; *Organic Noodles:* 40% Soba, Green Tea, Someh, Thai Rice; *Organic Ramen Noodles:* Ginger, Mushroom, Seaweed; *Organic Udon Noodles:* Brown Rice; *Soba Noodles:* 100% Buckwheat

VEGETALIA LIMITED

Gnocchi Pasta with Kamut; Macaroni with Quinoa and Beetroot; Mixture of Red Quinoa and Rice; Mixture of Wild Rice; Pasta with Spirulina and Parsley; Spirulina Spaghetti; Wonder Spelt; *Cultivos Marinos del Cantáábrico:* Dulse Seaweed, Kombu Seaweed, Sea Spaghetti Seaweed, Sea Spaghetti with Onion and Carrot in Oil, Wakame Seaweed

SAVOURIES - FROZEN

BEANIE'S HEALTH FOODS ™☺❶⊘

Fry's Special Vegetarian Frozen Foods: Veg Express Sausage Rolls

CALEDONIAN CURRY CO. ™⊘

Aloo Choley (Minted Potato & Chickpea); Baigan Nariyal (Hot Aubergine & Chilli); Baigan Tamatar (Spiced Aubergine & Tomato); Bombay Potato; Caledonian Chickpea; Channa Dhal Masala; Highland Beetroot Curry; Palak Choley (Spinach & Chickpea Curry); Saag Aloo; Tarka Dal

DALOON FOODS ⊘

Indian Classics: Mini Samosas, Mini Samosas & Onion Bhajis, Onion Bhajis, Vegetable Pakora; *Indian Snacks:* Onion Bhajis; *Oriental Classics:* Mixed Vegetable Spring Rolls; *Oriental Snacks:* Mini Spring Rolls

DRAGONFLY FOODS ⊘ ✿
Tatty Patty

G. COSTA & CO ⊘
Tipiak: Potato fecule

GOODLIFE FOODS ⊘
Butternut Squash Roast with Oven Roasted Tomato Sauce

HEINZ ™⊘
Aunt Bessies: Tidgy Roasties; *Ross:* Hash Browns, Jacket Wedges, Oven Crunchies, Potato Waffles; *Ross Chip Shop:* Chunky Chips, Oven Chips; *Weight Watchers from Heinz:* Bombay Potatoes, Low Fat Chips, Mediterranean Pot, Sea Salt and Black Papper Wedges

LINDA MCCARTNEY
Chilli Non Carne; Spicy Three Bean Bake

MCCAIN ⊘
5% Fat Roasts; 5% Fat Wedges; Baby Potatoes with Oven Roasted Tomatoes and Garlic; Chippy Chips; Crispy French Fries; Groovy Wedges; Hash Brown Bites; Hash Browns; Home Roasts; McCain Gold; Nicely Spiced Wedges; Quick Chippy Chips; Sea Salt & Cracked Black Pepper; Seasoned Curly Fries; Southern Fries; Steak Fry Chips; Super Value Chunky; Super Value Crinkle Cut; Super Value Straight Cut; Super Value Thin Fries; Traditional Roasts; *Home Fries:* Chunky, Crinkle Cut, Straight Cut, Thin & Crispy; *MicroChips:* Crinkle Cut, Straight Cut; *Oven Chips:* Crinkle Cut, Rustic, Straight Cut

REALEAT
Chicken Style Pieces; Fishless Fishcakes; VegeBangers; VegeMince

WESTLER FOODS LTD ⊘
Wayfarer: Vegetable Curry

SEASONAL FOODS

D & D CHOCOLATES ☺⊘
Carob: Chuckling Bunny Shapes, Hollow Easter Egg, Solid Hearts, Solid Mini Eggs; *Dark Couverture:* Chuckling Bunny Shapes, Hollow Easter Egg, Solid Mini Eggs

KINNERTON LTD
Childrens Dairy Free Easter Eggs; Luxury Dark Chocolate Easter Egg

KP
Luxury Roasted Pistachios (Xmas); Seasonal Fruit and Nut Mix (Xmas); *Big Nuts:* Red Hot Chilli Flavour

PAUL'S TOFU ™⊘ ⚬ ✿
Breads: **Organic Hot x Buns;** *Cakes:* **2 Organic Mince Pies with Miso & Kuzu, 2 Organic Mince Pies with Miso & Kuzu (Gluten Free), Gluten Free Christmas Cake, Gluten Free Christmas Pudding, Gluten Free Mince Pies, Organic Christmas Cake, Organic Christmas Pudding**

WARBURTONS ⊘
400g: Danish White

SEAWEED & SEAVEG

CLEARSPRING ™☺❶⊘✔👁
**Agar agar flakes(gelling agent);
Arame; Dulse; Green nori sprinkle
(flakes); Hijiki; Instant wakame
flakes; Kombu; Nori flavoured
strips; Nori sheets; Nori sushi
toasted sheets; Sea salad(dulse, sea
lettuce,nori); Sea vegetable salad -
Japanese; Wakame**

**INTERNATIONAL PARTNERSHIP LTD
(SEAGREENS DIVISION)** ™☺⊘
Seagreens: **Dulse Granules, Liquid
Ascophyllum, Nutri Puree;**
Seagreens- Pelvetia Pieces: **Salad
Condiment**

QUALITY SEA VEG ☺
Irish Carragheen; Irish Dulse; Irish Mixed
SeaVeg; Irish Nori; Irish Sea Spagetti;
Irish Spirulina; Irish Wakame; Sea Spice;
Sea Tangle; Smoked Dulse and sugar
kelp; Sweet Tangle

SANCHI ⊘
Seaweed: Kombu, Nori, Sushi Nori,
Wakame

SOURCE FOODS ☺✿
Herbs of The Sea; Nori; Sushi Sheets;
Wakame

SNACKS - SAVOURY

AJITAS VEGE CHIPS
BBQ; French Onion; Herbs & Garlic;
Lime Chilli; Natural; Sea Salt & Vinegar;
Sweet & Sour

ALNAVIT GMBH ™
Crispies pikant

BIOFAIR
Quinoa Snack w Oregano; Quinoa
Snack with Onion; Rice Quinoa
Crunchies

BLUE DRAGON
Rice Crackers: BBQ Flavour, Chilli
Flavour, Nori Flavour, Original Flavour

CLEARSPRING ™☺❶⊘✔👁
Organic: **Roasted seed and soya
snack, Roasted seeds and soya with
cranberry snack, Roasted Snack Mix,
Roasted Styrian pumpkin seeds,
Tamari roasted Sicilian almonds**

DISCOVERY FOODS
Gluten Free Tortilla Chips; Tortilla Chips

EAT ME LTD ☺
Rainbow: Flavours, Fruit Crisps

**ESSENTIAL TRADING
CO-OPERATIVE LTD** ™❶⊘✔
Essential Brand- Mixes: **Fruit Salad,
Organic Fruit & Nut Mix, Organic
Fruit Salad**

G. COSTA & CO ⊘
Old Ranch House Lorenz Snack World:
Ready Salted Chipsletten (Stackers)

GENERAL DIETARY
Pretzels: Rings, Sesame

GOLDEN WONDER ⊘
Crisps: Pickled Onion Flavour, Quite Hot
Curry Flavour, Ready Salted, Ready Salted
Flavour, Salt and Vinegar Flavour, Sausage
& Tomato Flavour, Smokey Bacon Flavour,
Tomato Ketchup Flavour; *Crunchy Fries:*
Salt and Vinegar Flavour; *Ringos:* Pickled
Onion Flavour, Salt and Vinegar Flavour

GREENCITY WHOLEFOODS ❶⊘
Bombay Mix; Chilli Rice Crackers; Garlic
Sticks; Japanese style Rice Cracker Mix;
Seaweed Peanut Crackers

HULA HOOPS
Hula Hoops: Original, Salt & Vinegar,
Smoky Bacon; *Hula Hoops Multigrain:*
BBQ Beef Flavour, Pickled Onion, Salt &
Vinegar, Salted, Saucy BBQ

KALLO FOODS ⊘
Whole Earth: SO Crispy Sea Salt and
Balsamic Vinegar, SO Crispy Smoky
Paprika

KETTLE CHIPS
Golden Parsnip; Lightly Salted; Mexican
Limes with a hint of Chilli; No Added
Salt; Sea Salt & Balsamic Vinegar; Sea
Salt with Crushed Black Peppercorns;
Sweet Chilli; Sweet Potato; *Kitchen:*
Aged Modena Balsamic Vinegar Sea

Salt and Basil, Maldon Sea Salt;
Organics: Lightly Salted, Sea Salt with
Crushed Black Peppercorns

KP
Big Nuts: Char Grilled Steak Flavour,
Hickory Smoked BBQ Flavour;
Brannigans Peanuts: Dry Roasted,
Roasted Salted; *Crisps:* Beef, Ready
Salted, Salt & Vinegar, Worcester
Sauce; *Jumbo Salted:* Peanuts; *KP:*
Bombay Mix, Fruit and Nut Mix;
Original Salted: Peanuts; *Peanuts:* Dry
Roasted, Salt & Vinegar, Spicy Chilli;
Roast Salted: Cashews, Pistachios

LIFEFOOD CZECH REPUBLIC S.R.O. ™
**Organic Bugs Chilli; Organic Bugs
Curry; Organic Bugs Provensal;
Organic Carrot Crackers; Organic
Figs and Spices Flax Rolls; Organic
Poppy Seed Balls**

MCCOYS
Potato Chips: Chicken Curry, Chicken
Madras, Chinese Sweet & Sour Ribs,
Mexican Chilli, Red Hot Chilli, Salt &
Malt Vinegar, Salted, Southern Fried
Chicken Wings, Spicy Paprika; *Specials
Tortilla Chips:* Red Chilli & Lime Flavour

MEDITERRANEAN FOODS
(LONDON) LTD ™☺
**Falafel; Falafel Meal with Couscous
Salad; Falafel Meal with Taboula;
Falafel Sandwich; Mixed Vegetable
Kebab; Mixed Vegetable Kebab
Sandwich; Spinach Kebab; Spinach
Kebab Sandwich**

MUNCHY SEEDS ™☺
Cajun Mix; Chilli Mix; Naked Mix; Omega Mix; Original Mix; Pumpkin Mix

NATASHA'S LIVING FOOD ☺⊘
Raw Sprouted Sunflower Crunch

NATURKRAFTWERKE ™
Mumbai mix

ORGANIX BRANDS PLC ⊘✿
Carrot Stix; Saucy Tomato Noughts & Crosses; Spicy Stars; *Rice Cakes:* Apple Rice Cakes, Orange Rice Cakes, Plain Rice Cakes

ORGRAN ☺
Crazy Jacks: Bombay Mix

PHILEAS FOGG
Classic Mexican Flavour Tortillas

PORTER FOODS CO LTD
Fruit Pyramid: Apricot & Pistachio, Fig & Almond, Pear & Hazelnut

POT NOODLE
Beef and Tomato; Bombay Bad Boy; Hot Chicken Curry; Lamb Hot Pot; Southern Fried Chicken; Sweet & Sour Flavour; *Posh Noodle:* Chilli, Spicy Chinese Chicken, Sweet & Sour

QUAKER OATS LTD ⊘
New Quaker Oats Bar Mixed Berry Flavour; New Quaker Oats Bar Original Golden Syrup Flavour; Quaker Jumbo Snack-Jacks Caramel Flavour; Quaker Seasons Lime & Coriander Flavour

RAW LIVING ™
Raw Cashew Nuts

SACLA
Green Olives with Chilli; Green Olives with Garlic; Mixed Olives

SANCHI ⊘
Brown Rice Chips; Brown Rice Crackers; Chilli Crackers; Hot and Spicy Wasabi Chips; Quinoa & Tamari Arare; Sanchi Nippers; Sea Vegetable Chips

SEABROOK POTATO CRISPS LTD ⊘
Crisps: Canadian Ham, Canadian ham crinkle cut, Pickled Onion, Salt & Vinegar, Sea Salt, Sea Salt & Black Pepper, Sea Salt Original, Smokey Bacon, Tomato, Unsalted

SHARWOODS ⊘
Poppodums: All

SUMA WHOLEFOODS
™❶⊘✦☺✖⨯1985
Bhusu; Bombay Mix; Dehli Mix; Garlic Sticks; Organic Bombay Mix; Spiced Roast Chick Peas; Spicy Noodles; Spicy Sticks

THE FOOD DOCTOR LTD ™☺
Seed Mix: Dry-Roasted Soy Nuts, Essential Omega Seed Mix, Essential Omega Seed Shake, Fennel & Caraway, Mixed Herb, Original, Rosemary & Onion, Spicy Mix, Thyme & Sage

TOPAS KLAUS GAISER GMBH ™☺☼
Spacebar Chorizo; Spacebar Nuts;
Spacebar Tofu; *Wheaty Snack Bars:*
Vegan Organic Spacebar "Hemp",
Vegan Organic Spacebar "Pyrossi",
Vegan Organic Spacebar "Red Hot
Chilli Peppers"

TRAIDCRAFT PLC ⊘
Bombay Mix; Savoury Snacks Variety
Pack; Spicy Plantain Chips

UNITED BISCUITS LTD ⊘
Brannigans - Peanuts: Dry Roasted,
Roasted Salted; *Crunchies:* Prawn
Cocktail Flavour; *Discos:* Salt &
Vinegar; *Frisps:* Ready Salted, Salt &
Vinegar; *Go Ahead Crinkle Cut Crisps:*
Lightly Salted, Salt & Vinegar; *Jacob's -
Bakes:* Garlic & Herb, Salt & Cracked
Black Pepper; *Jacob's - Essentials:*
Poppy Seeds & Herbs, Pumpkin Seeds &
Thyme, Sesame & Rosemary; *Mini
Chips:* Beef, Salt & Vinegar; *Nik Naks:*
Pickle N Onion, Rib N Saucy; *Space
Raiders:* Pickled Onion; *Wheat
Crunchies:* Worcester Sauce Flavour

VEG-OUT ™
Store Cupboard- Sandwiches:
**Redwood's cheatin' ham and
chicken; Pure, soya, lettuce, vegan
mayo**

WALKERS SNACK FOODS LTD
Sunbites Original; *Baked:* Mango Chilli,
Ready Salted, Salt and Vinegar; *Crisps:*
BBQ Rib, Cajun Spice, Chilli & Lemon,
Pickled Onion, Prawn Cocktail, Ready

Salted, Roast Gammon, Salt & Vinegar,
Salt 'n' Shake, Sweet Cumberland
Sausage, Worcester Sauce; *Doritos:*
Chilli Heatwave, Lightly Salted; *French
Fries:* Ready Salted, Salt & Vinegar;
Lights: Simply Salted; *Potato Heads:*
Ready Salted, Salt & Vinegar; *Quavers:*
Prawn Cocktail, Salt & Vinegar;
Sensations: Caramelised Onion & Sweet
Balsamic Vinegar, Gently Infused Lime
& Thai Spiced Flavour, Lime and
Coriander Chutney Flavour Poppadom
Bites, Sweet Chilli and Coriander
Flavour Corn Chips; *Smiths Chipsticks:*
Ready Salted, Salt 'n' Vinegar; *Squares:*
Ready Salted, Salt & Vinegar; *Wotsits:*
Flamin' Hot Flavour

YAOH ™☺❶⊘♨
**De-Hulled Hemp Seeds; Whole
Hemp Seeds**

SOUPS

BAXTERS ⊘
Autumn Vegetable; Carrot &
Butterbean; Carrot,Onion&Chick Pea;
Chunky Country Vegetable;
Mediterranian Tomato; Medley of
Country Vegetable; Minestrone; Red
Lentil & Vegetable; Tomato &
Butterbean; Winter Vegetable with
Yellow Split Peas; Italian Bean &Pasta

BLUE DRAGON
Spicy Red Curry Soup; Won Ton Soup

CLEARSPRING ™☺❶◌ℹ️👁️
Instant miso soup - Heart red with sea vegetables; Instant miso soup - mellow white with tofu; *Organic:* **Instant Miso Soup - Brown Rice with Sea Vegetables**

ESSENTIAL TRADING CO-OPERATIVE LTD ™❶◌ℹ️
Essential Brand- Soups: **Concentrated Organic Clear Vegetable Broth, Concentrated Organic Mediterranean Vegetable Bouillon with Organic Olive Oil, Organic Lentil & Pumpkin Soup, Organic Lentil Soup, Organic Pea Soup**

HEINZ ™◌
Autumn Lentil & Vegetable; Lentil; Spring Vegetable; Vegetable; Winter Vegetable; *Big Eat:* Veg and Tomato Hotpot; *Big Soups:* Spicy Mixed Bean; *Farmers Market:* Potato Leek and Thyme, Roast Parsnip; *Farmers Market Chilled Soups:* Tomato and Red Pepper with Basil; *Real Soups:* Homestyle Minestrone, Tuscan Tomato; *Soups of the World:* Homestyle Minestrone; *Special Soups:* Root Vegetable & Barley Broth, Tuscan Style Minestrone; *Weight Watchers from Heinz:* Carrot & Lentil, Country Vegetable, Country Vegetable Soup Cup, Hearty Vegetable, Meditarranean Tomato and Lentil, Mediterranean Tomato & Vegetable, Moroccan Tomato and Chickpea, Root Vegetable and Bean, Spiced Lentil and Potato, Tangy Tomato and Rice, Tomato & Red Pepper, Vegetable

JEREMY'S SOUPS ◌ℹ️
Soup: Chickpea & Harissa, Curried Parsnip, Gazpacho, Lentil, Minestrone, Red Pepper, Black Olive & Tomato, Sweetcorn & Chilli

JUST WHOLEFOODS ☺◌
Organic Soup in a Mug: Carrot & Coriander, Leek & Potato, Minestrone, Tomato & Basil, Vegetable

KNOBBLY CARROT FOOD COMPANY
Broccoli; Celery & Apple; Courgette & Lemon; Leek & Potato; Minestrone; Mushroom & Garlic; Spicy Tomato; Tomato & Orange

KNORR
Florida Spring Vegetable Packet Soup; French Onion; Highland Lentil; Highland Vegetable; Leek; Minestrone; Moroccan Chickpea; Spring Vegetable; *Soup:* Florida Spring Vegetable, Italian Tomato & Basil, Tomato & Pepper

ORGANICO ◌✿
Danival: Barley Miso, Japanese Pumpkin Cream, Miso Cubes, Miso Soup Powder, Rice Miso; *Serrra Rica:* Chesnut and Carrot with Ginger, Chesnut and Tomato, Gazpacho, Red Pepper and Toasted Almond, Tomato and Basil

ORGRAN ☺
Garden Vegetable Soup Mix

SAFE 2EAT LTD ☺
Soup: Carrot, Leek and Ginger, Italian Four Bean, Minestrone, Spicy Mexican Bean, Sweet Potato and Spinach, Tomato

SANCHI ⊘
Miso Soup: Instant with Seaweed, Organic, Organic Miso Soup with Mushroom

SANITARIUM HEALTH FOOD CO ⊘
John Tickell's 12 Vegetable Soup; Vegetable & Minestrone

SEEDS OF CHANGE
Spicy Lentil; Three Bean

SIMPLY ORGANIC ⊘ ✿
Pure & Pronto: Mixed Bean Chilli; *Soup:* Chunky Vegetable, Lentil & Parsley, Lentil Sweet Potato & Coconut, Minestrone, Tomato & Basil

SOMA ORGANIC ☺⊘ ✦ ✿
Nomato: Soup

SUMA WHOLEFOODS
™❶⊘✦ 👁⤴–1985
Broth Mix; *Organic Soups:* **Carrot & Coriander, Minestrone, Pea, Spicy Lentil, Thick Vegetable, Tomato, Tomato & Red Pepper**

SOYA AND OTHER 'MILKS'

ALPRO UK LTD ™☺⊘
Ambient Milk: **Light Calcium and Vitamins 1 Litre, Original Calcium and Vitamins 1 Litre/500ml/3x250ml, Soya Soleil Unsweetened 1 Litre;**
Fresh milk: **Chocolate shake calcium and vitamins 1 Litre, Chocolate Shake Calcium and Vitamins 500ml, Light Unsweetened Calcium and Vitamins 1 Litre, Organic 1 Litre;** *Organic Soya Fruity:* **Orchard, Tropical;** *Organic Soya Milk:* **Sweetened, Vanilla Flavour;** *Provamel Ambient Soya Milks:* **Organic sweetened plus calcium;** *Provamel Flavoured soya milk:* **Organic banana flavour shake 250ml, Organic chocolate drink, Organic chocolate flavour shake 250ml, Organic strawberry flavour shake 250ml, Organic vanilla drink 1litre, Organic vanilla flavour shake 250ml;** *Provamel Organic Soya Milk:* **Unsweetened;** *Provamel OY! Flavoured Soya Milk:* **Banana, Chocolate, Strawberry, Vanilla;** *Provamel Rice Drink:* **Organic, Organic rice & calcium, Organic rice drink with vanilla, with Calcium & Vitamins;** *Soya Milk:* **Sweetened, Unsweetened, with Calcium, with Calcium & Vitamins;** *Soya Soleil:* **Sweetened**

DIXIE DINERS CLUB
Moo NOT

FIRST FOODS LTD ☺⊘
Oat Supreme: Oat Milk

GRANOSE
All Soya Milks

GRANOVITA UK LTD ⊘ ✦
Soya Drink: Calcium Enriched, Organic Sugar Free

HOLLAND AND BARRETT RETAIL LTD ✔
Soya Alternative to Milk: Sweetened, Unsweetened

KALLO FOODS ⊘
Thin Slice Slightly Salted Rice Cakes

OATLY
Healthy Oat Alternative to Cream; Healthy Oat Organic

PLAMIL FOODS LTD ™☺❶⊘
Alternatives to Milk: **Organic Soya Milk**

RICE DREAM ☺
Rice Drinks

SANCHI ⊘
"Bonsoy" Soya Milk

SANITARIUM HEALTH FOOD CO ⊘
So Good Soya Milk: All Soya Milk including Active & Essential

SPIRAL FOODS
Original Bonsoy

VEGAN STORE ™☺❶⊘✔
Tam Tov: **Coffee Creamer**

WHITE WAVE ☺
All

SPICES

CHIMANS ™⊘
Aloo Gobi; Balti Pasta; Bean Curry;

Bombay Potatoes; Dal; Spicy Chick Peas; Spicy Vegetable Soup; *Organic:* **Aloo Gobi, Bean Curry, Bombay Potatoes, Dal, Spicy Chick Peas, Spicy Vegetable Soup**

DISCOVERY FOODS
Seasoning Mix: Cajun, Fajita, Taco

HOLISTIX ™❶
Mulled Wine Spice Powder; Mulled Wine Spice Whole

PATAKS FOODS ⊘
Curry Pastes: Balti, Bhuna, Biryani, Extra Hot Curry, Garam Masala, Jalfrezi, Kashmiri Masala, Korma, Madras, Mild Curry, Rogan Josh, Tandoori, Tikka, Tikka Masala, Vindaloo

SCOTTISH HERBAL SUPPLIES ™❶⊘✔
Dried Organic Herbs

SEASONED PIONEERS ⊘✔
Africa: Berbere, Harissa Spices, South African Curry Powder, Tsire Powder, Tunisian Five Spice, Tunisian Tabil, West African Pepper Seasoning, Zanzibar Curry Powder; *Balti:* Garam Masala; *Cajun:* Cajun Blackening, Cajun Spice Blend, Creole Spice Blend; *Caribbean:* Adobo Rub Caribbean, Caribbean BBQ Jerk Rub, Poudre de Colombo, Virgin Islands Spiced Salt, West Indian Curry Powder; *China:* Chinese Five Spice; *India:* Bombay Masala, Cardamom Masala, Char Masala, Chat Masala, Garam Masala, Gujarati Masala,

Kashmiri Masala, Madras Curry Powder, Panch Phoran, Punjabi Masala, Rose Petal Masala, Tandoori Masala; *Indonesia:* Seven Seas Curry Powder; *Japan:* Gomashio, Shichimi Tagarashi; *Mediterranean:* Quatre-ÉÉpices, Spice Parisienne; *Mexico:* Achiote Paste Spices, Adobo Rub Mexican; *Middle East:* Advieh (Iranian Rice Seasoning), Bahar (Kuwait), Baharat, Dukkah (Egypt), Hawaj (Yemen), Kabsa (Saudi), Sabzi Ghormeh (Iran), Zahtar (Za'atar); *Morocco:* La Kama, Ras-el-Hanout; *Mulling Drink Spices:* Cajun Cafe Brulot Rum Spices, Caribbean Sorrel Rum Spices, Hot Toddy Spices, Mulled Cider Spices; *South India:* Sambhar Masala, Sri Lankan Curry Powder; *Worldwide:* Aliñño (Chile), Celery Salt, Khmeli-Suneli (Georgia), Malay Curry Powder (Malaysia), Massaléé (Mauritius), Mixed (pudding) Spice, Pickling Spice

SPREADS - SAVOURY

ANGLESEY NATURAL FOODS ™☺◇✔
Alavon: **Coleslaw, Garlic Coleslaw, Potato Salad**

AROMAFOODS ™☺✔
Cajun Butternut Squash; Chilli Bean Spread; Coronation Spinach with Omega 3 seeds Sandwich Filling; Provencale Roast Veg; Roast Veg Houmus

BIONA
Black Olive Pate; Horseradish Relish; *Daily Balance Spread:* Country with Wild Garlic, Mexico with Corn Tomato & Cayenne Pepper, Styria with Pumpkin Seed, Tuscana with Olive Tomato & Basil

BUTE ISLAND FOODS LTD ™☺❶◇
Vegan Mayonnaise: **Curry Flavour Island Mayo, Garlic Flavour Island Mayo, Mexican Flavour Island Mayo, Original Flavour Island Mayo, Tartar Flavour Island Mayo**

ESSENTIAL TRADING CO-OPERATIVE LTD ™❶◇✔
Fairtrade tahini(light& dark); *Essential Brand:* **Tahini (Organic & Conventional);** *Essential Brand- Peanut Butters:* **All (Organic & Conventional)**

FIRST QUALITY FOODS ◇✔
Al'fez: Harissa paste 100g, Lemon tagine stir-fry paste 100g

GRANOVITA UK LTD ◇✔
Mushroom Savoury Pate in Chubb Pack; *Organic Ready Spready:* Garlic & Herb, Herb, Mushroom, Original; *Organic Tofu Pate:* Spicy Mexican (Yeast Free), Tomato (Yeast Free); *Ready Spready:* Herb Provence, Mushroom, Original; *Savoury Pate in Tin:* Mushroom, Olive, Vegetable

HIGHER NATURE PLC ™◇✔
Omega Excellence: **Organic Pumpkin Seed Butter**

LEEORA VEGETARIAN FOOD ™☺⃠
Mediterranean Cuisine: **Moroccan Style Matbucha;** *Spreads:* **Carrot & Chive, Green Lentil, Mushroom & Garlic, Spicy, Sundried Tomato**

MARMITE
Spread; Squeezy

MEDITERRANEAN FOODS (LONDON) LTD ™☺
Black Olive Houmus; Plain Houmus; Red Pepper Houmus

MERIDIAN FOODS ⃠
Free From: Creamy Tomato & Herb Sauce, Dopiaza Sauce, Green Pesto, Green Thai Sauce, Madras Sauce, Red Pesto

MH FOODS LTD ™⃠ ✐
Florentino- Pesto: **Basil - Cheese Free, Red - Cheese Free**

NATASHA'S LIVING FOOD ☺⃠
Raw Houmous 1; Raw Houmous 2

ORGANICO ⃠ ✿
Nate: Carrot and Paprika Pate, Garlic and Basil Pate, Hazelnut Pate, Provincial Herbs Pate, Shii-take Mushroom Pate; *Serrra Rica:* Artichoke Spread, Aubergine and Garlic Spread, Caramelised Onion Spread, Roasted Red Pepper Spread, White Bean & Capers Spread

PREMIER FOODS
Sun-Pat: Creamy Crunch Peanut Butter, Creamy Smooth Peanut Butter, Original

Crunchy Peanut Butter, Original Smooth Peanut Butter

REAL ORGANIC FOODS ⃠
Province of India Chutneys: Mango with Ginger & Roasted Cumin, Spicy Tomato with Caramelised Onion, Tangy Eastern

REDWOOD WHOLEFOOD COMPANY ™☺❶⃠
Beanfeast Pate; *Vegideli Organic Range:* **Organic Beanfeast Pate, Organic Brussels Pate**

SANITARIUM HEALTH FOOD CO ⃠
Yeast Extract; *Peanut Butter:* All Varieties

SUMA WHOLEFOODS
™❶⃠ ✐ ☜✂1985
Organic Tomato Paste; *Organic Pate:* **Herb, Mushroom;** *Organic Peanut Butter:* **Crunchy, Crunchy - No Salt, Smooth, Smooth - No Salt;** *Organic Pesto:* **Green, Red**

TOPAS KLAUS GAISER GMBH ™☺✿
Gourmet Pate soya spread with garlic; Gourmet Pate Soya Spread with marjoram; Gourmet Pate soya spread with mushrooms; Gourmet Pate Soya Spread with Red Bell Pepper

TYRRELLS POTATO CHIPS
Crisps: Lightly Sea Salted, Naked/No Salt, Sea Salt & Black Pepper, Sea Salt & Cider Vinegar, Spicy Jalapeno Chilli & Lemon, Sweet Chilli & Red Pepper

UNILEVER
Marmite: Yeast Extract

VEGETALIA LIMITED
Black Olive Pate; Fine Herbs Pate; Green Olive Pate; Mushroom Pate; Seaweed Pate; Tahini with Seaweed; Tofu & Miso Pate; White Tahini with Creamed Sesame (No Salt)

VEG-OUT ™
Store Cupboard: **Smoked tofu and almond pate**

WOJNAR'S WIENER LECKERBISSEN ™
Austrian Soy; Country Soy; French Soy; Hungarian Soy; Italian Soy; *Biona:* **Country, Mexico, Styria, Toscana**

SPREADS - SWEET

BAXTERS ⊘
Blackcurrant Conserve; Country Berry Conserve; Lemon Marmalade; Orange Marmalade; Orange,Lemon & Grapefruit Marmalade; Rhubarb & Ginger Conserve; Stawberry Conserve; Thin Cut Seville Orange Marmalade

BIONA
Apple & Cranberry Compote; Dark Chocolate Spread; Pear & Apple Spread

CLEARSPRING ™☺❶⊘✔👁
Organic: **Apricot fruit spread, Blackcurrant fruit spread, Blueberry fruit spread, Peach fruit spread,** **Prune fruit spread, Sour cherry fruit spread, Strawberry fruit spread**

CUISINE DE FRANCE
Seedless Raspberry Jam

ESSENTIAL TRADING CO-OPERATIVE LTD ™❶⊘✔
Fruit Spreads: **Organic Cherry, Organic Four Fruit, Organic Raspberry, Organic Strawberry, Organic Wild Bilberry;** *Spreads:* **Organic Apricot, Organic Blackberry, Organic Blueberry**

KALLO FOODS ⊘
Whole Earth: Apple and Raspberry, Apricot, Blueberry, Cherry, Forest Fruits, Orange Thick Cut, Orange Thin Cut, Raspberry, Strawberry

KITCHEN GARDEN PRESERVES ✔
Jams: Blackberry & Apple, Blackcurrant, Gooseberry & Orange, Kiwi & Gooseberry, Mango & Papaya, Plum, Raspberry, Rhubarb, Strawberry, Summer Berry; *Marmalade:* Grapefruit, Lime, Orange & Cranberry, Orange with Lavender, Seville Orange, Three Fruit; *Organic Chutney:* Beetroot, Country Fruit, Piccalilli; *Organic Jams:* Apricot & Almond, Blackcurrant, Blueberry & Apple, Plum, Raspberry, Rhubarb, Strawberry; *Organic Marmalade:* Grapefruit, Seville Orange, Three Fruit

LYME BAY WINERY
Chutney: Apple with Elderflower Wine, Black Beer with Raisin Wine, Spicy

Tomato with Jack Ratt Cider; *Extra Preserve:* Blackcurrant with Elderberry Port Liqueur, Strawberry with Summer Fruit Liqueur; *Marmalade:* Lyme Bay Sunrise with Apricot Brandy Liqueur, Red Onion with Damson Gin Liqueur, Vintage with Whisky & Ginger Liqueur

MERIDIAN FOODS ⊘

Fruit Spread: Apricot, Blackcurrant, Blueberry, Breakfast Seville Orange, Cherries/Berries, Cherry, Cranberry, Cranberry & Orange, Grapefruit Breakfast, Grapefruit Breakfast Spread, Morello Cherry, Pineapple & Ginger, Raspberry, Strawberry, Tropical, Wild Blueberry; *Fruit Spread - Organic:* Apricot, Blackcurrant, Blueberry, Cherries/Berries, Cherry, Cranberry

NATROL ✔

Mango Chutney

ORGANICO ⊘ ✿

Coteaux Nantais: Magic Apricot Jam, Magic Cherry Jam, Magic Raspberry Jam, Magic Strawberry Jam; *Serrra Rica:* Clementine Marmalade, Lemon Marmalade, Membrillo - Quince Paste, Seville Orange Marmalade, Valencia Orange Marmalade

PLAMIL FOODS LTD ™☺❶⊘

Organic Chocolate Spread: **Orange;** *Organic Chocolate Spreads:* **Plain**

PREMIER FOODS

Frank Cooper: All Jams & Marmalades; *Robertsons:* All Jams & Marmalades

REAL ORGANIC FOODS ⊘

Organic Conserve: Apricot, Blueberry, Raspberry with a hint of Citrus, Strawberry & Blackberry, Summer Fruits; *Organic Marmalade:* Seville Orange

TRAIDCRAFT PLC ⊘

Exotic Fruit Mix; Orange Marmalade; Strawberry Jam; Tropical Fruit Mix

TOFU, TEMPEH, MISO ETC

ALPRO UK LTD ™☺⊘

Meat free: **Tofu Mince, Tofu Pieces - Lightly Seasoned;** *Provamel Meat Free:* **Organic lightly seasoned tofu strips, Organic tofu mince**

ANGLESEY NATURAL FOODS ™☺⊘✔

Quinova: **Chunks, Mince;** *Quinova-Banyan:* **Indian Spice, Mediterranean, Plain, Welsh Onion & Chives**

BLUE DRAGON

Firm Silken Tofu

CAULDRON FOODS LTD ⊘

Tofu: Marinated Pieces, Organic Original, Organic Smoked, Original

CLEARSPRING ™☺❶⊘✔◉

Tekka(miso condiment); *Organic:* **Barley Miso, Hatcho miso, Sweet white miso**

DRAGONFLY FOODS ⊘ ✿
Organic Tofu: Deepfried, Natural, Smoked

FULL OF BEANS
Garlic & Coriander Tempeh; Marinated Tempeh; *Organic:* Indonesian Style Tempeh, Japanese Style Tofu, Soyabean Miso

MARIGOLD ❶⊘
Braised Tofu

ORGANICO ⊘ ✿
Danival: Ravioli Stuffed Tofu

PAUL'S TOFU ™⊘ 🥄 ✿
Savoures: **Abura Age Marinated Tofu, Nigari Tofu, Tempeh**

R & R TOFU ™☺⊘
Marinated Tofu; Naturally Smoked Tofu; Organic Tofu; Tofu Sea Cakes; Tofu Sesame Burgers

SANCHI ⊘
Miso: Genmai (Brown Rice), Hatcho (Soya Bean), Mugi (Barley), Organic Genmai (Brown Rice), Organic Mugi (Barley), Organic Unpasteurised Barley (Mugi), Shiro

SOURCE FOODS ☺✿
Low Sodium Rice & Soy Organic Miso: Mellow Brown, Sweet Brown; *Ohso Miso:* Yummo Sesame; *Ohso Miso - Organic Instant Soup:* Original; *Organic Instant Soup:* Beetroot, Ginger, Spirulina; *Organic Miso:* Field Bean Barley, Ginger, Hemp, Mellow Barley, Mellow Brown, Mex Chilli, Sweet Brown

TAIFUN ☺⊘
Pan Ready Tofu: Tofu filets Wild Garlic, Tofu Röösti; *Smoked Tofu:* Demeter, Smoked, With Almonds and Sesame Seeds; *Tofu:* Basil, Demeter, Kinugoshi, Natural, Nigari, Silken; *Tofu Terrine:* Graffiti

TOPAS KLAUS GAISER GMBH ™☺✿
Finest Smoked Tofu; *Wheaty:* **Vegan Organic Seitan "Classic"**

TURTLE ISLAND FOODS ☺
Tempeh: Organic Five Grain, Organic Soy, Spicy Veggie

VEGETALIA LIMITED
Seitan; Seitan with Spelt; Tempeh; Tofu

'YOGURTS'

ALPRO UK LTD ™☺⊘
Alpro Dairy Free Alternative to Yogurt Raspberry & Vanilla Flavour; Alpro Dairy Free Chocolate Flavoured Custard & Calcium; Exotic Fruits; Forest Fruits; Peach; Strawberry; *Organic Yofu:* **Plain, Summer Fruits;** *Provamel Yogurts:* **Bluberry 4x125g, Organic blueberry and peach 4X125g, Organic forest fruits 500g, Organic peach and**

mango 4x125g, **Organic Plain 500g, Organic red cherry 4x125g, Organic strawberry 500g;** *Yofu Junior:* **Peach & Pear, Strawberry & Banana;** *Yogurts:* **Forest Fruits Calcium and Vitamins 500g, Organic Red Cherry/Peach & Mango 4x125g, Peach Calcium and Vitamins 4x125g, Peach/Pear & Strawberry/Banana Calcium and Vitamins 4x125g**

GRANOVITA UK LTD ⊘ ◖

Deluxe Soyage: Banana, Black Cherry, Mango, Peach & Apricot, Plain, Raspberry, Strawberry, Tropical; *Organic Soyage:* Fruits of the Forest, Peach & Apricot, Strawberry

NOTES

■ **Banana chips** may have been dipped in honey.

■ **Bread:** a few pre-packed loaves contain either skimmed milk powder or vitamin D3. Most large producers use vegetable-based emulsifiers (E471, E472 etc). When buying bread from local bakers, check ingredients and the type of fat used to grease tins.

■ **Breakfast cereals and margarines** fortified with vitamin D may contain the animal-derived vitamin D3.

■ **Chocolate:** unfortunately, plain chocolate is not always animal-free and may contain milk powder. All of the chocolate products listed in the Animal Free Shopper have been made without animal-derived ingredients or processing aids, but may have been produced on the same lines as milk chocolate products, see **contamination** below.

■ **Contamination:** the *Animal Free Shopper* only lists products that we have been informed meet our ANIMAL-FREE CRITERIA. However, many of the foods listed will have been produced on the same lines as products containing animal-based ingredients. Although health and hygiene, and product quality requirements mean that machines are cleaned between different products, there is a very slight, theoretical, risk of contamination. This means, for example, that some listed products may not be suitable for dairy allergy sufferers.

■ **Crisps** may contain lactose, whey or animal derived additives.

■ **Fruit** may be glazed with animal (commonly beeswax or shellac) waxes. Contact manufacturers for further details as information changes regularly (according to season, supplier, etc).

■ **Gelatine carrier:** beta-carotene and vitamin D2 may be 'carried' in gelatine to maintain stability, e.g. orange coloured drinks may contain beta-carotene held in a gelatine suspension (see DRINK NOTES, page 177). In the case of beta-carotene, vegetable oil carriers are available and are generally animal-free.

■ **Natural Flavourings** may be animal derived.

■ **Processing aids** may be animal derived. There is no statutory requirement for these to be listed on products.

■ **Salt** is usually vegan, but some low salts may contain a milk derivative.

■ **Sugar:** bone char is sometimes used as a decolourant in sugar production. However, the largest suppliers of sugar to companies in the UK - British Sugar, Tate & Lyle and Billington - do not use any animal-derived ingredients (except for Tate & Lyle Traditional Royal Icing, which contains dried egg white powder). Most supermarkets' own-brand sugars are made for them by one of these companies.

■ **Vinegar:** although malt and spirit vinegars are generally animal-free, the production of wine, cider and sherry vinegars may involve the use of a fining agent of animal origin.

DRINK

BEER

ANHEUSER-BUSCH

Ascent 54; Bare Knuckle Stout; Busch; Busch Ice; Busch Light; Czechvar; Demon's Hop Yard IPA; Grolsch; Grolsch Amber Ale; Grolsch Blonde Lager; Grolsch Light Lager; Harbin Lager; Hurricane High Gravity; Hurricane Ice; Hurricane Malt Liquor; King Cobra; Kirin Ichiban; Kirin Light; Mule Kick Oatmeal Stout; Natural Ice; Natural Light; Ray Hill's American Pilsner; Redbridge; Rolling Rock; Tarpon Spoon; Tequiza; Tiger Beer; Tilt; ZiegenBock; ZiegenBock Amber; *Bacardi Silver:* All; *Seasonal Beers:* Beach Bum Blonde Ale, Jack's Pumpkin Spice; *Specialty Organic Beers:* Stone Mill Pale Ale, Wild Hop Lager

BLACK SHEEP BREWERY PLC ⊘ ⬤

Bottled Ales: Black Sheep, Emmerdale, Golden Sheep Ale, Monty Python's Holy Grail, Riggwelter Strong

BRAKSPEAR'S

Bottled: Oxford Gold Organic Beer

BUDWEISER

Bud Dry; Bud Extra; Bud Ice; Bud Ice Light; Bud Light; Budweiser; Budweiser Select

CALEDONIAN BREWING CO ⊘

Bottled Beers: Caledonian 80 (500ml bottle), Deuchars IPA (500ml bottle), Golden Promise Organic (500ml bottle)

CARLSBERG UK LTD ⊘ ⬤

Carlsberg; Carlsberg Edge; Carlsberg Elephant Beer; Carlsberg Export; Carlsberg Special Brew; Tuborg

CROPTON BREWERY

Balmy Mild; Endeavour; King Billy; Monkman's Slaughter; Scoresby Stout; Two Pints; Uncle Sam's; Yorkshire Moors Bitter; *Seasonal:* Haunting Hanks, Rudolph's Revenge

EVERARDS BREWERY

Hazy Daze

FREEDOM BREWERY LTD ™
Freedom Dark; Freedom Organic Lager; Freedom Pilsner

FULLERS

Bottled & Keg (NOT Draught): All except Honey Dew

GEORGE BATEMAN & SON ™⊘ ⬤
ALDI Specially Selected Range: **Golden Ale, India Pale Ale, Treble X Ale, XB English Ale; Bottled Beers: Combined Harvest, Combined Harvest Multigrain Beer, Dark Lord Premium Ale, Rosey Nosey, Rosey Nosey Premium Ale, Spring Breeze, Summer Swallow, Triple XB, Victory Ale, XXXB Classic Bitter, Yella Belly Organic Beer**

GROLSCH

Lager

HALL & WOODHOUSE LTD
Badger: Blandford Fly, First Gold, Fursty Ferret, Golden Champion, Golden Glory, Poacher's Choice, Pumpkin Ale, Stinger, Tanglefoot

HEINEKEN
Lager: Pilsener

HOLSTEN
Holsten Export; Holsten Pils; Holsten Super

INBEV ⊘ ⓘ
Beck's; Brahma; Hoegaarden; Stella Artois

LITTLE VALLEY BREWERY LTD ™
Bottle Conditioned: **Cragg Vale Bitter, Fairtrade Organic Ginger Pale Ale, Hebden's Wheat, Moor Ale, Stoodley Stout, Tod's Blonde, Withens IPA**

MICHELOB
Michelob; Michelob AmberBock; Michelob Golden Draft; Michelob Golden Draft Light; Michelob Light; Michelob Ultra; Michelob Ultra Amber; *Seasonal Beers:* Michelob Bavarian-Style Wheat, Michelob Ultra Fruit Infused

PITFIELD BREWERY ™⊘ⓘ
Bottled Beers: **Amber Ale, Black Eagle, Dark Ale, East Kent Goldings, Eco Warrior, Hoxton Heavy, Imperial Stout, India Pale Ale, London Porter, Mild Ale, N1 Organic Wheat Beer, Pitfield Organic Lager, Pitfield Original, Red Ale, Shoreditch Stout, XXXX Stock Ale**

ROBERT CAIN & COMPANY LIMITED ⊘ⓘ
Bottled Beers: 2008 Culture Beer, Bock Beer, Dragonheart Ale, FA Ale, Finest Lager, Organic Wheat Beer, Raisin Beer; *Canned:* Dark Mild, FA Ale, Finest Bitter, IPA beer, Liverpool Lager; *Keg:* Bitter, Finest Lager, IPA, Liverpool Lager, Mild

SAMUEL SMITH ™⊘ⓘ
Celebrated Oatmeal Stout; Cider Reserve; Extra Stout; Famous Taddy Porter; Imperial Stout; India Ale; Nut Brown Ale; Old Brewery Pale Ale; Organic Best Ale; Organic Cherry Fruit Beer; Organic Lager; Organic Raspberry Fruit Beer; Organic Strawberry Fruit Beer; Pure Brewed Lager; Sovereign Bitter; Taddy Lager; Winter Welcome Ale; *Ayingerbrau:* **D Pils Lager, Hefeweiss Lager, Lager, Low Alcohol Lager, Prinz Lager;** *Melbourn Bros:* **Apricot Fruit Beer, Cherry Fruit Beer, Strawberry Fruit Beer**

SKOL
Skol (Cans); Skol Special; Skol Super

SPECTRUM BREWERY
Bottled: 42, Bezants, Black Buffle, Capt. Scarlet, Dark Fantastic, Light Fantastic, Old Stoatwobbler, Solstice Blinder, Spring Promise, Trip Hazard, Wizzard, XXXX, Yule Fuel; *Cask:* Black Buffle, Dark Fantastic, Old Stoatwobbler

THE DURHAM BREWERY LTD
Bottle-Conditioned: Benedictus, Cloister, Evensong, St Cuthbert, Temptation

THE HOP BACK BREWERY
Entire Stout: Bottles, Cask

THE INNIS & GUNN
BREWING COMPANY ⊘
Blonde Oak Aged Beer; Original Oak
Aged Beer; Rum Cask Oak Aged Beer

TRADITIONAL SCOTTISH ALES
Bottled Ales: Bannockburn, Ben Nevis,
City of Stirling, Glencoe Stout, Lomond
Gold, Shefiffmuir, Stirling Brig, William
Wallace

VINTAGE ROOTS ⊘ ✿
Freedom; Prospect pale ale; Vintage
roots organic beer; *Brakspear:*
Brakspear bottle conditioned organic
beer; *Caledonian:* Golden promise;
Duchy: Duchy originals organic ale;
Dupetit: Cannabia; *Hall & woodhouse:*
River cottage stinger ale; *Hartsfelder:*
Vintage roots organic lager; *Hepworth
brewery:* Cool blonde lager;
Lammsbrau: Lammsbrau organic
pilsner; *Little valley brewery:* Stoodley
stout, Withens ipa; *Ridgeway brewery:*
Ridgeway rob; *Riedenburger:*
Reidenburger low alcohol,
Riedenburger organic lager,
Riedenburger wisse wheatbeer;
Westons: Westons organic cider

WELLS & YOUNG'S
Wells Banana Bread Bear: Canned
Bottled and Keg Varieties (Not Cask);
Wells Bombardier: Canned Bottled and
Keg Varieties (Not Cask); *Wells Eagle
IPA:* Canned Bottled and Keg Varieties

(Not Cask); *Wells John Bull:* Canned
Bottled and Keg Varieties (Not Cask);
Youngs Bitter: Canned Bottled and Keg
Varieties (Not Cask); *Youngs Special
Premium Ale:* Canned Bottled and Keg
Varieties (Not Cask); *Youngs
Waggledance:* Canned Bottled and Keg
Varieties (Not Cask)

WESTERHAM BREWAERY CO LTD
British Bulldog; Little Scotney Best
Bitter; Little Scotney Pale Ale; William
Wilberforce Freedom Ale

WYCHWOOD BREWERY
Circlemaster

CHAMPAGNE

SMITHFIELD WINE ™
Vegan Champagne: **Th. Blondel Roséé
Brut Premier Cru, Thierry Blondel
Premier Cru**

THOMAS LOWNDES & CO
Champagne Brut NV (Roséé) 12%;
Champagne Brut NV 12%; Marc de
Champagne 60%

VINTAGE ROOTS ⊘ ✿
Duval-leroy: AOC Authentis cumieres
2001; *Faust:* AOC Carte d'or

CIDERS & PERRIES

ASPALL ⊘ ⏺
Cyder: All

DUNKERTON'S
CIDER COMPANY ☺⊘ ⏺ ☼
Ciders: Black Fox Sparkling Medium Dry, Kingston Black, Premium Organic Sparkling, Sparkling Extra Dry; *Perries:* Sparkling, Still; *Still Blended Ciders:* Dry, Med, Med Sweet, Sweet

GWYNT Y DDRAIG CIDER
Cider: Black Dragon, Orchard Gold

LUSCOMBE
ORGANIC DRINKS ☺⊘ ⏺ ☼
Organic Devon Cider

LYME BAY WINERY
Cider: Jack Ratt Scrumpy, Jack Ratt Vintage, Lyme Bay Sparkling Cider

MERRYDOWN ☺⊘
Gold; Vintage

PITFIELD BREWERY ™⊘ ⏺
Fred's Perry; *Bottled Cider:* **Hoxton Farmhouse Dry Cider**

SAMUEL SMITH ™⊘ ⏺
Organic Cider

SEDLESCOMBE ORGANIC VINEYARD
™☺⊘ ⏺ ☼
Dry Cider

SHEPPY'S CIDER ⊘ ⏺
Bullfinch; Goldfinch; Oakwood Supreme; Organic Dry; Organic Medium; *Draught Cider:* Dry, Medium, Sweet; *Gold Medal Vintage Cider:* Dry, Medium, Sweet; *Oakwood Draught Cider:* Dry, Medium; *Oakwood Special:* Dry, Medium, Sparkling; *Single Variety Ciders:* Dabinett, Kingston Black, Taylor's Gold, Tremlett's Bitter

SOMERSET CIDER BRANDY
COMPANY & BURROW HILL CIDER ☺
Ciders: All

VINTAGE ROOTS ⊘ ☼
Cinq autels: Normandy cider; *Dunkertons:* Black fox cider, Premium organic cider, Vintage cider 2004/05; *Sheppy's:* Sheppy's organic cider

WESTON & SONS LTD ☺⊘
Oak Conditioned Cider: Henry Westons Vintage Reserve, Medium Sweet, Strong Extra Dry, Strong Medium Dry, Vintage Cider; *Organic Cider:* Draught Vintage, Westons Organic; *Perries:* Herefordshire Country, Original; *Scrumpy Cider:* 1st Quality Cider, Bounds Brand Scrumpy Cider, Extra Strong Scrumpy, Old Rosie Scrumpy, Traditional Scrumpy Cider; *Speciality Ciders:* 1880 Anniversary Cider; *Stowford L.A.:* Low Alcohol; *Stowford Press Cider:* Dry, Export, Medium Dry, Medium Sweet, Supreme

'HOT'

A. VOGEL
Bambu

CADBURY TREBOR BASSETT
Bournvita

CLEARSPRING ™☺❶⊘✓👁
Hasucha Lotus Tea; Mu Tea -16 herbs; *Organic:* **Genmaicha Green Tea/Roasted Rice - Bags, Genmaicha Green Tea/Roasted Rice - Loose, Hojicha Roasted Green Tea - Bags, Hojicha Roasted Green Tea - Loose, Hojicha Tea bags, Kukicha Roasted Twig Tea - bags, Kukicha Roasted Twig Tea - loose, Sencha Green Tea - loose, Sencha Green Tea bags**

ESSENTIAL TRADING CO-OPERATIVE LTD ™❶⊘✓
Essential Brand- Organic Coffee: **All;**
Essential Brand- Organic Demeter Teas: **All**

GUARANA COMPANY ™
Hot Guarana Punch

HERBS HANDS HEALING LTD ™⊘✓
Herbal Tea Blends & Single Herb Teas: **Basil, Burdock Root, Cassia Split Bark, Catnip, Dandelion Coffee, Dandelion leaf, Fennel Seeds, Hibiscus Flower, Lavender Flowers, Lift and Calm, Liquorice root, Marigold Flowers, Marjoram, Mellissa, Oregano, Parsley, Pau d'arco, Peppermint, Sage, Spearmint, St. John's Wort, Thyme, Uva Ursi, White Willow Bark, Wild Cherry Bark**

KALLO FOODS ⊘
Whole Earth: No Caf, Wake Cup

KITCHEN GARDEN
SoyCaf

MONTEZUMAS CHOCOLATES
Drinking Chocolate: Omacati Dos, Omacati Uno

NATROL ✓
Laci Le Beau Teas: All

OPTIMAH HEALTH & NUTRITION ⊘✓⅃1995
Vital Health Foods: Organic Rooibos Tea Bags

RAWCREATION LTD ™☺
Immunitea; Olive Leaf Tea; Pau D'arco Tea; Rise and Shine; Teatox; Tranqilitea; Yerba Mate Tea

REDBUSH TEA CO
Redbush: Apple, Finest, Lemon, Spiced, with Lemon Oil

SIMPLY SOAPS™❶⊘✓👁⅃ 2003
Gift Sets: **Yogi Tea 'Calming' Gift Box, Yogi Tea 'Detox' Gift Box, Yogi Tea 'Harmony' Gift Box**

THE CHOCOLATE ALCHEMIST ⊘✿
Dark Drinking Chocolate: Plain, with Chilli, with Nutmeg

TRAIDCRAFT PLC ⊘
Drinking Chocolate

LOW & NON-ALCOHOLIC

BRITVIC ⊘ 🍷
Shandy Bass: Shandy

**LUSCOMBE ORGANIC
DRINKS** ☺⊘ 🍷 ✿
Organic Ginger Beer: Cool, Hot

SOFT

ARCIM HYPOGEEN B.V. ™
Hypo-Fit Direct Energy for Diabetics

ASPALL ⊘ 🍷
Apple Juice

BELVOIR FRUIT FARMS ☺⊘
Cordials: Elderflower, Ginger,
Gooseberry & Mint, Lime &
Lemongrass, Passion Fruit & Mango,
Pomegranate & Raspberry, Raspberry &
Rose Cordial, Spiced Winter Berries,
Summer Berries; *Organic Cordials:*
Blackcurrant, Blood Orange &
Mandarin, Blueberry, Cranberry,
Elderflower, Ginger

BRITVIC ⊘ 🍷
American Ginger Ale; Bitter Lemon;
Blackcurrant Cordial; Lime Cordial; Low
Calorie Tonic Water; Orange Cordial;
Soda Water; *7UP:* Cherry, Free, Regular;
Ame: Elderberry and Lemon, Grape and
Apricot, Orange and Grape, Raspberry
and Blackberry; *Aqua Libra:* Original;
Bass: Indian Tonic Water; *Britvic 55:*
Apple, Apple Raspberry and Cranberry,
Orange; *Cordial:* Blackcurrant; *Drench:*
Spring Water; *Gatorade:* Lemon, Orange;
Idris: Fiery Ginger Beer, Red Devil; *J2O:*
Apple and Mango, Apple and Melon,
Apple and Raspberry, Orange and
Cranberry, Orange and Passionfruit,
Orange and Pomegranate; *Pennine:*
Citrus Mineral Water, Strawberry Mineral
Water; *Pennine Spring - Mineral Water
Drink:* Citrus, Orange and Peach,
Strawberry; *Pepsi:* Diet, Max, Regular;
Purdey's: Multi Vitamin Juice Drink; *R
Whites:* Diet, Premium; *R. Whites:*
Lemonade; *Really Wild Drinks:* Apple and
Blackcurrant Still, Apple Blackcurrant
Sparkling, Orange and Pineapple
Sparkling, Orange and Pineapple Still;
Robinsons - Barley Water: Lemon,
Orange; *Robinsons - For Milk:* No Added
Sugar Fruity Banana Soft Drink;
Robinsons - Fruit & Barley: Apple & Pear
Soft Drink, Apple and Blackcurrant,
Citrus, Orange, Peach, Pink Grapefruit,
Strawberry and Kiwi, Summer Fruits,
Tropical Soft Drink; *Robinsons - Fruit
Shoot:* Apple, Apple No Added Sugar,
Blackcurrant and Apple, Blackcurrant
and Apple No Added Sugar, No Added
Sugar Tropical Soft Drink, Orange and
Peach, Orange and Peach No Added
Sugar, Still Spring Water Apple Soft
Drink, Still Spring Water Blackcurrant
Soft Drink, Still Spring Water Orange
Soft Drink, Strawberry, Strawberry No
Added Sugar, Tropical No Added Sugar;

Robinsons - *Fruit Shoot H2O:* Apple, Blackcurrant, Orange; *Robinsons - Fruit Spring:* Apple & Cranberry, Blackcurrant & Raspberry, No Added Sugar Apple & Cranberry Juice Drink, No Added Sugar Blackcurrant and Raspberry Juice Drink, No Added Sugar Orange and Mandarin Juice Drink, Orange & Mandarin; *Robinsons - Fruit Squash:* Apple and Blackcurrant, Apple and Blackcurrant No Added Sugar, Lemon No Added Sugar, Orange, Orange and Pinapple (No Added Sugar), Orange and Pineapple, Orange No Added Sugar, Summer Fruits, Summer Fruits No Added Sugar; *Robinsons - High Juice:* Apple, Apple Cherry and Raspberry, Apple Strawberry and Lychee, Apple Strawberry and Lychee Drink, Grape and Melon, Orange, Peach, Pink Grapefruit; *Robinsons - Smooth Juice:* Apple, Apple and Blackcurrant, Orange; *Tango:* Apple, Cherry, Citrus, Diet Orange, Orange; *Tango - Clear:* No Added Sugar Apple and Watermelon Drink, No Added Sugar Lemon and Kiwi Soft Drink, No Added Sugar Orange Soft Drink, Raspberry and White Cranberry Soft Drink; *The Really Wild Drinks Co.:* Apple and Blackcurrant Juice Drink, Apple and Prickly Pear Juice From Concentrate, Orange and Mango Juice From Concentrate, Orange and Pineapple Juice Drink

CHEGWORTH VALLEY JUICES ☺
Certified Organic Juices: Bramley Apple, Cox Apple, Discovery Apple, Pear; *Classic Apple Juices:* Bramley, Cox & Bramley, Discovery, Discovery & Bramley,

Russet, Worcester & Bramley; *Pear Juice & Special Variety Juices:* Apple & Beetroot, Apple & Blackberry, Apple & Blackcurrant, Apple & Cranberry, Apple & Elderflower, Apple & Raspberry, Apple & Rhubarb, Apple & Strawberry, Pear

ELLA DRINKS ☺ ⊘ ✔

FENTIMANS LTD ☺ ⊘
Curiosity cola; Dandelion & Burdock; Mandarin and Seville Orange Jigger; Traditional Brewed Shandy; Traditional Ginger beer; Victorian Lemonade

G & G VITAMINS
Aktiv Ingredient Energy Drink

GERBER JUICE COMPANY
Libby's: Apple C Juice Drink, Blackcurrant C Juice, NAS Tropical Drink, Orange C Juice Drink, Tomato Juice with Vitamins C and E, Um Bongo; *Ocean Spray:* Cranberry & Blackcurrant Juice Drink, Cranberry & Blueberry Juice Drink, Cranberry & Mango Juice Drink, Cranberry & Orange Juice Drink, Cranberry & Raspberry Juice Drink, Cranberry and Acerola Juice Drink, Cranberry Juice Drink - Classic; *Scooby Doo:* Tropical Juice Drink; *Sunpride:* Cranberry Juice Drink, Exotic Juice Drink, Mango Juice Drink; *Thomas the Tank Engine:* Apple & Blackcurrant Juice Drink, Orange Juice Drink; *Welch's:* Grape & Mango Juice Drink, White Grape & Peach Juice Drink, White Grape & Pear Juice Drink, White Grape, Pear & Apple Juice Drink

GUARANA COMPANY ™
Cold Guarana Punch

HYPOGEEN
Hypo-Fit Direct Energy

KALLO FOODS ⊘
Whole Earth: Sparkling Cola, Sparkling
Cranberry, Sparkling Elderflower,
Sparkling Ginger, Sparkling Lemonade

KNORR
Vie Shots: Apple, Carrot & Strawberry,
Kiwi, Pumpkin & Banana, Orange,
Carrot & Banana

LUSCOMBE ORGANIC
DRINKS ☺⊘✔✿
Organic Apple & Apricot Juice; Organic
Apple & Pear Juice; Organic Apple
Juice; Organic Apple with Elderflower;
Organic Apple with Ginger; Organic
Elderflower Bubbly; Organic Lime
Crush; Organic Raspberry Lemonade;
Organic Sicilian Lemonade; Organic St.
Clements; Organic Strawberry
Lemonade

LYME BAY WINERY
Dorset Ginger Cordial

MCKEITH ☺
Organic Juice: Berry Chi, Cherry Chi,
Peach Chi; *Organic Smoothie:* Groovy
Guava, Mango Mania, Veggie Vitality

MERIDIAN FOODS ⊘
Fruit Juice Concentrates: Apple, Apple
& Blackcurrant, Organic Apple, Pear

ORGANICO ⊘✿
The Organic Collection: Blueberry
Sparkle Juice, Raspberry Sparkle Juice

PENNARD ORGANIC WINES
& CIDER ⊘✿
Pennard Organic: Apple Juice

PURELY WICKED SHAKES LIMITED ™
Soya Fruit Milkshakes - All Flavours

RED BULL ☺⊘
Red Bull: Energy Drink, Stimulation,
Sugar Free

ROCKS ORGANIC CORDIALS ⊘✿
Juice Drinks: Bella Blackcurrant; *Organic
Cordials:* Blackcurrant, Cranberry,
Elderflower, Fruit Punch, Ginger, Lemon,
Lime, Summer Fruit; *Squashes:* Lizzy
Lemon, Olly Orange

RUBICON DRINKS LTD.
Sparkling Juice Drinks: Guanabana,
Guava, Lychee, Mango, Passion,
Pomegranate, Tropical; *Still Juice Drinks:*
Coconut Water, Guanabana, Guava,
Guava Berry, Lychee, Mango, Mango
Apple, Papaya, Passion, Pomegranate,
Blueberry & Cranberry, Tropical

SCIENCE IN SPORT
GO Electrolyte: All Flavours; *PSP22:* All
Flavours; *REGO Recovery:* All Flavours

SEDLESCOMBE ORGANIC VINEYARD
™☺⊘✔✿
Apple Juice; Blackberry & Apple
Juice; Bramley Apple Juice; Cox
Apple Juice; Grape Juice; Pear Juice

SOMA ORGANIC ☺🚫◀ ☼
Lemonade; Original; *Pure Fruit Smoothies:* Blackberry & Blueberry, Mango & Passionfruit, Peach & Strawberry, Raspberry & Blackcurrant; *Super smoothies:* Blueberry Bliss, Fruity Roots, Jungle Juice, Tropical Twist

THE HIBISCUS DRINKS COMPANY LIMITED ™
Hibiscus & Grape; Hibiscus & Peppermint; Hibiscus Classic; Hibiscus Cordial

UNILEVER
AdeZ Fruit Drink with Soya: Mango & Apricot, Orange & Peach, Pineapple & Passionfruit; *Lipton Ice Tea:* Lemon, Mango, Peach

VEGETALIA LIMITED
Organic Pomegranate Juice; Organic Rose Elixir

VIMTO
Cordial: Apple, No Added Sugar, Orange, Original; *Fizzy:* No Added Sugar, Original; *Ready to Drink:* No Added Sugar, Original

VINCEREMOS ORGANIC WINES ™🚫◀ ☼
Rocks: **Blackcurrant squash 74cl, Lemon squash 74cl, Orange squash**

X35 ENERGY LTD ™☺
X35 Body Fuel- energy drink- 250ml and 500ml sizes.

SPIRITS & APÉRITIFS

ARCHERS
Schnapps: All

BARON WINE CELLARS, LTD T/A TISHBI ESTATE WINERY ™🚫
Port 45; White Brandy

CLEARSPRING ™☺🅾🚫◀ 👁
Shizengo Sake; Tamaki Sake

FONSECA
Ports: All Vintage, Terra Prima Oganic Reserve

JOHNNIE WALKER
Johnnie Walker Whisky: Black Label, Blue Label, Gold Label, Green Label, Red Label

LYME BAY WINERY
Fruit Liquers: Apricot Brandy, Blackcurrant Rum, Damson, Elderberry & Port, Plum, Sloe, Summer Fruit, Whisky & Ginger; *Somerset Cider Brandy Company:* 10 Years Old Cider Brandy, 3 Years Old Cider Brandy, 5 Years Old Cider Brandy, Eau de Vie Cider Brandy, Kingston Black Aperitif Cider Brandy

PENNARD ORGANIC WINES & CIDER 🚫☼
Pennard Organic: Ginger Liquor, Raspberry Liquor

PERNOD RICARD
Malibu

SEDLESCOMBE ORGANIC VINEYARD
™☺🚫♨ ✿
**Blackberry Liqueur; White Grape
Liqueur**

**SOMERSET CIDER BRANDY COMPANY
& BURROW HILL CIDER** ☺
Eau De Vie; Kingston Black Apple
Aperitif 18%; Somerset Pomona 20%;
Brandy: Somerset Alchemy, Somerset
Five Year Old, Somerset Royal,
Somerset Ten Year Old

THE ORGANIC SPIRITS COMPANY
☺🚫♨ ✿
Highlands Harvest: Organic Scotch
Whisky; *Juniper Green:* Organic Gin;
Papagayo: Organic White Rum; *UK5:*
Organic Vodka; *Utkins:* Fairtrade White
Rum

THOMAS LOWNDES & CO
Amaretto 50%; Calvados 40%;
Coconut Liqueur Extract 50%; Coffee
Liqueur Extract 50%; Creme de Menthe
Extract 60%; Culinary French Brandy
40%; Culinary Jamaican Rum 40%;
Culinary Malt Whisky 60%; French Dry
White Tolosan 11.5%; Kirsch 50%;
Marsala Superiore 18%; Medium Dry
Amontillado Sherry 18.5%; Oloroso
Cream Sherry 17.5%; Peach Schnapps
50%; Rich Ruby Port 20%; Scotch
Whisky 60%; Single Speyside Malt
Whisky (6 year old) 40%; Vodka 40%;
Cockburn's Special Reserve: Port 20%;

Courvoisier V.S.: Cognac 40%;
Courvoisier V.S.O.P.: Cognac 40%;
Courvolsier: V.S. Cognac 60%;
Drambuie: Liquor 40%; *Grand Marnier:*
Liqueur 40%; *Harveys:* Orange 17.5%;
Harveys Bristol Cream: Sherry 17.5%;
Jim Beam: Black Bourbon Whiskey
43%, White Bourbon Whiskey 50%;
Lambs Navy: Rum 60%; *Laphroaig:*
Single Islay Malt Scotch Whisky 40%

VINCEREMOS ORGANIC WINES
™🚫♨ ✿
Casal dos Jodoes (Portugal): **Majara
Finest Reserve Port Quinta da
Esteveira;** *Highland Harvest:* **Highland
Harvest organic whisky;** *Utkins:*
Fairtrade white rum

VINTAGE ROOTS 🚫 ✿
Benromach: Speyside single malt
whisky; *Beucher:* Calvados; *Da mhile:*
Da mhile blended whisky, Da mhile
highland whisky; *Dwersteg:* Amaretto
liqueur; *Organic spirit company:*
Highland harvest whisky, Juniper green
organic london dry gin, Papagayo
organic spiced golden rum, Utkins
fairtrade premium single estate white
rum, Utkins uk5 organic vodka; *Pinard:*
Cognac napoleon, Cognac VSOP,
Cognac***; *Saoubis:* Bas Armagnac;
Verdet: Creme de cassis(blackcurrant),
Creme de framboise(raspberry), Creme
de mure(blackberry), Creme de
peche(peach)

WILLIAM GRANT & SONS 🚫
Glenfiddich Scotch Whisky: All

SPORTS DRINKS

HYPOGEEN
Hypo-Fit - Sachets: Direct Energy Mint, Direct Energy Orange, Direct Energy Tropical

WINES

CARMEL WINERY ☺◒
All

CONSTELLATION WINES
Counry Manor: All; *Rougemont:* All

EMILIANA ORGANICO ◒✿
Colchagua Valley 2003; Coyam Colchagua Valley 2004/2005; *Winemakers Selection:* Novas Casablanca Valley Syrah Sauvignon 2005, Novas Colchagua Valley Mourvedre 2004/2005, Novas Colchagua Valley Syrah 2004/2005

NO COWS ☺❶
Mixed Case: Connoisseurs' Organic Selection, Friends For Dinner Mixed Selection, MIxed case of 12 Organic Wines

WINES - FRUIT

BROUGHTON PASTURES ◒✈✿
Elderflower; Ginger (Fairtrade); Sparkling Elderflower

LYME BAY WINERY
Apricot; Birch; Blackbeer & Raisin; Blackberry; Blackberry & Apple; Blackcurrant; Cowslip; Cranberry; Damson; Dandelion; Dry Damson; Dry Gooseberry; Elderberry; Elderflower; Ginger; Gooseberry; Parsnip; Peach; Plum; Raspberry; Raspberry & Apple; Rhubarb; Sloe; Strawberry; Strawberry & Apple

PENNARD ORGANIC WINES & CIDER ◒✿
Pennard Organic: Apple, Elderberry, Folly, Ginger, Gooseberry, Plum, Raspberry, Tayberry

SEDLESCOMBE ORGANIC VINEYARD ™☺✈✿
Black Cherry Wine; Blackberry Wine; Elderberry Wine; Elderflower Wine; Ginger Wine; Golden Apple Wine; Plum Wine

SPLASH ENGLISH WINES ☺
Apricot Wine; Elderberry Wine; Elderflower Wine; Hibiscus; Peach Wine; Rhubarb Wine

VINTAGE ROOTS ◒✿
Irjimpa: DO La mancha caballero de mesarrubbias 2005/06; *Pinol:* DO Terra alta sacra natura 2005/06

WINES - RED

A'BECKETT'S VINEYARD ™
Estate Red 2004; Estate Red 2005

BARON WINE CELLARS, LTD
T/A TISHBI ESTATE WINERY ™⊘
Jonathan Tishbi Special Reserve Series:
**Cabernet Sauvignon Blend (Sde
Boker), Cabernet Sauvignon Gush
Etzion, Merlot;** *The Vineyards:*
**Cabernet Sauvignon, Carignan,
Merlot, Red Dessert Muscat, Ruby
M;** *Tishbi:* **Cabernet Petite Syrah;**
Tishbi Estate: **Cabernet Sauvignon,
Merlot, Pinot Noir, Shiraz**

EMILIANA ORGANICO ⊘✿
Adobe Carmenere 2005/2006; Adobe
Colchagua Valley Syrah 2005/2006;
Novas Central Valley Cabernet Merlot
2005; Novas Central Valley Cabernet
Sauvignon 2005; Novas Colchagua
Valley Cabernet Sauvignon 2005; Novas
Colchagua Valley Carmenere 2005

HARBOURNE VINEYARD ☺⊘ ✦
2002 Harbourne

MAJESTIC WINE WAREHOUSE LTD
Agramont Crianza 2004 Navarra; Aloxe
Corton 1er Cru 2005 Domaine
Chevalier Pèère et Fils; Aloxe-Corton
2004 Domaine Maillard; Beaune Rouge
2004 Domaine Maillard Pèère et Fils;
Bonterra Vineyards Zinfandel 2005
Mendocino; Bourgogne Côte
Chalonnaise Les Gorgères 2005 Michel

Sarrazin; Bourgogne Pinot Noir 2006
Cave Co-op de Buxy; Bourgogne Rouge
2005 Domaine Sarrazin; Caracol
Serrano 2005 Jumilla; Carmen
Winemaker's Reserve 2002 Maipo
Valley; Castillo Rioja 2006 Bodegas
Palacio; Cavas de Weinert Merlot 2002
Mendoza; Chapoutier Organic Tricastin
2006 Côteaux du Tricastin; Château
Batailley 2001 Pauillac, Crème Cru
Classé; Chââteau Bel Air 2003 Haut
Médoc, Cru Borgeois; Château du Cray
Bourgogne Rouge 2003/2004 Côôte
Chalonnaise; Château Guiot 2006
Costières de Nîmes; Château Haut
Franquet 2002 Bordeaux; Château
Potensac 2002 Médoc Cru Borgeois
Exceptionnel; Chénas 2005 Cave du
Château de Chénas; Chianti Classico
Riserva Carpineto 2000/2003 DOCG;
Clos d'Yvigne Le Petit Prince 2005
Côtes de Bergerac; Clos d'Yvigne Le
Rouge et Le Noir 2004; Collection
Privée de l'Oratoire 2006 Vin de Pays
de Vaucluse, Léonce Amouroux;
Corbières La Combe des Oliviers 2005;
Cuvée de Richard Red 2006 Vin de Pays
de l'Aude; Domaine de l'Amauve
Séguret Rouge 2006 Côtes du Rhône
Villages; Domaine Delubac 'Les Bruneau'
2005 Côtes du Rhône Villages Cairanne;
Fairhills Fairtrade Pinotage Cabernet
2006 Western Cape; Gevrey Chambertin
2005 Domaine Chevalier Père et Fils;
IIIB Merlot, Jean-Claude Mas 2006 Vin
de Pays d'Oc; King's River Shiraz 2006
Robertson; La Chapelle de Pitray 2005
Côtes de Castillon; La Motte Shiraz
2005 Franschoek; Ladoix Rouge 1er

Cru 'Clou d'Orge' 2005 Domaine Chevalier Père et Fils; Ladoix Rouge 2005 Domaine Chevalier Père et Fils; Les Fontanelles Cabernet Sauvignon 2006 Vin de Pays d'Oc; Les Fontanelles Merlot 2006 Vin de Pays d'Oc; Mâcon Rouge 2006 Les Vignerons des Grandes Vignes; Martin Sarmiento 2004 Bierzo; Paul Mas Cabernet de Cabernet 2006 Vin de Pays d'Oc; Pinot Noir Domaine de Valmoissine 2005 Louis Latour, Vin de Pays des Côteaux du Verdon; Pommard 'La Chanière' 2004 Domaine Maillard Père et Fils; Sablet Le Rêve de Marine 2004 Domaine de Piaugier; Sancerre Rouge 2006 Paul Thomas; Saumur Rouge 2005 Réserve des Vignerons; Savigny-Lès-Beaune Rouge 2004 Domaine Millard Père et Fils; Spy Mountain Pinot Noir 2006 Marlborough; Swartland Winery Pinotage 2006; Tatachilla Foundation Shiraz 2003 McClaren Vale; Tempranillo La Serrana 2006 Vino de la Tierra Castilla y León; Vergelegen Cabernet Sauvignon 2004 Stellenbosch; Vergelegen Mill Race Cabernet Sauvignon Merlot 2005 Stellenbosch; Vino Nobile di Montepulciano 'La Ciarliana' 2004; Yering Frog Cabernet Shiraz 2006 Yarra Valley; Yering Frog Pinot Noir 2006 Yarra Valley; Yering Station Pinot Noir 2004/2005 Yarra Valley; Yering Station Shiraz/Viognier 2005 Yarra Valley

NO COWS ☺❶

Aroa Tempranillo 2004; Camino Los Robles - Tempranillo Roble; Can Vendrell Tempranillo Garnatxa; Chateau Grolet La Coccinelle 2003; Chateau Grolet Le G 2003; Compte Cathare - Domaine Maris La Touge; Compte Cathare Maris Grenache 2002; Compte Cathare Syrignan; Domaine Majelus Merlot; L'Esprit de Valeriane; Novas Carmenere Cabernet; Pech-Roc Cabernet 2005

PETER LEHMANN
All Red Wine

SANT'OR ™☺◇
Red Wine

SEDLESCOMBE ORGANIC VINEYARD ™☺◇✔☼
Regent Dry Red English Wine

SMITHFIELD WINE ™
Azcunaga Semi Crianza; Casa Viva Pinot Noir; Casas del Bosque Pinot Noir Reserva; McGuigan Bin 2000 Shiraz; Palandri Estate Chardonnay; Poco Mas Cabernet Sauvignon; Poco Mas Merlot; Rincon Privada Cabernet Sauvignon; Rincon Privado Malbec; Rosario Carmenere Reserva; Rosario Merlot; Santa Luisa Malbec; Santa Luisa Merlot; Santa Luisa Syrah; *Australian Wines:* **Jarrah Ridge Red, McGuigan Bin 4000 Cabernet Sauvignon, McGuigan Black Label Merlot, McGuigan Black Label Shiraz;** *French Wines:* **Chateau Leon, Chateau Taillefer, Chateauneuf du Pape La Roche, Cotes du Rhone Caves St- Pierre, Cotes du Rhone Village, Dom. de la Garelle, Cote du**

Luberon Cuvee Pere Antoine Rouge, Domaine de La Garelle Merlot VDP de Vaucluse, Domaine de la Garelle, Cote du Luberon Cuvee Speciale; *Israeli Wines:* Dalton Merlot, Tishbi Cabernet Petit Syrah, Tishbi Special Reserve Merlot, Tishbi Vineyards Cabernet Sauvignon, Tishbi Vineyards Merlot; *New Zealand Wines:* Springbank Pinot Noir; *South African Wines:* Cape Bay Mellow Red, Cape Bay Pinotage, Neil Joubert Pinotage, Peaks View Pinotage; *Spanish Wines:* Bodega Palacio de Villachica 5T, Bodegas 1877 Arx Crianza, Bodegas 1877 Arx Negro Tempranillo/Merlot, Bodegas Bilbainas La Vicalanda Gran Reserva, Bodegas Bilbainas La Vicalanda Reserva, Bodegas Bilbainas Vina Pomal Reserva, Bodegas Entrecepas Crianza, Bodegas Irius Absum Varietales Tempranillo Merlot, Bodegas Valdevinas Tinar Crianza, Castillo Viejo Catamayor Merlot, Castillo Viejo Catamayor Merlot Tannat, Cune Crianza, Cune Reserva, Imperial Gran Reserva, Imperial Reserva, Montalvo Wilmot, Mynus& Tinto, Palaciego Rioja Red, Rioja Palaciego Crianza DOC, Rioja Valsarte Crianza DOC, Rioja Valsarte Reserva, Vallformosa Cabernet Sauvignon, Vallformosa Val Reserva, Vina Real Crianza, Vina Real Gran Reserva, Vina Real Reserva

TRAIDCRAFT PLC ⊘
Argentinian Shiraz; Chilean Cabernet Merlot; South African Cabernet Sauvignon Merlot; South African Pinotage

VINCEREMOS ORGANIC WINES ™⊘✓✿
Iberum Tinto DO Navarra 2005&2006; *Arlindo da Costa Pinto E Cruz:* Quinta da Esteveira DOC Douro 2004; *Bon Cap:* Syrah -Cabernet "The Ruins" 2005; *Bon Cap Winery (South Africa):* 'The Ruins' Pinotage; *Bucaro:* Montepulciano d'Abruzzo Riserva; *Chatelaine Stephanie:* VDT rouge- 10 litres bag in box; *Domaine de Clairac:* Cuvee des Cinq Filles, French Organic Red, Joubio Rouge, Marsanne, Syrah, Vin de Pays de l'Herault, Cabernet-Merlot 2004&2005; *Dominio Basconcillos:* Ribera del duero DO 2005; *Eden Collection Wines (Spain):* Tempranillo; *Era (Italy):* Primitivo; *Jacques Frelin (France):* Cuvee Olivier Vin de Table Rouge (10L Box), Merlot Cuvéée la Marouette, Vin de Pays du Gard; *La Nature Wines (France):* Cabernet Sauvignon; *Pircas Negras (Argentina):* Torrontes Barbera Malbec Syrah; *Ventura:* Cabernet Sauvignon 2005, Pinot Noir 2006; *Wilkie Estate (Australia):* Cabernet Merlot

VINTAGE ROOTS ⊘✿
Albet i noya: DO penedes tempranillo col.leccio 2000/01; *Azul y garanza:* DO Navarra 2006, DO Navarra seis 2004/05; *Barra:* Zinfandel 2005/06;

Basconcillos: DO Ribera del duero roble 2005; *Beausejour:* Puisseguin St Emilion 2004/2005, Puisseguin St Emilion Petit Beusejour Tradition 2005; *Bioghetto:* de l'Herault RN13 Vin de Pique-nique Rouge 2005; *Blanchard:* AOC Pineau des charenes; *Brau:* Cabardes 2004/2005, Cabardes Cuvee Exquise 2004/2005, Cite de Carcassonne Meditation Syrah/Egiodola 2004/2005, de l'Aude 2005, de l'Aude 'Pure' Cabernet Sauvignon 2006, de l'Aude 'Pure' Pinot Noir 2006, d'Oc Cuvee Gabriel Merlot 2005/2006; *Buis Rond:* Beaujolais 2006; *Casal dos jordoes Fortified Wine:* Finest Reserve Port, Tawny Port, Vintage port 2004; *Chapoutier:* AOC Coteaux du tricastin 2006; *Clos Plince:* Pomerol 2003; *CLVD:* d'Oc WWF Element Terre Merlot/Cabernet Sauvignon 2005; *Combebelle:* St Chinian Syrah/Grenache 2006; *Comte Cathare:* Minervois Domaine Maris La Touge Syrah 2004/2005; *Couronneau:* Bordeaux Superieur 2005/2006, Bordeaux Superieur Cuvee Pierre de Cartier 2005/2006, Bordeaux Superieur L'Ecuyer de Couronneau 2005; *Fasoli gino:* IGT La calle merlot 2004/05, IGT Rosso veronese pinot noir sande 2005; *Ijalba:* DO Rioja crianza 2003/04, DO Rioja dionisio ruiz ijalba 2004, DO Rioja graciano 2004, DO Rioja livor 2006/07, DOC Rioja genoli 2006/07; *Irjimpa:* DO Lamancha shiraz 2006; *Javillier:* Pommard Premier Cru 2005, Volnay Premier Cru 2004/2005; *Joliette:* AOC Muscat de rivesaltes 2005/06, Cotes du Roussillon Cuvee Andre Mercier 2003/2004, Cotes du Roussillon Villages Cuvee Romain Mercier 2002/2003; *La raia:* DOCG Gavi la raia 2006/07, DOCG Gavi la raia pise 2006/07; *Mas igneus:* DO Priorato Costers De Mas Igneus 2001, DO Priorato FA206 2004; *Moulin de Cadet:* St Emilion Grand Cru Classe 2004; *OVA:* Five Plots Merlot/Ruby Cabernet/Cabernet Sauvignon 2004/2005, Jamberoo Cabernet Sauvignon/Merlot 2003, Jamberoo Shiraz/Cabernet Sauvignon 2004/2005; *Palacios duque:* DOC Rioja buradon 2005, DOC Rioja padus 2004; *Pech-Latt:* Corbieres Selection Vielles Vignes 2005; *Perrini:* IGT Salento primitvo 2004/05; *Purisma:* DO Yecia Cerro Campana Old Vine Nonastrell 2006; *Quinta do coa:* Quinta do coa branco; *Richard:* Bergerac 2006, Bergerac Les Charmes Merlot/Cabernet Franc 2006, Bergerac Rouge 2006; *Rizzotti:* DOCQ Chianti san donato a lucardo 2005/06; *Robinvale:* Shiraz/Cabernet Sauvignon/Merlot 2005/2006; *San polino:* DOC Brunello di montalcino 2001, DOC rosso di montalcino 2004; *St Paul:* d'Oc Viognier 2006; *Stellar:* Cabernet sauvignon 2006/07, Heaven-on-earth sweet muscat, Live-a-little really ravishing red 2005, Live-a-little really revealing rose 2006/07, Merlot 2006/07; *Tsantali:* Merlot 2004/05; *Viberti:* DOC Barbera d'alba 2004, DOC Barolo 2001, DOC Langhe nebbiolo 2003/04; *Vintage Roots Own-label:* Organic rouge, Organic Tinto

VIVA! ☺❶⊘🐟
All

WINES - ROSÉ

HARBOURNE VINEYARD ☺⊘✔
2001 Dry Roséé Pinot Meunier

MAJESTIC WINE WAREHOUSE LTD
Lawson's Dry Hills Pinot Noir Rosé 2006
Marlborough; Pinot Grigio Rosé 2006
Cantina Beato Bartolomeo di Breganze;
Puig Ventos Garnacha 2005 Terra Alta

MEINKLANG
Pinot Noir Frizzante 2005/2006; Pinot
Noir Frizzante 2006

NO COWS ☺❶
Camino Los Robles - Rosado; Pech-Roc
Syrah

SEDLESCOMBE ORGANIC VINEYARD
™☺⊘✔✿
English Wine

SMITHFIELD WINE ™
South African Wines: **Peaks View
Pinotage Rose;** Spanish Wines:
**Mynus& Rose 2007, Vallformosa
Gran Reserva**

VINCEREMOS ORGANIC WINES
™⊘✔✿
La Mancha Blanco; Bon Cap:
Pinotage rose"The Ruins" 2006;
Domaine de Clairac: **Cabernet
Sauvignon Rosé, Joubio Rosé;**
Ventura: **Carmenere Rose 2006**

VINTAGE ROOTS ⊘✿
Albet i noya: DO Penedes Pinot
Moir/Merlot Classic Rosat, Penedes
Pinot Noir/Merlot Classic Rosat
2006/2007; Azul y garanza: DO
Navarra rosa 2006/07, Navarra Rosa;
Bassac: Organic Rose; Bettili: Serenel
Vivace Rosato 2006/2007; Bioghetto:
de l'Herault, de l'Herault RN13 Vin de
Pique-nique Rose 2006/2007, Vin de
Pique-nique Rose 2006/2007; Brau: de
l'Aude Brau Rose 2006/2007; Emiliano
Organico: Touchstone Rose; Fabril Alto
Verde: Buenas Ondas Syrah Rose
2006/2007; Jas d'esclans: AOC Cotes
de provence cru classe 2006/07; Jas
d'Esclans: Cotes de Provence Cru Classe
2006/2007; Meinklang: Pinot Noir
Frizzante 2006/2007; Stellar: Live-a-litle
rather revealing rose 2006/07, Live-a-
Little Rather Revealing Rose; Vintage
Roots Own-label: Organic rose, Organic
Rosso

WINES - SPARKLING

A'BECKETT'S VINEYARD ™
a'Beckett's Sparkly 2005

LIMNEY ☺⊘✔✿
Quality Sparkling Wine 2004

NO COWS ☺❶
Albet I Noya - Classic Xarel.lo K; Can
Vendrell Cava; Canals Brut Nature
Rosat; Limney Estate Sparkling

SEDLESCOMBE ORGANIC VINEYARD
™☺◎✔ ✿
Cuvee Bodiam Brut English Sparkling Wine; Cuvee Pinot Noir Regent Brut Rosé English Sparkling Wine 2002; Elderflower Sparkling Wine

SMITHFIELD WINE ™
Palandri Solora Sauvignon Blanc; *Israeli Wines:* **Tishbi Estate Chardonnay;** *Spanish Wines:* **Vallformosa Winery Cava Brut;** *Vegan Sparkling Wines:* **Old Acres Cava brut/rose**

VINTAGE ROOTS ◎✿
Albet i noya: DO Cava brut 21, DO Cava brut reserva, DO Cava brut rosat, DO Cava can vendrell; *Bosca del merlo:* IGT Prosecco del veneto 2006; *Mont'albano:* IGT Prosecco; *Naturian:* Ffizz! Organic brut; *Vintage Roots Own-label:* Organic bianco; *Zuccardi:* Santa julia organica sparkling chardonnay 2004

WINES - WHITE

A'BECKETT'S VINEYARD ™
Estate Blend 2004; Estate Blend 2005; Sevyal 2004; Sevyal 2005

BARON WINE CELLARS, LTD T/A TISHBI ESTATE WINERY ™◎
Jonathan Tishbi Special Reserve Series: **Chardonnay;** *The Vineyards:* **Dry French Colombard, Emerald Riesling, Sauvignon Blanc;** *Tishbi:* **Chenin Blanc, French Riesling, Muscat Alexandroni, Semi Dry French Colombard;** *Tishbi Estate:* **Chardonnay, Riesling Late Harvest, Sauvignon Blanc, White Riesling**

EMILIANA ORGANICO ◎✿
Adobe Casablanca Valley Sauvignon Blanc 2007; Novas Casablanca Valley Chardonnay 2005/2006; *Winemakers Selection:* Novas Casablanca Valley Chardonnay 2004/2006, Novas Casablanca Valley Marsanne 2004/2006, Novas Casablanca Valley Viognier 2004/2006

FETZER VINEYARDS ☺
All White Wines

HARBOURNE VINEYARD ☺◎✔
1995 Harbourne Medium Dry;1999 Harbourne Seyval Blanc;1999 Harbourne Ortega/Regner Dry; 2000 Harbourne Ortega/Muller Thurgau Unfiltered Dry; 2002 High Halden Estate Dry; 2003 Seyval Blanc; Harbourne High Halden Medium Dry

LIMNEY ☺◎✔ ✿
Horsmonden Dry 2006/2007

MAJESTIC WINE WAREHOUSE LTD
Argento Chardonnay 2006 Mendoza; Argento Pinot Grigio 2007 Mendoza; Bonterra Vineyards Chardonnay 2005 Mendocino; Chablis 2006 Domaine Servin; Cheverny Le Vieux Clos 2006 Emmanuelle Delaille; Chorey-Lès-Beaune Blanc 2004 Domaine Maillard

Père et Fils; Clos d'Yvigne Princesses de Clèves 2006 Bergerac Blanc Sec; Clos d'Yvigne Cuvée Nicolas 2006 Bergerac Sec; Corton-Charlemagne Grand Cru 2005 Domaine Chevalier Père et Fils; Coulée d'Argent Vouvray Sec 2006 Bourillon-Dorléans; Crios Torrontes 2007 Susana Balbo; Cuvée Elise Demi Sec 2006 Vin de Pays du Comté Tolosan; Domaine Begude Chardonnay 2006 Vin de Pays d'Oc; Domaine Caillaubert Sauvignon 2006 Vin de Pays des Côôtes de Gascogne; Drylands Sauvignon Blanc 2006 Marlborough; Finca Las Moras Viognier 2007 San Juan; Five Rivers Chardonnay 2005 Monterey County; Grechetto di Todi 2006 Franco Todini; Greco di Tufo 2006 Vesevo; Grüner Veltliner 2006 Weingut Pfarre Weissenkirchen; Kangarilla Road Viognier 2006 Mclaren Vale; King's River Chardonnay 2006 Robertson; King's River Pinot Grigio 2006 Robertson; King's River Viognier 2007 Robertson; Klein Constantia Chardonnay 2005 Constantia; La Nuit Blanche' Roussanne 2006 Domaine Sainte Rose; La Serrana Chardonnay 2006 Vino de la Tierra Castilla y León; 'Le Vent du Nord' Roussanne Chardonnay 2005 Domaine Sainte Rose, Vin de Pays d'Oc; Lirac Blanc 2006 Château d'Aquéria; Marc Ducournau Grand Heron 2006 Vin de Pays des Côtes de Gascogne; Meursault 2005 Domaine Vincent Bouzereau; Montagny 1er Cru 2004 Cave de Buxy; Montagny 1er Cru 2005 Domaine Vincent Bouzereau; Montes Limited Selection Sauvignon Blanc 2007 Leyda

Valley; Muscadet 2006/2007 Jacques Arnoult; Muscadet de Sèvre et Maine Sur Lie 2006 Domaine de la Tourmaline; Paulett's Riesling 2006 Polish Hill River, Clare Valley; Pinot Grigio 'Punggl' Single Vineyard 2006 Alto Adige, Nals & Margreid; Pinot Grigio Superiore 2007 Cantina Breganze; Pouilly-Fumé 'Les Ferrées' 2006 Marcel Sautejeau; Robert Mondavi Winery Fumé Blanc 2005 Napa Valley; Robertson Winery Chenin Blanc 2007; Sancerre Blanc 2005 Thauvenay Masson Blondelet; Sancerre Vielles Vignes 2005 Domaine Paul Cherrier et Fils; Saumur Blanc 2006 Réserve des Vignerons; Sauvignon de Touraine 2006 Domaine de La Prévôté; Sauvignon Les Fumées Blanches 2006 J&F Lurton, Vin de Pays d'Oc; St Clair Estate Selection Sauvignon Blanc 2007 Marlborough; St Clair Pioneer Block 6 Sauvignon Blanc 2006/2007 Marlborough; St-Véran 2006 Les Vignerons des Grandes Vignes; Vasse Felix 'Adams Road' Chardonnay 2006 Margaret River; Vergelegen Chardonnay 2006 Stellenbosch; Vergelegen Sauvignon Blanc 2007 Stellenbosch; Vignes de Nicole Chardonnay Viognier 2006 Vin de Pays d'Oc; Viognier Collection 2006 Gérard Bertrand, Vin de Pays d'Oc; Yering Frog Chardonnay 2006 Yarra Valley; Yering Station Chardonnay 2005 Yarra Valley; Zonda Chardonnay Chenin 2007 Mendoza; Zondernaam Sauvignon Blanc 2007 Stellenbosch

MEINKLANG
Burgenland White 2005/2006; Eiswein 2003; Gruner Veltliner 2006/2007

NO COWS ☺❶
Borghi Pinot Grigio; Camino Los Robles - Airen; Chianti Majnoni; Domain Majelus Chardonnay Rousane; Domaine Begude Sauvignon Blanc; Horsmonden 2006; M Chapoutier - Mirabel Viognier; Pech-Roc Sauvignon Blanc; Rolly Gassman - Reisling

PENNARD ORGANIC WINES & CIDER ⊘ ✿
Pennard Organic: Dry White English Table Wine

SANCHI ⊘
Sake

SANT'OR ™☺⊘
Dry White Wine

SEDLESCOMBE ORGANIC VINEYARD ™☺⊘ ✚ ✿
Bodiam Harvest English Wine; Dry White English Wine; Reserve English Wine

SMITHFIELD WINE ™
Casa Viva Sauvignon Blanc; Casas del Bosque Sauvignon Blanc; Domaine de la Garelle Chardonnay VDP de Vaucluse; McGuigan Black Label Chardonnay; Mynus & Blanco; Palandri Chardonnay; Palandri Riesling; Palandri Sauvignon Blanc; Palandri Solora Chardonnay; Poco

Mas Chardonnay; Poco Mas Sauvignon Blanc; Rincon Privada Torrontes; Rosario Chardonnay; Rosario Chardonnay Reserva; Rosario Sauvignon Blanc; Santa Luisa Chardonnay; Vistamar Chardonnay; Vistamar Sauvignon Blanc; *Australian Wines:* Jarrah Ridge Colombard Chardonnay, McGuigan Black Label Chardonnay, McGuigan Estates Bin 7000 Chardonnay; *Chilean Wines:* Los Robles Sauvignon Blanc; *Israeli Wines:* Carmel Vineyard Select Sauvignon Blanc, Dalton Canaan White, Dalton Fume Blanc, Dalton Safsufa Sauvignon Blanc, Tishbi Emerald Riesling, Tishbi Special Reserve Chardonnay; *New Zealand Wines:* Tohu Sauvignon blanc; *South African Wines:* Neil Joubert Chenin Blanc, Peaks View Chenin Blanc, Peaks View Sauvignon Blanc; *Spanish Wines:* Bodegas Irius Absum Varietales, Castillo Viejo Catamayor Chardonnay, Vallformosa Chardonnay

TRAIDCRAFT PLC ⊘
Chilean Chardonnay; South African Chenin Blanc; South African Sauvignon Blanc

VINCEREMOS ORGANIC WINES ™⊘ ✚ ✿
Aquis Celenis DO Rias Baixas: Albarino 2004; *Chatelaine Stephanie:* La Mancha Blanco, 10 litres bag in box; *Domaine de Clairac:* Joubio Blanc;

Domaine de la Parentiere: **French Organic White, Muscadet de Sevre et Maine sur lie;** *Eden Collection Wines (Spain):* **La Mancha Blanco;** *Jacques Frelin (France):* **Cuvee Olivier La Mancha Blanc (10L Box);** *Millton (New Zealand):* **Chardonnay Gisborne;** *Ventura:* **Chardonnay 2006, Sauvignon blanc 2006;** *Weingut Stefan Sander:* **Kerner Kabinett Lieblich, Riesling Kabinett Trocken, Riesling Spatlese Trocken;** *Wilkie Estate (Australia):* **Verdelho**

VINTAGE ROOTS ◎ ✿

Organic blanc; *Albet i noya:* DO Penedes cabernet suavignoncol.leccio 2000/01, DO Penedes can vendrell petit albet chardonnay/xarel.lo 2006/07, DO Penedes can vendrell petit albet tempranillo/garnacha 2006/07, DO Penedes lignum blanc 2006/07, DO Penedes lignum negre 2003/05, DO Penedes reserva marti1998, DO Penedes syrah col.leccio 2000, DO Penedes tempranillo classic 2006, DO Penedes xarel.lo classic 2006/07; *Andre:* AOC Chateauneuf-du-pape 2001/03; *Barra:* Pinot noir 2005/06; *Bettili:* IGT Veneto frizzante 2006/07, IGT Veneto pinot grigio 2006/07, IGT Veneto serenael vivace rosato 2006/07, Veneto Frizzante 2006/2007; *Bioghetto:* de l'Herault RN13 Vin de Pique-nique Blanc 2006; *Bonterra:* Chardonnay 2005/06; *Bossard:* AOC Muscadet de servre et maine sur lie, AOC Muscadet de sevre et maine, VDP Du jardin de la France cabernet franc 2005/06;

Boudonno: DOCG Chianti classico 2005/06, DOCG Chianti classico riserva 2003/06; *Bousquet:* Chardonnay 2006; *Brau:* d'Oc Blanc de Brau Chardonnay/Roussanne 2006/2007, d'Oc Chardonnay Finement Boise 2005/2006; *Brocard:* Chablis Jean-Marc Brocard 2005; *Cantine bricco:* IGT Sicilia inzolia bricco al sole 2006, IGT Sicilia nero d'avola bricco al sole 2005; *Casale mattia:* DOC Frascati superiore 2006/07; *Chapoutier:* VDP Des coteaux de l'ardeche domaine des granges de miriblat viognier 2006; *Clos du caveau:* AOC Vacqueras 2004; *Clos du joncuas:* AOC Gigondas 2000; *CLVD:* d'Oc WWF Element Terre Chardonnay 2006; *Cossentino:* IGT Sicilia gadi catarratto 2006, IGT Sicilia nero d'avola 2005; *Couronneau:* Bordeaux Superieur 2006; *Dauny:* AOC Sancerre 2006/07; *Fabril alto verde:* Buenas ondas chardonnay 2006/07, Buenas ondas malbec 2006/07, Buenas ondas syrah rose 2006/07, Semental gran reservado 2005; *Fasoli gino:* DOC Soave borgoletto 2006/07, DOC Soave pieve vecchia 2004/05, DOC Valpolicella 2006/07, DOC Valpolicella amarone alteo 2001/03, DOC Valpolicella amarone la corte del pozzo 2004, DOC Valpolicella classico la corte del pozzo 2005/06, DOCG Recioto di soave san zeno 2004/05, Grappa di chardonnay; *Ferraton:* AOC Hermitage blanc le miaux 2006, AOC Hermitage le miaux 2004; *Foraci:* IGT Sicilia sollatio rosso 2005/06; *Gaudry:* AOC Sancerre le tournebride 2006, AOC Sancerre melodie de vieilles vignes 2006; *Giol:* Prosecco Frizzante; *Goulley:* Chablis 2006/2007, Chablis Premier Cru Montmains 2002/2003, Petit Chablis 2005/2006; *Guillemot Michel:* Macon-Villages Quintaine 2005; *Guyot:* Puligny Montrachet 2004/2005; *Jasci:* DOC Montepulciano d'abruzzo barrique domino 2006, DOC Monttepulciano d'abruzzo 2006/07, DOC Trebbiano d'abruzzo 2006, IGT Atteso pecorino 2006; *Javillier:* Meursault Les Tillets 2005/2006, Meursault Poruzot Premier Cru 2005/2006; *Jeandeau:* Pouilly-Fuisse Les Progues 2004/2006; *Knobloch:* QMP Rheinhessen riesling 2006/07; *La fourmente:* AOC Cotes du rhone 2005/06; *Longchamp:* VDP des bouches du rhone 2004/06; *Maisons brulees:* AOC touraine sauvignon blanc 2006/07; *Mant'albano:* DOC Friuti grave pinot grigio 2006/07; *Moncaro:* d'Oc Verdicchio Dei Castelli Di Jesi 2006/07; *Mont'albano:* IGT Delle venezie pinot bianco/pinot grigio 2006/07; *OVA:* Five Plots Semillon; *Pajot:* Des Cotes de Gascogne 2006/2007; *Passavant:* AOC Anjou sec 2006; *Plouzeau:* AOC Chinon chateau de la bonneliere 2005, AOC Touraine sauvignon blanc chateau de la bonneliere 2006; *Pulmary:* Cuq 2004/06; *Richard:* Bergerac Sec 2006/2007, Bergerac Sec Les Charmes Semillon/Sauvignon Blanc 2006/2007, Saussignac Coup de Coeur 2004, Saussignac Cuvee Noble 2003; *Richmond plains:* Nelson sauvignon blanc 2006/07; *Robinvale:* Cabernet Sauvignon/Cabernet Franc/Merlot/Ruby Cabernet 2005/2006, Chardonnay/Chenin Blanc/Sauvignon Blanc 2006/2007; *Sedlescombe:* Dry White 2005/2006; *Sonop:* Organic terroir chardonnay 2007, Organic terroir shiraz 2007; *St Paul:* d'Oc Sauvignon Sur Lie 2006; *St ursula:* QBA St ursula ornament 2006; *Stellar:* Stellar sauvignon blanc 2007; *Stentz:* Alsace Gewurztraminer 2006, Alsace Gewurztraminer Grand Cru Steingruber 2004, Alsace Pinot Blanc 2005; *Tulbagh mountain:* Syrah/mourvedre 2003/04, Theta 2003; *Vida buena:* Vida buena red, Vida buena white; *Vintage Roots Own-label:* Organic Blanco; *Zuccardi:* Santa julia organia torrontas 2006/07, Santa julia organica bonarda/sangiovese 2006, Santa julia organica chenin blanc, Santa julia organica tempranillo 2006/07

VIVA! ☺❶⊘♂
All

NOTES

■ **Beers:** As a general rule traditional, cask-conditioned beers ('real ales') are usually clarified (cleared) with isinglass finings (see GLOSSARY OF ANIMAL SUBSTANCES page 45). The addition of the finings speeds up a process that would otherwise occur naturally. Keg, canned, beers and some bottled beers are usually filtered without the use of animal substances. Lagers are generally chill-filtered but some may involve the use of isinglass. Keg beers may contain the foam-control agent Glyceryl Monostearate (E471), which can be animal-derived; alternatives are available and are widely used.

■ **Fruits** used for producing fruit juices are not normally coated with shellac. However some fruits coated with shellac and originally destined for sale as whole fruit may be used to produce juices (see FOOD NOTES, page 152).

■ **Soft drinks and alcopops** may contain animal-derived colorants such as cochineal / carmine (see GLOSSARY OF ANIMAL SUBSTANCES page 45). Orange coloured drinks may contain beta-carotene held in a gelatine suspension. For example some Coca-Cola products use gelatine as a stabiliser for beta-carotene: these include Fanta Orange, Fanta Zero Orange, Lilt, Lilt Zero, Five Alive Citrus Burst and Tropical Hit squash and some

of the Kia-Ora, Minute Maid and Schweppes drinks. An up to date list can be found at *www.coca-cola.co.uk/faq* or telephone 0800 22 77 11. Also see FOOD NOTES, page 152.

■ **The production of spirits** does not usually involve the use of animal substances. However some red drinks may contain cochineal / carmine as a colouring agent.

■ **Wines** (including fortified wines such as sherry and port), may be fined using one of the following: blood, bone marrow, chitin, egg albumen, fish oil, gelatine, isinglass, milk or milk casein (see GLOSSARY OF ANIMAL SUBSTANCES page 45). Non-animal alternatives include limestone, bentonite, kaolin and kieselguhr (clays), plant casein, silica gel and vegetable plaques.

The Co-op labels those wines that are suitable for vegans and declares all processing aids used in their manufacture. Several major off-licences now have vegan lists available so do ask.

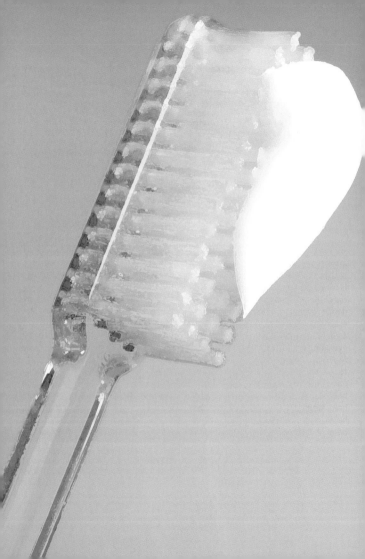

TOILETRIES & COSMETICS

AFTERSHAVE

ANIMAL AID SOCIETY™☺❶◎ ✔ ✄~1976
Aftershave Lotion

ANNEMARIE BORLIND ✔
Natural Care - For Men: Aftershave
Balm, Aftershave Gel

BEAUTY NATURALS ✔
David Hill for Men: Skin Calming
Aftershave Balm, Skin Refreshing
Aftershave Gel

BURT'S BEES ◎ ✔ 👁
Bay Rum: Aftershave Balm

DOLMA ™☺❶◎ ✔ 👁✄~1976
Especially For Men: **'Imagine'**
Aftershave/Cologne, 'Kwame'
Aftershave/Cologne, 'Sirius'
Aftershave/Cologne, De-luxe
Aftershave Balm

ESSENTIALLY NATURAL ™
Sandalwood Aftershave (Organic)

FLORIS ☺ ✔
Aftershave Balm: Elite, JF, No 89, Santal;
Aftershave Splash: Elite, JF, No 89

LAVERANA ™ ✔
Men SPA: **Aftershave Balm,**
Aftershave Balm - Aqua Fresh,
Aftershave Balm - Cool Lime,
Aftershave Balm - Relaxing Santal,
Aftershave Lotion

QUINESSENCE AROMATHERAPY
☺◎ ✔ 👁
Aftershave Balm

SOLARAY NUTRITIONAL
SUPPLEMENTS
Northwoods Aftershave

VERDESATIVA S.R.L. ™☺
Anti Age Face Cream and
Aftershave; Anti-Age Face Cream &
Aftershave; Dopobarba Canapa
(Aftershave Hemp); Dopobarba
Canapa e Menta (Aftershave Hemp
and Mint)

BATH & SHOWER

ABSOLUTE AROMAS ™◎ ✔
Ord River: **Bath & Shower Gel 250ml**

AHIMSA COSMETICS ™☺
Bath Soak; Face and Body Wash

AKAMUTI
Himalayan Salts; *Bath Salts:* Fragrant
Tranquility, Tropical Zest

ALTERNATIVE STORES ™☺❶
All products are vegan

ALVIN CONNOR LIMITED ™☺◎
Natural Balance: **Natural Bath Soak,**
Unscented Bath Soak

AMAZENE ™
Phytophilo Aromatherapy Range- Bath
and shower gels: **Cocoa & Cupuacu,**

Green Tea, Aloe Vera & Anise, Lavender, Calendula & Primrose, Papaya, Passion Fruit & Acerola, Strawberry n Cream; *Phytophilo Aromatherapy Range- Bath Salts:* **Cocoa & Cupuacu, Green Tea, Aloe Vera & Anise, Lavender, Calendula & Primrose, Papaya, Passion Fruit & Acerola, Strawberry n Cream;** *Phytophilo Aromatherapy Range- Fizz Balls:* **Cocoa & Cupuacu, Green Tea, Aloe Vera & Anise, Lavender & Calendula, Papaya, Passion Fruit & Acerola, Strawberry n Cream;** *Phytophilo Aromatherapy Range- Gift Sets- 2 piece:* **Cocoa & Cupuacu, Green Tea, Aloe Vera & Anise, Strawberry n Cream;** *Phytophilo Aromatherapy Range- Gift Sets- 4 piece:* **Cocoa & Cupuacu, Green Tea, Aloe Vera & Anise;** *Phytophilo Aromatherapy Range- Gift Sets-2 piece:* **Lavender, Calendula & Primrose, Papaya, Passion Fruit & Acerola;** *Phytophilo Aromatherapy Range- Gift Sets-4 piece:* **Lavender, Calendula & Primrose, Papaya, Passion Fruit & Acerola, Strawberry n Cream**

ANIMAL AID SOCIETY™☺◇❶◇ ✦–1976
Violet & Almond Foaming Bath Oil; *Body Wash:* **Amber Body Wash, Woodspice Body Wash;** *Foam Bath:* **Calendula & Vanilla, Vanilla & Passion Flower Foam Bath;** *Shower Gel:* **English Rose, Tropical**

ANNEMARIE BORLIND ✦
Bodyvital Body Crèème Scrub; *Anne Lind:* Cranberry Body Scrub, Shower Gels (All); *Body Lind:* Shower Gel; *Body*

Lind Sportiv: Shower Gel; *Natural Care - For Men:* Revitalizing Shower Gel

AROMA COMFORTS ™☺◇
Anti Stress Body&Bath Oil

BAREFOOT BOTANICALS ◇ ✦
SOS: Bodyguard Soothing Body Wash, Lifesaver Moisturising Bath Oil

BEAMING BABY ™
Organic Lavender Shampoo and Body Wash

BEAUTY NATURALS ✦
Gently Exfoliating Seaweed Body Scrub; *Bath Oil:* Citrus Refreshing, Lavender Relaxing, Rose Geranium Harmonising, Seaweed Therapeutic; *Body Wash:* Citrus Refreshing, Lavender Relaxing, Rose Geranium Harmonising, Seaweed Therapeutic; *Martha Hill:* Citrus Refreshing Body Wash, Lavender Relaxing Bath Oil, Lavender Relaxing Body Wash, Rose Geranium Harmonising Body Wash

BRONNLEY & CO LTD ✦
Bath & Shower Gel: Africa, Asia, Caribbean, Europe, India, Mediterranean; *Bath Foam:* Apricot & Almond, English Fern, Lavender, Orchid, Pink Bouquet, White Iris; *Bath Gel:* Bird of Paradise, Tulip; *Bath Relaxant:* Passion Flower, Rose; *Bath Soak:* Gardener's; *Body Care for Men:* Bath Relaxant, Hair & Body Wash; *Body Scrub:* Bird of Paradise, Tulip; *Royal Horticultural Society - Bath Relaxant:* Passion Flower, Rose; *Royal*

Horticultural Society - Bath Seeds:
Passion Flower, Rose; *Royal Horticultural
Society - Bath Soak:* Gardener's; *Royal
Horticultural Society - Shower Gel:*
Gardener's, Passion Flower, Rose;
Shower Gel: Apricot & Almond, English
Fern, Lavender, Orchid, Pink Bouquet,
White Iris

BURT'S BEES ⊘ 🦊 👁
All-In-One Wash; Therapeutic Bath
Crystals; *Face & Body:* Vitamin E Body
& Bath Oil

CAURNIE SOAPERIE ☺⊘ 🦊 ⅓ 1976
Marigold & Orange Shower Gel

CAWARRA COSMETICS LTD ™
OrganicSpa: **Body Salt Scrub**

CEBRA ETHICAL CHIC ™⊘ 🦊
Cebra- ethical skin care: **Calm Me
Down Body Wash, Make Me Smile
Body & Hair Wash, Total Detox Bath
Salt, Wake Me Up Body Wash**

DANIEL FIELD LABORATORY LTD ™☺
*FFP Research Limited- Free From
Sensitive Skin Body Care:* **Body Wash**

DESERT ESSENCE ⊘ 🦊 ⅓ 1985
Organics Body Wash: Green Apple &
Ginger, Italian Red Grape, Red Raspberry

**DM-DROGERIE MARKT
GMBH & CO KG** ™
dm alverde: **Meeres-Badesalz Limone
Mandarin, Meeres-Badesalz
Orchidee, Pflegedusche Grapefruit**
**Bambus, Pflegedusche Olive Aloe-
Vera**

DOLMA ™☺❶⊘ 🦊 👁⅓ 1976
Aromatic Body Shampoos: **Antiseptic,
Deep Relaxing, Invigorating,
Relaxing, Relaxing & Refreshing**

DR HAUSCHKA ⊘ 🦊
Bath: Lavender, Lemon, Rose,
Rosemary, Sage, Spruce

ESSENTIAL CARE
Bath Products: Aloe Vera Bodywash,
Lavender Hand & Bodywash,
Lemongrass Hand & Bodywash, Ylang
Ylang & Orange Bodywash

ESSENTIALLY YOURS LTD ™☺⊘ 🦊 👁
**De-Stress Shower Gel; Hypnotic
Shower Gel; Morning Shower Gel;
Sports Shower Gel; Wellbeing
Shower Gel;** *Fragrance Free Range:*
Shampoo&body wash; *LYB Range:*
**Bath Oil, Eucalyptus shower gel,
Grapefruit shower gel, Patchouli
shower gel, Rose bath foam;** *Natural
Elements:* **Anti-Fatigue Shower Gel,
Anti-Stress Shower Gel;** *Therapeutics
Range:* **Bath Oil, Body Wash, E Bath
Oil**

FAITH PRODUCTS LIMITED
™ 🦊 👁⅓ 1988
**Aloe Vera Shower Gel / Foam Bath
400ml / 5 Ltr; Chocolate Shower Gel
/ Foam Bath 400ml / 5 Ltr; Hemp
and Meadowfoam Shower Gel /
Foam Bath 400ml / 5 Ltr; Lavender**

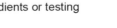

and Geranium Shower Gel / Foam Bath 400ml / 5 Ltr; Mum's relaxing bath oil; Purifying Face and Body Scrub 150ml; Seaweed Shower Gel / Foam Bath 400ml / 5 Ltr; Tea Tree Shower Gel / Foam Bath 400ml / 5 Ltr

FIGS & ROUGE ™☺
Bath Soak; Bath Soak- Palmarosa; Bath Soak- Petitgrain; Shower Gel

FLORAROMA LTD ™
Little Me- Mummylicious: **Mum To Be Luxury Bath Soak**

FLORIS ☺ ⓘ
Concentrated Bath Essence: Edwardian Bouquet, Florissa, Lily of the Valley, Rose Geranium, Seringa, Stephanotis; *Foaming Bath & Shower Gel:* Elite, JF, Santal; *Moisturising Bath & Shower Gel:* Cefiro, China Rose, Edwardian Bouquet, Fleur, Florissa, Lily of the Valley, Night Scented Jasmine, No 89, Rose Geranium, Seringa Moisturising, Stephanotis, White Rose; *Natural Benefits:* Energising Body Wash, Invigorating Body Polish

FOREVER LIVING PRODUCTS
Aloe Bath Gelee

FREERANGERS ™☺ ⓘ
Arnica Bath Soak; Power Shower Gel; Stress-Less Bath Soak; *Pamper Products:* **Bath Melts**

FUNK BUBBLE ™☺
Bath&Body Melts: **Blueberry, Cherry,**

Chocolate/orange, Coconut, Rose; *Bubble Bath:* **Lavender/Geranium, Tea Tree;** *Fizzers and Bath Bombs:* **Lavender, Orange/Grapefruit, Rose, Strawberry, Vanilla Bath Bomb, Vanilla Fizzer;** *Organic Bubble Bath:* **Aloe Vera, Chocolate;** *Organic Shower Wash:* **Aloe Vera, Chocolate;** *Shower Wash:* **Lavender/Geranium, Tea Tree**

GEO ORGANICS ⊘
Atlantic Bath Salt with Aloe Vera 250g

GREEN PEOPLE CO. ™⊘ ⓘ
Nourishing Spa Shower Wash; *Hair & Body Care:* **Aloe Vera Shower Gel, Moisturising Shower Bath, Rosemary & Pink Clay Shower Gel, Vita Min Fix Shower Wash;** *Men's Range:* **Cool Style Hair & Body Wash;** *Organic Base:* **Shower Bath;** *Sugar Scrub:* **Sensuous Sugar Scrub**

GREEN VALLEY TRADING CO. ™☺
All products are vegan

GREEN WYCH ™☺❶
Natural Bath Salts: **Bergamot, Geranium, Lavender, Orange**

HEALTHQUEST LIMITED ™⊘ ⓘ
Organic Blue- Body Care: **Shower Gel;** *Organic Blues - Mens:* **Bath Soak, Hair & Body Wash, Shower Scrub;** *Pure Adore:* **Chamomile Bubblebath, Lavender Bubblebath, Mandarin Bubblebath**

TOILETRIES & COSMETICS

HEDGECRAFT ™☺⃠
Bath Bomb Range: **Groovy Grapefruit, Muscle Ease, Orange and Patchouli, Simply Lavender, Simply Rose, White Chocolate, Ylang Ylang and Orange**

HEMP GARDEN ™
Hand & Body Wash; *Bath Oil:* **Sensual, Soothing, Stimulating**

HERBS HANDS HEALING LTD ™⃠ ⌕
Organic Bitter Orange Body Oil; Organic Lavender and Mint Bodywash

HIGHER NATURE PLC ™⃠ ⌕
Alka-Bathe (Powder); Special Sea Soak

HOLISTIX ™❶
Bath Salts - 580g Kilner Jar: **All**

HONESTY COSMETICS LTD
™☺❶⃠ ⌕ ☜⌖-1976
Foam Bath: **Orange Geranium & Lavender;** *Honesty Essential Range:* **Mandarine, Ginger & Ylang Ylang Shower Gel, Orange, Geranium & Lavender Foam Bath, Rose Shower & Bath Gel;** *Honesty Fruit Range:* **Apple & Mint Shower & Bath Gel, Green Tea & Citrus Shower & Bath Gel, Strawberry & Papaya Shower & Bath Gel;** *Shower Gel:* **Apple & Mint, Mandarine Ginger & Ylang Ylang, Strawberry & Papaya**

I AM NATURAL ™
Organic Lavender & Chamomile Shower Gel; *Shower Gel:* **Organic Mint & Rosemary, Organic Tea Tree with Coriander & Ginger**

ID AROMATICS
Bubble Bath Base (Essential Oils Can Be Added); *Bubble Bath and Shower Gel:* Refreshing - Geranium & Lime, Relaxing - Lavender & Marjoram; *Mind, Body and Spirit Range:* Soothing

INNGINNI LIMITED (OHSOBO) ™☺
Ohsobo: **Shower Gel - Citrus Medley, Shower Gel - Orange Tree, Shower Gel - Rose & Lavender Burst, Shower Gel - Skin Bliss, Shower Gel - Tropical Sunset**

ITS ELIXIR UK LIMITED ™⃠ ⌕ ☜
Body scrubbing gel

JASON NATURAL PRODUCTS ⌕ ☜
Satin Shower Body Wash: Aloe Vera, Apricot, Chamomile, Citrus, Herbal Extracts, Lavender, Mango, Rosewater, Tea Tree

JR LIGGETT ☺ ⌕ ☜
Body Scrub: Lemon & Lime, Unscented, Western Slope, White Sage

KOBASHI ™☺⃠ ⌕ ☜⌖-1976
Bath: **Fragrance Free Bath Base, Refreshing Fruit Bath, Relaxing Bath, Wild Flower Shower Gel**

B *Never Too Busy to be Beautiful*
is the only UK company to carry an entire colour cosmetics line that has been especially made for Vegans. Founded by Vegan and Vegetarian partners, our products have been lovingly created using the finest of essential oils and wonderfully vivacious colours. Being compassionate has never been so glamorous!

If that isn't irresistable enough, B Never Too Busy to be Beautiful is also proud to say all its sparkly packaging is fairly traded by local artisans in India and Morocco through a number of grass roots projects helping displaced people.

Pop into one of our vibrant boutiques to experiment with our kaleidoscope of colours and nine beautiful fragrance ranges. Our team of expert staff are always on hand to advise and create the perfect look for you.

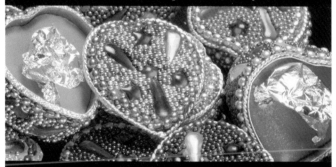

B *Never Too Busy to be Beautiful*
New stores opening all the time - phone **01202 493789** for shop addresses or visit us at
www.bnevertoobusytobebeautiful.com

LAVERANA ™ 🌿

Lavera Body Spa: **Shower & Bath Gel (Almond/Vanilla), Shower & Bath Gel (Avocado/Ginger), Shower & Bath Gel (Bamboo/Green Tea), Shower & Bath Gel (Blood Orange/Lemongrass), Shower & Bath Gel (Citrus), Shower & Bath Gel (Grapefruit/Mint), Shower & Bath Gel (Lavender/AloeVera), Shower & Bath Gel (Lemon/Cypress), Shower & Bath Gel (Olive/Fig), Shower & Bath Gel (Orange/Sea Buckthorn), Shower & Bath Gel (Peach/Apricot), Shower & Bath Gel (Sandalwood/Jojoba), Shower & Bath Gel (Tiare/Lilly), Shower & Bath Gel (Vanilla/Coconut), Shower & Bath Gel (Velvet and Silk), Shower & Bath Gel (Vervain/Lemon), Shower & Bath Gel (Wild Rose), Shower & Bath Gel (WildBerry), Shower & Bath Gel Christmas Chocolate, Shower & Bath Gel Spiced Apple;** *Lavera Body Spa Bath Oil:* **Eucalyptus-Rosemary, Lavender-Aloe Vera, Orange-Sea Buckthorn, Vanilla-Coconut, Vervain-Lime, Wild Rose;** *Lavera Body Spa Sea Bath Salts:* **Lavender-Aloe Vera, Orange-Sea Buckthorn, Vanilla-Coconut, Vervain-Lime, Wild Rose;** *LaveraBody Spa:* **Shower & Bath Gel (Violet/Rose);** *Lavere:* **Body-Effect Active Shower;** *Men SPA:* **Shower Shampoo, Shower Shampoo - Aqua Fresh, Shower Shampoo - Cool Lime, Shower Shampoo - Relaxing Santal**

LIZ EARLE 🌿 👁

Bath Sponge; Deep Cleansing Mask Sponges; Orange Flower Botanical Body Wash; Vital Oils for the Bath

LONGCROFT SOAP COMPANY ™

Bounce Around Salt Scrub; Sugar Rush Sugar Scrub; Wee Choccy Poke Soak; Wee Poke Bath Soak

LOVE THE PLANET ™ ⊘

Grapefruit Sugar Scrub; Lime Sugar Scrub; Mandarin Body Wash; Mandarin Sugar Scrub; Peppermint Sugar Scrub; Tea Tree Body Wash

LUSH ™ 🌿

Flosty Gritter; Green Day; Guantanamo Garden; Happy Bubble Bar; Ne Worry Pas Bath Ballistic; Pop In The Bath Bubble Bars; Rub Rub Rub Shower Gel; Sunnyside; The Comforter; *Bath Ballistics:* **Absolute Delight, Avobath, Big Blue, Blackberry Bath Bomb, Bon Bain Bonnard, Bon Bomb, Butterball, Butterfly Ball, Champagne Supernova, English Countryside, Fairy Jasmine, Fizz-O Therapy, Fox in the Flowers, Geo Phyzz, Gingerman, Haagenbath, Hot Java, Ickle Baby Angel, Ickle Baby Baff, Ickle Baby Devil, Kiss Me Klimt, Luverly, Rainbow Worrier, Sakura, Sex Bomb, Sicilian, Softy, The Happy Pill, Tisty Tosty, Uluru, Vanilla Fountain, Waving Not Drowning, White Wedding, World Piece, Youki-Hi;** *Bubble Bar Slices:* **A French Kiss,**

Amandapondo, Auntie Pamela, Aura Suavis, Bathos, Blue Skies and Fluffy White Clouds, Elixir, Hot Milk?, Ice Hotel, It's a Date, Ma Bar, Marzibain, Melomint, Playdoze, Pleasure Dough, Psychodelic, The Phoenix, The Wuss; *Emotibombs:* **Sex in the Shower, Up the Wooden Hill, Up You Gets;** *Karma Products:* **Karma Bubble Bar;** *Luxury Bath Melts:* **Ceridwen's Cauldron, Dreamtime, Floating Island, Melting Marshmallow Moment, You've Been Mangoed Bath Melt;** *Shower:* **13 Rabbits, Chai, Freeze, Narcotick;** *Shower Gels:* **Happy Hippy, Sonic Death Monkey, The Olive Branch, Tramp;** *Shower Jellies:* **Deep Sleep, Party On, Sweetie Pie, The Big Calm, The Joy Of Jelly;** *Smoothie Shower Soaps:* **Creamed Almond and Coconut Smoothie, Dreamwash**

MAJIK BLANKIT SKIN CARE ™☺✓
Comfrey Root Shower Jelly

MANDALA AROMA LTD ™☺⊘
Body Wash: **Courage, Love, Skin Soothing;** *Organic Bath Oils:* **Courage Stress Relief, Love Nurturing & Balancing, Skin Soothing, Strength Muscle Relief, Wisdom Relaxing**

MONTAGNE JEUNESSE ⊘✓
Eucalyptus & Camphor Anti Cold Bath; *Bath:* Dead Sea Aches-Away

NATURA ORGANICS ⊘✓✿
Shower Gel: Nourishing with Aloe Vera, Vitamin E and Soft Almond Oil, Revitalising with Vitamin E, Lemon and Mandarin, Soothing with Vitamin E, Lemon and Rosemary

NATURAL SENSE ™
Himalayan Bath Salts; Luxury Bath Oil

NATURE'S GATE
Organics - Advanced Care: Natural Results Acne Body Wash; *Organics - Fruit Blend Body Washes:* Grapefruit & Wild Ginger, Mandarin Orange & Patchouli, Persimmon & Rose Geranium; *Organics - Fruit Blend Liquid Soaps:* Asian Pear & Red Tea; *Organics - Herbal Blend Body Washes:* Chamomile & Lemon Verbena, Cucumber & Mint, Lavender & Aloe, Lemongrass & Clary Sage

NEAL'S YARD REMEDIES
⊘✓👁⚘1998
Aromatic Foaming Bath; *Bath & Shower Gel:* Baseline; *Bath Oil:* Baseline, Exotic, Geranium & Orange, Silver Birch, Soothing; *Bath Salts:* Lavender; *Foaming Bath:* English Lavender; *Shower Gel:* Lavender & Tea Tree

NEVER TOO BUSY TO BE BEAUTIFUL ™✓
2 Hearts Beating As One: **Bath Powder;** *B Scent:* **Ballistic;** *Botanomancy:* **Serendipity Phytofoam, Smaragadine Phytofoam;** *Breath of God:* **Bath Oil;** *Keep It Fluffy:* **Bath Powder;** *Ladyboy:* **Lemon Melt Shower Jelly;** *Love:* **Apple Bubble Bar**

NEW SEASONS ⊘ 🖑
Hair & Body Wash; *Neutral & Toiletry Bases:* Foam Bath Base, Shower Gel Base

NO COWS ☺❶
No Cows Exotic Shower Gel; No Cows Fruity Shower Gel; No Cows Shower Gel for Men

NOTHING NASTY 🖑
Bath Salts: Lavender & Calendula, Rose & Calendula

OPTIMAH HEALTH & NUTRITION ⊘ 🖑 ⅍ 1995
Raw Aloe: Shower Gel with Tea Tree & Citrus Oils

POTIONS AND POSSIBILITIES ⊘ 🖑
Bath & Shower Gels: ...And To Sleep, Anti-fatigue, Detox, Divinity, English Garden, English Lavender, English Rose, Relax & Unwind, Serenity Perfume, Sleepy Prince, Sleepy Princess, Traditional Lavender; *Bath Sizzlers & Bath Salts:* Bath Salt Pouch Lavender, Bath Salt Pouch Rose, Bath Salts Cook, Bath Salts Gardener, Bath Salts Golfer, Champagne Message Bombs, English Garden Bath Salts Pouch, English Lavender Bath Salts Pouch, English Rose Bath Salts Pouch, Heart Shaped Sizzler In Net, Luxury Bath Sizzler Cracker (Energizing), Luxury Bath Sizzler Cracker (Relaxing), Therapeutic Bath Salts, Therapeutic Bath Salts Joint & Muscle,

Therapeutic Bath Salts Stress Ease,
Tudor Sleep Parcels; *Clinical Bath Oils:*
All; *Luxury Bath Oils:* All

PURATY LTD ☺ 🐇
Balancing Shower Wash; Refreshing
Shower Wash

PURE GAISHA ™☺❶ 🐇
**Fragrant Shower Gel; Kindred Spirit
Bath Soak; Tranquility Bath Soak;
Vegan Bath Milk - Exotic Gaisha**

PZ CUSSONS UK LTD ™⊘ 🐇
Original Source Bath: **White Tea &
Grapefruit Bath Tea;** *Original Source
Bath Foam:* **Tea Tree & Lavender;**
Original Source Body Scrub: **Detoxifying,
Moisturising;** *Original Source Body
Wash:* **Eucalyptus & Lime oil Body
Wash, Orange Oil Ginger Body
Wash, Sea Kelp & Rock Salt Body
Wash;** *Original Source Deep Soak
Foam Bath:* **Almond and Coconut;**
Original Source Shower: **Almond and
Coconut, Cocoa & Vanilla Shower
Gel, Dragon Fruit and Capsicum
Shower Gel, Lime, Mango &
Macadamia Shower Smoothie,
Organic Black Pepper & Cardamom,
Organic Goji Berry & Mallow
Shower Gel, Organic Grapefruit &
Gingerlily Shower Gel, Pomegranate
& Fig Shower Juice, Tea Tree &
Lavender, Tea Tree & Lemon, Tea
Tree & Mint, Watermint &
Lemongrass Shower Sorbet**

QUINESSENCE AROMATHERAPY
☺⊘ 🐇 👁
Bath Base; Muscle Ease Bath Soak;
Relaxing Bath Soak; Sensual Bath Soak;
Shower Gel Base

REN ⊘
High Altitude Lavender Body Wash;
Moroccan Rose Otto Bath Oil; Moroccan
Rose Otto Body Wash; Multi Vitamin
Apricot Shower Wash; Neroli and
Grapefruit Body Wash; Rhassoul and
Moroccan Rose Thalassotherapy Bath
Soak; Seaweed and Sage Body Wash

SAAF INTERNATIONAL LIMITED ™
Pure Shower Gel

SANMAR GMBH ™
Body and Hair Shampoo

SHANTI PRODUCTS ⊘ 🐇
Bath Bombs: Bath Truffles, Mini Fizzers,
Relaxing, Uplifting

SHELLBELLES ☺❶
Bath Bombs: Aniseed, Choc Vanilla,
Lavender and Neroli, Lemongrass and
Jasmine, Orange and Lemon, Rose;
Bath Fizz: Aniseed, Lavender and Neroli;
Bath Melts: Lavender and Neroli, Lime
and Ylang Ylang, Rose Geranium

SIMPLE 🐇
Moisturise Bath Cream; Refreshing
Shower Gel; Relax Bath Soak; Soothe
Bath Milk; Soothe Shower Cream; *Body
Polish:* Energise; *Body Wash:* Exfoliate,
Moisturise, Nourishing, Relax

SIMPLY SOAPS ™❶⊘ ✦ ☞ ⚶2003
Bath Salts: **Citrus, Love, Relax, Woodland Calm;** *Hedgerow Herbals:* **Aaag Bath Bag, Grrr Bath Bag, Mmm Bath Bag, Oooo Bath Bag, Oww Bath Bag, Scrumptious Bath Bar Treats, Zzzzz Bath Bag;** *Hedgerow Herbals- Queen of Sheba:* **Bath Herb Tea Bags;** *Salt Scrub:* **Aphrodisia, Exfoliating, Invigorating, Stimulating**

SKIN BLOSSOM LIMITED ™⊘
Body Wash

SOLARAY NUTRITIONAL SUPPLEMENTS
Rosa Mosquesta Bath & Shower Gel

STELLA MCCARTNEY
Stella: Soft Bath Oil; *Stella in Two:* Exfoliating Shower Gel

TAOASIS GMBH AROMA-KOSMETIK & VERLAG ™
Zaubernuss Duschgel; Zitrusgarten Duschgel

THE HIGHLAND SOAP COMPANY ™⊘
Bath Bombes: **Citrus Delight, Highland Lavender, Mango Butter, Rose&Patchouli, Rose&Ylang Ylang, Scottish Heather, White Jasmine;** *Bath Salts:* **Highland Lavender, Rose&Patchouli, Rose&Ylang Ylang, Scottish Heather, White Jasmine;** *Body Wash:* **Ginger&Lemongrass, Rosemary& Wild Nettle, Wild Nettle&Heather;** *Bubble Bath:*

Highland Lavender, Mango Butter, Rose&Patchouli, Rose&Ylang Ylang, Scottish Heather, White Jasmine; *Dead Sea Salt Scrubs:* **Ginger&Lemongrass, Rosemary&Wild Nettle, Ylang & Ylang Patchouli**

THE NATURAL SPA COMPANY LIMITED ™☺
All products are vegan

TISSERAND AROMATHERAPY PRODUCTS ™☺
Bath and shower oil collection: **Rebalance, Relax, Revive;** *Bath Care:* **Awaken Shower Gel, Indulge Bath Soak, Rejuvenate Shower Gel, Relax Bath Soak;** *Lavender Products:* **Lavender Bath Soak, Lavender cream body wash;** *Wash, bath and shower:* **Essential oil Rich Awaken Shower and Bath Gel, Essential oil Rich Indulge Bath Soak, Essential oil Rich Rejuvenate Shower and Bath Gel, Essential oil Rich Relax Bath Soak, Tea tree and Grapefruit skin wash, Tea tree and Lime cream body wash**

TRUTHFUL CO. LTD (PURELY SKINCARE) ™☺⊘
Purely Skincare: **Shower/bath wash-female variant, Shower/bath wash-male variant, Shower/bath wash-refreshing variant, Shower/bath wash- sensitive variant**

URTEKRAM ⊘ ✔ ☜ ⚹ 1998
Shower Gel: All

VERDESATIVA S.R.L. ™☺
Bagno Doccia Canapa e Agrumi (Bath and Shower Gel Hemp and Citrus Fruit); Bagno Doccia Canapa e Lavanda (Bath and Shower Gel Hemp and Lavender); Bagno Doccia Canapa, Vetiver e Arancia (Bath and Shower Gel Hemp, Vetiver and Orange); Shampoo Doccia Canapa e Ylang Ylang (Shampoo and Bath/Shower Gel Hemp and Ylang Ylang); Shampoo Doccia Frutti e Fiori (Shampoo & Bath/Shower Gel Hemp Fruits and Flowers)

VISIONARY SOAP COMPANY ™☺
Bath Melts: **Eucalyptus Lime, Geranium Rose, Lavender, Lemongrass, Patchouli and Ylang Ylang, Peppermint Orange**

WELEDA ⊘ ✔ ⚹ 1985
Chestnut Toning Bath Soak; Citrus Creamy Body Wash; Citrus Refreshing Bath Milk; Lavender Relaxing Bath Milk; Pine Reviving Bath Milk; Rosemary Invigorating Bath Milk; Sea Buckthorn Creamy Body Wash; Wild Rose Creamy Body Wash

BRUSHES ETC

ABSOLUTELY PURE ⊘
Vegan Kabuki Brushes

BEAUTY NATURALS ✔
Complexion Massage Brush; *Cosmetic Brushes:* All

ESSENTIALLY NATURAL ™
Cotton Exfoliating Face Cloths

ESSENTIALLY YOURS LTD ™☺⊘ ✔ ☜
Wish Range: **Shampoo**

HOLISTIX ™❶
Body Brush / Massager; Facial Loofah; Pumice; Terry / Loofah Palm Pad; Wooden Massager

INIKA ™ ✔
Eyeshadow Brush; Kabuki Brush

LIZ EARLE ✔ ☜
Body Exfoliating Gloves; Natural Bristle Body Brush

NEAL'S YARD REMEDIES
⊘ ✔ ☜ ⚹ 1998
Ayate Cloth; Back Brush; Massage Mitt; Nail Brush

QUALITY SEA VEG ☺
Sea Bath and Skin pads

THE ESSENTIAL OIL COMPANY ⊘ ✔ ☜
Natural Sisal Body Brush

CONDITIONERS & HAIR CARE

ABSOLUTE AROMAS TM ⊘ ✐
Ord River: **Conditioner 250ml**

AHIMSA COSMETICS TM☺
Hair Conditioner

AKAMUTI
Hair Care Products: All

ALOE PURA ✐
Organic Aloe Vera Herbal Shampoo
Dry/Damaged Hair

ALTERNATIVE STORES TM☺❶
All products are vegan

ANIMAL AID SOCIETY TM☺❶⊘ ✐ ⅍1976
Coconut Conditioner

ANNEMARIE BORLIND ✐
Ceramide Cream Rinse; Vital Hair Care
Fluid

BAREFOOT BOTANICALS ⊘ ✐
SOS: Intensive Care Dry Scalp
Conditioner

BEAUTY NATURALS ✐
Conditioner: Deep Moisturising; *Martha
Hill:* Conditioning Hair Gel; *Martha Hill
Purely Natural Haircare Conditioner:*
Mild & Gentle, Moisturising,
Reconstructive, Treatment

CAWARRA COSMETICS LTD TM
OrganicSpa: **Conditioner For Dry Hair,
Conditioner For Normal Hair,
Conditioner For Treated Hair;**
Sanctum: **Conditioner - Dry,
Conditioner - Normal**

CEBRA ETHICAL CHIC TM⊘ ✐
Cebra- ethical skin care: **Make Me
Shine Conditioner**

DANIEL FIELD LABORATORY LTD TM☺
*FFP Research Limited- Free From
Sensitive Skin Hair Care:*
**Smooth&shine conditioner,
Volumising conditioner spray**

DESERT ESSENCE ⊘ ✐ ⅍1985
Organics: Green Apple & Ginger, Italian
Red Grape, Lemon Tea Tree, Red
Raspberry

**DM-DROGERIE MARKT
GMBH & CO KG** TM
dm alverde: **Pflegespüülung Aloe /
Hibiskus**

DOLMA TM☺❶⊘ ✐ ⅍1976
Hair Preparations: **Cedarwood &
Cypress Hair Conditioner, Lavender
& Jojoba Hair Conditioner, Rosemary
Nettle & Marigold Hair Lotion**

DOME ☺
Extensions: Monofibre Hair Extensions:
Free from glues, chemicals and acetones,
Prolin Hair Enhancers

DR HAUSCHKA ⊘ ⓘ
Neem Hair Lotion; Neem Hair Oil

ESSENTIAL CARE
Skincare: Hair Lice Therapy Oil

ESSENTIALLY YOURS LTD ™⊘☺ ⓘ ◉
Fragrance Free Range: **Conditioner;**
LYB Range: **Orange shower gel;**
Therapeutics Range: **Shampoo;** *Wish
Range:* **Conditioner**

FAITH PRODUCTS LIMITED
™ ⓘ ◉✈1988
Aloe Vera 400ml / 5 Ltr; Chocolate
conditioner; Gingko Biloba 400ml /
5 Ltr; Hemp and Meadowfoam;
Jojoba 400ml / 5 Ltr; Lavender and
Geranium 400ml / 5 Ltr; Rosemary
400ml / 5 Ltr; Seaweed 400ml / 5
Ltr; Tea Tree 400ml / 5 Ltr

FIGS & ROUGE ™☺
Conditioner

FOREVER LIVING PRODUCTS
Aloe Jojoba Conditioner

FUNK BUBBLE ™☺
Conditioner: **Jojoba,**
Lavender/Geranium, Tea Tree; *Organic
Conditioner:* **Aloe Vera, Chocolate**

GREEN PEOPLE CO. ™⊘ ⓘ
**Nourishing Spa Conditioner; Volume
Building Spa Conditioner;** *Hair &
Body Care:* **Aloe Vera Herbal
Conditioner, Aloe Vera Styling Gel,
Intensive Repair Conditioner,**

**Rosemary Conditioner, Vita Min
Conditioner;** *Organic Base:* **Conditioner**

GREEN VALLEY TRADING CO. ™☺
All products are vegan

HEALTHPOL ⊘ ⓘ
Herbacet Herbal Hair Balsam

HEALTHQUEST LIMITED ™⊘ ⓘ
Organic Blue- Body Care: **Conditioner**

HEMP GARDEN ™
Conditioner: **For all hair types**

HERBSGO LIMITED
T/A CLIVE FOOT ™☺
Clive Foot: **Sunflower and Tea Tree
Conditioner, Walnut and Tea Tree
Conditioner**

HONESTY COSMETICS LTD
™☺ⓘ⊘ ⓘ ◉✈1976
Conditioner: **Coconut & Avocado,
Jojoba & Peach;** *Honesty Essential
Range:* **Nettle, Lavender and Olive
Conditioner;** *Honesty Fruit Range:*
**Coconut & Avocado Conditioner,
Jojoba & Peach Conditioner**

I AM NATURAL ™
Organic Lavender & Geranium Hair
Conditioner; Organic Lime &
Grapefruit Hair Conditioner; Organic
Tea Tree & Neem Conditioner

ID AROMATICS
Conditioner Base (Essential Oils Can Be
Added)

INNGINNI LIMITED (OHSOBO) ™☺
Ohsobo: **Anti-Dandruff Conditioner, Conditioner - Original Formula**

ITS ELIXIR UK LIMITED ™⊘ ⅰ ☜
Hair treatment oil dandruff; Hair treatment thinning

JASON NATURAL PRODUCTS ⅰ ☜
84% Pure Aloe Vera Conditioner; Damage Control Creme Conditioner; Hemp Super Moisturizing Conditioner; Henna Hi-lights Conditioner; Incredible Thin-to-Thick™ Revitalizing Scalp Elixir; Lavender Conditioner – 70% Organic; Natural Apricot Conditioner; Natural Biotin Conditioner; Natural Sea Kelp Conditioner; Pro-Vitamin Thin-to-Thick™ Conditioner; Rosewater Conditioner – 70% Organic; Scalp Balancing Natural Jojoba Conditioner; Swimmers & Sports™ Revitalizing Conditioner; Tall Grass™ High-Protein Conditioner; Tea Tree Scalp Normalizing Conditioner; Vitamin E with A & C Conditioner; *All Natural Color Enhancing Temporary Shampoos:* Color Sealant Conditioner; *Natural Salon Hair Care:* Kiwi & Apricot Root Boot, Kiwi & Apricot Volumizing Conditioners, Mint & Rose Intense Moisture Treatment, Plumeria & Sea Kelp Moisturizing Conditioners, Plumeria & Sea Kelp Moisturizing Leave-In Conditioning Spray, Rosewater & Chamomile Normalizing Conditioners

LAVERANA ™ⅰ
Lavera HAIR: **Mango Milk Care Conditioner, Mango Milk Care Treatment, Rose Milk Repairing Conditioner**

LIVE NATIVE ™☺
Deep Hair Repair

LOVE THE PLANET ™⊘
Lemon & Lime Conditioner; Mandarin Conditioner; Tea Tree & Mint Conditioner

LUSH ™ⅰ
Hair Moisturisers: **Jasmin and Henna Fluff-Eaze, Marilyn;** *Liquid Conditioner:* **Veganese;** *Solid Conditioners:* **Jungle**

MONTAGNE JEUNESSE ⊘ ⅰ
Miracle Hair: Frizz Pink Grapefruit, Lime Oil Reconstructer, Seville Orange Emergency Repair

MORROCCO METHOD
Euro Organic Oil Hair & Scalp Conditioning Therapy; Zen Detox Hair & Scalp Therapy; *Instant Hair Conditioner:* Chi, Diamond Crystal Mist

NATURA ORGANICS ⊘ ⅰ ✿
Nourishing with Shea Butter, Vitamin E and Orange

NATURE'S GATE
Aloe Vera Moisturizing Conditioner; Awapuhi Volumizing Conditioner; Biotin Strengthening Conditioner; Chamomile Replenishing Conditioner; Hemp

Nourishing Conditioner; Henna Shine Enhancing Conditioner; Herbal Daily Conditioner; Jojoba Revitalizing Conditioner; Pomegranate Sunflower Conditioner; Tea Tree Calming Conditioner; *Masques:* Aloe Vera Moisturizing, Chamomile Replenishing, Herbal Hair Hydrating, Jojoba Revitalizing; *Organics - Fruit Blend:* Asian Pear & Red Tea, Grapefruit & Wild Ginger, Mandarin Orange & Patchouli, Persimmon & Rose Geranium; *Organics - Herbal Blend:* Chamomile & Lemon Verbena, Lavender & Aloe, Lemongrass & Clary Sage, Tea Tree & Blue Cypress

NEAL'S YARD REMEDIES
◌ ♦ ☞ ⪍ 1998
Rosemary & Cedarwood Hair Treatment; *Conditioner:* Chamomile & Jojoba

NEVER TOO BUSY TO BE BEAUTIFUL
™ ♦
Botanomancy: **Tangle Re-Conditioner**

NEW SEASONS ◌ ♦
Neutral & Toiletry Bases: Conditioner, Conditioning Shampoo Base

NO COWS ☺ ❶
No Cows Everyday Conditioner; No Cows Extra Help Conditioner

OPTIMAH HEALTH & NUTRITION
◌ ♦ ⪍ 1995
Raw Aloe: Medicated Shampoo

PAUL PENDERS CO ™
Hair Repair Conditioning Treatment;

Holy Basil Conditioning Scalp Toner; Pegaga Scalp Cleansing Treatment

PZ CUSSONS UK LTD ™◌ ♦
Original Source Conditioner: **Almond & Coconut, Lime and Guarana, Tea Tree & Mint, White Pear and Avocado**

QUINESSENCE AROMATHERAPY
☺ ◌ ♦ ☞
Protein Conditioner; Protein Conditioner Base

REN ◌
Conditioners: Manketti Conditioner, Monoi Conditioner, Phytokeratin Volumising Conditioner, Tomato Bioferment Conditioner

SAAF INTERNATIONAL LIMITED ™
Organic Enriching Hair Oil

SIMPLE ♦
Conditioner: Colour Protect, Frequent, Intensive

SIMPLY SOAPS ™❶◌ ♦ ☞ ⪍ 2003
Hair Care: **Conditioning Oil, Strengthening Oil**

SOLARAY NUTRITIONAL SUPPLEMENTS
Ginseng Biotin Hair Repair; Green Tea Finishing Cream Rinse; Mandarin Gingko & Ginseng Moisturising Jelly; Primrose Tangle-Go Hair Conditioner; White Camelia & Jasmine Conditioner Spray; *Hair Conditioner:* Calaguala Fern Texturising Leave-In Treatment,

Camomile Luxurious Volumising, Honeysuckle Rose, Jojoba & Aloe Desert Herb, Rosa Mosqueta Rose Hip, Swimmers

SUKI PURE SKIN CARE
Clean Balance with Horsetail Yerba Lavender & Rosemary

TARA SMITH LIMITED ™⊘
Tara Smith: **Base Coat Serum, Big Baby Conditioner, C Curl Hair Conditioner, Feed The Root Conditioner, Serum, Straight Away Conditioner, Top Coat Glosser**

THE CRUELTY FREE SHOP ™☺❶
All products are vegan

THE HIGHLAND SOAP COMPANY ™⊘
Conditioner: **Rosemary&Wild Nettle, Wild Nettle&Heather**

THE NATURAL SKINCARE COMPANY LTD ™
Paul Penders: **Holy Basil, Holy Basil Conditioning Scalp Toner, Intensive Hair Repair Therapy, Leave-In Defrizzing Balm, Pegaga Scalp Cleansing Treatment, Rinse GENTLE, RinseFORTE, RinseGENTLE**

TINTS OF NATURE ⊘ 𝄞
Conditioner; Natural Scalp Treatment; Seal & Shine Conditioner

TISSERAND AROMATHERAPY PRODUCTS ™☺
Lavender Products: **Lavender and**

Mint conditioning shampoo; *Tea Tree Products:* **Tea Tree, Lemon and Rosemary Balancing Conditioner, Tea tree, Lemon and Rosemary shampoo**

TRUTHFUL CO. LTD (PURELY SKINCARE) ™☺⊘
Purely Skincare: **Hair Conditioner - (normal/oily variant), Hair Conditioner (smooth and sleek variant), Hair Conditioner- (sensitive variant), Hair Conditioner (volumising variant)**

URTEKRAM ⊘ 𝄞 ☻⚘ 1998
Conditioner: All

VERDESATIVA S.R.L. ™☺
Balsamo (Hair Conditioner); Revitalizing Hair Conditioner

WELEDA ⊘ 𝄞 ⚘ 1985
Calendula Conditioner; Lemon Balm Conditioner; Rosemary Conditioner; Rosemary Hair Lotion; *Mens Range:* Shaving Lotion

YAOH ™☺❶⊘ 𝄞
Conditioner

DEODORANTS & ANTIPERSPIRANTS

A. VOGEL
Deodorant: Crystal Spring

ALTERNATIVE STORES ™☺❶
All products are vegan

ALVIN CONNOR LIMITED ™☺⊘
Natural Balance: **Natural Body Stick Deodorant, Natural Bodyspray Deodorant**

ANN ELISE SKINCARE ☺
Natural Deodorant

ANNEMARIE BORLIND ✦
Body Lind: Deodorant Spray; *Body Lind Sportiv:* Deodorant Spray; *Natural Care For Men:* Deostick

BEAUTY NATURALS ✦
Herbal; *Deodorant:* Pure

BRONNLEY & CO LTD ✦
Body Care for Men: Deodorant

BURT'S BEES ⊘✦☻
Doctor Burt's Herbal Deodorant

CAWARRA COSMETICS LTD ™
Sanctum: **Men's Deodorant**

DANIEL FIELD LABORATORY LTD ™☺
FFP Research Limited- Free From Sensitive Skin Body Care: **Anti-odorant**

DM-DROGERIE MARKT GMBH & CO KG ™
dm alverde: **Deo Balsam Calendula**

DOLMA ™☺❶⊘✦☻⊱1976
Miscellaneous Products: **Roll-On Deodorant**

DR HAUSCHKA ⊘✦
Deodorant: Floral, Fresh

ESSENTIAL CARE
Bath products: Deodorant Stone

ESSENTIALLY NATURAL ™
Fresh Man Deodorant (Organic); Lemon and Coriander Deodorant (Organic)

FAITH PRODUCTS LIMITED ™✦☻⊱1988
Body deodorant; Spray deodorant

FLORIS ☺✦
Deodorant Stick: Cefiro

FOREVER LIVING PRODUCTS
Aloe Ever-Shield Deodorant

GREEN PEOPLE CO. ™⊘✦
Deokrystal Spray; *Gentle Control:* **Aloe Vera Deodorant;** *Hair & Body Care:* **No Scent Deodorant, Rosemary Deodorant;** *Men's Range:* **Stay Cool Deodorant, Stay Fresh Deodorant;** *Organic Base:* **Deodorant**

GREEN VALLEY TRADING CO. ™☺
All products are vegan

GREEN WYCH ™☺❶
Natural Cream Deodorant: **Bergamot, Fragrance free, Geranium, Lavender, Orange Zest;** *Perfumed Body Spray:* **Bergamot, Geranium, Lavender, Orange Zest**

I AM NATURAL ™
Deodorant: **Organic Cypress & Tea Tree, Organic Lavender & Frankincense**

ICE GUARD ☺ ✦
Natural Crystal Deodorant Roll-on;
Natural Crystal Deodorant Spray;
Natural Crystal Deodorant Twist Up

J&D BLACK LTD ☺⊘ ✦ ☉
Hollytrees: Deodorant

JASON NATURAL PRODUCTS ✦ ☉
Aloe Vera Deodorant Roll; Aloe Vera
Deodorant Stick; Apricot Deodorant
Roll; Apricot Deodorant Stick; Herbs &
Spice Deodorant Stick; Lavender
Deodorant Roll-on; Lavender Deodorant
Stick; Naturally Fresh for Men
Deodorant Stick; Naturally Fresh for
Women Deodorant Stick; Tea Tree
Deodorant Roll-on; Tea Tree Deodorant
Stick; Wild Yam Deodorant Stick

LAVERANA ™ ✦
Lavera Basis Sensitiv: **Deo Roll-On;**
Men SPA: **Deodorant Active Spray,
Deodorant Active Spray - Aqua
Fresh, Deodorant Active Spray -
Cool Lime, Deodorant Active Spray -
Relaxing Santal**

LUSH ™ ✦
Deodorant Powder: **The Greeench;**
Deodorant Powders: **Coconut, Mr T;**
Solid Deodorants: **Aromaco,
Aromacreme, Aromarant;** *Solid
Deodorants - Krysztals:* **T'Eo**

NATURAL SENSE ™
Natural Deo Krystal

NATURE'S GATE
Organics - Fruit Blend: Asian Pear & Red
Tea, Grapefruit & Wild Ginger,
Mandarin Orange & Patchouli,
Persimmon & Rose Geranium; *Organics
- Herbal Blend:* Chamomile & Lemon
Verbena, Lavender & Aloe, Lemongrass
& Clary Sage, Tea Tree & Blue Cypress;
Roll-on: Autumn Breeze, Spring Fresh,
Summer Spice, Winter Clean; *Stick:*
Autumn Breeze, Spring Fresh, Summer
Spice, Winter Clean

NEAL'S YARD REMEDIES
⊘ ✦ ☉⚘1998
Lavender & Aloe Vera Deodorant;
Lemon & Coriander Deodorant

PITROK LTD ⊘ ✦
Crystal Deodorant: Original, Push-up;
Spray Deodorant: Fragrance, Natural

PURPLE FLAME AROMATHERAPY
⊘ ✦
Deodorants: All

PZ CUSSONS UK LTD ™⊘ ✦
Original Source Deodorant: **White
sage & Juniper Anti Perspirant
Deodorant**

SANMAR GMBH ™
Olive and Bio Melisse

SIMPLE ✦
Deodorant: Roll On, Stick

SOLARAY NUTRITIONAL SUPPLEMENTS
Calendula Blossom Spray; E Plus High C Roll-On; Northwoods Herbal Pine Deodorant

STELLA MCCARTNEY
Stella: Soft Deodorant Roll On

TAOASIS GMBH AROMA-KOSMETIK & VERLAG ™
Zaubernuss Deo; Zitrusgarten Deo

TAWAS CRYSTAL UK ™
Tawas Crystal: **Body Cyrstal, Gift Boxes, Mini Crystal, Natural Deodorant, Powder, Spray**

THE DEODORANT STONE (UK) LTD ☺◎✔
Deodorant Stone; *Roll-On Stone:* Aloe & Cucumber, Herbal Spice, Tea Tree, Unscented; *Spray-On Stone:* Aloe & Cucumber, Herbal Spice, Tea-Tree, Unscented

THE NATURAL SKINCARE COMPANY LTD ™
Spa Exotiques: **Lavender Body Deodorant**

TISSERAND AROMATHERAPY PRODUCTS ™☺
Deodorants: **Tea tree, Lemon and Rosemary deodorant, Wild rose & Lemon Leaf Deodorant;** *Lavender Products:* **Lavender and Lemon deodorant;** *Tea Tree Products:* **Tea Tree Lemon & Rosemary Deodorant, Tea Tree, Lemon and Rosemary Deodorant**

TOMS OF MAINE ◎✔
Natural Long-Lasting Deodorant Roll On: Lavender, Unscented; *Natural Long-Lasting Deodorant Stick:* Apricot, Lavender, Lemongrass, Unscented; *Natural Original Deodorant Stick:* Calendula, Honeysuckle Rose, Unscented, Woodspice; *Natural Sensitive Care Deodorant Stick:* Bay-Lime, Cucumber-Grapefruit, Fragrance Free

URTEKRAM ◎✔◉✈1998
Deo Crystal: All

WELEDA ◎✔✈1985
Citrus Deodorant; Sage Deodorant; Wild Rose

YAOH ™☺❶◎✔
Hemp Seed Oil Deodorants: **Cool, Neutral, Original**

ESSENTIAL OILS & MASSAGE PRODUCTS

A. VOGEL
Po-Ho Oil; St John's Wort Oil

ABSOLUTE AROMAS ™◎✔
Ord River: **Pure Tea Tree Oil 10ml & 25ml**

AKAMUTI
Mum's Special Oil Blend; Mum's Tummy

Butter; *Body Oils:* All; *Cold Pressed Tea Tree Oils:* All; *Essential Oils:* All

ANN ELISE SKINCARE ☺
Joint & Muscleez

BAREFOOT BOTANICALS ⊘ ♂
Rosa Fina: Secret Essence Face & Decolletage oil

BRONNLEY & CO LTD ♂
Royal Horticultural Society - Massage Oil: Gardener's

CAPITELLI OILS ⊘ ♂
Essential Oil Mixtures: Dolci Bambini 1, Dolci Bambini 2, Dormi Bene, Prima, Testa Fresca, Versatilata, Zanzara Via
CAWARRA COSMETICS LTD ™
Face Massage Oil; *Sanctum:* **Massage Oil**

DOLMA ™☺❶⊘ ♂ ☻⅋1976
Massage Oils: **Anti-Cellulite, Invigorating, Relaxing, Soothing**

ESSENTIAL CARE
Skincare: Mosimix, Muscle Ease Therapy Oil, Organic Relaxing Body Oil

ESSENTIALLY NATURAL ™
Car Aromatherapy Difuser (with Stay Awake Organic Oil)

ESSENTIALLY YOURS LTD ™☺⊘ ♂ ☻
For Play: **Anticipation Penis Cream, Discovery Cream, Divine Nipple Gel, Everlasting Gel, Fantasy Massage Oil, Interplay Lubricating Gel, Yin-**

Yang Lubricating Oil; *Natural Elements:* **Body massage oil, Facial Massage Oil, Refreshing Massage Oil, Relaxing Massage Oil**

HARLOW LUBRICANTS ™☺
Astroglide Liquid Products

HEALTHQUEST LIMITED ™⊘ ♂
Organic Blue- Massage Oils: **Muscle Rub, Relaxing, Sensual;** *Organic Blue-Mood Blends:* **Easy Breathe, Energising, Meditation, Relaxing, Restful Night, Sensual**

HERBS HANDS HEALING LTD ™⊘ ♂
Base Oils: **Castor, Nutmeg Kernel, St John's Wort Oil, Sweet Almond, Wheatgerm;** *Essential Oils:* **All;** *Massage Oils:* **Deep Tissue, Earth Song, Flower, Hot Zing, Intimate, Relaxing;** *Pure Essential Oils:* **Basil, Benzoin, Bergamot, Black Pepper, Cajaput, Camphor, Cardamom, Cedarwood, Chamomile (Roman), Cinnamon, Clary Sage, Clove, Eucalyptus, Fennel, Frankincense, Garlic, Geranium, Ginger, Juniper, Lavender, Lemon, Lime, Mandarin, Marjoram, Orange, Peppermint, Petitgrain, Rosemary, Rosewood, Sage, Spearmint, Tea Tree, Thyme, White Pine, Ylang Ylang**

HERBS OF GRACE ™⊘ ♂
Essential Oils: **All;** *Organic Carrier Oils:* **All**

TOILETRIES & COSMETICS

HOLISTIX ™❶
Bath/Massage Oils: **Luscious, Recovery, Relaxing, Sensual, Skincare, Warming Circulation;** *Carrier Oils:* **All;** *Essential Oils:* **All;** *Festive:* **Festive Essential Oil;** *Tinctures:* **All**

HOWAD LTD T/A INCOGNITO ™❶⊘✦
Lemongrass, Citronella & Jasmine Rice Oil

I AM NATURAL ™
Organic Avocado Oil; Organic Hemp Oil; Organic Macadamia Nut Oil; Organic Sweet Almond Oil; *Essential Oils:* **Organic Ginger Essential Oil, Organic Lavender Essential Oil, Organic Peppermint Essential Oil, Organic Sweet Orange Essential Oil, Organic Tea Tree Essential Oil;** *Massage Oil:* **Calming Massage Oil, Sensual Massage Oil, Uplifting Massage Oil, Warming Massage Oil**

ID AROMATICS
Essential Oils: All; *Facial Oils:* For combination Skin, For dry skin, For mature skin, For oily skin; *Fixed Oils:* All; *Hydolats & Floral Waters:* All; *Mind, Body and Spirit Range:* Aphrodisiac, Balancing, Calming, De-Stressing, Empowering, Insomnia, Invigorating, Meditation, Purifying, Relaxing, Revitalising; *Synergy Blends:* Anti-Allergy, Anti-Bacteria, Bug off, Citrus, Decongestant, Detoxifying, Early Morning, Night Time, Relaxation, Romantic, Warming; *Therapeutic Massage Blends:* Anti-Asthma Massage

Oil, Anti-Cellulite Massage Oil, Astral Massage Oil, Cough & Cold Massage Oil, Digestion Massage Oil, Hair & Scalp Massage Oil, Head Lice blend, Labour Blend for Pregnancy, LMJ Massage Oil, Menopause Massage Oil, Nail Oil, Period Pains Massage oil, Skin Soothe Oil, Sports Massage Oil, Stretch Mark Massage Oil

INNOCENT OILS ™☺⊘✦
Innocent Massage Oil

ITS ELIXIR UK LIMITED ™⊘✦👁
Joint&muscle gel

JR LIGGETT ☺✦👁
Pure Tea Tree Oil Roll On; *Moisturizing Oils Kit:* with Nut Oil, Without Nut Oil

JUNGLESALE LIMITED ™
Neem Massage Oil; Neem Oil

KOBASHI ™☺⊘✦👁⚕1976
Baby; Detox; Harmony; Neroli facial oil; Rose facial oil; *Blended Massage Oils:* **Anti-Cellulite, Relaxing, Sensual, Sports;** *Misc:* **Carrier Oils, Essential Oils, Poster, Vitamin E**

KOOCHIE KOO ™
aromababy: **Great Expectations Oil**

LUSH ™✦
Business Time Massage Bar; *Massage Bars:* **Amazonian, Bewitched, Cosmic Dreamcatcher, Each Peach (and Two's a Pear), Fever, Nutts, Snake Oil Scalp Bar, Sore Labours, Therapy, Wiccy Magic Muscles;** *Massage Bars*

With Glitter: **Iridescent Glitterbug, Shimmy Shimmy**

MAJIK BLANKIT SKIN CARE ™☺ ♪
Veon Sensuous Organic Jojoba & Jasmine Massage Balm

NATURAL BY NATURE OILS
™☺ ♪ ☞ ⚘–1976
Bath Oils: **Jasmine, Lavender, Meditation, Rose, Seduction, Tranquility;** *Massage Blends:* **Baby & Toddler, Cellulite, Hair & Scalp, Muscle & Joint, Rose, Seduction, Tranquility**

NATURAL SENSE ™
Joint Ease; Massage Oil; Muscle Rub

NATURALLY GIFTED ™
Bath & Massage Oil: **Citrus & Lavender, Neroli & Rose**

NEAL'S YARD REMEDIES
⊘ ♪ ☞ ⚘–1998
Aromastream; Cellulose Herb Bags; Citronella Formula; Essential Oils; Flower Essence Blends; Kaolin; Rosewater; *Aromatherapy for:* Balance, Energy, Relaxation; *Facial Oil:* Orange Flower; *Macerated Oil:* Arnica, Calendula, Comfrey, Mullein, St John's Wort; *Massage Oil:* Aromatic, Base, Baseline, Geranium & Orange, Mother's; *Oils:* Apricot Kernel, Coconut, Detox Toning, Evening Primrose, Ginger & Juniper Warming, Grapeseed, Inhalation, Jojoba, Neem, Organic Almond, Rosehip Seed, Sweet Almond, Wheatgerm; *Spritzer:* Calm, Renew, Zest

NEVER TOO BUSY TO BE BEAUTIFUL ™ ♪
2 Hearts Beating As One: **Massage Oil**

NOTHING NASTY ♪
Rosemary Energising Body Oil

OPTIMAH HEALTH & NUTRITION
⊘ ♪ ⚘–1995
Cariad: All Essential Oils and Carrier Oils

ORGANIC BOTANICS ™⊘ ✧
Certified Organic French Lavender Essential Oil; Certified Organic Pure Tea-Tree Essential Oil

OSHADHI ☺ ♪
Essential Oils and Carrier Oils: All

PINKS BOUTIQUE ™☺
Himalayan Organic Massage Oil; Indonesian Organic Massage Oil

POTIONS AND POSSIBILITIES ⊘ ♪
Carrier Oils: All; *Essential Oils:* All; *Massage:* ...And To Sleep Blend, Detox Blend, Fatigue Blend, Intimate Blend, Joint & Muscle Blend, Relaxation Blend; *Organic Range:* Detox Facial Massage, Energy Lift Body Massage, Gentle Facial Massage, Stress Ease Massage

PURPLE FLAME AROMATHERAPY
⊘ ♪
Cocoa Butter; *Carrier Oils:* All; *Chakra Mists:* All; *Essential Oils:* All; *Extract:* Arnica, Comfrey, Grapefruit Seed; *Hot Stone Blends:* All; *Massage Oils:* All; *Precious Oils in Jojoba:* All; *Ready*

Blended Essential Olis: All; *Synergistic Skin & Massage Oils Blends:* All; *Tinctures:* All

QUINESSENCE AROMATHERAPY
☺⊘◢👁
Vegetable Solubiliser; *10% Dilutions:* All; *5% Dilutions:* All; *Absolutes and Phytols:* All; *Essential Oil Synergies:* After Flight, Cellulite, Energising, Foot Ease, Head Ease, Immune Optimise, Problem Skin, Relaxing, Uplifting; *Hydrosols:* All; *Massage Oils:* Athletic, Cellulite, Invigorating, Joint Mobility, Muscle Ease, Relaxing, Stress, Stretch Marks; *Pure Essential Oils:* All

SCENT BY NATURE ☺⊘◢✄ 1986
Aromatherapy: Apricot Carrier Oil, Discounted Essential Oil Multi-Packs, Dispersable Vegetable Bath Carrier Oil, Essential Oil Collections, Grapeseed Carrier Oil, Self-Selection Gift Packs, Sweet Almond Carrier Oil, Tea Tree Antiseptic Cream; *Essential Oils:* All

SCOTTISH HERBAL SUPPLIES ™❶⊘◢
Organic & Non-Organic Essential Oils; Vegetable Creams; Vegetable Oils

SIMPLY SOAPS ™❶⊘◢👁✄ 2003
Faerie Therepy: **3 Colour Candle & Oil Gift Box;** *Hedgerow Herbals:* **Finest Rose Body Oil;** *Hedgerow Herbals-Rosa Passionata:* **Rosa Body Oil;** *Oils:* **Aphrodisia, Invigorating, Relaxing**

SOLARAY NUTRITIONAL SUPPLEMENTS
Natural Spa Sea Wonders Relaxing Massage Oil

SOPHYTO LTD ™
Feminine Massage Butter; Masculine Massage Butter; Meditation Massage Butter; Unfragranced Massage Butter

SUKI PURE SKIN CARE
Clean Balance Treatment Oil with Lavender & Rosemary

THE ESSENTIAL OIL COMPANY
⊘◢👁
Carrier Oils: All; *Pure Essential Oils:* All

THE NATURAL SKINCARE COMPANY LTD ™
Spa Exotiques: **Lavender Body Oil, Lime Body Oil, Tangerine Body Oil**

THE ORGANIC HERB TRADING COMPANY ⊘
Organic Macerates & Flower Waters: All

TISSERAND AROMATHERAPY PRODUCTS ™☺
After Treatment Products: **After Wax Oil;** *Blended Essential Oils:* **Jasmine/Jojoba, Linden Blossom/Jojoba, Orange Blossom/Jojoba, Rose/Jojoba;** *Blended Massage Oils:* **Cellulite Treatment Oil, Muscle Fatigue Treatment Oil, Relaxing Body Oil, Sensual Body Oil;** *Essential Oils:* **Basil (Herb), Benzoin (resinoid 50%) Wild Crafted, Benzoin (Trees), Bergamot, Bergamot (Rind of the Fruit), Black Pepper, Black Pepper (Peppercorns), Camphor White, Cardomon (Seeds),**

Carrot Seed (Seeds), Cedarwood (Virginian) (Trees), Cedarwood Atlas (Trees), Chamomile (Roman), Chamomile Blue (Flowers), Chamomile Roman (Flowers), Cinnamon, Citronella, Citronella (Grass), Clary Sage - ethically harvested, Clary Sage (Herb), Clove, Coriander (Dried Fruits), Cypress - wild crafted, Cypress (Leaves of the Tree), Eucalyptus, Eucalyptus (Leaves of the Tree), Fennel (Herb), Frankincense - wild crafted, Frankincense (Tree Resin), Geranium - ethically harvested, Geranium (Leaves), Ginger, Ginger (Root of the Plant), Grapefruit, Grapefruit (Rind of the Fruit), Immortelle (Flowers), Jasmine absolute - ethically harvested, Jasmine Absolute (Flowers), Juniper, Juniper (Berries), Kanuka (Foliage), Lavender, Lavender - ethically harvested, Lavender (Flowers), Lemon, Lemon (Rind of the Fruit), Lemongrass, Lemongrass (Grass), Lemon-Tea tree, Lime, Lime (Rind of the Fruit), Linden Blossom Absolute (Flowers), Mandarin, Mandarin (Rind of the Fruit), Marjoram (Spanish) wild crafted, Marjoram French (Herb), Marjoram Spanish (Herb), May Chang - ethically harvested, May Chang (Fruit), Melissa (Leaves & Flowers), Myrrh (Tree Resin), Orange, Orange (Rind of the Fruit), Orange Blossom (Neroli) (Flowers), Orange Blossom (Neroli)- ethically harvested, Palmarosa (Grass), Patchouli, Patchouli (Herb), Peppermint, Peppermint (Herb), Petitgrain (Orange Tree Leaf), Pine - wild crafted, Pine (Trees), Rose (absolute) - ethically harvested, Rose Absolute (Flowers), Rose otto - ethically harvested, Rose Otto (Flowers), Rosemary, Rosemary (Herb), Rosewood - tomar, Rosewood (Tree), Sandalwood - wild crafted, Sandalwood (Tree), Tea tree, Tea tree (Leaves of the Tree), Thyme, Turmeric, Vetiver (Grass), Yarrow (Milfoil) (Flower Heads), Ylang-Ylang (Flowers); *Lavender Products:* **Lavender body Lotion, Lavender roller ball;** *Massage Oil Base:* **Face & Body Massage Oil Base, Grapeseed, Jojoba, Peach Kernel, Sweet Almond, Wheatgerm;** *Mixing bottle:* **Calibrated glass mixing bottle;** *Rescue Roller Balls:* **Concentrate Remedy Roller Ball, De-Stress Remedy Roller Ball, Goodnight Remedy Roller Ball, Travel Ease Remedy Roller Ball;** *Softening pre-blended body oils for massage:* **Cellulite detox body massage oil, Muscle ease body massage oil, Relaxing body massage oil, Sensuous body massage oil;** *Tea Tree Products:* **Natural Antiseptic Cream, Tea Tree & Kanuka Blemish Stick, Tea Tree & Kanuka Gel, Tea Tree & Lime Cream Body Wash, Tea Tree & Manuka Cream, Tea Tree Lotion, Tea Tree Moist Tissues, Tea Tree Roller Ball**

TREE-HARVEST ⊘ ✦
Linden Relaxation Oil; *Body Oils:* Aches
and Pains, Detox, Renewed Energy,
Sensuality, Soothing, Sports, Tranquility;
Essential Oils: All; *Oils & Hydrolats:* All;
Precious Oils & Absolutes: All; *Pulse
Points:* Lavender, Linden, Rose, Willow

URTEKRAM ⊘ ✦ ☜ ⤲ 1998
Body Oil: All

VERDESATIVA S.R.L. TM☺
**Olio Aromatico (Red Velvet Oil);
Olio Balsamico (Balsamic Oil); Olio
Fitness (Benessere); Olio Gloreale
(Flower Garden Oil); Olio Relax
(Relax Oil)**

VISIONARY SOAP COMPANY TM☺
Body Oils: **Recuperate, Rejuvenate,
Relax, Romance**

YAOH TM☺❶◐ ✦
Massage Oil

EYE PRODUCTS

AKAMUTI
Rose Berry Eye Reviitaliser

ANNEMARIE BORLIND ✦
Eye Make Up Remover; Pura Soft Q10
Eye Area Care

BAREFOOT BOTANICALS ⊘ ✦
Rosa Fina: Revelation Intensive Eye Serum

BEAUTY NATURALS ✦
Eye Care: Contour Balm, Elderflower
Contour Gel, Gentle Cleansing Gel;
Gentle Cleansing for Eyes: Lotion

CAWARRA COSMETICS LTD TM
OrganicSpa: **Eye Balm, Eye Gel;**
Sanctum: **Energising Eye Gel,
Firming Eye Balm**

DANIEL FIELD LABORATORY LTD TM☺
*FFP Research Limited- Free From
Sensitive Skin Skin Care:* **Eye lines
serum, Eye makeup remover**

DOLMA TM☺❶⊘ ✦ ☜ ⤲ 1976
Honesty Eye Gel; *Eye Care:*
**Chamomile & Aloe Vera Eye Cream,
Chamomile & Fennel Eye Make-up
Remover**

DR HAUSCHKA ⊘ ✦
Eye Solace

ESSENTIALLY NATURAL TM
**Anti-Wrinkle Eye Pillow; Calming
Eye Pillow; Hangover Eye Pillow;
Relaxing Eye Pillow**

ESSENTIALLY YOURS LTD TM☺⊘ ✦ ☜
Eye cream; *Free&Organic Range:* **Eye
cream, Eye make-up remover;** *Men's
Range:* **Eye firming serum;** *Natural
Elements:* **Eye Cleansing Liquid, Eye
Cream, Eye firming serum, Eye gel,
Eye make-up remover**

FAITH PRODUCTS LIMITED
TM *i* ☻ ⤴-1988
Replenishing Aloe Vera Eye Gel 50ml

GREEN PEOPLE CO. TM⊘ *i*
Skin Care: **Eye Cream (Night), Eye Gel (Day)**

HERBS HANDS HEALING LTD TM⊘ *i*
Eyebright & Goldenseal Eyewash;
Allergies: **Eyebright & Goldenseal Eyewash Formula**

HERBS OF GRACE TM⊘ *i*
Eyewash Powder

HONESTY COSMETICS LTD
TM☺❶⊘ *i* ☻⤴-1976
Honesty Unscented Range: **Eye Gel with Eyebright**

ID AROMATICS
Eye Cream

JASON NATURAL PRODUCTS *i* ☻
Alpha Hydroxy Acids: 3-1/2% Plus Gentle Eye Gel New Cell Eye Area Therapy™ Alpha Hydroxy Acids; *Ester-C®®️ Skin Care:* Ultra-C™ Eye Lift

JUICE BEAUTY *i* ☻
Green Apple Nutrient Eye Cream; Smoothing Eye Concentrate

LAVERANA TM *i*
Lavere: **Hydro Energy Cool Eye, Solution Power Eye Glow**

LIZ EARLE *i* ☻
Daily Eye Repair; Day & Night Eye Care Duo; Eyebright Soothing Eye Lotion; Smoothing Line Serum

NATURE'S GATE
Ultimate Comfort Eye Cream

NEAL'S YARD REMEDIES
⊘ *i* ☻⤴-1998
Eye Gel: White Tea

NO COWS ☺❶
No Cows Eye Gel

ORGANIC BOTANICS TM⊘ ✧
Pink Lotus & Aloe Vera Creamy Eye Gel

PAUL PENDERS CO TM
Plantago Essential Eye Gel

POTIONS AND POSSIBILITIES ⊘ *i*
Beauty: Firming Eye Gel

RAW GAIA TM⊘ *i*
Revitalising Eye Oil with Sea Buckthorn Fruit

REN ⊘
Active 7 Radiant Eye Maintenance Gel; Conditioning Eye Make Up Remover; Lipovector Peptide Anti-Wrinkle Eye Cream

SAUFLON PHARMACEUTICALS ⊘ *i*
Contact Lens Care Solution: All In One Light Multipurpose Solution, Comfort Drops, ConfortVue Multipurpose Solution, CyClean®®️ Multipurpose

Solution, Multi™ Hydrogen Peroxide Solution, Preservative Free Saline, Sauflon 7 Comfort Solution, Synergi Preservative Free Multipurpose Solution; *Contact Lenses:* Bioclear™ 1Day Biomimetic Daily Disposables, Bioclear™ Biomimetic Monthly Disposables, Bioclear™ Biomimetic Toric Monthly Disposables, ClearComfort Aspheric Monthly Disposables, NewDay® Aspheric Daily Disposables, Sauflon UV55 Monthly Disposables

SIMPLE ✔
Conditioning Eye Make-Up Remover; Conditioning Eye Make-Up Remover Pads; Kind To Eyes Balm; *Eye Cream:* Age Resisting, Anti-Wrinkle, Daily Radiance

SOLARAY NUTRITIONAL SUPPLEMENTS
Lumessence Rejuvanating Eye Cream

SUPERDRUG
Amie: Bright Eyes Very Gentle Eye Make-Up Remover

THE NATURAL SKINCARE COMPANY LTD ™
Paul Penders: **Plantago Essential Eye Gel**

TREASURED EARTH SKINCARE ™☺⊘
Eye Cream

TREE-HARVEST ⊘ ✔
Elderflower Eye Gel

VEGAN STORE ™☺❶⊘ ✔
Vizulize: **Contact Lens Cleaner, Herbal Eye Drops**

FEMININE HYGIENE

HIGHER NATURE PLC ™⊘ ✔
V Gel; VagiClear

LIVE NATIVE ™☺
Love Lube

MOONCUP LTD. ™☺
Mooncup

NATRACARE
Baby Wipes; Intimate Wipes; *Organic Applicator Tampons:* Regular, Super; *Organic Tampons:* Regular, Super, Super Plus; *Pads:* Dry & Light Incontinence, Maternity, Night Time, Nursing, Regular, Slender, Super; *Panty Liners:* Breathable, Curved, Tanga, Ultra Thin; *Ultra Pads:* Long with Wings, Regular with Wings, Super Plus, Super w Wings

SANMAR GMBH ™
Lacta Femina Wash sanmar; *Vleur:* **Femina Wash**

VERDESATIVA S.R.L. ™☺
Unisex Mild Intimate Cleanser

FOOT & LEG CARE

AKAMUTI
Foot Spray; Shea Cocoa Mint Foot Butter

ALVIN CONNOR LIMITED ™☺⊘
Natural Balance: **Natural Foot Powder**

ANIMAL AID SOCIETY ™☺❶⊘ ✔ ⊱1976
Cool Mint Foot Lotion

BAREFOOT BOTANICALS ⊘ ✔
SOS: Foot Soldier Soothing Foot Balm

BEAUTY NATURALS ✔
Moisturising Foot Balm; *Martha Hill:* Energising Leg Gel

CAWARRA COSMETICS LTD ™
Sanctum: **Reviving Foot Balm, Reviving Foot Soak**

DESERT ESSENCE ⊘ ✔ ⊱1985
Organics: Pistachio Foot Repair

DOLMA ™☺❶⊘ ✔ ☞ ⊱1976
Hand & Foot Care: **Aromatic Foot Shampoo with Lemongrass & Cypress, Aromatic Foot Shampoo with Peppermint & Tea Tree, Honesty Foot Lotion**

ESSENTIALLY NATURAL ™
Raspberry & Lemon Footpowder

ESSENTIALLY YOURS LTD ™☺⊘ ✔ ☞
Natural Elements: **Anti-Microbial Foot Cream, Anti-Microbial Foot Soak, Anti-Microbial Foot Spray, Foot cream, Foot Massage Cream, Foot scrub, Foot soak, Refreshing Foot Scrub, Refreshing Foot Soak, Warming Foot Cream, Warming Foot Soak**

FREERANGERS ™☺ ✔
Minty foot Scrub; Zingy Lemon Foot Cream

HEALTHY HERBS ™☺
Herbytoes

HOLISTIX ™❶
Lavender Water Foot Spray

HONESTY COSMETICS LTD
™☺❶⊘ ✔ ☞ ⊱1976
Honesty Essential Range: **Peppermint, Tea Tree & Lemon Foot Lotion**

I AM NATURAL ™
Organic Peppermint Foot Cream with myrrh & camphor

INNOCENT OILS ™☺⊘ ✔
Innocent Angel Butter Mint; Innocent Buff Paste; Innocent Pinkie Drops

ITS ELIXIR UK LIMITED ™⊘ ✔ ☞
Foot gel

LIVE NATIVE ™☺
Fresh Feet

TOILETRIES & COSMETICS

LUSH ™ ⚘
Volcano Foot Mask

MONTAGNE JEUNESSE ⊘ ⚘
Ice Blueberry & Balm Mint Foot Cooler;
Morella Cherry & Iced Mint Tired Leg
Gel; Pink Grapefruit & Balm Mint Foot
Soak; Spearmint & Balm Foot Lotion;
Watermelon & Balm Mint Foot Scrub

NATURAL SENSE ™
Hot Feet Oil

NOTHING NASTY ⚘
Breeze Foot Spray

PINKS BOUTIQUE ™☺
Crystal Sanitising Spritz; Himalayan
Crystal Foot Soak; Himalayan
Organic Foot Balm

PURE GAISHA ™☺❶ ⚘
Fantasy Foot Cream; Fantasy Foot
Scrub; Fragrant Garden Foot Soak

QUINESSENCE AROMATHERAPY
☺⊘ ⚘ ❶ 👁
Foot Balm

REN ⊘
Revivo-Tonic Cool Comfort Leg and
Foot Gel

SAAF INTERNATIONAL LIMITED ™
Organic Foot Softening Balm

SOLARAY NUTRITIONAL SUPPLEMENTS
Feet Relief Massage Cream; Neat Feet
Foot Scrub

THE DEODORANT STONE (UK) LTD
☺⊘ ⚘
Peppermint Foot Spray-On Stone

**THE NATURAL SPA
COMPANY LIMITED** ™☺
All products are vegan

**TISSERAND AROMATHERAPY
PRODUCTS** ™☺
Hand & Foot Care: **Foot Lotion;**
Restored feet: **White mint and
Kanuka foot balm**

WELEDA ⊘ ⚘ ⅍ 1985
Birch Cellulite Oil

GIFT BOXES & PACKS

HOLISTIX ™❶
Aromatherapy Scent: **Oil Burner,
Essential Oil, Candle;** *Calendula:*
Cream, Soap, Bath Oil; *Feet Treat:*
Pumice, Foot Balm, Soap; *Hard-
Worker's Treat:* **Back Rub, Bath Oil,
Soap;** *Pamper 1:* **Spritzer, Soap,
Cream, Flannel;** *Pamper 2:* **Cream,
Bath Oil, Soap;** *Sensual:* **Massage Oil,
Geranium & Ylang-Ylang Cream, Lip
Balm, Candles;** *Winter Warmer 1:*
Ointment, Bath Oil, Soap, Candles;
Winter Warmer 2: **Xmas Spray,
Ointment, Wine Spice**

HONESTY COSMETICS LTD
™☺❶ ⚘ 👁 ⅍ 1976
Honesty Essential Range: **Essential**

Range Gift Bag; *Honesty Fruit Range:* **Fruit Range Gift Bag;** *Honesty Unscented Range:* **Unscented Range Gift Bag**

KOBASHI ™☺⊘ *i* ◉⅋1976
Misc: **Starter Baskets/Gift packs**

NO COWS ☺❶
No Cows Beautiful Home Kit; No Cows Pamper Me Kit; No Cows Spa Day Kit

SHANTI PRODUCTS ⊘ *i*
Glycerine Soaps: Boxed Humming Bird Soap, Daisy Gift Soaps, Dragonfly boxed soaps, Large cupcake soap in Box, Mini Cupcake Soaps, Rose Shaped Soap, Soap Scroll, Vintage Collection Black & White Soaps

ULTRA GLOW COSMETICS ☺ *i*
Latex free accessory set; Mirror accessory

HAIR DYES

ALTERNATIVE STORES ™☺❶
All products are vegan

DANIEL FIELD *i*
Classics: Natural Lights; *Watercolour:* All Colours

LUSH ™ *i*
Les Cacas Hair Colours: **Caca Brun, Caca Marron, Caca Noir, Caca Rouge**

MANIC PANIC
All

NEAL'S YARD REMEDIES
⊘ *i* ◉⅋1998
Henna

RENBOW *i*
Crazy Color: All

SMART BEAUTY *i*
Smart Blonde: Champagne, Platinum; *Smart Colour:* Hot Chocolate, Midnight Blue, Pure Purple, Real Red, Total Blonde; *Smart Highlights:* Carmine Pink, Cool Blonde, Hot Chocolate, Intense Red, Pure Purple; *Smart Multi Tonal Highlights:* Fiery Red, Hazelnut, Hot Chocolate, Mahogany

SOLARAY NUTRITIONAL SUPPLEMENTS
Colour Me Natural Hair Dye Dark Brown

SPECIAL EFFECTS HAIR DYES
All

TINTS OF NATURE ⊘ *i*
Changes Semi-Permanent Hair Colour: All (8 Shades Available); *Permanent Hair Colour:* All (24 Shades Available), Highlight Kit, Lightener Kit

HAIR REMOVAL

AQUA NATURAL ™☺⊘ *i*
Aqua Natural; Simply Smooth

BOOTS COMPANY PLC
Expert Sensitive Hair Removal Strips

MOOM UK
M4Men Organic Refill Jar; Moom 4 Men Organic Hair Removal; Moom Organic Refill Jar; Organic Hair Removal Extra Sensitive Skin; Organic Hair Removal Mature Skin; Organic Hair Removal Normal/Sensitive Skin

HAIRSPRAYS, GELS ETC

AVEDA
Air Control Hairspray

BEAUTY NATURALS ✔
Natural Style Conditioning Hair Gel

DANIEL FIELD ✔
Anti Frizz Hairspray; Smooth & Shine Serum

ESSENTIALLY YOURS LTD ™☺⊘ ✔ ☻
Natural Elements: **Anti-Tangle Spray, Hair & Scalp Fluid, Hair Oil**

FOREVER LIVING PRODUCTS
Aloe Pro-Set

GREEN PEOPLE CO. ™⊘ ✔
Volume Building Spa Hair Mist

HOLISTIX ™❶
Hair Oil

JASON NATURAL PRODUCTS ✔ ☻
All Natural Mousse; Fresh Botanicals Hairspray Super Style Holding Mist; Hi-Shine Styling Gel; Pro-VitaminThin-to-Thick™ Hair Spray; Stuck-Up!™ Hair Wax; *Natural Salon Hair Care:* Aloe Vera & Bergamot Finishing Spray, Aloe Vera & Bergamot Shine Spray, Aloe Vera & Bergamot Styling Gel, Aloe Vera & Bergamot Texturizing Cream, Citrus & Mandarin Wax Pomade, Kiwi & Apricot Volumizing Mousse

LAVERANA ™ ✔
Lavera Basis Sensitiv: **Special Hair Treatment**

LUSH ™ ✔
Hair Styling: **Goth Juice, King Of The Mods, The Big Tease**

MONTAGNE JEUNESSE ⊘ ✔
Miracle Hair: Wild Strawberry Boost & Bounce

MORROCCO METHOD
Volumizer Mist Conditioner & Hairspray

SOLARAY NUTRITIONAL SUPPLEMENTS
B5 Design Gel; Natural Misst Super Hold Herbal Hairspray

TARA SMITH LIMITED ™⊘
Tara Smith: **Hard Hold Gel**

HAND & NAIL PRODUCTS

ALTERNATIVE STORES ™☺❶
All products are vegan

ANIMAL AID SOCIETY
™☺❶◎ ✿ ⅍1976
Marigold & Marshmallow Handcream

ANNEMARIE BORLIND ✿
Anne Lind: Lemon Grass Hand Balm;
Beauty Extras: Hand Balm

AROMA COMFORTS ™☺◎
Rich Moisture Lemon Hand Cream

ASTONISH ✿ ☻
Travelmate Palm Clear; *Liquid Hand Wash:* Blueberry, Coconut, Kiwi; *Lquid Hand Wash:* Waterlilly
BAREFOOT BOTANICALS ◎ ✿
SOS: Safety Gloves Barrier Hand Cream

BARRY M COSMETICS ✿ ⅍1982
Nail Whitener Pencil; *3 in 1 Nail Paint:* All; *Glitter Nail Paint:* All; *Nail Paint:* All; *Neon Nail Paint:* All

BEAUTY NATURALS ✿
Gardener's Cream; Nourishing Nail Oil; Skin Smoothing Hand Scrub; *Cuticle Cream:* Gentle, Nourishing; *Martha Hill:* Nourishing Cuticle Cream, Nourishing Nail Oil

BEAUTY WITHOUT CRUELTY
☺ ✿ ☻ ⅍1996
High Gloss Nail Colour: Birch, Candyfloss, Cassis, Clear, Coral Mist, Flame, Fuschia, Pink Shimmer, Pink Whisper, Praline, Raspberry, Silver Lilac

BOURGEOIS BOHEME ™☺
Beauty Without Cruelty: **High Gloss Nail Colour**

BRONNLEY & CO LTD ✿
Hand and Nail Cream: Apricot & Almond, Bird of Paradise, Gardener's, Lavender, Orchid, Passion Flower, Pink Bouquet, White Iris; *Royal Horticultural Society - Hand & Nail Cream:* Gardener's, Passion Flower; *Royal Horticultural Society - Hand Conditioner:* Passion Flower, Rose; *Royal Horticultural Society - Hand Wash:* Rose

CAWARRA COSMETICS LTD ™
Sanctum: **Hand & Nail Repair Cream**

CELLANDE MIDLANDS ◎ ✿
Hand Cleaner: Coconut, Lavender & Avocado Oil, Pine

DANIEL FIELD LABORATORY LTD ™☺
FFP Research Limited- Free From Sensitive Skin Body Care: **Hand wash**

DESERT ESSENCE ◎ ✿ ⅍1985
Organics: Pumpkin Hand Repair

DOLMA ™☺❶◎ ✿ ☻ ⅍1976
Hand & Foot Care: **Lemongrass Hand Cream, Nail & Cuticle Oil, Wild Poppy Hand Cream**

DR HAUSCHKA ⊘ 𝒊
Neem Nail Oil; Neem Nail Oil Pen

ESSENTIALLY NATURAL ™
Lavender and Coconut Hand Balm
(Organic); Lemon Cuticle Conditioner
(Organic); Orange and Frankincense
Hand Balm (Organic); Organic
Castor Oil Nail Strengthener

ESSENTIALLY YOURS LTD ™☺⊘ 𝒊 ☜
Fragrance Free Range: **Passion to
Garden hand lotion, Passion to
Garden hand wash;** *Free&Organic
Range:* **Hand cream;** *Natural Elements:*
**Extra Rich Hand Cream, Hand cream,
Hand wash;** *Passion to Garden:* **Luxury
Hand Lotion, Luxury Hand Wash**

FAITH PRODUCTS LIMITED
™ 𝒊 ☜⚮1988
Aloe Vera and Tea Tree 300ml / 5 Ltr;
Lavender and Geranium 300ml / 5
Ltr; Restorative Hand Cream 50gm;
Seaweed 300ml / 5 Ltr

FIGS & ROUGE ™☺
Hand Cream

FLORIS ☺ 𝒊
Natural Benefits: Gently Cleansing Hand
Wash, Nourishing Hand and Nail Cream

GREEN WYCH ™☺❶
Hand Cream: **Bergamot, Fragrance
free, Geranium, Lavender, Orange**

HEALTHY HERBS ™☺
Lem-Nail Oil

HONESTY COSMETICS LTD
™☺❶⊘ 𝒊 ☜⚮1976
Honesty Essential Range: **Orange
Geranium & Lavender Hand Wash,
Orange, Geranium & Lavender Hand
Cream;** *Honesty Unscented Range:*
**Hand Cream with Comfrey, Hand
Wash with Chamomile**

I AM NATURAL ™
Organic Macadamia Nut Hand
Cream with Myrrh

LAVERANA ™ 𝒊
Lavere: **Body-Effect Protection
Intensive Hand Cream**

LIZ EARLE 𝒊 ☜
Hand Repair

LUSH ™ 𝒊
Handy Gurugu Hand Cream; *Hand
and Body Creams:* **Potion**

MANDALA AROMA LTD ™☺⊘
Conditioning Hand Lotion

**NATURAL HOUSE PRODUCTS
LIMITED** ™☺ 𝒊
Organic Liquid Handsoap

NATURAL SENSE ™
Hand Cream; Nail Oil

NEAL'S YARD REMEDIES
⊘ 𝒊 ☜⚮1998
Citrus Hand Wash; *Hand Lotion:*
Garden Mint & Bergamot, Geranium &
Orange, Juniper & Black Pepper; *Hand*

Wash: Garden Mint & Bergamot, Juniper & Black Pepper

NEVER TOO BUSY TO BE BEAUTIFUL ™ 🖤
Botanomancy: **Qushion - Hand Cream**

NEW SEASONS ⊘ 🖤
Rich Moisturising Hand Cream; *Neutral & Toiletry Bases:* Hand Cream

NO COWS ☺❶
No Cows Hand Cream

ORGANIC BOTANICS ™⊘✿
Intensive Daily Hand Treatment

PINKS BOUTIQUE ™☺
**Indonesian Organic Hand Balm;
Indonesian Organic Hand Exfoliant;
Indonesian Organic Hand Soak;
Organic Cuticle Oil**

POTIONS AND POSSIBILITIES ⊘ 🖤
Hand & Nail Cream: English Garden, English Lavender, English Rose; *Hand Wash:* English Garden, English Lavender, English Rose

PURE GAISHA ™☺❶ 🖤
Gardener's Hand Cream; Gardener's Hand Scrub

QUINESSENCE AROMATHERAPY ☺⊘ 🖤 👁
Cleanser Base; Hand Cream; Hand Cream Base

SANMAR GMBH ™
Hand and Nail Creme; *Handcreme:* **Liposomes and Bio Sheabutter**

SHANTI PRODUCTS ⊘ 🖤
Almond & Sandalwood Hand Cream

SIMPLE 🖤
Anti-Ageing Hand Treatment; Moisturising Hand Wash; Nourish Hand & Nail Lotion; *Hand Cream:* Intensive, Night Care; *Handwash:* Antibacterial, Deep Clean

SKIN BLOSSOM LIMITED ™⊘
Organic: **Organic Bloom rose geranium hand cream**

SPARITUAL ™☺
Affirming Scrub Masque; Amigo; Cuti-Clean; Cuti-Cocktail; Cuti-Quench; DBP Free Nail Lacquer; Eloquent Toner; Farewell; Fluent Conditioning Lacquer Remover; Harmonising Soak Tonic; Impeccable; Infinitely Loving Oil; Infinitely Wise Fragrant Mist; Instinctual Moisturising Lotion; Lacquer Lock; Look Inside 21 Mineral Bath Salts; Multi-Tasker; Nail Lacquer Thinner; Nail Lacquers; Nutri-Thick; Protein Boost; Resurface; Tout de Suite; Visionary Cleanser; Well-Connected Massage Creme

THE HIGHLAND SOAP COMPANY ™⊘
Hand Wash: **Ginger&Lemongrass, Scottish Heather, Tea Tree&Lavender**

**THE NATURAL SPA
COMPANY LIMITED** TM☺
All products are vegan

**TISSERAND
AROMATHERAPY PRODUCTS** TM☺
**Wild rose & Lemon Leaf handwash;
Wild rose & Lemon Leaf
rejuvenating hand and nail cream;**
Hand & Foot Care: **Hand & Nail
Cream;** *Hand nourishment:* **Essential
oil Rich Hand and Nail Cream;** *Hand
washes:* **Tea tree, Mandarin and
Bergamot Hand Wash;** *Lavender
Products:* **Lavender and Balm Mint
Hand Wash, Lavender Hand Cream**

TREASURED EARTH SKINCARE TM☺⊘
Hand Cream

ULTRA GLOW COSMETICS ☺✔
High gloss nail colour: Birch, Candyfloss,
Classic, Clear, Flame, Fushia, Pink
shimmer, Praline, Raspberry, Silver lilac

VERDESATIVA S.R.L. TM☺
Barrier Hand Cream

VINDOTCO UK LTD TM☺⊘✔
Really Works: **Nail Polish Remover**

LIP PRODUCTS

BEAUTY NATURALS ✔
Aloe Vera Lip Balm

BURT'S BEES ⊘✔👁
Medicated Lip Balm

DOLMA TM☺❶⊘✔👁⚹1976
Honesty Lip Balm

ECO LIPS, INC TM
Lip Balms: **Bee Free Lemon & Lime**

EVEOLUTION BEAUTY LIMITED ☺
Mystery Kiss Lip Enhancer

GREEN PEOPLE CO. TM☺✔
Cool Lips Lip Balm; *Lip Care:* **Soft
Lips ("No Scent")**

GREEN WYCH TM☺❶
Lip Balm: **Bergamot, Fragrance free,
Peppermint**

HEDGECRAFT TM☺⊘
Kiss This! Lip Balm Range: **Mandarin,
Peppermint & vit E, Peppermint and
grapefruit, Sweet Orange&vit E,
Vanilla**

HOLISTIX TM❶
Choc Orange Lip Balm

HONESTY COSMETICS LTD
TM☺❶⊘✔👁⚹1976
Honesty Unscented Range: **Lip Balm**

I AM NATURAL TM
Lip Balm: **Organic Chamomile &
Cocoa Lipbalm, Organic Hemp
Lipbalm, Organic Lime & Lavender**

LAVERANA ™ ✔
Basis Sensitiv: **Lip Balm SPF15**

LONGCROFT SOAP COMPANY ™
Minty Vegan Lip Butter

MAJIK BLANKIT SKIN CARE ™☺ ✔
**Coconut Shimmer Lip Balm; Hint
&Tint Lip balm; Lemon & Lime Lip
Balm; Natural Lipbalm; Orange &
Mandarin Lip Balm; Peppermint Lip
Balm; Spearmint Hemp Lip Balm;
Sweet Fennel Lip Balm; Vitamin E &
Mango Butter Lip Balm SPF 5**

NEVER TOO BUSY TO BE BEAUTIFUL
™ ✔
Lip Barrier

NO COWS ☺❶
No Cows Lip Balm

NOTHING NASTY ✔
Rosemary & Vanilla Balm

PURE GAISHA ™☺❶ ✔
Lip Balm

RAW GAIA ™☺ ✔
**Lip Balm - Sweet Orange; Lip Balm -
Sweet Peppermint**

SHELLBELLES ☺❶
Lip Balm: Lemon and Lime, Peppermint,
Raw Chocolate, Vanilla

**TISSERAND AROMATHERAPY
PRODUCTS** ™☺
Fresh face: **Tea tree and Mandarin lip**

butter; *Tea Tree Products:* **Tea Tree &
Mandarin Lip Balm**

VEGAN STORE ™☺❶⊘ ✔
All

VISIONARY SOAP COMPANY ™☺
Lip Balms: **Grapefruit, Lemon,
Orange, Peppermint**

YAOH ™☺❶⊘ ✔
Salve; *Lip Balm:* **Blueberry, Coconut,
Mango, Spearmint, Strawberries
and Cream**

PERFUMES ETC

AKAMUTI
Flower Waters: All; *Pulse Points:* All

BRONNLEY & CO LTD ✔
Body Care for Men: Eau do Toilette;
Cologne: Apricot & Almond, English
Fern, Lavender, Orchid, Pink Bouquet,
White Iris; *Eau de Parfum:* Tulip; *Eau de
Toilette:* Apricot & Almond, Lavender,
Pink Bouquet, White Iris; *Eau Fraiche:*
Africa, Asia, Caribbean, Europe, India,
Mediterranean; *Royal Horticultural
Society - Eau Fraiche:* Passion Flower,
Rose

BURT'S BEES ⊘ ✔ 👁
Bay Rum Cologne

DOLMA ™☺❶⊘ ✔ ✈ 1976
Vegan Perfumes: **Amethyst Mist,
Anahita, Calista, Compassion,**

Cushie B, Keltina, Prelude, Raga, Sarabande, Sonata, Vegamusk

ESSENTIALLY NATURAL ™
Chill Out! Lavender Roll-On (Organic); Chill Out! Sandalwood Roll-On (Organic)

FLORIS ☺ ❤
Eau de Parfum Atomiser: Bouquet De La Reine, Cefiro, China Rose, Edwardian Bouquet, Night Scented Jasmine, Seringa, White Rose; *Eau de Toilette Atomiser:* Cefiro, China Rose, Edwardian Bouquet, Fleur, Florissa, Lily of the Valley, Malmaison, Night Scented Jasmine, No. 127, Seringa, Stephanotis, White Rose, Zinnia

GREEN VALLEY TRADING CO. ™☺
All products are vegan

LUSH ™ ❤
Fragrance: **Ginger;** *Fragrance Spritzer:* **Dirty, Go Green;** *Fragrances:* **Flower Market, Icon;** *Karma Products:* **Karma Atomiser;** *Solid Perfumes:* **American Cream, Dirty, Fever, Go Green, Honey I Washed The Kids, Karma, Potion, Silky Underwear**

NATURE'S GATE
Organics: Labrinto, Presento, Sicuro

NEAL'S YARD REMEDIES
⊘ ❤ 👁 ✈ 1998
Cologne

NEVER TOO BUSY TO BE BEAUTIFUL ™ ❤
1000 Kisses Deep: **Fragrance, Pomander;** *2 Hearts Beating As One:* **Fragrance;** *B Scent:* **Body Spray, Fragrance;** *Breath of God:* **Exhale body spray, Fragrance, Inhale body spray;** *Cocktail:* **Fragrance;** *Dear John:* **Body Spray, Fragrance;** *Dirty:* **Body Spray, Fragrance;** *Keep It Fluffy:* **Creme Perfume, Fragrance;** *Love:* **Body Spray, Fragrance**

POTIONS AND POSSIBILITIES ⊘ ❤
Perfumes: Divinity Cologne, Energy Perfume, Serenity Perfume

PURE GAISHA ™☺❶❤
Solid Perfume

RAW GAIA ™☺ ❤
MSM Beauty Spray - Frankincense & Argan

REN ⊘
Cologne

STELLA MCCARTNEY
Sheer Stella: Eau de Toilette; *Stella:* Eau de Parfum, Eau de Parfum Natural Spray, Parfum; *Stella in Two:* Peony Eau de Toilette Natural Spray (Not Amber); *Stella Rose Absolute:* Eau de Parfum, Eau de Parfum Natural Spray

THE PERFUMERS GUILD ☺❶⊘ ❤
All

TISSERAND AROMATHERAPY PRODUCTS ™☺
Wild rose pulse point perfume; *Pure skin perfumes- precious oils in organic jojoba:* **Jasmine absolute in Organic Jojoba, Orange blossom (neroli) in Organic Jojoba, Rose absolute in Organic Jojoba**

TREE-HARVEST ⊘ 🖐
Frankincense & Geranium Moisturiser; Tea Tree Cream; *Tree Colognes:* Cypress, Juniper, Moss, Rowan

VEGAN STORE ™☺❶⊘ 🖐
All

SHAMPOOS

A. VOGEL
Neemcare: Riddance

ABSOLUTE AROMAS ™⊘ 🖐
Ord River: 250ml

AHIMSA COSMETICS ™☺
Hair Shampoo

ALOE PURA 🖐
Organic Aloe Vera Herbal Shampoo Normal/Frequent Use

ALTERNATIVE STORES ™☺❶
All products are vegan

ANIMAL AID SOCIETY ™☺❶⊘ 🖐♨1976
Amber Shampoo; Jojoba Orange &

Rosemary; Sea Spray; Tea Tree & Coconut; Woodspice Shampoo

ANN ELISE SKINCARE ☺
Nourishing & Conditioning Shampoo with Organic Lavender, Chamomile and Rosemary

BAREFOOT BOTANICALS ⊘ 🖐
SOS: Intensive Care Dry Scalp Shampoo

BEAUTY NATURALS 🖐
Deep Moisturising; Gentle Balancing; Protein Enriched; *Martha Hill Purely Natural Haircare:* Enhancing, Mild & Gentle, Moisturising, Treatment, Volumising

BURT'S BEES ⊘ 🖐 👁
Rosemary Mint Shampoo Bar

CAURNIE SOAPERIE ☺⊘ 🖐♨1976
Shampoo: All

CAWARRA COSMETICS LTD ™
OrganicSpa: **Shampoo For Dry Hair, Shampoo For Normal Hair, Shampoo For Treated Hair;** *Sanctum:* **Men's Shampoo / Body Wash, Shampoo - Dry, Shampoo - Normal, Shampoo - Treated**

DANIEL FIELD LABORATORY LTD ™☺
FFP Research Limited- Free From Sensitive Skin Hair Care: **Frequent shampoo, Smooth&shine shampoo, Volumising shampoo**

DESERT ESSENCE ⊘ ✦ ⚹ 1985
Organics: Green Apple & Ginger, Italian Red Grape, Lemon Tea Tree, Red Raspberry

DM-DROGERIE MARKT GMBH & CO KG ™
dm alverde: **Pflege Shampoo Aloe / Hibiskus, Pflege Shampoo Birke / Salbei, Pflege Shampoo Olive / Henna**

DOLMA ™☺❶⊘ ✦ ⚖ ⚹ 1976
Hair Preparations: **Jojoba & Sandalwood;** *Nettle & Pectin Hair Shampoos:* **Bitter Orange & Tangerine, Cedarwood & Cypress, Lavender & Sage, Rosemary, Tea Tree & Thyme**

EARTHPURE ☺ ✦
Luxury Shampoo Bar: Geranium and Lavender (Normal Hair), May Chang (Normal to Oily Hair)

ESSENTIAL CARE
Haircare: Gentle Herb Shampoo, Tea Tree & Herb Shampoo

ESSENTIALLY NATURAL ™
Chamomile Soother Shampoo Bar (Organic); Nettle, Marshmallow and Rosemary Shampoo Bar (Organic)

ESSENTIALLY YOURS LTD ™☺☺ ✦ ⚖
Natural Elements: **Conditioning;**
Therapeutics Range: **E Hair & Body**

FAITH PRODUCTS LIMITED
™ ✦ ⚖ ⚹ 1988
Aloe Vera 400ml / 5 Ltr; Chocolate 400ml / 5 Ltr; Ginkgo Biloba 400ml / 5 Ltr; Hemp and Meadowfoam 400ml / 5 Ltr; Jojoba 400ml / 5 Ltr; Lavender and Geranium 400ml / 5 Ltr; Rosemary 400ml / 5 Ltr; Seaweed 400ml / 5 Ltr; Tea Tree 400ml/ 5 Ltr

FIGS & ROUGE ™☺
Shampoo

FLORIS ☺ ✦
Conditioning Shampoo; *Natural Benefits:* Shine Boosting Conditioning Shampoo

FOREVER LIVING PRODUCTS
Aloe Jojoba Shampoo

FREERANGERS ™☺ ✦
Mane Taming Conditioning Shampoo

FUNK BUBBLE ™☺
Jojoba; Lavender/Geranium; Tea Tree; *Organic:* **Aloe Vera, Chocolate**

GREEN PEOPLE CO. ™⊘ ✦
6 Vitamin Boost Hair & Body Wash; Nourishing Spa Shampoo; Volume Building Spa Shampoo; *Hair & Body Care:* **Aloe Vera Herbal, Intensive Repair, Moisturising Shampoo, Rosemary Herbal, Vita Min Fix;** *Men's Range:* **Itch Away;** *Organic Base:* **Shampoo**

GREEN VALLEY TRADING CO. ™☺
All products are vegan

GREEN WYCH ™☺❶
Shampoo: **Bayleaf and Sweet Orange, Nettle and Lavender, Rosemary and Geranium**

HEALTHQUEST LIMITED ™⊘✔
Organic Blue- Body Care: **Normal/Dry, Normal/Greasy;** *Pure Adore:* **Chamomile Shampoo & Bodywash, Lavender Shampoo & Bodywash, Mandarin Shampoo & Bodywash**

HEMP GARDEN ™
Shampoo: **Carrot & Nettle for dry/damaged hair, Kelp & Cucumber for all hair types, Sage and Echinacea for lacklustre/greasy hair**

HERBS HANDS HEALING LTD ™⊘✔
Head & Hair

HERBSGO LIMITED T/A CLIVE FOOT ™☺
Clive Foot: **Kelp and Olive Oil, Orange and Cider, Patchouli and Tea Tree, Soya and Kelp**

HOLISTIX ™❶
Neem Shampoo Bar

HONESTY COSMETICS LTD
™☺❶⊘✔👁⚓1976
Chamomile & Orange; Hair & Body; Lemon & Vanilla; Nettle & Lavender; Peach & Coconut; *Honesty Essential Range:* **Nettle & Lavender Shampoo;** *Honesty Fruit Range:* **Apple &**

Rosemary Conditioning Shampoo, Lemon & Vanilla Shampoo, Orange & Chamomille Shampoo, Peach & Coconut Shampoo; *Honesty Unscented Range:* **Hair & Body Shampoo**

HOWAD LTD T/A INCOGNITO ™❶⊘✔
Java Citronella 2 in 1 Shampoo&Conditioner

I AM NATURAL ™
Shampoo: **Organic Lavender & Geranium Shampoo for Dry Hair, Organic Lime and Rosemary For Oily Hair, Organic Tea Tree - Anti Dandruff**

ID AROMATICS
Shampoo Base (Essential Oils Can Be Added); *Organic shampoo bars:* Neem& kukui psoriasis soap shampoo

INNGINNI LIMITED (OHSOBO) ™☺
Ohsobo: **Anti-Dandruff Shampoo with Bergamot, Shampoo - Original Formula**

JASON NATURAL PRODUCTS ✔👁
84% Pure Aloe Vera Shampoo; Damage Control; Dandruff Relief™; Hemp Super Moisturizing; Henna Hi-Lights; Lavender Shampoo Hair Strengthening; Natural Apricot; Natural Biotin Shampoo; Natural Jojoba Shampoo; Natural Sea Kelp; Pro-Vitamin Thin-to-Thick™; Rosewater Shampoo – 70% Organic; Swimmers & Sports™; Tall Grass™; Tea Tree Scalp

TOILETRIES & COSMETICS

Normalizing; Vitamin E with A & C Shampoo; *All Natural Color Enhancing Temporary Shampoos:* Black Hair, Blonde Hair, Brown Hair, Red Hair; *Natural Salon Hair Care:* Kiwi & Apricot Volumizing, Plumeria & Sea Kelp Moisturizing, Rosewater & Chamomile Normalizing

JR LIGGETT ☺ 🐰 👁

Shampoo Bars: Damaged Hair Formula, Herbal Formula, Jojoba & Peppermint, Original Formula

JUNGLESALE LIMITED ™
Neem Herbal Shampoo

KOBASHI ™☺◯ 🐰 👁 ⚘ 1976
Shampoo: **Fragrance Free Base, Wild Tea Tree & Mandarin, Wild Thyme & Lime**

LAVERANA ™ 🐰
Lavera Basis Sensitiv: **Balm Shampoo, Regenerative Shampoo, Vital Shampoo;** *Lavera HAIR:* **Almond Milk Shampoo, Apple Milk Shampoo, Cornflower Shampoo, Lemon Milk Shampoo, Mango Milk Shampoo, Orange Milk Shampoo, Rose Milk Shampoo;** *Lavera Neutral:* **Shower**

LITTLE SATSUMA ™
Little Satsuma: **Rosemary & Tea Tree shampoo bar**

LOVE THE PLANET ™◯
Lemon & Lime Shampoo; Mandarin Shampoo; Tea Tree & Mint Shampoo

LUSH ™ 🐰
Ice Blue Shampoo; Washday Greens Shampoo; *Hair care:* **Antiphilitron Shampoo, Gentle Lentil Solid Shampoo, Ibiza Party;** *Liquid Shampoos:* **Big, Cynthia Sylvia Stout, Daddyo, I Love Juicy, Rehab;** *Shampoo Bars:* **Jumping Juniper, Karma Comba, New, Seanik, Soak and Float, Soft, Squeaky Green, Ultimate Shine;** *Solid Shampoos:* **Reincarnate, The Blonde, Trichomania**

MORROCCO METHOD
Apple Cider Vinegar Natural Holistic; *Holistic Organic:* Earth Essence, Pine Shale, Sea Essence

NATURA ORGANICS ◯ 🐰 ✿
Fortifying with Vitamin E, Nettle and Lemon; Nourishing with Jojoba, Vitamin E and Aloe Vera

NATURAL SENSE ™
Shampoo

NATURE'S GATE
Aloe Vera Moisturizing Shampoo; Awapuhi Volumizing Shampoo; Biotin Strengthening Shampoo; Chamomile Replenishing Shampoo; Hemp Nourishing Shampoo; Henna Shine Enhancing Shampoo; Herbal Daily Shampoo; Jojoba Revitalizing Shampoo; Pomegranate Sunflower Shampoo; Rainwater Clarifying Shampoo; Tea Tree Calming Shampoo; *Organics - Fruit Blend:* Asian Pear & Red Tea, Grapefruit & Wild Ginger, Mandarin Orange & Patchouli,

Persimmon & Rose Geranium; *Organics - Herbal Blend:* Chamomile & Lemon Verbena, Lavender & Aloe, Lemongrass & Clary Sage, Tea Tree & Blue Cypress

NEAL'S YARD REMEDIES

⊘ 🖋 ☻ ⚘ 1998
Baseline; Calendula; Chamomile & Orange Flower; Coconut & Jojoba; Nettle & Sage; Rosemary & Thyme; Seaweed

NEVER TOO BUSY TO BE BEAUTIFUL ™ 🖋

Botanomancy: **Black Tang Shampoo, Serpentine Shampoo;** *Dirty:* **Shampoo**

NO COWS ☺❶

No Cows 2 in 1 Shampoo and Conditioner; No Cows Everyday Shampoo; No Cows Extra Help Shampoo

OPTIMAH HEALTH & NUTRITION

⊘ 🖋 ⚘ 1995
Raw Aloe: Shampoo with Tea Tree, Vitamin B5 & Citrus Oils

ORGANIC SOAP COMPANY ™⊘✿

Organic Shampoo Bars: **Anti dandruff shampoo- Seaweed and Sage, Anti headlice shampoo- Neem and Tea Tree, Chamomile and Orange, Mandarin and Orange Blossom, Nettle and Horsetail, Organic Shampoo For Dogs, Tea Tree, Tea Tree and Peppermint;**
Shampoo/Conditioner Bars: **Anti**

Headlice, Chamomile & Orange Blossom, Nettle & Horsetail, Seaweed & Sage, Specially for Mums - Orange Blossom

PAUL PENDERS CO ™

Jasmine Shampoo; Lemon Perfecting Rinse; Rosemary Shampoo; Walnut Oil Shampoo

POTIONS AND POSSIBILITIES ⊘ 🖋

Hair Shampoo: Essential Moisture Repair, Tea Tree Shampoo

PZ CUSSONS UK LTD ™⊘ 🖋

Original Source Shampoos: **Almond & Coconut, Tea Tree & Mint, White Pear and Avocado**

QUINESSENCE AROMATHERAPY

☺⊘ 🖋 ☻
Frequent Shampoo; Mild Shampoo Base; Tea Tree

REN ⊘

Moringa Seed Micro-Protein Universal Shampoo

SANMAR GMBH ™

Repair Shampoo; *Hair and Body:* **Ylang Ylang;** *Repair Shampoo:* **Lemongrass**

SHANTI PRODUCTS ⊘ 🖋

Herbal Shampoo

SIMPLE 🖋

Shampoo: Colour Protect, Frequent

SIMPLY SOAPS ™❶◇✎✍●⚡ 2003
Cleansing Body Shampoo; Invigorating Shower Shampoo; *Shampoo Bars:* **Chamomile, Rosemary & Lavender**

SOLARAY NUTRITIONAL SUPPLEMENTS
Blue Camomile Hydrating; Calaguala Fern Treatment; Chamomile Luxurious Volumising; Ginseng Biotin; Green Tea; Honeysuckle Rose Moisturising; J.A.Y. Revitalising; Primrose & Lavender Scalp-Soothing; Rosa Mesqueta Rose Hip Nourishing; Selenium Natural Treatment; Swimmers

SUKI PURE SKIN CARE
Clean Balance with Yerba Protein & Sugar Extracts

SUMA WHOLEFOODS
™❶◇✎✍●⚡1985
Clear & Simple; Grapefruit & Aloe Vera; Rose Petal & Geranium; White Lavender

TARA SMITH LIMITED ™◇
Tara Smith: **Big Baby Shampoo, C Curl Shampoo, Feed The Root Shampoo, Shampoo for Straight Hair**

THE CRUELTY FREE SHOP ™☺❶
All products are vegan

THE HIGHLAND SOAP COMPANY ™◇
Rosemary&Wild Nettle; Shampoo Bar; Wild Nettle&Heather Shampoo

THE NATURAL SKINCARE COMPANY LTD ™
Paul Penders: **Jasmine Shampoo,**

Rosemary Shampoo, ShampooFORTE, ShampooGENTLE

TINTS OF NATURE ◇✎
Shampoo (Not sulphate Free)

TISSERAND AROMATHERAPY PRODUCTS ™☺
Lavender Products: **Lavender & Mint Conditioning;** *Tea Tree Products:* **Tea Tree Lemon & Rosemary, Tea Tree, Lemon and Rosemary Balancing Shampoo**

TREE-HARVEST ◇✎
Organic shampoo bars: Neem, Tropical Coconut

TRUTHFUL CO. LTD (PURELY SKINCARE) ™☺◇
Purely Skincare: **Shampoo- normal/oily variant, Shampoo- sensitive variant, Shampoo- Volumising Variant, Shampoo-Smooth and Sleek variant**

URTEKRAM ◇✎●⚡1998
Shampoo: All

VERDESATIVA S.R.L. ™☺
Purifying Cream Shampoo - Hemp and White Mud; Restoring Shampoo - Shine and Volume; Shampoo Antiforfora Canapa e Betulla (Anti-dandruff Shampoo Hemp and Birch); Shampoo Delicato Canapa e Proteine Del Grano(Mild Shampoo Hemp and Wheat Proteins); Shampoo Doccia Fitness & Sport - 200ml(Fitness & Sport Shampoo and

Bath/Shower Gel); Shampoo Energizzante Canapa e Ginseng(Energising Shampoo for Prevention of Hairloss); Shampoo Fitness and Sport - 1 litre; Shampoo per Capelli Grassi Canapa e Tea Tree(Equilibratine Shampoo for Greasy Hair)

VINDOTCO UK LTD TM☺⊘ ⒤
Really Works: **Hand & Body Soap/Shampoo**

WELEDA ⊘ ⒤ ⅍ 1985
Calendula Shampoo; Lemon Balm Shampoo; Rosemary Shampoo; Rosemary Shampoo (tube)

YAOH TM☺❶⊘ ⒤
Shampoo

SHAVING PRODUCTS

ANNEMARIE BORLIND ⒤
Natural Care - For Men: Caring Shaving Cream

BAREFOOT BOTANICALS ⊘ ⒤
SOS: Calm Down Post-Shave Face Balm, Close Shave Hydrating Shaving Cream

BEAUTY NATURALS ⒤
David Hill for Men: Cleansing & Shaving Gel, Skin Calming Shaving Oil, Skin Soothing Cream Shave

BRONNLEY & CO LTD ⒤
Body Care for Men: After Shave, After Shave Balm, Shaving Cream

BURT'S BEES ⊘ ⒤ ☻
Bay Rum: Shaving Soap

CAWARRA COSMETICS LTD TM
Organic Soap Shave; *Sanctum:* **Men's Shaving Gel**

DOLMA TM☺❶⊘ ⒤ ☻⅍ 1976
Especially For Men: **Freedom After Shave Cologne, Wet Shaving Fluid**

DROYT PRODUCTS ⊘ ⒤ ⅍ 1984
Shaving Soap

EARTHPURE ☺ ⒤
Soap Bars: Shaving Bar

ESSENTIALLY NATURAL TM
Lime and Lavender Shaving Soap (Organic)

ESSENTIALLY YOURS LTD TM☺⊘ ⒤ ☻
Men's Range: **Shave gel, Shave oil;** *Natural Elements:* **Depilatory Shave Oil, Easy Shave for Men**

FLORIS ☺ ⒤
Conditioning Shaving Cream: Elite, JF, No 89, Santal; *Eau de Toilette Atomiser:* Elite, JF, Limes, No 89, Santal, Vetiver; *Shaving Soap and Bowl:* Elite, JF, No 89; *Shaving Soap Refill:* Elite, JF, No 89

TOILETRIES & COSMETICS

GREEN PEOPLE CO. ™⊘✔
Men's Range: **Pre-Shave Face Wash, Shave Now Shaving Gel**

HERBS HANDS HEALING LTD ™⊘✔
Splash on Toner; Sunrise After Shave Water

INNOCENT OILS ™☺⊘✔
Innocent Shave Oil

ITS ELIXIR UK LIMITED ™⊘✔☜
Shaving oil - women; Shaving oil Men; Shaving oil men sensitive

JASON NATURAL PRODUCTS ✔☜
All Natural After Shave Tonic; All Natural Shaving Lotion

JR LIGGETT ☺✔☜
Shaving Foam

LIZ EARLE ✔☜
Skincare for Men: After-Shaving Moisturiser, Sensitive Shave Cream

LUSH ™✔
Shave the Planet Shaving Cream

MAJIK BLANKIT SKIN CARE ™☺✔
Jojoba & Cocoa Butter Shave Lotion; Organic Calendula and Rosewood shave oil

NATURAL SENSE ™
Shaving Oil

NATURE'S GATE
Organics - Herbal Blend Shave Tubes:
Cucumber & Mint, Lavender & Aloe, Lemongrass & Clary Sage

NEAL'S YARD REMEDIES
⊘✔☞1998
After Shave Balm; Lavender & Vitamin E Shaving Soap; Shaving Oil; *Shaving Cream:* Red Clay

NEVER TOO BUSY TO BE BEAUTIFUL ™✔
Dirty: **Shaving Cream**

NEW SEASONS ⊘✔
After Shave Gel

NOTHING NASTY ✔
Smoothly Does it Shave Oil

ORGANIC SOAP COMPANY ™⊘✿
Organic Shaving Bars: **Buccaneer Shave, Old Original Shave, Patchouli Shave, Tea Tree Shave, Zanzybar shaving bar;** *Shaving Soaps:* **Old Original, Patchouli Peculier Shave, Tea Tree**

PURE GAISHA ™☺❶✔
Soothing Shaving Balm - For Men

PZ CUSSONS UK LTD ™⊘✔
Original Source Shave Gel: **Tea Tree & Mint;** *Original Source After Shave:* **Whole Leaf Aloe Ginseng After Shave Balm;** *Original Source Shave Gel:* **Avocado & Aloe Vera Shave Gel, Lime**

REN ⊘
Multi-Tasking After Shave Balm;
Tamanu High Glide Shaving Oil

SIMPLE ✔
Daily Face Wash; *Balm:* Cooling,
Soothing; *Shave:* Foam, Gel, Silicon Gel

SIMPLY SOAPS ™❶⊘✔☜❄ 2003
Shaving Bars: **Eucalyptus & Lavender**

**SOLARAY NUTRITIONAL
SUPPLEMENTS**
Northwoods Shaving Cream

THE HIGHLAND SOAP COMPANY
™⊘
Soaps: **Shaving soap**

TREE-HARVEST ⊘✔
Shaving Soap Bowl: Bay, Juniper,
Patchouli & Sandlewood

VERDESATIVA S.R.L. ™☺
**Emulsione Post Depilazione (Post-
Depilation Lotion)**

SKIN CARE
- MASKS, WRAPS, ETC

AKAMUTI
Clay Mask Pack

ANNEMARIE BORLIND ✔
Beauty Extras: Anti-Stress Mask,
Exfoliating Peel; *LL Regeneration Series:*

Moisturising Cream Mask, Vital Cream
Mask; *Purifying Care Series:* Cleansing
Mask

BAREFOOT BOTANICALS ⊘✔
Rosa Fina: Masquerade Rejuvenating
Masque

BEAUTY NATURALS ✔
Facial Care - Treatments: Seaweed
Peeling Mask; *Skin Revivals - Refining:*
Hydrating Gel Mask

BIO-OIL
Specialist Skincare Oil: For the
Treatment of Scars and Stretch Marks

BURT'S BEES ⊘✔☜
Healthy Treatment: Pore-Refining Mask

CAWARRA COSMETICS LTD ™
OrganicSpa: **Body Mask, Clay Mask,
Face Exfoliant, Gel Mask, Treatment C,
Treatment Clay Mixed;** *Sanctum:*
**Hydrating Gel Mask, Purifying Clay
Mask**

CEBRA ETHICAL CHIC ™⊘✔
Cebra- ethical skin care: **Glacial Mud
Masque**

DAIVITA ™☺
Mantra: **Scrub**

DOLMA ™☺❶⊘✔☜❄1976
Skin Care: **Honesty Facial Mask**

DR HAUSCHKA ⊘✔
Facial Steam Bath

ESSENTIALLY YOURS LTD ™☺⊘✍👁
Fragrance Free Range: **Face mask;**
Men's Range: **Face mask, Scrub;**
Natural Elements: **Combination/Oily Face Mask, Dry/Mature Face Mask, Face mask, Normal Face Mask**

FAITH PRODUCTS LIMITED
™✍👁⚹1988
Purifying Facial Wash 150ml

FOREVER LIVING PRODUCTS
Aloe Scrub

GREEN PEOPLE CO. ™⊘✍
Spa Purifying Mineral Mask; *Skin Care:* **Vita Min Mask**

HERBS OF GRACE ™⊘✍
Miscellaneous: **Bentonite Clay**

HOWAD LTD T/A INCOGNITO ™❶⊘✍
100% Natural Deep Sea Scrub

I AM NATURAL ™
Organic Ylang Ylang & Tea Tree Face Mask

INNOCENT OILS ™☺⊘✍
Innocent Angel Face Scrub

ITS ELIXIR UK LIMITED ™⊘✍👁
Face scrubbing gel; Peeling cream-dry skin; Peeling cream- oily skin; Peeling cream- sensitive skin

JASON NATURAL PRODUCTS ✍👁
Ester-C®® Skin Care: C-Lite™ Skin Tone Balancer, Ester-C®® Hydrating

Masque, Hyper-C Serum™ Anti-Aging Therapy, Vita-C Max™ One Minute Facial

LAVERANA ™✍
Lavere: **Body-Effect Active Body Scrub, Hydro Energy Effect Gel Facial Mask, Hydro Energy Peel**

LIZ EARLE ✍👁
Energising Hip and Thigh Gel; New Energising Body Scrub

LONGCROFT SOAP COMPANY ™
Kiwi Face Mask

LUSH ™✍
Bio Fresh: **Catastrophe Cosmetic, Cupcake**

MAJIK BLANKIT SKIN CARE ™☺✍
Mandarin & Apricot Body Scrub

MONTAGNE JEUNESSE ⊘✍
Green Tea Chin & Forehead Strips; Orange Nose Strips; Tea Tree Blemish Dots; *Face Masque:* Collagen, Cucumber Peel-Off, Dead Sea Mud Tired Skin Reviving, Microderma Abrasion, Peach Kernel & Walnut Exfoliating, Peel Off Deep Pore Cleaning, Pore Refining, Red Hot Earth Sauna; *Masque:* Algae & Dead Sea Salt Cellulite Body Mud, Anti Cellulite Body Mud; *Night Face Masque:* Marine Algae & Shea Butter Ultra Firming, Pomegranate & Nori Juice Ultra Moisturising

NATURA ORGANICS ⊘ ☼
Hydrating Mask; Purifying Mask

NATURAL SENSE ™
Chocolate Dreams Face Mask

NATURE'S GATE
Organics - Advanced Care: Microdermabrasion System, Natural Results Acne Extra Strength Spot Corrector, Natural Results Acne Treatment Kit

NEVER TOO BUSY TO BE BEAUTIFUL ™
Mint Julips Sugar Scrub

NEW SEASONS ⊘
Gentle Face Mask

OPTIMAH HEALTH & NUTRITION
⊘ ✂1995
Raw Aloe: Cellulite Massage Gel

ORGANIC BOTANICS ™⊘☼
Refining French Clay & Seaweed Creamy Face Mask

PAUL PENDERS CO ™
Ceramide Recovery Lipo A, C & E; Ceramide Recovery LipoA, C&E; Rescue Blemish Away; Whitening Aqualuna

PINKS BOUTIQUE ™☺
Himalayan Rock Salt Foot Scrub

PURE GAISHA ™J❶
Clay Face Mask - Mature Skin; Clay Face Mask - Normal Skin; Wake Up and Smell The Coffee Scrub

PURPLE FLAME AROMATHERAPY
⊘
Green Clay Powder

PZ CUSSONS UK LTD ™⊘
Original Source Body Scrub: **Bitter Orange & Crushed Sweet Almond Body Scrub**

QUINESSENCE AROMATHERAPY
☺⊘ 👁
Marine Clay Mask

RARE NATURAL CARE, INC. ™☺⊘
Rare2B Vegan Skincare: **Detox facial Mask**

RAW GAIA ™☺
Raw Chocolate Face Pack; Sun-Dried Green Clay Face Pack

REN ⊘
Body Scrubs: Ginger, Revivo-Tonic Two Sugar Body Scrub, Guerande Salt Exfoliating Body Balm, Monoi and Shea Butter Body Balm; *Face Masks:* F10 Enzymatic Smooth Radiance Facial Mask, Glycolactic Skin Renewal Peel Mask, Jiaogulan Revitalising Facial Mask, Multi-Mineral Detoxifying Facial Mask, Phyto-Dynamic Instant Lifting Gel

SANMAR GMBH ™
2 Phases Mask; Bodypeeling; Kaolina; Terra Vita Pure; *Vleur:* **Kaolin Maske, Peeling 2 in 1, Terra Vital Maske**

SHELLBELLES ☺❶
Face Mask: Green Clay for Normal-Oily Skin, Pink Clay for Sensitive Skin

SIMPLE ✔
Deep Cleansing Face Mask; Nourishing Moisture Mask

SIMPLY SOAPS ™❶⊘✔ ☞⅄ 2003
Hedgerow Herbals: **Purifying Green French Clay**

SKINCARE CAFE LTD ™☺
Organic grapeseed & aloe vera exfoliator; Organic rose petals body scrub

SKINVAC ™☺⊘✔
Exfoliation Cloth

SOLARAY NUTRITIONAL SUPPLEMENTS
Mask: Blue Green Algae, Green Tea & Green Clay, Natural Herbal Sea Clay with Goa Herb Oil, Rosa Mosqueta Jojoba & Oatmeal, Sea Buckthorn, Vegecol with Organic Aloe & Oatmeal

SOPHYTO LTD ™
Polyphenol Skin Drops; Purifying Active Mask; Refining Active Mask; Revitalising Active Mask

SUKI PURE SKIN CARE
Transformative Facial Clay with Green Tea Roses & White Willow

SUPERDRUG
Amie: New Leaf Skin Exfoliating Polish

THE NATURAL SKINCARE COMPANY LTD ™
Paul Penders: **Intensive Clarifying Therapy**

THE NATURAL SPA COMPANY LIMITED ™☺
All products are vegan

TISSERAND AROMATHERAPY PRODUCTS ™☺
Skin treatments and solutions: **Tea tree and Kanuka gel**

TREASURED EARTH SKINCARE ™☺⊘
Face Scrub

WELEDA ⊘✔ ⅄1985
Almond Range: Facial Masque; *Iris Range:* Iris Facial Masque, Iris Intensive Treatment Masque; *Wild Rose Facial Care:* Wild Rose Intensive Facial Masque

SKIN CARE - MOISTURISERS & BODY LOTIONS

ABSOLUTE AROMAS ™⊘✔
Ord River: **Hand & Body Lotion 250ml**

ABSOLUTELY PURE ⊘
Shea Butter

AHIMSA COSMETICS ™☺
Fab Face and Body Oil (For Dry Skin); Fab Face and Body Oil (For Grease Prone Skin); Fab Face and Body Oil

(For Mature Skin); Face and Body Butter; Face and Body Polish

AINSWORTHS
Recovery Cream

AKAMUTI
Replenishing Rose Facial Oil; Shea Soothing Salve; *Body Butter:* Cocoa & Almond, Shea & Olive, Shea Mandarin; *Butter:* Mango, Murumuru, Neem, Organic Cocoa Butter, Red Palm, Shea, Sweet Almond Tree

ALOE PURA ✔
Organic Aloe Vera Gel; Organic Aloe Vera Gel with Tea Tree; Organic Aloe Vera Gel with Vitamins A, C & E

ALTERNATIVE STORES ™☺❶
All products are vegan

ALVIN CONNOR LIMITED ™☺⊘
Natural Balance: **Lavender Body Polish, Natural Body Polish, Rose Body Polish**

AMAZENE ™
Phytophilo Aromatherapy Range- Body Cremes: **Cocoa & Cupuacu, Papaya, Passion Fruit & Acerola, Strawberry n Cream;** *Phytophilo Aromatherapy Range- Body Lotions:* **Green Tea, Aloe Vera & Anise, Lavender, Calendula & Primrose**

ANIMAL AID SOCIETY ™☺❶⊘ ✔ ⚘1976
Apricot & Jojoba Moisturising Cream; Olive Body Cream; Vanilla &

Macadamia Nourishing Cream; *Body Lotion:* **Calendula and Vanilla Moisturising Lotion, Exotic Body Lotion, Unscented Vitamin E Cream, Unscented Vitamin E Lotion**

ANN ELISE SKINCARE ☺
Pure Magic Moisture

ANNEMARIE BORLIND ✔
Aqua Bleu Vitality Gel; *Anne Lind:* Body Lotions (All); *Beauty Extras:* Ceramide Vital Fluid, Facial Firming Gel, Natursome, Skin Whitening Fluid; *Body Effect:* Anti Cellulite Gel, Energising Scrub, Firming Cream; *LL Regeneration Series:* Concentrate Ampoules, Decollete Cream, Moisturising Ampoules; *Natural Care - For Men:* Anti-Ageing Revitalizing Cream, Revitalizing Body Lotion; *Purifying Care Series:* Facial Cream For Day and Night, Ultra Stick; *Young Beauty - Peach Series:* Facial Cream

AROMA COMFORTS ™☺⊘
Ma Ma's Belly Butter; Organic Almond & Cocoa Butter Body Lotion; Skin Comforting Creamy Body Butter

AZIZ CHAIR ™
Argan Oil Basic; Argan Oil Pure

BAREFOOT BOTANICALS ⊘ ✔
Rosa Fina: Hourglass Lifting & Firming Body Lotion, Radiance Anti-ageing Day Cream, Supernatural Instant Youth Serum; *SOS:* Protect Me Daily Body Lotion, Rescue Me Face & Body Cream

BEAUTY NATURALS ✔

Body Oil: Evening Primrose & Lavender, Orange; *Camomile Skin Care:* Moisture Milk; *David Hill for Men:* Extra Rich Treatment Cream, Skin Soothing Daytime Moisturiser; *Evening Primrose:* Moisturiser; *Herbal Skin Care:* No 3 Day Cream; *Martha Hill:* Enriched Body Moisturiser; *Martha Hill Evening Primrose:* Body Lotion; *Moisturiser:* Enriched Body; *Seaweed:* Body Toning Gel, Enriched Body Treatment Cream; *Skin Revivals - Moisturising:* Pure Skin Treatment, Revitalising Cream

BIO-HEALTH LTD ⊘ ✔

Vitamin E Cream; Vitamin E Lotion

BRONNLEY & CO LTD ✔

Body Balm: Africa, Asia, Bird of Paradise, Caribbean, Europe, India, Lavender, Medterranean, Passion Flower, Rose, Tulip; *Body Lotion:* Apricot & Almond, English Fern, Lavender, Orchid, Pink Bouquet, White Iris; *Royal Horticultural Society - Body Balm:* Passion Flower, Rose

BURT'S BEES ⊘ ✔ 👁

Miracle Salve; Peppermint Foot Lotion; Radiance Body Lotion; Repair Serum; *Body Butter:* Richly Repairing, Therapeutic

CAWARRA COSMETICS LTD ™

OrganicSpa: **Body Butter, Body Oil, Day Moisture, Face Oil, Intense Moisture, OS Age Vita Renewal Treatment(Mixed), OS Clay Renewal**

Body Cocoon, OS Hydra Herbal Body Indulgence, Rose Hip Oil, Skin Whitening Cream, Vitamin C Serum, Wrinkle Defense Cream; *Sanctum:* **Body Detox, Body Polish, Body Soothe, Hy C Intensive Repair Cream, Hy C Recovery Serum, Men's Moisture Balance, Moisture Balance Gel, Moisture Concentrate, Moisture Replenish, Night Conditioning Cream, Pure Brightening Serum**

CEBRA ETHICAL CHIC ™⊘ ✔

Cebra- ethical skin care: **Calm Me Down - Skin Soothing Mango Shea Butter, Chocolate Orange Body Soufflé, Perk Me Up Body Oil, Pina Colada Body Soufflé, Summer Fruit Body Soufflé, Whipped Perk Me Up Body Soufflé, Whipped Shea Butter Cream**

DAIVITA ™☺

Mantra: **Anti-Ageing Cream, Body Lotion, Day Cream, Hydration Cream, Night Cream**

DANIEL FIELD LABORATORY LTD ™☺

FFP Research Limited- Free From Sensitive Skin Body Care: **Hand&body moisturiser, Intensive skin balm;** *FFP Research Limited- Free From Sensitive Skin Skin Care:* **Day complex, Face firming serum, Face moisturiser, Night complex**

DESERT ESSENCE ⊘ ✔ ⚶ 1985

Organics Hand and Body Lotion: Almond, Bulgarian Lavender, Coconut, Spicy Citrus, Vanilla Chai

**DM-DROGERIE MARKT
GMBH & CO KG** ™
Alverde Planten & Kosmetik:
**Feuchtigkeits - Ampulle
Meeresalge, Gesichtsööl - Kapseln
Wildrose, Regenerations - Ampulle
Ginseng;** *dm alverde:* **Cellulite
Köörper -ÖÖl Zitrone Rosmarin,
Pflegelotion Olive Aloe-Vera**

DOLMA ™☺❶◎ ✔ ☜ ☞⌇1976
Miscellaneous Body Preparations: **Aloe
Vera Hand & Body Lotion, Ho-Leaf
& Orange Moisturising Body Wash,
Niamh De-luxe Body Lotion;** *Skin
Care:* **Avocado & Ylang Ylang
Moisture Cream, Carotene Enriched
Fragrance Free Moisture Cream,
Carotene Ho-Leaf & Orange
Moisture Cream, Chamomile
Moisture Lotion, De-luxe Facial Oil,
Facial Oil for Dehydrated Skin,
Facial Oil for Dry Skin, Facial Oil for
Mature Skin, Facial Oil for Sensitive
Skin, Facial Oil for Thread Veins,
Fragrance Free Moisture Lotion,
Geranium & Evening Primrose Night
Cream, Wheatgerm & Lavender
Moisture Cream**

DR HAUSCHKA ◎ ✔
Moisturising Day Cream; Normalising
Day Oil; Quince Body Moisturiser; *Body
Oil:* Birch Arnica, Blackthorn, Lavender,
Lemon, Moor Lavender, Rose,
Rosemary, St. John's Wort

EARTHPURE ☺ ✔
Moisturiser: Eastern Rose, Luxurious

Rose, Orange and Frankincense, Pure
and Rich

ESSENTIAL CARE
Skincare: Organic Avocado Replenishing
Cream, Organic Hand & Body Lotion,
Organic Repair Lotion, Organic Rose
Moisturiser

ESSENTIALLY YOURS LTD ™☺◎ ✔ ☞
Day serum; *Fragrance Free Range:*
Moisturiser; *Free&Organic Range:*
Facial oil, Night serum; *LYB Range:*
Body firming gel, Body Lotion;
Men's Range: **Facial oil, Moisturiser;**
My Baby Range: **Body Lotion;** *Natural
Elements:* **Body Lotion,
Combination/Oily Moisturiser,
Combination/Oily Night Gel,
Combination/Oily Serum Gel,
Contour serum, Day serum,
Dry/Mature Cleanser, Dry/Mature
Moisturiser, Dry/Mature Night
Cream, Eye/Neck Gel, Face
Contouring Serum, Firming Gel,
Holistic facial oil, Luxury facial oil,
Moisturiser, Night gel, Night serum,
Normal Moisturiser, Normal Night
Cream, Regenerating facial oil,
Rehydrating facial oil, Seaweed
body lotion;** *Sundry Products:*
**Afterwax lotion, Body wrap gel,
Prewax toner;** *Therapeutics Range:*
**Body Lotion, E Extra Rich Barrier
Cream, E Hand & Body Lotion, E
Moisturising Oil, Extra rich
moisturising cream, Moisturising oil**

EVEOLUTION BEAUTY LIMITED ☺
Base Cream; Body Glow; Body Slender; Body Soufflée

FAITH PRODUCTS LIMITED
™ ✦ ☞ ⚹ 1988
Deep Moisturising Night Cream 50g; Pre natal leg lotion; Preventive stretch mark lotion; Replenishing Moisturising Body Lotion 150ml; Replenishing Moisturising Cream 50ml; Stretch mark lotion

FIGS & ROUGE ™☺
Body Lotion; Body Lotion- rose; Body Lotion-Sweet geranium

FLORAROMA LTD ™
Little Me- Mummylicious: **Mum to Be Care & Cocoon Body Cream, Mum To Be Stretch Mark Body Oil**

FLORIS ☺ ✦
Enriched Body Moisturiser: Cefiro, China Rose, Edwardian Bouquet, Fleur, Florissa, Lily of the Valley, Night Scented Jasmine, Seringa Enriched, Stephanotis, White Rose; *Natural Benefits:* Soothing Skin Balm

FOREVER LIVING PRODUCTS
Aloe Activator; Aloe Vera Gelly; Alpha - E Factor

FREERANGERS ™☺ ✦
Arnica Gel; Funky Finger Hand Cream; Self tan cream; *Pamper Products:* **Hand & Foot Balm**

FUNK BUBBLE ™☺
Jasmin/Lemon Cream; Rose/Wheatgerm Cream; *Body Cream:* **Aloe Vera/Lemon, Chocolate/Orange, Jojoba/Ylang Ylang**

GREEN PEOPLE CO. ™⊘ ✦
Aloe Vera Hand Lotion; Sheer Pamper Body Oil; *Men's Range:* **Cool Down Moisturiser;** *Organic Base:* **Hand/Body Lotion;** *Skin Care:* **Body Comfort (Body Lotion), Day Solution (Day Cream), Fruitful Nights (Night Cream), Vita Min Fix (Day & Night Cream)**

GREEN VALLEY TRADING CO. ™☺
All products are vegan

GREEN WYCH ™☺❶
Cocoa & Almond Body Butter: **Bergamot, Geranium, Lavender, Orange;** *Cocoa & Almond Body Butter:* **Fragrance free;** *Face Cream:* **Bergamot, Fragrance Free, Geranium, Lavender, Sweet Orange**

HEALTHQUEST LIMITED ™⊘ ✦
Earth Friendly Baby: **Chamomile Body Lotion, Lavender Body Lotion, Mandarin Body Lotion;** *Organic Blue-Body Care:* **Body Lotion;** *Organic Blues - Mens:* **Body Lotion;** *Pure Adore:* **Baby Oil, Chamomile Body Lotion, Lavender Body Lotion, Mandarin Body Lotion**

HEMP GARDEN ™
Refining Face Cream; Revitalising

Body Lotion; *Body Oil:* Sensual, Soothing, Stimulating

HERBS HANDS HEALING LTD ™⊘✔
Organic Rose Geranium Body Moisturiser

HIGHER NATURE PLC ™⊘✔
Aloe Vein Gel; MSM Cream Light; MSM Cream Rose; MSM Lotion Rose; Ultimate Aloe Vera Skin Gel

HOLISTIX ™❶
Moisturising Skincare Cream: Calendula, Lavender & Mandarin, Orange, Geranium & Palmarosa, Rose & Frankincense

HONESTY COSMETICS LTD
™☺❶⊘✔👁⚘1976
Honesty Essential Range: Geranium & Ylang Ylang Moisturising Lotion, Lavender & Geranium Moisturising Cream, Olive Body Cream, Rose & Shea Butter Body Cream, Rose Body Lotion; *Honesty Unscented Range:* Cocoa Butter Moisturising Lotion, Grapeseed Oil, Moisturising Cream with Vitamin E, Rich Moisture Cream with Carrot & Jojoba, Sweet Almond Oil; *Unscented Moisturiser:* Cream with Vitamin E, Lotion with Cocoa Butter, Rich Cream with Carrot & Jojoba

HOWAD LTD T/A INCOGNITO ™❶⊘✔
Calendula, ginseng and aloe vera body moisturising lotion

I AM NATURAL ™
Calendula Healing Cream; Organic Cocoa Butter; Organic Cocoa Butter with Ginger; Organic Cocoa Butter with Orange; Organic Frankincense Face Cream; Organic Hemp Protection Balm; Organic Shea Butter; Organic Sweet Orange Body Cream; Organic Tea Tree Gel

ID AROMATICS
Aloe Vera Gel; Cream Base (Essential Oils Can Be Added); Seaweed Cream; *Body Lotions:* Champagne Lotion, Grapefruit & Geranium, Lavender & Rosewood, Peppermint Foot Lotion; *Luxurious Moisturising Creams:* All the Roses, Lavender Flowers, Orange Blossom, Turkish Balsam

INNOCENT OILS ™☺⊘✔
100% Innocent Hemp Seed Oil; Innocent Angel Body Silk; Innocent Angel Butter; Innocent Hemp Seed Oil Balm; Innocent Lavender and Geranium Balm

ITS ELIXIR UK LIMITED ™⊘✔👁
Aloe vera cream; Aloe Vera Gel; Cellulite Gel; Dry skin cream; Evening primrose cream; Night cream; Problem skin cream; Pseudo collagen cream; Rose&lavender; Rosehip cream; Rosehip&vitamin cream; Shea butter moisturiser F; Shea butter moisturiser G; Shea butter moisturiser L; Shea butter moisturiser P; Silk cream; Simple moisturiser; Vitamin C cream; Vitamin cream

TOILETRIES & COSMETICS

JASON NATURAL PRODUCTS 🦋 👁
25,000 IU Vitamin E Age Renewal Moisturizing Crème 70% Organic; Aloe Vera 70% Comforting Moisturizing Crème 70% Organic; Aqua Moist™Balancing Moisture Lotion; Cocoa Butter,Intensive Moisturizing Crème 70% Organic; Hemp Ultra-Rich Moisturizing Crème 70% Organic; Mango Butter; Pro-Vita Moisture Plus; Quick Recovery™Re-Hydrating Lotion; Tea Time Anti-Aging Moisturizing Crème 70% Organic; Wild Yam Balancing Moisturizing Crème 70% Organic; *Alpha Hydroxy Acids:* 10% Plus Nighttime Creme New Cell Therapy™ Alpha Hydroxy Acids Night Time Creme, 12-1/2% Plus Oil-Free Gel New Cell Therapy™ Alpha Hydroxy Acids, 12-1/2% Plus with SPF 12-1/2 Protective Moisturizer New Cell Therapy™ Alpha Hydroxy Acids; *Ester-C®® Skin Care:* Ester-C®® Crème, Ester-C®® Lotion; *Hand & Body Therapy:* Chamomile 70% Organic Hand & Body Therapy, Hemp 70% Organic Hand & Body, Lavender 70% Organic Hand & Body, Vanilla 70% Organic Hand & Body Therapy, Wild Yam 70% Organic Hand & Body Therapy; *Jason:* 5,000 I.U. Vitamin E Revitalizing Moisturizing Crème70% Organic, Aloe Vera 84% Ultra-Comforting Moisturizing Crème70% Organic; *Organic Hand & Body Lotion:* 84% Pure Aloe Vera 70% Organic Hand & Body Lotion, Cocoa Butter 70% Organic Hand & Body Lotion, Glycerine & Rosewater 70% Organic Hand & Body Lotion, Natural Apricot 70% Organic Hand & Body Lotion, Natural EFA 70% Organic Hand and Body Lotion, Vitamin E 70% Organic Hand and Body Lotion; *Organic Pure Beauty Oils:* All; *Red Elements™ Antioxidant Skin Care:* Daily Moisturizing Lotion with SPF 15, Exfoliating Scrub, Hydrating Night Crème, Lifting Eye Crème, Red Clay Masque

JR LIGGETT ☺ 🦋 👁
Body Oil Spray: Lavender, Lemon Lime, White Sage

JUICE BEAUTY 🦋 👁
Antioxidant Serum; Blemish Clearing Serum; Soothing Serum

JUNGLESALE LIMITED ™
Neem Herbal Oil

KOBASHI ™☺⊘ 🦋 👁✈1976
Aloe Vera: **Gel, Liquid;** *Luxury Lotions:* **Fragrance Free Moisturiser, Rose Facial**

KOOCHIE KOO ™
aromababy: **Stretched To The Limit Cream**

LAVERANA ™🦋
Lavera Basis Sensitiv: **Moisturizing Body Lotion;** *Lavera Body Spa:* **Body Lotion (Citrus), Body Lotion (Lavender/Aloe Vera), Body Lotion (Orange/Sea Buckthorn), Body Lotion (Peach/Apricot), Body Lotion (Tiare/Lilly), Body Lotion**

(Vanilla/Coconut), Body Lotion
(Vervain/Lemon), Body Lotion (Wild
Rose), Body Lotion (WildBerry);
Lavera BodySPA Body Oil: **Lavender-
Aloe Vera, Orange-Sea Buckthorn,
Vanilla-Coconut, Vervain-Lime, Wild
Rose;** *Lavera Faces:* **Moisturizing
Cream Wild Rose;** *Lavera Neutral:*
**Body Lotion, Cleansing Gel, Facial
Fluid;** *Lavere:* **Body-Effect Active
Care Body Lotion, Body-Effect
Active Control, Body-Effect Active
Silhouette Spray, Hydro Energy Lift,
Hydro Energy Sensation Cream,
Repair Relax Absolute Day, Repair
Relax Absolute Night, Repair Relax
Impression, Repair Relax Meeting,
Solution Power Glamour, Solution
Power Performance, Solution Power
Promise, Solution Power Royal Day,
Teint Balance;** *Men SPA:* **All-Round
Moisturizing Cream**

LITTLE SATSUMA ™
Lavender, Frankincense and Geranium
Moisturiser; Unscented Moisturiser

LIVE NATIVE ™☺
Essential Woman; Every Body Every
day; Head To Toe For Men; Pure Natal

LIZ EARLE 🖌 👁
Brightening Treatment Mask; Intensive
Nourishing Treatment Mask; Nourishing
Botanical Body Cream; Sheer Gold
Shimmer; Superskin Concentrate; Vital
Oils Body Sprays; *Skin Repair:* Light -
Oily, Moisturiser - Dry, Moisturiser -
Normal

LONGCROFT SOAP COMPANY ™
Orchid Drops Facial Serum; Paradise
Shea Butter; Vanilla Shea Butter

LOVE THE PLANET ™⊘
Eyebright Gel; Grapefruit Body
Butter; Lime Body Butter; Mandarin
Body Butter; Neroli & Bergamot
Moisture Cream; Tea Tree & Lemon
Gel; Tea Tree Moisture Cream

LUSH ™🖌
Paradise Regained Moisturiser; *Body
Butters:* **Aqua Mirabilis, Buffy, King
of Skin, Running To The Embassy,
You Snap The Whip;** *Butter Creams:*
**A Ring Of Roses, Almond Butter,
Lemslip, Skinny Dip;** *Hand And Body
Creams:* **Charity Pot, Dream Cream,
Pied de Pepper, Sympathy for the
Skin;** *Karma Products:* **Karma Kream;**
Moisturisers: **Almond Kisses, Celestial,
Enzymion, Imperialis, Skin Drink,
Ultralight**

MAJIK BLANKIT SKIN CARE ™☺🖌
Hand & Body Cocoa Butter Cream;
Hand & Body Shea Butter Cream;
Veon Organic Shea & Pumpkin Body
Quench

MANDALA AROMA LTD ™☺⊘
Body Lotions: **Courage, Love, Skin
Soothing;** *Organic Body Treatment
Oils:* **Courage, Love, Strength, Wisdom**

MJ HEALTH(NZ) LTD ™☺⊘🖌
*Dr Wendy's 100% Pure Botanical Skin
Care:* **Balanced cream, Gentle**

Moisturiser, Replenish Cream, Ultra Treat Moisturiser

MONTAGNE JEUNESSE ⊘ ✦
Face Tonic: Dead Sea Fabric, Spearmint & Tea Tree Fabric

NATURA ORGANICS ⊘ ✦ ✿
Body Lotion: Nourishing with Aloe Vera, Vitamin E and Grapefruit, Revitalising with Shea Butter, Vitamin E and Mandarin, Soothing with Shea Butter, Vitamin E and Rosemary; *Face Cream:* Hydrating Cream, Purifying Cream

NATURAL SENSE ™
Body Butter; Face and Body Cream; Fade Away Balm

NATURE'S GATE
Colloidal Oatmeal For Itchy Dry Sensitive Skin; Daily SPF 15 Moisture Cream; Fragrance Free Moisturizing Sensitive; Hemp Moisturizing; Herbal Moisturizing Lotion All Types; Papaya Moisturizing All Skin Types; Pomegranate Sunflower Lotion; Skin Therapy Moisturizing; Tea Tree Calming Lotion; Vitamin E Oil; Vitamin E Roll-on; *Organics - Advanced Care:* C For Yourself Serum, Forget Your Lines Serum, Have A Vine Day Cream, Light Switch Serum, Oh What A Night Cream; *Organics - Fruit Blend:* Asian Pear & Red Tea, Grapefruit & Wild Ginger, Mandarin Orange & Patchouli, Persimmon & Rose Geranium; *Organics - Herbal Blend:* Chamomile, Lavender & Aloe, Lemongrass & Clary Sage, Neroli Orange & Chocolate Mint Lotion

NEAL'S YARD REMEDIES
⊘ ✦ ☞⚡1998
Chamomile & Aloe Vera Lotion; Cocoa Butter; Frankincense Nourishing Cream; Jasmine Enriching Cream; *Body Lotion:* English Lavender; *Facial Oil:* Rose; *Night Cream:* Vitamin E & Avocado; *Skin Oil:* Jasmine Nourishing, Soothing; *Toning Body Cream:* Frankincense

NEVER TOO BUSY TO BE BEAUTIFUL ™ ✦
Crème Anglaise; *2 Hearts Beating As One:* **Hand & Body Cream;** *Botanomancy:* **Ianthine - Body Lotion;** *Cocktail:* **Body Lotion;** *Dirty:* **Face Protector;** *Keep It Fluffy:* **Body Lotion, Turkish Bath Body Polish;** *Love:* **Body Lotion**

NEW SEASONS ⊘ ✦
Men's Moisturiser; Relaxing Moisturising Lotion; Rich Rose Moisturising Cream; Travel Moisturiser; *Neutral & Toiletry Bases:* Aloe Vera Gel Base, Moisturising Cream, Moisturising Lotion

NO COWS ☺❶
No Cows Body Lotion; No Cows Day Cream; No Cows Night Cream

NOTHING NASTY ✦
Big Belly Pregnancy Moisturiser; *Facial Moisturiser:* Flawless for Problem Skin, Ideal for Normal Skin, Prime for Mature & Sensitve Skin; *Moisturiser:* Bliss Sensual, Chill Relaxing, Zest Uplifting

ORGANATURAL ™☺ ✦ ◉
Forest Secrets Skincare: **Rejuvenate Step 1 Lifting Pro-Youth Face Oil, Rejuvenate Step 2 Regenerating Skin Serum**

ORGANIC BOTANICS ™⊘✿
Damask Rose & Orange Flower Daily Elixir; Moisturising Nutritive (Extra Rich); Moisturising Nutritive (Medium/Light); Organic Damask Rose and Orange Flower Daily Moisturising Elixir; Organic Fragrance Free Satin Body Lotion; Organic Satin Hand & Body Lotion; Pink Lotus & Jasmine Facial Elixir; Simpler Daily Moisturiser (Essential oil free)

PAUL PENDERS CO ™
Aloe and Lavender AM Moisturiser; Avocado and Cranberry PM Moisturiser; Bio-Marin Aloe Vera Gel; Carotene Body Lotion; Herbal Citrus Fruit Exfoliant; Hibiscus Rose Daytime Moisturiser; Hydrating Control Serum; Intensive Clarifying Therapy; Lavender Body Lotion; Lemon Body Lotion; Mangosteen and Nettle PM Moisturiser; St Johns and Hibiscus AM Moisturiser; Wheatgerm Night Time Moisturiser

PINKS BOUTIQUE ™☺
Himalayan Elixir; Indonesian Elixir

POTIONS AND POSSIBILITIES ⊘ ✦
Beauty: English Garden Hand & Body Lotion, English Lavender Hand & Body Lotion, English Rose Hand & Body Lotion, Essential Night Repair Formula, Evening Primrose Moisture Relief For The Complexion, Hand & Body Lotion, Luxury Body Souffle, Moisture Repair For Complexion Of Men; *Essentials:* Heavy Duty Relief Gel; *Hand & Foot Care:* Foot Relief Cream, Luxury Hand Cream w Lavender; *Organic Range:* Day Cream, Hand & Body Lotion, Night Cream

POTTER'S HERBAL MEDICINE ✦
Skin Clear Ointment

PURATY LTD ☺ ✦
Balancing Body Moisturizer; Balancing Facial Moisturizer; Refreshing Body Moisturizer

PURE GAISHA ™☺❶ ✦
Creamy Body Whip; Decadent Body Lotion; Facial Moisturiser - Dry/Mature Skin; Facial Moisturiser - Normal Skin; Facial Moisturiser - Oily Skin; Facial Toner - Dry/Mature Skin; Mens Hydrating Face Cream; Mineral Body Shimmer; Mineral Bronzer; Rich Body Butter

PURE HEALTH LIMITED ™
100% Shea Butter; 100% Shea Oil

PURPLE FLAME AROMATHERAPY ⊘ ✦
Moisture Lotion Base

QUINESSENCE AROMATHERAPY ☺⊘ ✦ ◉
Age Defying Cream; Aloe Vera & Lavender Gel; Aloe Vera & Seaweed

Gel; Anti Wrinkle Cream; Anti Wrinkle Cream Base; Hydrating Cream Base; Hydrating Day Cream; Hydrating Night Cream; Moisture Lotion Base; Night Repair Cream Base; Reflex Cream Base; Shea Butter Cream Base; Vitamin E Cream; Vitamin E Cream Base; *Lotion:* After Sun, Antiseptic, Base Carrier, Hand and Body, Insect Repellent, Moisture, Problem Skin

RARE NATURAL CARE, INC. ™☺⊘
Rare2B Vegan Skincare: **Body Lotion, Hydrating Day Cream, Restorative Night Cream**

RAW GAIA ™☺ ⸙
Body Bar - Detox; Body Bar - Lavender; Coconut Body Butter; Living Hemp Moisturizer; Living Moisturiser - for her daughters; Living Moisturiser - for her sons; Living Moisturiser For Her Babies; Living MSM Beauty Cream; Red Palm Kernel Body Butter; Shea Body Butter

REN ⊘
Body Products: Damask Rose Ramnose Biosaccharide Body Cream, Grapeseed, Jojoba and Shea Butter Body Cream, Laminaria Firming Body Gel, Monoi Moisturising Body Rinse, Monoi Nourishing Body Oil, Moroccan Rose Otto Ultra Nourishing Body Oil, Wild Yam Omega 7 Firming Body Repair Cream; *Face Care:* Calendula Omega 3/7 Hydra-Calm Moisturiser, Frankincense and Boswellia Serrata

Revitalising Repair Cream, Mayblossom and Konjac Balancing Moisturiser, Omega 3 Overnight Lipid Renewal Serum - All skin types, Phyto-Dynamic Instant Lifting Gel, Phytostimuline Instant Replenishment Moisturiser, Revivo-Lift H11 Intensive Night Serum, Revivo-Lift Radiant Day Serum, Rose Complex Moisturiser - Normal skin

SAAF INTERNATIONAL LIMITED ™
Organic Complexion Boosting Serum; Organic Eraser Body Oil; Organic Hydrating Face and Lip Balm; Organic Super Hydrating Body Balm; Organic Ultimate Moisturising Serum

SANMAR GMBH ™
24H Cream; Bodylotion sanmar; Crème Purifiante; Crème Teintée; Hautgel braun; Hautgel weiss / Daily Protective Moisturiser; Nightcream; Terra Vita 2 in 1; *Vleur:* **24H Pflege, Creme Balance, Getöönte Pflege, Nachtpflege, Tinktur Bei Hautröötungen, Tinktur Bei Pigmentierter Haut, Tinktur Bei Sensibler Haut, Tinktur Bei Unreiner Haut, Tinktur Füür Straffere Haut**

SHANTI PRODUCTS ⊘ ⸙
Face Care: Apricot Kernal Facial Scrub, Frankincense & Rose Face Cream, Rich Borage Night Cream

SHEA BY NATURE ™☺
Body Oil; Shea Body Butter; Shea Body Butter with Green Tea

SHEACARE ☺
Shea Butter

SIMPLE 🖊
Age Resisting Night Renewal; Hydrate Body Moisturiser; Intensive Line Reducing Serum; Moisture Rich Anti-Wrinkle Cream; Nourish Body Cream; Protecting Moisture Cream; Summer Look Body Lotion; *Day Cream:* Age Resisting, Anti-Wrinkle; *Men:* Advanced Moisturiser, Daily Moisturiser; *Moisturiser:* Daily Radiance spf 10, Hydrating Light, Oil Balancing, Replenishing Rich; *Night Cream:* Anti-Wrinkle, Restoring

SIMPLY NATURE ❶ ⊘ 🖊
Beauty Extras: Velvet Cream

SIMPLY SOAPS ™❶⊘ 🖊 ✍ ⚓ 2003
Hydrating Face Oil; *Hedgerow Herbals- Black Palm Natural Range:* **Wild Shea Butter;** *Hedgerow Herbals-Rosa Passionata:* **Rose Night Butter**

SKIN BLOSSOM LIMITED ™⊘
Body Lotion

SKINCARE CAFE LTD ™☺
Organic Almond & Patchouli Anti-ageing Night Oil; Organic Anti-cellulite Body Firming Gel; Organic Chinese Geranium Anti-Ageing Night Oil; Organic Grapeseed & Aloe Vera Cleanser; Organic Lemongrass Purifying Face Mask; Organic Mandarin & Chamomille Body Conditioning Lotion; Organic

Orange & Chamomile Body Wash; Organic Rose Geranium Moisturiser w 5 vitamins; Organic Vitamin Enriched Anti-ageing Day Serum

SOLARAY NUTRITIONAL SUPPLEMENTS
Men's Daily Moisturiser; Organic 100% Aloe Vera Gel; Rosa Mosquesta Hand & Body Lotion; Rosa Mosquesta Rose Hip Moisturiser; Rose Mosqueta Night Creme; Sparkling Mineral Water Complexion Mist; Vegecell Nighttime Hydrator w Green Tea; *Moisturising Cream:* Blue Green Algae SPF15, Green Tea & Gingko SPF15, Natural Herbal Maintenance Oil, Rosa Mosqueta w Rose Hip, Sea Buckthorn, Vegecol w Organic Aloe; *Ultimate Moist Hand & Body Lotion:* Passionflower, Unscented

SOPHYTO LTD ™
Skin Energising High Potency Concentrate

STELLA MCCARTNEY
Care: 5 Benefits Moisturising Cream, 5 Benefits Moisturising Fluid, Calming and Soothing Elixir, Nourishing Elixir, Radiance and Youth Elixir; *Stella:* Soft Body Milk; *Stella in Two:* Moisturising Body Milk

SUKI PURE SKIN CARE
Delicate Moisture Body Oil w Cedar Rose & Bergamot; Velvet Hand & Body Creme; *Facial Moisture Serum:* Blue Chamomile & Echinacea, Carrot, Myrrh & Sandalwood

SUPERDRUG
Amie: Morning Dew Matte Finish
Moisturiser; *Optimum:* Line Decrease
Radiance Balm

**TAOASIS GMBH AROMA-KOSMETIK
& VERLAG**
**Lavendel Nachtcreme; Mandel
Sensitiv Creme; Neroli Intensiv
Creme; Teebaum Intensiv Creme;
Wildrose Tagescreme; Zaubernuss
Lotion; Zitrusgarten Lotion**

THE CRUELTY FREE SHOP TM☺❶
All products are vegan

**THE NATURAL SKINCARE
COMPANY LTD** TM
Caribbean Blue: **Aloe After-Bite;** *Paul
Penders:* **Aloe & Lavender AM
Moisturiser, Avocado & Cranberry
Moisturiser, Bio-Marine Aloe Vera
Gel, Carotene Body Lotion, Herbal
Citrus Fruit Exfoliant, Hydrating
Control Serum, Kigelia Lipo &
Phyto-Tocotrienol Firmer Curves,
Lavender Body Lotion, Lemon Body
Lotion, Mangosteen & Nettle PM
Moisturiser, St Johns & Hibiscus AM
Moisturiser, Wheatgerm Night Time
Moisturiser, Whitening AquaLuna,
Wild Thyme & Lupin Lipo & Phyto-
Tocotrienol Firmer Curves;** *Spa
Exotiques:* **Lavender Body Mist,
Lavender Body Wash, Lime Body
Mist, Lime Body Wash, Tangerine
Body Mist, Tangerine Body Wash**

**THE NATURAL SPA
COMPANY LIMITED** TM☺
All products are vegan

**TISSERAND AROMATHERAPY
PRODUCTS** TM☺
**Essential Oil Rich Hydrating Body
Lotion; Lavender, Sweet orange and
Bergamot body butter; Lavender,
Ylang Ylang and bergamot body
lotion; Orange and Jasmine Body
Lotion; Wild rose & Lemon Leaf
Body Lotion;** *Body moisturisers:* **Bitter
orange hand and body lotion;**
Lavender Products: **Lavender gel,
Lavender hand and body lotion;**
Skin nourishing pure blending oils:
**Face and body base, Grapeseed,
Jojoba, Peach kernel, Sweet
almond, Wheatgerm;** *Skin treatments
and solutions:* **Essential rich
antiseptic cream, Tea tree and
Manuka cream, Tea tree skin balm;**
Tea Tree Products: **Tea Tree &
Grapefruit Skinwash, Tea Tree,
Rosemary and Shea Skin Care**

TREASURED EARTH SKINCARE TM☺⊘
Moisturiser; Night Cream

TREE-HARVEST ⊘🖌
Avocado & Geranium Night Cram;
Frankincense Rejuvenating Cream; Holy
Thorn Healing Cream; Horsechestnut &
Rowan Gel; Pau d'Arco; *Tropical Skin
Butters:* All

TRUTHFUL CO. LTD (PURELY SKINCARE) ™☺⊘
Purely Skincare: **Intense Moisturiser (female variant), Light Moisturiser (male variant), Light Moisturiser (refreshing variant), Moisturiser-sensitive variant**

URTEKRAM ⊘ ✔ ☜ ⅍ 1998
Body Lotion: All

VERDESATIVA S.R.L. ™☺
Bioactive Day and Night Face Cream; Crema Idratante Bioattiva (BioActive Moisturising Face Cream); Crema Lifting Bioattiva (BioActive Eye Contour Cream); Crema Piedi & Gambe (Leg & Foot Cream); Crema Viso Antirughe (Anti-age Face Cream); Latte Corpo Canapa e aloe (Body Lotion Hemp and Aloe); Latte Corpo Canapa e Calendula (Body Lotion Hemp and Marigold)

VINDOTCO UK LTD ™☺⊘ ✔
Really Works: **Anti-Bacterial Hand Spray**

VISIONARY SOAP COMPANY ™☺
Body Butters: **Geranium, Lavender, Lemongrass, Patchouli, Unscented**

WELEDA ⊘ ✔ ⅍ 1985
Mallow Body Lotion; *Almond Range:* Facial Oil; *Sea Buckthorn Body Care:* Sea Buckthorn Body Lotion, Sea Buckthorn Body Oil; *Specialist Skin Care:* Aknedoron Lotion

YAOH ™☺❶⊘ ✔
Body Lotion; Coco Bean Moisturiser; Moisturiser; Papaya Moisturiser

SKIN MAKE-UP

ALTERNATIVE STORES ™☺❶
All products are vegan

ANNEMARIE BORLIND ✔
Eyebrow Crayons; Kohl Crayons; Lip Liner; Powder Eye Shadow; Powder Make-Up; Powder Rouge; *Beauty Extras:* Cosmetic Sponges; *Compact Powder:* All; *Fluid Make Up:* All; *Natural Velvet Cream:* All

BARRY M COSMETICS ✔ ⅍ 1982
Dazzle Dust; Face and Body Shimmer Powder; Fine Glitter Dust; Natural Dazzle Powder Loose (Not Compact); Translucent Powder Loose (Not Compact); *Glitter Eye Crayon:* All; *Glitter Liquid Eyeliner:* All; *Kohl Pencils:* All; *Lip Glosses:* Glossy Tubes; *Lip Liners:* All; *Liquid Eyeliner:* All; *Neon Kohl Pencils:* All

BEAUTY NATURALS ✔
Dual Concealer & Eye Stick; Dual Wet & Dry Foundation; Herbal Enriched Lip Twist; Herbal Lip Primer; Ultra Sheer Liquid Foundation; Vitamin E Lip Treatment; *Eye Colours:* Eye Crayon, Eye Liner Pencil, Herbal Silky 'Diamonds' Shadow, Powder Eye Shadow Duos

BEAUTY WITHOUT CRUELTY

☺ ✔ 👁 ⚘ 1996

Clear Lip Gloss; *Concealer:* Fair, Medium; *Eye Defining Pencil:* Black, Soft Brown; *Full Volume Mascara:* Black, Brown; *Jojoba Lip Gloss:* Apricot Shimmer, Coral Mist, Deeply Berry, Gold Sunset, Pink Crush, Rosewood, Silver Lilac; *Lip Defining Pencil:* Brown, Pinky Brown; *Liquid Eyeliner:* Black; *Moisturising Lipstick:* Barely Pink, Birch, Butterscotch, Cappuccino, Caramel Cream, Chilli Red, Clover Pearl, Coppernob, Coral, Mulberry, Peach Dream, Perfect Plum, Rebel Rose, Red Red, Rosewood, Silver Rose, Soft Pink, Spiced Grape, Sugar Plum, Sweet Apricot, Tangerine, Tansy Tease, Terracotta, Toffee Apple; *Moisturising Make Up Matte:* Beige Matte, Fair Matte, Light Matte, Natural Matte; *Moisturising Make Up Satin:* Bronze Satin, Gold Satin, Light Satin, Warm Satin; *Natural Look Tinted Moisturiser:* Light, Medium; *Satin Finish Blusher:* Cranberry, Hot Chestnut, Rosetta, Sun Gold, Tawny Whisper; *Satin Finish Eye Shadow Duo:* Aquamarine, Graphite, Lilac, Oakmoss, Tamarind; *Soft Kohl Pencil:* Black, Walnut; *Ultrafine Loose Powder:* Fair Translucent, Light, Medium; *Ultrafine Pressed Powder:* Fair Translucent, Light, Medium, Sheer Translucent, Warm; *Waterproof Mascara:* Black, Brownish Black

BOURGEOIS BOHEME ™☺

Beauty Without Cruelty: **Cream Concealer, Eye Defining Pencil, Lip Defining Pencil, Lip Gloss, Liquid Eyeliner, Moisturising Lipstick, Natural Look Tinted Moisturiser, Satin Finish Blusher, Superfine Pressed Powder, Ultrafine Loose Powder;** *Beauty Without Cruelty Eyeliner:* **Soft Kohl Pencil;** *Beauty Without Cruelty Eyeshadow:* **Satin Finish Duos;** *Beauty Without Cruelty Mascara:* **Full Volume, Waterproof;** *Beauty Without Cruelty Moisturising Makeup:* **Matte, Satin**

BURT'S BEES ⊘ ✔ 👁

Healthy Treatment: Parsley Blemish Stick; *Natural Remedies:* Doctor Burt's Herbal Blemish Stick

DR HAUSCHKA ⊘ ✔

Concealer: 01, 02, 03; *Kajal Eyeliner:* 02, 03, 04, 05

EARTH'S BEAUTY ✔ 👁

Blush: All; *Eye Shadow:* All; *Foundation Powders:* All; *Loose Eye Liner:* All

ECCO BELLA ✔

FlowerColor Blush: All Except Burgundy Rose Wild Rose Orchid Rose and Coral Rose; *FlowerColor Face Powder Compact:* All; *FlowerColor Natural Liquid Foundation:* All; *FlowerColor Natural Mascara:* All; *FlowerColor Powder Eye Liner:* All; *FlowerColour Bronzing Powder:* All; *FlowerColour Eye Shadow:* All; *Good for you Gloss:* Colours Peace and Pleasure (Not the Colours Passion and Power); *Paperback Duo Compact:* All; *Shimmer Dust:* All;

Soft Eyeliner Pencils: All; *Vitamin E Lip Smoother:* All

FOREVER LIVING PRODUCTS
Lip/Eye Pencil; Mascara/Eyebrow Fix; Sonya Eye Makeup Remover

GREEN VALLEY TRADING CO. ™☺
All products are vegan

INIKA ™ ⚘
Blusher; Body Bronze/Mousse; Bronzer; Eye & Lip Liner; Eye Shadow; Foundation; Lip Gloss; Lipsticks - All; Mascara; Primer; Setting Powder

LAVERANA ™ ⚘
Lavera Trend Sensitiv: **Lipstick No. 21**

LVF MINERAL MAKEUP ⚘
All Blushers/Bronzers; All Foundation; All Illuminisers; All Makeup; All Multipurpose Powders; All Setting Powders; All Ultra Matte/Liners

MAJIK BLANKIT SKIN CARE ™☺⚘
Gentle Self-Tanner; Peppermint Pout Lip Ploss; Strawberry Glimmer Lip Gloss

NEVER TOO BUSY TO BE BEAUTIFUL ™ ⚘
Blushers: **B Hold, Bashful, Bliss, Blush, Bongo;** *Body Glitter:* **Glitter Pot - Dusty Pink, Glitter Pot - Emerald Green, Glitter Pot - Gold, Glitter Pot - Iridescent, Glitter Pot - Iris, Glitter Pot - Poodle Pink, Glitter Pot - Silver, Glitter Pot - Sky Blue;** *Cleansers:* **B Gone;** *Cocktail:* **Body Lustre;** *Cover Sticks:* **Bambi, Bedouin, Binky, Biscuit, Blithe, Honey B;** *Cream Blushers:* **Bashful, Bliss, Blush, Bongo;** *Cream Eye Shadow:* **Bullet;** *Cream Eye Shadows:* **B Black, Banky, Bdazzled, Beam, Beast, Bedroom, Beezer, Beleek, Biz, Bleep, Bluemer, Bondage, Bramble, Brazened, Brook, HB;** *Cream Eyeshadow:* **Battleship, Boosh, Bossy, Bottle Green, Bramley, Broider, Busy;** *Cream Foundation:* **Bambi, Bedouin, Binky, Biscuit, Blithe, Honey B;** *Face Powder:* **Bermuda, Burlesque;** *Glitter Eye Shadow:* **Bolly;** *Glitter Eyeshadows:* **Babylon, Bamboozle, Blessed, Bodicea, Boo, Brite, Butterfly;** *Highlighters:* **Blazer, Bon Bon;** *Kohl:* **Kohl - Black;** *Lip Creams:* **B Cause, Babe, Baffle, Ballet, Banter, Bardot, Beijing, Belle, Bellflower, Bilingual, Bingo, Bitten, Blab, Blast, Bonfire, Pretty B;** *Lip Gloss:* **B Have, Bebe, Beret, Blip, Blue Tooth, Bombay, Bounce, Bow, Brill;** *Lip Sticks:* **Ballyho, Biatch, Boudoir;** *Lip Tints:* **Bluff, Bodice, Breeze, Bustle;** *Lipstick:* **Bandana, Banquet, Beanie, Belter, Blown, Bond, Bruton;** *Loose Eye Powder:* **Big Shot Loose Eye Powder;** *Loose Powders:* **Bali, Ballroom, Beverly Hills, Bollywood, Bora Bora;** *Mascara:* **Bananza, Bark Mascara, Bewitched Mascara, Bienvenue, Blanket, Bothered Mascara, Bracken, Bunny Mascara;** *Pressed Eye Shadow:* **Bethlehem, Broadway;** *Pressed Eyeshadows:* **2B, B Delight, B Friend,**

B Lo, B Never, Baker, Banger, Bay, Beach, Beatrix, Beck, Beelzebub, Belize, Bentley, Birdy, Blossom, Bluebell, Blur, Boogie, Boston, Botswana, Boxster, Brag, Brogue, Bubble, Bugatti, Burke, Burnish, Buttercup, OB1; *Sheer Lipstick:* **Bravo, Buzz**

PAUL PENDERS CO ™
Make Up Remover; Nutritious Colour Mascaras

PURE GAISHA ™☺❶🐇
All Nautral Lipstick; Eye Pencils; Mineral Brow Dust; Mineral Corrector; Mineral Foundation Powder; Mineral Foundation Stick; Mineral Lip Pencils; Mineral Lipgloss; Mineral Powder Blusher; Mineral Powder Eyeshadow; Mineral Setting Powder; Natural Mascara

SAVVY COSMETICS ™
Blush; Bronzer; Eyeshadow; Foundation

SIMPLY NATURE ❶⊘🐇
Annemarie Böörlind: Compact Powder, Fluid Make-Up

THE NATURAL SKINCARE COMPANY LTD ™
Paul Penders: **Make-up Remover, Nutritious Colour Mascaras**

ULTRA GLOW COSMETICS ☺🐇
Eye defining pencil: Black, Soft brown;

Full volume mascara: Black, Brown; *High gloss nail colour:* Coral mist, Pink whisper; *Jojoba Lip gloss:* Apricot Shimmer, Coral mist, Deeply berry, Gold sunset, Pink crush, Rosewood, Silver lilac; *Lip defining pencil:* Morello, Pinky brown; *Lip gloss:* Clear; *Liqiud concealer:* Fair, Medium; *Liqiud eyeliner:* Black; *Moisturing lipstick:* Spiced grape; *Moisturing makeup satin:* Beige Matte, Bronze Satin, Gold satin, Light matte, Natural matte, Warm satin; *Moisturising Lipstick:* Barely Pink, Birch, Butterscotch, Cappuccino, Caramel Cream, Chilli red, Clover pearl, Coppernob, Coral, Mulberry, Peach dream, Perfect plum, Rebel rose, Red red, Rosewood, Silver rose, Soft pink, Sugar plum, Sweet apricot, Tangerine, Tansy tease, Terracotta, Toffee apple; *Moisturising makeup satin:* Light satin; *Natural look tinted moisturiser:* Light, Medium; *Satin finish blusher:* Cranberry, Hot chestnut, Rosetta, Sun gold, Tawny whisper; *Satin Finish Eye Shadow Duo:* Aquamarine, Graphite, Lilac, Oakmoss, Tamarind; *Soft kohl pencil:* Black, Walnut; *Ultrafine loose powder:* Fair translucent, Medium; *Ultrafine loose power:* Light; *Ultrafine pressed powder:* Fair translucent, Light, Medium, Sheer translucent, Warm; *Waterproof mascara:* Black, Brownish black

VEGAN STORE ™☺❶⊘🐇
All

VICTORIA MANOR SPA RETREAT T/A LIVINIA NATURAL SKINCARE ™�⦸ⓘ
Mineral Blush; Mineral Bronzer; Mineral Cream Foundation; Mineral Eyeshadow; Mineral Liners; Mineral Lipgloss; Mineral lipsticks; Mineral Mascara; Mineral Powder Foundation

SKINCARE
- CLEANSERS & TONERS

AKAMUTI
Toners: All

ALTERNATIVE STORES ™☺❶
All products are vegan

ANIMAL AID SOCIETY
™☺❶ⓘ ⚗-1976
Aloe & Papaya Cleansing Lotion; Aloe & Papaya Toner; Fruit & Nut Scrub; *Facial Wash:* Kiwi & Grapefruit Facial Wash

ANN ELISE SKINCARE ☺
Deep Cleansing Oil; Revitalising Toner

ANNEMARIE BORLIND ⓘ
Aqua Rose Vitality Essence; *Combination Series:* Cleansing Gel, Day Essence, Facial Toner; *LL Regeneration Series:* Blossom Dew Gel, Cleansing Milk; *Purifying Care Series:* Cleansing Gel, Facial Toner; *Rosedew Series:* Cleansing Milk, Facial Toner; *System*

Absolute Series: Beauty Fluid, Cleanser; *Young Beauty – Peach Series:* Cleanser; *ZZ Sensitive Series:* Cleansing, Facial Toner

AQUA NATURAL ™☺⦸ⓘ
Toner spray

AROMA CRYSTAL THERAPY ⦸ⓘ
Acne Face Wash

BAREFOOT BOTANICALS ⦸ⓘ
Rosa Fina: Innocence Creamy Face Wash, Naked Beauty Nourishing Cleansing Milk; *SOS:* Lifeguard Soothing Face Wash

BEAUTY NATURALS ⓘ
Camomile Skin Care: Cleansing Gel; *David Hill for Men:* Deep Cleansing Lotion; *Evening Primrose:* Cleansing Lotion, Toning Gel; *Herbal Skin Care:* No 1 Cleansing & Conditioning Milk, No 2 Toning Gel; *Herbal Skin Tonic:* Cucumber, Rosewater; *Skin Revivals:* Harmonising Cream Cleanser; *Skin Revivals - Reviving:* Harmonising Tonic

BURT'S BEES ⦸ⓘ👁
Deep Clean Cleanser; Deep Pore Scrub; *Complexion Mist:* Carrot Seed Oil, Cucumber Chamomile, Grapefruit, Lavender; *Face & Body:* Citrus Facial Scrub, Garden Tomato Toner; *Healthy Treatment:* Rosewater & Glycerin Toner

CAWARRA COSMETICS LTD ™
OrganicSpa: **Cream Cleanser, Foam Cleanser, Toner;** *Sanctum:* **Body Buff,**

Body Spa, Gentle Face Exfoliant, Men's Face Exfoliant, Men's Purifying Face Cleanser, On The Spot, Purifying Foam Cleanser, Skin Renewal Treatment, Skin Whitening Lotion, Soothing Cream Cleanser, Tone & Refresh Mist

DAIVITA TM☺
Mantra: **Astringent, Cleanser**

DANIEL FIELD LABORATORY LTD TM☺
FFP Research Limited- Free From Sensitive Skin Skin Care: **Face cleanser, Face wash, Gentle toner**

DESERT ESSENCE ⊘ ✿ ⚘-1985
Organics: Age Reversal Pomegranate Facial Cleansing Gel

DOLMA TM☺❶⊘ ✿ ☺⚘-1976
Skin Care: **Aromatic Face Shampoo, Astringent Toner, Chamomile & Mint Facial Wash, Evening Primrose & Marigold Moisture Cream, Fragrance Free Cleansing Lotion, Freshening Toner, Gentle Toner, Honesty Spicy Orange Scrub, Lavender & Chamomile Cleansing Lotion, Oil Free Cleanser, Purifying Toner**

DR HAUSCHKA ⊘ ✿
Cleansing Clay Mask; Cleansing Cream; Cleansing Milk; *Toner:* Clarifying, Facial, Rosemary Leg & Arm

EARTHPURE ☺ ✿
Cleanser: Pure and Rich Cleansing

Cream; *Toner:* Luxurious Rose Cleanser and Toner

ESSENTIAL CARE
Skincare: Creamy Coconut Cleanser, Lemon & Tea Tree Facial Wash, Organic Citrus Fruit Tonic, Organic Rose Petal Tonic

ESSENTIALLY NATURAL TM
Elderflower and Glycerine Toner (Organic); Fennel Soother Rinse (Organic); Luxury Rose and Glycerine Cleanser (Organic); Orange Flower and Rose Toner (Organic); Tangerine Toner (Organic)

ESSENTIALLY YOURS LTD TM☺☺ ✿ ☺
Fragrance Free Range: **Cleanser, Exfoliating lotion, Face wash, Toner;** *Free&Organic Range:* **Face wash;** *Men's Range:* **Toner;** *Natural Elements:* **Cleanser, Combination/Oily Antimicrobial Face Wash, Combination/Oily Cleanser, Combination/Oily Exfoliating Lotion, Combination/Oily Toner, Dry/Mature Face Wash, Dry/Mature Toner, Exfoliating lotion, Face wash, Normal Cleanser, Normal Face Wash, Normal Toner, Toner**

FAITH PRODUCTS LIMITED TM ✿ ☺⚘-1988
3-In-1 Facial Wipes; Purifying Cleansing Lotion 150ml; Refining Toning Lotion 150ml

FOREVER LIVING PRODUCTS
Exfoliating Cleanser

GREEN PEOPLE CO. TM⊘✔
Rejuvenating Facial Oil; *Organic Base:* **24-Hour Cream, Cleanser;** *Skin Care:* **Fruit Scrub, Gentle Cleanse, Gentle Tone**

GREEN WYCH TM☺❶
Face Toner: **Lavender, Rose;** *Facial Toner:* **Lavender, Rose**

HEALTHQUEST LIMITED TM⊘✔
Pure Adore: **Baby Wipes**

HEDGECRAFT TM☺⊘
Main Soap Range: **Kitchen Garden Coffee Scrub**

HEMP GARDEN TM
Face Oil: Sensual for all skin types; Face Oil: Soothing for dry, mature and weathered skin; Face Oil: Stimulating for greasy skin; Renewing Cleanser

HERBS HANDS HEALING LTD TM⊘✔
Herbs & Flowers Skin Toner; Lavender Skin Water; Rose Water Facial Tonic; Skin Guard Water

HERBS OF GRACE TM⊘✔
Organic Flower Waters: **All**

HOLISTIX TM❶
Rosewater Spritzer; Rosewater Toner; Teatree & Orange Cleanser 60ml

HONESTY COSMETICS LTD
TM☺❶❶✔☙✂1976
Cleansers: **Lavender & Geranium, Unscented w Chamomile;** *Facial Toners:* **Lavender & Geranium, Unscented w Chamomile;** *Honesty Essential Range:* **Face Mask with Tea Tree & Lavender, Lavender & Geranium Cleanser, Lavender & Geranium Toner, Spicy Orange Scrub;** *Honesty Fruit Range:* **Papaya Facial Wash;** *Honesty Unscented Range:* **Cleansing Lotion with Chamomille, Toner with Chamomille**

I AM NATURAL TM
Fruit Facial Scrub; Organic Avocado Face Cream with Vitamin E; Organic Balancing Toner; Organic Coconut Cleanser; Organic Healing Toner; Organic Hemp Cleanser; Organic Macadamia Cleanser; Organic Nourishing Toner

ID AROMATICS
Skin Cleanser

ITS ELIXIR UK LIMITED TM⊘✔☙
Acne oil; Aloe&avocado lotion; Cleansing cream- dry skins; Cleansing cream- oily skins; Cleansing cream-sensitive skins; Cleansing Gel; Cleansing oil dry skin; Cleansing oil sensitive skin; Tea tree gel; Vitamin lotion

JASON NATURAL PRODUCTS ✔☙
Apricot Scrubble Wash and Scrub; Beta-Gold™Re-Hydrating Freshener; Citrus

TOILETRIES & COSMETICS

6-in-1 Wash and Scrub with Ester-C®®; Clean Start™Refreshing Cleanser; D-Clog Naturally™Balancing Cleanser; Fruit Cooler™Refreshing Toner; Vegee Tonic™Balancing Astringent; *Ester-C®® Skin Care:* Super-C Toner, Super-C™ Cleanser Gentle Facial Wash; *Red Elements™ Antioxidant Skin Care:* Calming Toner, Gentle Gel Cleanser, Hydrating Lotion Cleanser

JUICE BEAUTY 🌿 👁
Cleansing Gel; Cleansing Milk; Hydrating Mist

KOBASHI ™☺️🚫🌿👁✂️1976
Spritzer; Witchhazel; *Misc:* **Chamomile Water, Dill Water, Lavender Water, Neroli Water, Peppermint Water, Rose Water**

LAVERANA ™🌿
Lavera Basis Sensitiv: **Cleansing Gel, Cleansing Milk 2 in 1;** *Lavera Body Spa:* **Body Peeling (Luffa/Jojoba);** *Lavera Young Faces:* **Toner Mint;** *Lavere:* **Active Cleansing, Hydro Energy Cleanser 2-Phase Cleansing Mousse, Hydro Energy Splash, Repair Relax Cleanser, Repair Relax Splash, Solution Power Cleansing, Solution Power Splash**

LIZ EARLE 🌿 👁
Instant Boost Skin Tonic; Spot-On; *Skincare for Men:* Face and Body Wash

LOVE THE PLANET ™🚫
Tea Tree & Lavender Cleanser

LUSH ™🌿
Tea Tree Toner Tab; Vit C Toner Tab; Vit E Toner Tab; *Cleansers:* **Angels on Bare Skin, Aqua Marina, Baby Face, Coalface, Fresh Farmacy, Herbalism, Sweet Japanese Girl;** *Soap:* **Temptation;** *Toners:* **Breath of Fresh Air, Eau Roma Water, Tea Tree Water**

MAJIK BLANKIT SKIN CARE ™☺️🌿
Organic Jojoba & Apricot Face Cleanser

MJ HEALTH(NZ) LTD ™☺️🚫🌿
Dr Wendy's 100% Pure Botanical Skin Care: **Balance Cleanser, Balance Toner, Gentle Cleanser, Gentle Toner, Replenish Cleanser, Replenish Toner**

NATURA ORGANICS 🚫🌿☼
Hydrating Cleansing Milk; Hydrating Toner Spray; Purifying Cleansing Gel; Purifying Toner Spray

NATURAL SENSE ™
Face Mister; Marigold Cleanser; Orange Flower Toner; Rose Flower Toner

NATURE'S GATE
Deep Cleansing Face Wash; Gentle Moisturizing Facial Toner; Revitalizing Facial Scrub; *Organics - Advanced Care:* In The Beginning Cleanser, Tone Back the Clock Toner

NEAL'S YARD REMEDIES ⊘ ✍ ☞ ✂—1998
Aloe Vera Cooling Spray; Calendula
Cleanser; *Flower Water:* Lavender, Orange

NEW SEASONS ⊘ ✍
Creamy Body Scrub; Rose Cleanser;
Neutral & Toiletry Bases: Cleanser, Facial
& Body Scrub

NO COWS ☺❶
No Cows Cleanser; No Cows Toner

NOTHING NASTY ✍
Facial Toner: Flawless for Problem Skin,
Ideal for Normal Skin, Prime for Mature
& Sensitve Skin

ORGANIC BOTANICS ™⊘✿
**Fragrance Free Organic Deep
Cleansing Milk; Organic Tea Tree &
Lavender Face & Body Wash**

PAUL PENDERS CO ™
**Alpinia and Teatree Cleansing Wash;
Body Firming and Cellulite Serum;
Calendula Cleansing Milk; Chamomile
& Orange & Moringa Herbal Skin
Toner; Kigelia Lipo and Phyto-
Tocotrinol Firmer Curves; Moringa
Skin Toner; Orangeblossom Skin
Toner; Rosemary and Calendula
Cleansing Milk**

POTIONS AND POSSIBILITIES ⊘ ✍
Beauty: Essential Cleanser, Essential
Toner, Invigorating Salt Scrub For Men,
Tea Tree & Lavender Facial Cleanser;
Organic Range: Facial Cleanser, Facial
Scrub, Facial Toner, Gentle Facial Wash

PURATY LTD ☺ ✍
Balancing Facial Wash

PURE GAISHA ™☺❶ ✍
**Aloha Sugar & Salt Scrub; Creamy
Cleanser - Dry/Mature Skin; Creamy
Cleanser - Sensitive Skin; Facial Toner
- Normal Skin; Facial Toner - Oily
Skin; Facial Toner - Sensitive Skin;
Floral Waters; Foamy Cleanser -
Normal Skin; Foamy Cleanser - Oily
Skin; Luxury Facial Scrub and Polish;
Mens Reviving Face & Body Polish**

PURPLE FLAME AROMATHERAPY ⊘ ✍
Hygenic Moist Wipes; *Flower Waters:* All

QUINESSENCE AROMATHERAPY
☺☺✍ ✍
Damask Rose Toner; Facial Exfoliator;
Rose Facial; *Lotion:* Cleansing

RAW GAIA ™☺ ✍
**Facial Cleanser; Floral Face Toner;
MSM Beauty Spray**

REN ⊘
Calendula and Arctic Blackcurrant Seed
Cleansing Milk Wash; Jojoba Micro
Bead Purifying Facial Scrub;
Mayblossom and Blue Cypress Facial
Wash; Phyto-Dynamic Instant Lifting
Facial Spray; Rosa Centifolia Facial
Wash; Zostera Marina Cleansing Milk
Wash

SAAF INTERNATIONAL LIMITED ™
Organic Pure Face Cleanser

SANMAR GMBH ™
24hr Liposomecreme; Anti-aging Nightcreme; Fitness Gel; *Body Lotion:* **Liposomes with Bio Jojoba and Bio Sheabutter;** *Vleur:* **Lifting Serum, Lifting Serum Plus, Tiefenreinegung / Make Up Remover;** *White Skin Gel:* **Liposomes and Bio Jojoba**

SIMPLE ✔
Age Resisting Facial Wash; Cleansing Glycerine Bar; Daily Radiance Foaming Cream Cleanser; Energise Body Bar; Men's Face Scrub; Moisturising Foaming Facial Wash; Oil Balancing Exfoliating Wash; Purifying Cleansing Lotion; Refreshing Facial Wash Gel; Smoothing Cleansing Scrub; Softening Facial Cleansing Mousse; Soothing Facial Toner; *Cleansing Wipes:* Oil Balancing, Original, Regeneration, Revitalising Exfoliating, Smoothing Facial

SIMPLY SOAPS ™❶⊘✔👁✂️ 2003
Exfoliating Facial Scrub; Lavender Toner; *Hedgerow Herbals:* **Gentle Rose Wash Grains;** *Hedgerow Herbals- Rosa Passionata:* **Rosa Facial Steam Bags, Rosa Organic Hydrosol, Rose Facial Serum**

SKINCARE CAFE LTD ™☺
Organic aloe vera toner

SKINVAC ™☺⊘✔
Deep Daily Cleansing Cloth; Pore Gripper Acne Control Cloth
SOLARAY NUTRITIONAL SUPPLEMENTS
Herbessence Make Up Remover; Natural Herbal Facial Astringent; *Facial*

Cleansing Cream: Sea Buckthorn, Seaware w Rosa Mosqueta; *Facial Cleansing Lotion:* Blue Green Algae, Green Tea & Gingko, Natural Herbal, Vegecol w Organic Aloe; *Facial Toner:* Blue Green Algae, Green Tea & Gingko, Rosa Mosqueta & English Lavender, Sea Buckthorn, Vegecol w Organic Aloe Alcohol Free

SOPHYTO LTD ™
Deep Pore Foaming Cleanser; Ultra Mild Silken Gel Cleanser

STELLA MCCARTNEY
Care: Gentle Cleansing Milk, Purifying Foaming Cleanser, Toning Floral Water; *Stella:* Gentle Body Cleanser, Precious Body Cream

SUKI PURE SKIN CARE
Exfoliating Lemongrass Cleanser w Chamomile & Vitamin C; *Concentrated Toner:* Shitake, Burdock & Olive Leaf, White Willow, Aloe, Chamomile & Tea Tree

SUPERDRUG
Amie: Morning Clear Purifying Facial Wash, Petal Perfect Refreshing Cleansing Lotion

THE CRUELTY FREE SHOP ™☺❶
All products are vegan

THE NATURAL SKINCARE COMPANY LTD ™
Paul Penders: **Alpinia & Tea tree Cleansing Wash, Body Firming & Cellulite Serum, Calendula Cleansing**

Milk, Ceramide Recovery Lipo A,C & E, Chamomile, Orange & Moringa Herbal Skin Toner, Moringa Skin Toner, Orangeblossom Skin Toner, Rescue Bleamish Away, Rosemary & Calendula Cleansing Milk, Rosemary Cleansing Milk

THE NATURAL SPA COMPANY LIMITED ™☺
All products are vegan

TISSERAND AROMATHERAPY PRODUCTS ™☺
Lavender Products: **Lavender facial cleansing foam, Lavender Foaming Face Wash;** *Skin treatments and solutions:* **Tea tree and Kanuka blemish stick;** *Tea Tree Products:* **Tea Tree and Manuka Anti Blemish Roller ball**

TREASURED EARTH SKINCARE ™☺◌
Body Scrub; Cleanser; Toner

TRUTHFUL CO. LTD (PURELY SKINCARE) ™☺◌
Purely Skincare: **Face wash - refreshing variant, Face wash (female variant), Face wash (male variant), Face wash- sensitive variant**

URTEKRAM ◌ ✦ ◉ ⅍ 1998
Body Scrub: All

VERDESATIVA S.R.L. ™☺
Cleansing Lotion - Hemp and Red Grape; Latte Detergente Canapa e Malva (Cleansing Lotion Hemp and Mallow)

WELEDA ◌ ✦ ⅍ 1985
Almond Range: Cleansing Lotion; *Iris Range:* Iris Facial Toner; *Wild Rose Facial Care:* Wild Rose Cleansing Lotion, Wild Rose Facial Toner

SOAPS

ABSOLUTE AROMAS ™◌ ✦
Ord River: **Ord River Handwash 250ml, Tea Tree & Lavender 125g**

AKAMUTI
African Black Soap Bars; *Liquid African Black Soap:* Scented, Unscented; *Soap:* Red Palm, Shea Butter & Baobab, Shea Butter & Neem

AMAZENE ™
Phytophilo Aromatherapy Range- Liquid Soaps: **Cocoa & Cupuacu, Green Tea, Aloe Vera & Anise, Lavender, Calendula & Primrose, Strawberry n Cream;** *Phytophilo Aromatherapy Range- Vegetable Bar Soaps:* **Acerola, Passion Fruit & Avocado, Andiroba, Buriti, & Aroeira, Calendula, Carombinha & Cupuacu, Cocoa, Coconut, Buriti & Brazil Nut, Lavender, Passion Fruit, Strawberry n Cream;** *Phytophilo Aromatherapy Range-Liquid Soaps:* **Papaya, Passion Fruit & Acerola**

ANIMAL AID SOCIETY ™☺❶◌ ✦ ⅍ 1976
Calendula & Vanilla Liquid Soap; Lavender&Aloe Vera Liquid Soap

BIO-D ™☺◯ ♂ ☜☞~1988
Hemp Bran; Hemp Oil

BRACKENCRAFT ™☺❶ ♂
Bsoaps: **Chamomille & Lemon Soap, Cinnamon Swirl Soap, Lavender & Coconut Soap, Natural Unfragranced Soap, Orange & Geranium Soap, Patchouli &Orange Soap, Peppermint &Green Tea with Nettles Soap, Rose & Geranium Soap, Unfragranced with Cranberries Soap, White Cinammon Soap**

BRONNLEY & CO LTD ♂
Body Care for Men: Soap; *Face Wash:* Bird of Paradise, Tulip; *Royal Horticultural Society - Hand Wash:* Gardener's, Passion Flower; *Royal Horticultural Society - Soap:* Passion Flower, Rose; *Royal Horticultural Society- Soap:* Gardener's; *Soap Body Bar:* Bird of Paradise, Tulip; Africa; Apricot & Almond; Asia; Caribbean; English Fern; Gardener's; India; Lavender; Lemon; Orchid; Passion Flower; Pink Bouquet; White Iris

BURT'S BEES ◯ ♂ ☜
Face & Body: Garden Carrot Complexion Soap, Wild Lettuce Complexion Soap; *Natural Remedies:* Poison Ivy; *Shower Soap:* Citrus Spice Exfoliating, Peppermint

CALDER VALLEY SOAP ™☺◯ ♂ ☜
Almond Blossom; Aloe Vera; Anise; Avocado & Cucumber; Coconut Palm; Grapefruit; Lavender; Lemongrass; Minted Lime; Oatmeal Scrub; Orchard Apple; Peppermint & Poppyseed; Rose; Sea Kelp; Tea Tree; Vanilla; Violet; Wild Raspberry

CAURNIE SOAPERIE ☺◯ ♂ ☜~1976
Soap: All

CAWARRA COSMETICS LTD ™
Organic Soap Cedarwood & Olive Leaf; Organic Soap Lavender & Chamomille; Organic Soap Lemongrass & Witch Hazel; Organic Soap Rose Geranium & Calendula; Organic Soap Sanctum

CELLANDE MIDLANDS ◯ ♂
Liquid Soap: Almond, Mint Bactericidal

DM-DROGERIE MARKT GMBH & CO KG ™
dm alverde: **Flüüssigseife Zintronengras - Limette**

DOLMA ™☺❶◯ ♂ ☜☞~1976
Glycerine Soap: **'Niamh' De-luxe, Carrot Ho-Leaf & Orange, Hemp Seed Fragrance Free, Lavender & Jojoba, Tea-Tree & Calendula**

DROYT PRODUCTS ◯ ♂ ☜~1984
Bath Bar: Fresh Green, Lavender, Lemon, Mint, Pine & Juniper; *Craft Collection:* Eau de Cologne, Fresh Green, Red Rose, Unperfumed; *Glycerose:* Avocado, Mandarin, Rose Scented, Yellow Rose; *Liquid Soap:* Glycerine Soap, Glycerine Soap Refill; *Organic Range:* Liquid Soap with

TOILETRIES & COSMETICS

Glycerine, Soap Bar with Glycerine; *Original:* Glycerine Soap, Unperfumed Glycerine Soap; *Soap Bars:* Lavender Soap, Vegetas; *Soap Square:* Apple, Avocado, Chamomile, Coconut, Fresh Green, Lavender, Lemon, Mandarin, Mint, Pine; *Stripe Soaps:* Coconut & Vanilla, Mint

EARTHPURE ☺ ♦
Soap Bars: Eastern Rose, Geranium and Lavender, Lavender, Neem &, Peppermint, Eucalyptus & Clove, Pure Soap, Spiced Orange, Vetivert and Lavender

ECOSOAPIA ☺
Liquid Soap: Almond, Eucalyptus, Lavender, Peppermint, Rose Geranium, Tee Tree, Unscented

ESSENTIALLY NATURAL ™
Cucumber and Almond Scrub (Organic); Cucumber and Elderflower Soap (Organic); Feet Treat Soap; Gardener's Delight Soap with Pumice (Organic); Gardener's Delight Soap without Pumice (Organic); Hemp and Patchouli Soap (Organic); Hemp Soap (Organic); Insect Repellent Soap (Organic); Luxury Rose and Cocoa Butter Soap (Organic); Oranges & Lemons Soap

FAITH PRODUCTS LIMITED
™ ♦ ☞ ⚕ 1988
Aloe Vera 100g / unwrapped; Chocolate 100g / unwrapped; Gingko Biloba 100g / unwrapped;

Hemp with Lemongrass & Green Tea 100g / unwrapped; Lavender 100g / unwrapped; Orange 100g / unwrapped; Pine (Loose and unwrapped only); Rosemary 100g / unwrapped; Seaweed 100g / unwrapped; Tea Tree 100g / unwrapped

FLORIS ☺ ♦
Luxury Soap: Cefiro Luxury, China Rose, Edwardian Bouquet, Elite, Fleur, Florissa, Guest Soap, JF, Lily of the Valley Luxury Soap, Luxury Soap Collection, Night Scented Jasmine, No 89, Rose Geranium, Santal, Seringa, Stephanotis, White Rose

FOREVER LIVING PRODUCTS
Aloe Liquid Soap

FREERANGERS ™☺ ♦
Lavender Lullaby Soap; Lemon Zing Soap; Summer Garden Soap; *Pamper Products:* **Pack 3 Soaps, Presentation Pack 3 Soaps (1 of each variety), Single Soap, Soap Gift Pack**

FUNK BUBBLE ™☺
Chocolate/Orange; Cinnamon/Oatmeal; Orange/Lemon; Rose; Tea Tree; Ylang Ylang/Neroli

GREEN PEOPLE CO. ™⊘ ♦
Aloe Vera Liquid Soap; Antibacterial Liquid Soap; Rosemary Liquid Soap; *Organic Base:* **Liquid Soap**

GREEN WYCH ™☺❶
Bergamot; Geranium; Lavender; Orange Zest

GREENCITY WHOLEFOODS ❶⊘
Organic Soaps: Geranium & Rose Petal, Grapefruit & Aloe Vera, Hemp Oil Fragrance Free, Lime & Lemongrass, Mandarin & Ginger, Sandalwood & Cedar, White Lavender

HEDGECRAFT ™☺⊘
Castile Soap Range: **Lavender, Lavender and Oat;** *Main Soap Range:* **Grapefruit, Lavender, Lavender and Oat, Orange and Patchouli, Ylang Yland and Orange**

HOLISTIX ™❶
Handmade Soap: **Calendula, Hardworking Hands, Hemp, White Lavender**
HOWAD LTD T/A INCOGNITO ™❶⊘✓
Ginger&Citronella Soap; Lemongrass &Citronella Soap

HOWDEN SOAP CO. ™✓
Chamomille and Vanilla Soap; Citrus Morning Bar Soap; Hippy Daze Soap; Lavender Soap; Natural Nude Soap Bar; Oregano and Lime Soap; Oriental Bouquet Soap; Spicy Red Bush Tea Soap; Sweet Peppermint Soap; Woodland Soap

I AM NATURAL ™
Organic Tea Tree Hand Soap

ID AROMATICS
100% Pure & Natural Aromatherapy Soaps: Baby Soap, French Clay Soap, Geranium Soap, Neem Soap, Patchouli Soap, Vanilla Soap; *Aromatherapy Soaps:* All That Jas, Aloe Vera Gel Sensitive Cleansing Bar, Coconut & Mango Moisture Bar, Flower Ramedies, Honeysuckle & Chamomile, Indian Rose, Lavender Provence, Sandalwood & Spice, Sea Spray, Tea Tree & Witch-Hazel

JASON NATURAL PRODUCTS ✓☞
All-Natural Liquid Satin Soaps: Aloe Vera, Apricot, Chamomile, Glycerine & Rosewater, Herbal Extracts, Lavender, Mango & Papaya, Tea Tree Oil

KOBASHI ™☺⊘✓☞⚖-1976
Liquid Soap: **Fragrance Free Soap Base, Protect hand wash, Tea Tree & Lemon**

KOOCHIE KOO ™
aromababy: **Pure Rainwater Cleansing Bar**

LAVERANA ™✓
Basis Sensitiv: **Liquid Soap - Almond Milk & Shea Butter, Liquid Soap - Calendula & Sea Buckthorn;** *Lavera Young Faces:* **Exfoliant Wash Mint;** *Men SPA:* **Face Wash with Scrub Effect**

LITTLE SATSUMA ™
Apple & Green Tea; Dewberry; Frankincense and Myrrh; *Little*

Satsuma: **Aloe & Cucumber, Banana, Chocolate, Exfoliating Oatmeal, Fresh Citrus, Fresh Lavender, Fresh Rose, Lemongrass & Kelp, Poppy & Peppermint, Rosemary & Tea Tree, Shea & Simple;** *Scouse Soap Company:* **A Little Kelp From My Friends, Albert Choc, All You Need Is Lavender, Aloe, Goodbye & Cucumber, Calm Down, Calm Down, Dewberry Fields Forever, Goodison Day Sunshine, Lennon & Lime Street, Let It Be Rosemary & Tea Tree, Magical Mystery, Scrubber Soul, Sergeant Peppermint, Shea (Butter) Loves You, Welcome to the Little Apple, Yellow Scrub 'n' Clean, You'll Never Wash Alone**

LONGCROFT SOAP COMPANY ™
Cheer Up Lemonhead; French Laundry; Gracefruit; Holiday In Tangier; Holiday with Cary; In The Rainforest With Lula; Love Potion; Nettle The Score; Oh Pear!; Pomegranate Martini; Spiced Umeshu; Vigor & Verve; *Limited Edition:* **Secret Crush, Turn On, Tune In, Wash Up**

LUSH ™ ⏺
B Scent Electro Soap; Godmother; Keep It Fluffy B; You Wash My Back; *Karma Products:* **Karma Soap;** *Soap:* **Bamboo Soap, Beautiful Pea Green Soap, Gingerman Soap, Icon, Pineapple Grunt, Queen of Hearts Complexion Soap, Quinquereme of Nineveh, Soap Sod, Spice Curls, Tiptoe Through the Tulips, Waylander Rhassoul; Big Hugs; Bohemian; Demon In The Dark; Extra Virgin Olive; Figs and Leaves; I Should Coco; Ice Blue; Lily Savon; Milky Bar; Miranda; Mud Flats; Ooh La La; Porridge; Red Rooster; Rock Star; Sandstone; Sea Vegetable; Sexy Peel; Soft; Sultana of Soap**

MANDALA AROMA LTD ™☺◌
Conditioning Liquid Soap; *Soap Bars:* **Love, Wisdom**

MAXIM MARKETING COMPANY ™
Amber: **Sandalwood Beauty**

NATURAL HOUSE PRODUCTS LIMITED ™☺⏺
Orange and Apricot Hand Soap

NATURAL SENSE ™
Aleppo Cubes; Aleppo Soap with Damascus Rose Oil; Aleppo Soap with Oil of Jasmine; Aleppo Soap with Oil of Nigella; Liquid Soap

NATURALLY GIFTED ™
Bed of Roses; Citrus Grove Bar; Hemp & Walnut; Herbal Mint; Oatmeal & Spice Scrub; Olive Oil; Seaweed Bar; Summer Solstice; T Tree

NATURE'S GATE
Liquid Soaps: Deep Cleansing, Moisturizing, Purifying, Soothing; *Organics - Fruit Blend Liquid Soaps:* Asian Pear & Red Tea, Grapefruit & Wild Ginger, Mandarin Orange & Patchouli, Persimmon & Rose

Geranium; *Organics - Herbal Blend Liquid Soaps:* Lavender & Aloe, Lemongrass & Clary Sage, Neroli Orange & Chocolate Mint, Tea Tree & Blue Cypress

NEAL'S YARD REMEDIES
⊘ ✔ ☞⅄ 1998

Calendula; French Almond; French Lavender (Hand Made); Geranium & Orange; Lavender & Olive Oil; Lavender & Tea Tree; Marseille Block; Neem; Simple Oat

NEVER TOO BUSY TO BE BEAUTIFUL
TM ✔

Botanomancy: **True Grit - Washball Soap;** *Dirty:* **Face Scrub**

NEW SEASONS ⊘ ✔

Liquid Soap; *Neutral & Toiletry Bases:* Liquid Soap

NO COWS ☺❶

Gardeners Gift Box; Natural Mini Soap Gift Box; Natural Soap Gift Box; No Cows Liquid Soap; Organic Mini Soap Gift Box

NOTHING NASTY ✔

Liquid Castille Soaps: Lavender, Mandarin, Rosemary, Tea Tree

OPTIMAH HEALTH & NUTRITION
⊘ ✔ ☞⅄ 1995

Olivera: Olive Oil & Aloe Vera Soap, Olive Oil & Aloe Vera Soap with Lavender Essential Oil, Olive Oil & Aloe Vera Soap with Tea Tree Antiseptic, Olive Oil & Aloe Vera Soap with Vitamin E Moisturiser

ORGANIC BOTANICS ™⊘☼
Organic Bar Soap With Flower Oils; Organic Soap With Flower Oils

ORGANIC SOAP COMPANY ™⊘☼
Adam the Gardener's Tea Tree Scrub; Aloe Vera & Lavender; Bergamot; Cheer Up; Frankincense & Myrrh; Geranium & Orange Blossom; Lavender; Lavender & Chamomile; Lavender Scrub; Lemongrass & Rosemary; Patchouli; Patchouli Soap; Relax & Chill Out; Rose & Jasmine; Rose & Vanilla; Rose Garden; Sandalwood; Soothing Smoothing; Tea Tree & Lavender; Vanilla Marble; *New:* **No Worries, Rosemary, Soothing Smoothing 1, Soothing Smoothing 2;** *Soap:* **Adam the Gardener's Hand Scrub, Avocado Soap / Baby Soap, Buzz Off / Midge Repellent Soap, Cheer Up Soap, Cinnamon and Oatmeal Scrub, Frankincense and Myrrh, Lavender and Aloe Vera, Lavender and Chamomile, Lavender Flowers Scrub, Lemon Sorbet, No Worries, Olive Oil, Patchouli, Patchouli, Bergamot, Geranium, Rose and Jasmine, Rose Garden, Sandalwood, Soothing Smoothing, Spice Island, Tea Tree, Tea Tree and Lavender, Venus Aphrodite**

POTIONS AND POSSIBILITIES ⊘ ✔
Double Luxury Soaps: Bergamot,

English Garden, English Jasmine, English Lavender, English Rose, Frankincense, French Lavender & Evening Primrose, Orange & Calendula, Rose & Cinnamon, Rosemary & Wild Mint, Violet; *Luxury Soap Stack:* Contemporary Soap Collection, Traditional Soap Collection; *Organic Range:* Luxury Double Soap

PURPLE FLAME AROMATHERAPY ☺◒⚲
All

QUINTESSENTIAL SOAPS ☺
Calendula Comfort; Essential Spice; Sublime; Terra Rosa; Citrus Swirl; Cobblestone; Pure and Natural; Rosemary and Time

RAW GAIA ™☺⚲
Organic Raw - clear and refreshing; Organic Raw - Lavender; Organic Raw - Rose Geranium

RED STAR NATURAL LIQUID SOAPS
™☺◒⚲✂−1980
Hard Bar Soaps: **Smooth as a Baby's Bum;** *Natural Hard Bar 125g Soaps:* **Lavender;** *Natural Hard Bar 125g Soaps:* **Fragrance Free, Lemon & Lime, Marjoram & Fennel, Peppermint, Tea Tree;** *Natural Liquid Soaps 250ml:* **Fragrance Free, Lavender, Lemon & Lime, Marjoram & Fennel, Peppermint, Tea Tree**

REDBUSH TEA CO
Redbush Exfoliating Soap; Redbush Soap

SCENT BY NATURE ☺◒⚲✂−1986
100% Plant-Based Essential Oil Soap: Tea Tree & Eucalyptus

SHANTI PRODUCTS ◒⚲
Christmas Range: Christmas Cake Soap Slice, Christmas Cupcake, Cinnamon Christmas Cake Slice; *Cold Process Bars:* Cinnamon & Nutmeg, Coconut Soap, English Rose Soap, Eucalyptus & Tea Tree Soap, Garden Mint, Gardener, Lavender Soap, Lemon Zest Soap, Lime & Patchouli Soap, Ocean Fresh, Pure & Simple, Rosemary Soap, Sandalwood Soap, Sweet Orange & Patchouli, Vanilla Soap

SHEA BY NATURE ™☺
Liquid Soaps: **African Black Soap - Cocovanille, African Black Soap - Coffee Fragrance, African Black Soap - Exotica with Lemongrass, Lemon and Orange, African Black Soap - Jungle Spice, African Black Soap - Strawberry and Vanilla, African Black Soap - Sweet Romance (Geranium, Lavender and Ylang, African Black Soap - Tea Tree and Peppermint, African Black Soap - Unscented;** *Soap Bars:* **African Black Soap - Unscented, African Black Soap - with Lemongrass,Lavender and YlangYlang**

SHELLBELLES ☺❶
Soap: Anise Star, Bergamot and Ho Leaf, Juniper Berry and Ylang Exfoliating, Lemongrass and Jasmine, Lime and Ylang Ylang

SIMPLY SOAPS ™❶⊘✔☞⅍ 2003
Banana & Citron; Calendula & Lavender; Cedarwood; Geranium & Rose; Guys Bar Natural and Organic; Hemp; Liquid Soap; Mandarin Liquid Soap; Orange, Neroli & Sandalwood; Poppy Bar; Rosemary & Lavender; Seaweed; Tea Tree; *Gift Sets:* **3-Soap Gift Box, 5-Soap Gift Box;** *Hedgerow Herbals:* **Comfrey & Calendula, Rose & Oatmeal;** *Hedgerow Herbals- Black Palm Natural Range:* **Natural Soft Soap**

SODASAN ™
Bar Soap; Body Care Soaps; Olive Soaps

SOLANO TRADING ™⊘✔
Rampal Patou: **Almond Soap, Lavender Soap, Olive Oil Soap, Scented Soap;** *Savon Liquide:* **Lavande, The Vert**

SOLARAY NUTRITIONAL SUPPLEMENTS
Herbal Liquid Every Day Body Soap; Men's Cleansing Bar; Rosa Mosqueta Cleansing Bar; Rosa Mosqueta Luxurious Bodywash; Sea Buckthorn w Sandalwood; White Camelia w Jasmine

SONETT OHG ™
Citrus Handsoap; Curd Soap; ÉÉpure; Lavender Handsoap; Liquid Soap; Neutral Handsoap; Neutral Plant Soap Bar; Rose Handsoap

SUMA WHOLEFOODS
™❶⊘✔☞⅍1985
Country Garden: **Chamomile, Mixed Pack, Rosemary, Violet;** *Exotic:* **Cinnamon & Sandalwood, Mixed Pack, Nutmeg & Vanilla, Tea Tree;** *Extra Gentle:* **Avocado & Cucumber, Desert Aloe Vera, Fragrant Coco Palm, Mixed Pack;** *Glycerine Soaps:* **Grapefruit & Aloe Vera, Hemp & Vitamin E, Rose & Geranium, White Lavender;** *Handmade Gifts:* **Box of Soaps - Gift Box;** *Old English:* **Elderflower & Apple, English Lavender Blossom, Mixed Pack, Rose of York;** *'Winter Collection giftbox handmade soaps':* **Frankincense and Lemongrass/Orange and Clove/ Ylang Ylang/Cinnamon and Sandalwood**

TANJERO ™☺⊘✔
Aloeswood; Apple & Orchid; Aquarius; Aries; Cancer; Capricorn; Carrot & Hempseed; Chamomile; Coconut & Kelp; Cucumber & Mint; Gardenia; Gemini; Geranium; Geranium & Lime; Grapefruit & Orange; Jasmine; Just Carrot; Kitchen Coffee Bar; Lavender; Lavender & Aloe Vera; Lavender & Chamomile; Lavender & Oatmeal; Lavender with Flowers; Leo; Libra; Litsea Cubeba; Musk; Patchouli; Pisces; Pure Aloe Vera; Rose; Sagittarius; Scorpio; Sea Breeze; Strawberry; Sultan; Tanjero No. 1; Tanjero No. 2; Tanjero No. 3; Taurus;

Tea Tree & Aloe Vera; Tea Tree & Lavender; Tea Tree & Lavender with Oatmeal; Tea Tree & Mint; Tea Tree & Oatmeal; Violet; Virgo; Ylang Ylang

THE HIGHLAND SOAP COMPANY ™◯
Aloe&White tea; Chamomille; Cinnamon&Orange; Gardeners Soap; Highland Lavender; Lavender Luxury Soap; Lemongrass; Lemongrass&Ginger Soap; Mango Butter; Passion Fruit; Red Clay&Ylang Ylang; Rose Geranium&Lavender Soap; Rose&Patchouli; Rose&Ylang Ylang; Rosehip&Patchouli Soap; Rosemary&Wild Nettle; Sandalwood; Scottish Heather; Tea Tree&Peppermint; White Jasmine; Wild Nettle&Heather; Wild Scottish Strawberry

TISSERAND AROMATHERAPY PRODUCTS ™☺
Lavender Products: **Lavender & Evening Primrose, Lavender and Evening Primrose;** *Skin softening soaps:* **Bitter Orange and Jasmine, Tea Tree and Avocado;** *Tea Tree Products:* **Tea Tree, Tea Tree & Avocado**

TOMS OF MAINE ◯✦
Natural Clear Body Bar: Lavender, Unscented; *Natural Deodorant Body Bar:* Lemongrass, Unscented; *Natural Moisturising Body Bar:* Calendula, Lavender, Unscented

TREASURED EARTH SKINCARE ™☺◯
Soaps

TREE-HARVEST ◯✦
Artisan Handmade Soap: Bay, Calendula, Cedar & Lemon, Forest Spice, Frankincense & Myrrh, Gardener's, Geranium Lavender & Chamomile, Hemp, Orange Cardamon & Clove, Patchouli & Sandalwood, St Clement's, Tea Tree

TROPICAL WHOLEFOODS
Clean: Aloe Vera and Baobab Purity, Neem, Seaweed & Lemongrass Scrub

URTEKRAM ◯✦◉⚹1998
Handsoap: All

VERDESATIVA S.R.L. ™☺
Liquid Soap - Hemp and Citrus Fruit; Sapone Canap e Papavero (Hemp and Poppy Soap); Sapone Canapa e Aloe (Hemp and Aloe Soap); Sapone Canapa e Argilla (Hemp and Clay Soap); Sapone Canapa e Arumi (Hemp and Citrus Fruits Soap); Sapone Canapa e Calendula (Hemp and Marigold Soap); Sapone Canapa e Camomilla (Hemp and Chamomile); Sapone Canapa e Crusca (Hemp and Bran); Sapone Canapa e Fior di Loto (Hemp and Lotus Flower); Sapone Canapa e Lavanda (Hemp and Lavender Soap); Sapone Canapa e Mango (Hemp and Mango); Sapone Canapa e Menta (Hemp and Mint); Sapone Canapa e Neem (Hemp and Neem Soap);

Sapone Canapa e Papaia (Hemp and Papaya); Sapone Canapa e Pezzetti di Canapa (Hemp and Hemp Pieces Soap); Sapone Canapa e Rosa (Hemp and Rose); Sapone Canapa e Sandalo (Hemp and Sandalwood Soap); Sapone Canapa e Spirulina (Hemp and Spirulina); Sapone Canapa e Tea Tree (Hemp and Tea Tree); Sapone Canapa e Uva Rossa (Hemp and Grapeseed Oil); Sapone Canapa e Vetiver Java (Hemp and Vetiver Java Soap); Sapone Variegato Canapa e Argilla (Marble Soap Hemp and Clay); Sapone Variegato Canapa e Menta (Marbled Hemp and Mint); Sapone Variegato Canapa e Pezzetti di Canapa(Marble Soap Hemp and Hemp Pieces); Sapone Vegetale Canapa e Olio di Oliva Delicato(Pure Vegetable Soap Hemp and Olive Oil); Sapone Vegetale Canapa e Spirulina Levigante(Pure Vegetable Soap Hemp and Spirulina); Spone Canapa e Malva (Hemp and Mallow); Sapone Canapa ed Olio di Oliva Levigante (Hemp and Olive Oil)

VINDOTCO UK LTD ™☺◇ ✓
Really Works: Gel Citrus Hand Cleaner with Pumice, Gel Citrus Hand Cleaner without Pumice, Lotion Hand

VISIONARY SOAP COMPANY ™☺
Anise Poppy Seed; Bergamot Pine; Cinnamon Orange Clove; Eucalyptus Lime; Geranium Rose; Lavender; Lemon Lavender; Lemongrass; Patchouli; Peppermint Orange;

Rosemary Spearmint; Shea Butter and Oatmeal; Tea Tree; Unscented; Ylang Ylang

WELEDA ◇ ✓ ⚘ 1985
Iris; Rose; Rosemary

YAOH ™☺❶◇ ✓
Liquid Soap

SUN CARE

ALTERNATIVE STORES ™☺❶
All products are vegan

ANNEMARIE BORLIND ✓
After-Sun Gel; Sun Lotion Factor 15; Sun Milk Factor 10; Sun Milk Factor 15; Sunless Bronze

BEAUTY NATURALS ✓
Hair Protection Mist; *After Sun:* Skin Calming Gel, Skin Repair Lotion; *Martha Hill:* After-Sun Skin Calming Gel, After-Sun Skin Repair Lotion; *Sun Protection Lotion:* SPF 15, SPF 25; *Sun Protection Oil:* SPF 10

FOREVER LIVING PRODUCTS
Aloe Sunless Tanning Lotion; Aloe Sunscreen SPF30

GREEN PEOPLE CO. ™◇ ✓
Self Tan Lotion; *Skin Care:* Day Solution SPF15 (Day Cream); After Sun; Edelweiss Sun Lotion - SPF8/SPF15

HOWAD LTD T/A INCOGNITO ™❶⊘ⓘ
100% Natural After Sun

JASON NATURAL PRODUCTS ⓘ 👁
Active Block SPF40; Complete Block SPF26; Daily Block SPF30; Family Block SPF 36; Kid's Block SPF46; Natural Lip Care SPF 20; Sunbrellas®® Chemical Free Sun Block SPF30&; Sunbrellas®® Complete Block Spray SPF 26; Sunbrellas®® Facial Block SPF20; *After Sun:* Aloe Vera 98% Moisturizing Gel, Tea Tree Soothing Gel

LAVERANA ™ⓘ
Sun Sensitiv: **Sun Spray Hawaii SPF 20**

LIZ EARLE ⓘ 👁
Sun Shade Botanical Aftersun Gel; Sun Shade Botanical Self-Tan Spray; Sun Shade SPF15 Body Protector; Sun Shade SPF25 Face Protector

NATURE'S GATE
Aqua Block SPF 50; Kids Block Giggleberry SPF30; Kids SPF 30; Lotion SPF 30; Mineral Kidsblock SPF20; Mineral Sportblock SPF20; Mineral Sunblock SPF20; Sport SPF 30; *Organics - Advanced Care:* Be Selective SPF30 for face, Happy Glow Lucky Citrus Bronzer, Happy Glow Lucky Floral Bronzer, Sundercover SPF30 for body, Tanagement Self Tanner

NEW SEASONS ⊘ⓘ
After Sun Gel

SIMPLE ⓘ
Face Protector Hydrolotion SPF 30; Face Self Tan Hydrolotion; Lip Protector; Lotion SPF 30; Tender Places SPF 50; *Aftersun:* Balm, Hydrating Lotion, Insect Repellant Lotion; *Babies:* Baby Cream SPF 50, Baby Lotion SPF 50; *Body Self Tan:* Lotion, Mousse, Spray; *Children:* Kid's Lotion SPF 30, Kid's Lotion SPF 50, Kid's Spray SPF 30

SOLARAY NUTRITIONAL SUPPLEMENTS
Green Tea Sunblock for Children SPF25; Rosa Mosqueta Sun Protection Herbal Butter SPF12

SUN ZAPPER ☺
Lip Balm; *Sun Block:* Blue Zinc Stick, Pink Zinc Stick, Skin Tone Colour Zinc Stick, White Zinc Stick

WELEDA ⊘ⓘ⚘1985
Edelweiss Sun Cream PF20; Edelweiss Sun Lotion PF15

YAOH ™☺❶⊘ⓘ
AfterSun; Sun Cream; Sunblock 15; Sunblock 30

TALCUM POWDERS

BEAUTY NATURALS ⓘ
Body Talc; Lavender

BRONNLEY & CO LTD ⓘ
Body Care for Men: Talc; *Dusting Powder:* Apricot & Almond, English Fern, Lavender, Orchid, Passion Flower, Pink

Bouquet, Rose, White Iris; *Royal Horticultural Society - Dusting Powder:* Passion Flower, Rose; *Talcum Powder:* Apricot & Almond, English Fern, Lavender, Orchid, Pink Bouquet, White Iris

ESSENTIALLY NATURAL ™
**Lavender Body Powder;
Sandalwood Body Powder**

GREEN WYCH ™☺❶
Dusting Powder: **Bergamot, Geranium, Lavender, Orange Zest**

JASON NATURAL PRODUCTS ✔ ☞
Aloe Vera Body Powder Talc Free; Tea Tree Body Powder Talc Free

LUSH ™ ✔
Dusting Powders: **Bare Naked Lady, Candy Fluff, Silky Underwear, T for Toes;** *Karma Products:* **Karma Dusting Powder**

NEVER TOO BUSY TO BE BEAUTIFUL ™ ✔
Keep It Fluffy: **Bronze Powder Puff, Dusting Powder**

SIMPLE ✔
Pure Fine Talc

TOOTHPASTES & ORAL HYGIENE

A. VOGEL
Echinacea Toothpaste; *Dentaforce:* Mouthspray and Wash, Toothpaste

ABSOLUTE AROMAS ™⊘ ✔
Ord River: **Tea Tree Toothpaste 75 g**

ABSOLUTELY PURE ⊘
Peppermint Dental Soap

ALOE DENT
Aloe Vera Mouthwash with Vitamin K & Tea Tree; Childrens Toothpaste - Strawberry Flavour; Night Time Aloe Vera Toothpaste with Chamomile - Mint Flavour; Sensitive Aloe Vera Toothpaste with Silica - Mint Flavour; Wake Up Aloe Vera Toothpaste with Ginseng - Mint Flavour; Wake Up Toothpaste with Ginseng; Whitening Aloe Vera Toothpaste with Echinacea - Mint Flavour

ALTERNATIVE STORES ™☺❶
All products are vegan
BURT'S BEES ⊘ ✔ ☞
Peppermint Breath Drops; *Doctor Burt's Toothpaste:* Cinna-Mint, Lavender Mint

CLEARSPRING ™☺❶⊘ ✔ ☞
Dentie toothpaste; Dentie toothpowder

DR HAUSCHKA ⊘ ✦
Wala Vita Lemon & Salt Toothpaste

FLORIS ☺ ✦
Concentrated Mouthwash: Rose

GREEN PEOPLE CO. ™⊘ ✦
Oral Hygiene: **Citrus Herbal Fresh Toothpaste, Mint Herbal Fresh Toothpaste, Mint Mouthwash, Minty Cool Toothpaste**

GREEN WYCH ™⊘☺❶
Toothpaste: **Lemon, Peppermint**

HERBS HANDS HEALING LTD ™⊘ ✦
Ears, Eyes & Mouth: **Mouthwash Water;** *Herbal Formula:* **Mouthwash**

HERBS OF GRACE ™⊘ ✦
Miscellaneous: **Photodent**

J&D BLACK LTD ☺⊘ ✦ ◉
Hollytrees: Citrus Toothpaste, Fennel Mouthwash, Fennel Toothpaste, Garden Mint Mouthwash, Garden Mint Toothpaste, Sage and Calendula Mouthwash

JASON NATURAL PRODUCTS ✦ ◉
Healthy Mouth Toothpaste and Mouthwash; NutriSmile Toothpaste and Mouthwash; PowerSmile Toothpaste and Mouthwash; PowerSmile®® Cinnamon Mint Mouthwash; PowerSmile®® Cinnamon Mint Toothpaste; PowerSmile®® Vanilla Mint Toothpaste; Sea Fresh Toothpaste and Mouthwash

JUNGLESALE LIMITED ™
Neem Mouthwash

KINGFISHER NATURAL TOOTHPASTE ☺ ✦ ◉✂1981
Toothpaste: Aloe Vera Tea Tree Fennel, Aloe Vera Tea Tree Mint, Baking Soda Mint, Fennel, Fennel Fluoride Free, Mint with Lemon, Mint with Lemon Fluoride Free

LAVERANA ™✦
Lavera Basis Sensitiv: **Toothpaste Mint;** *Lavera Neutral:* **Neutral Tooth Gel**

MAXIM MARKETING COMPANY ™
Amber: **Toothpaste (Sugar Free)**

NATURAL SENSE ™
Natural Toothpastes (all flavours)

NATURE'S GATE
Cherry Gel; Cool Mint Gel; Crème de Anise; Crèème de Mint; Crème de Peppermint; Whitening Gel; Wintergreen Gel; *Organics - Advanced Care:* Peppermint Mouthwash, Peppermint Whitening Toothpaste, Raspberry Mint Mouthwash, Raspberry Mint Whitening Toothpaste

NEAL'S YARD REMEDIES ⊘ ✦ ◉✂1998
Lemon & Mint Mouth Freshener; *Toothpaste:* Fennel, Gardenmint

SANMAR GMBH ™
Zahngel

TOMS OF MAINE ⊘ 🍖
Natural Anticavity Fluoride Mouthwash: Spearmint; *Natural Anticavity Fluoride Mouthwash for a Dry Mouth:* Lemon Lime; *Natural Anticavity Fluoride Toothpaste:* Peppermint Baking Soda, Spearmint; *Natural Antiplaque Plus Tatar Control and Whitening Toothpaste:* Fennel, Peppermint, Spearmint; *Natural Antiplaque Plus Whitening Gel Toothpaste:* Peppermint; *Natural Clean and Gentle Care Fluoride Free Toothpaste:* Cinnamon-Clove, Spearmint; *Natural Clean and Gentle Care SLS-Free:* Apricot, Lemon-Lime; *Natural Clean and Gentle Care SLS-Free Plus Dry Mouth Soother:* Apricot, Lemon-Lime; *Natural Clean and Gentle Care SLS-Free Plus Whitening:* Fennel, Peppermint; *Natural Cleansing Mouthwash:* Cinnamint, Peppermint Baking Soda, Spearmint; *Natural Sensitive Care:* Black Currant, Wintermint; *Natural Tartar Control Mouthwash:* Peppermint; *Natural Whole Care Toothpaste:* Cinnamon-Clove, Peppermint, Spearmint, Wintermint; *Natural Whole Care Toothpaste Gel:* Cinnamon-Clove, Orange-Mango, Peppermint, Spearmint

TRINITY LIFECARE(HOLDINGS) LIMITED ™⊘
Peri-Gum

URTEKRAM ⊘ 🍖 👁 🌿 1998
Aloe Vera Toothpaste

VICCO
Vicco Vajradanti

WELEDA ⊘ 🍖 🌿 1985
Calendula Toothpaste; Plant Gel Toothpaste; Ratanhia Toothpaste; Salt Toothpaste

NOTES

■ **Contact lenses** are classed as a medicine under the Medicines Act, all contact lens solutions and associated products have been safety-tested (which invariably entails animal testing at some point). Such products are listed in the Animal Free Shopper *only* if the company under whose name they are sold meets our animal testing criterion (see **ANIMAL-FREE CRITERIA**, page 42).

■ **Dental floss** may contain beeswax or propolis, Desert Essence produces a dental floss that is suitable for vegans.

■ **Disposable razors** may include a moisturising strip that could contain animal-tested or animal-derived ingredients. Veganstore.co.uk sells a range of shaving products that are free from animal ingredients and animal testing, including disposable and refillable razors and shaving brushes.

■ **Mascara** may contain silk, as can other types of make-up products.

■ **The Body Shop** cannot state that any of their products are free from animal derived ingredients.

■ **Toothpastes and mouthwashes** may contain glycerine, which can be animal-derived.

VEG 1

VEGAN MULTIVITAMIN
90 chewable tablets

Suitable for everyone
Perfect for vegans

HEALTHCARE

CONTRACEPTIVES

DUREX
Condoms: Avanti Ultima

GLYDE HEALTH PTY LTD ™
Latex Condoms; Sheer Glyde Dams

PASANTE HEALTH CARE
Condoms: Delay, Extra, Large, Mixed
Flavours, Naturelle, Ribbed, Trim, Xtra
Sensitive

INSECT REPELLENTS

A. VOGEL
Neemcare: Shampoo

BURT'S BEES ⊘ 🖊 👁
Bug Bite Relief; *Natural Remedies:*
Herbal Insect Repellent

KOBASHI ™☺⊘ 🖊 👁⤙ 1976
Luxury Lotions: **Insect Repellent**

**THE NATURAL SKINCARE
COMPANY LTD** ™
Carribean Blue: **Natural Insect
Repellant**

LUBRICANTS

BODYLOVE
Anal Joy Intimate Lubricant; Orgasm
Gel, Ultra Gel Lubricant

GLYDE HEALTH PTY LTD ™
Lubricant

JASON NATURAL PRODUCTS 🖊 👁
Women Wise Intimate Lubricant

REMEDIES

(The Vegan Society cannot vouch
for the effectiveness of the
products in this section)

A. VOGEL
Aesculus Gel; Aesculus Tablets; Atro Bath
Oil; Atrogel; Comfrey Cream; Echinacea
Cream; Hypericum Tablets; Luffa Nasal
Spray; Silecea Gel; Silicea Cold Sore Lip Gel;
Animal Essence Range: All; *Jan de Vries
Essences:* All; *Jan de Vries Range Tincture
Range:* All; *Neemcare:* Oil; *Tinctures:* All

ABSOLUTE AROMAS ™⊘ 🖊
Ord River: **Tea Tree Antiseptic Cream
50ml**

AINSWORTHS
Recovery Plus Emergency Formula;
Recovery Remedy; *Bach Flower
Remedies:* All; *Homeopathic Remedies:*
All (Pills & Coarse Granules)

Kudos

VITAMINS AND HERBALS

www.kudosvitamins.com
Freephone:
0800 3895476

ANN ELISE SKINCARE ☺
Relief from Eczema

AROMA CRYSTAL THERAPY ⊘ *i*
Natures First Defence

BIO-HEALTH LTD ⊘ *i*
Licensed Herbal Medicinal Products:
Blue Fag Rood Compound, Boldo Aid
to Slimming, Damiana, Digestive,
Echinacea, Garlic, Lobelia Compound,
Motherworth Compound, Natural Herb
Laxative; *Ointments:* Arnica,
Chamomile, Chickweed, Comfrey,
Echinacea, Garlic, Marigold, Tea Tree,
Witch Hazel; *The Star Range:*
Goodnight, Lowater, Neurotone, Runo,
Strength

CEDAR HEALTH LTD
Ortis: Devils Claw Gel

DENDRON LTD *i*
Adios: A Natural aid for Slimming;
Stressless: A Natural Remedy For Stress;
Yariba: A Natural Way to Revive Your
Day

DIOMED DEVELOPMENTS LTD ⊘
Headache Relief Stick

DOLMA ™☺❶⊘ *i* ◉⊁ 1976
Miscellaneous Products: **Avasafab
Antiseptic Cream**

ESSENTIALLY NATURAL ™
Organic Acne Astringent

ESSENTIALLY YOURS LTD ™☺⊘ *i* ◉
Free&Organic Range: **Spot serum;**
Natural Elements: **Spot serum**

HALLS
Cough Sweets: Blackcurrant, Cherry
Sugar Free, Original, Original Mentho-
Lyptus Medicated; *Soothers:*
Blackcurrant, Cherry, Peach and
Raspberry, Strawberry

HARLOW LUBRICANTS ™☺
**Follicel All Natural Head Lice
Treatment**

HEALTHY HERBS ™☺
**Aloe Vera Gel; Balancing-The-
Change Oil; Burdock&Chickweed
Oil; Calendula Oil; Chamomille OIl;
Comfrey; Evening Primrose Oil;
Herb Oil; Manuka Stick; Musc-Ease
Gel; Nit-Away Oil; Pilewort Oil;
Soothing Botanical Oil; Sportshyp
Oil**

HERBS HANDS HEALING LTD ™⊘ *i*
**Adrenal; Bringing on a period;
Cystitis; Endometriosis; Fibroid;
Galactogogue (for bringing on
breast milk postnatal); Libido &
Fertility; Ovulation Pain; PCO
(polycystic Ovary); Strong
Fibroid/Heavy Bleeding; Underactive
Thyroid; Womb Lining and
Thickening;** *Bowel Cleanse:* **Olive &
Artemisia Formula;**
*Capsules/Powders/Culinary & Medicinal
Herbs:* **Cayenne Powder, Chickweed
Powder, Clay & Linseed, Comfrey**

Root Powder, Deep Repair Powder, Marigold Powder, Marshmallow Powder, Mediterranean Medley Culinary Herbs, Milk Thistle Seeds, Organic Pot Barley Seeds, Poultice Powder, Slippery Elm Powder, Tumeric Powder; *Colds & Chest Support:* Cherry Bark & Elderberry Syrup, Onion & Horseradish Elixir; *Digestive Assistance:* Cleanse & Balance Heb Tea, Digestion Heal Pack, Meadowsweet Herb Tea, Meadowsweet Tincture; *Ears, Eyes & Mouth:* Dr. Christopher's B & B Ear Formula; *For all Menopausal Stages:* Chamomile & Vervain Formula, Siberian Ginseng Tincture, Valerian & Passionflower Formula, Vitex & Black Cohosh Formula (Menopause); *Fungal Overload:* Pau d'Arco & Chamomile Formula, Pau d'Arco Bark Tea; *Heart & Circulatory Health:* Ginger & Hawthorn Formula, Ginkgo & Rosemary Formula, Hawthorn Tincture; *Heart & Circulatory Heath:* Prickly Ash & Rosemary Formula; *Herbal Formula:* Burdock & Silver Birch, Sarsaparilla & Tumeric; *Hormone Assistance for Men:* Saw Palmetto & Damiana Formula; *Immune Stimulation:* Echinacea & Thyme Formula, Echinacea Tincture, Immuno Herbal Tea; *Immune Tonics:* American Ginseng & Astragalus Formula, Gentian & Liquorice, Siberian Ginseng & Liquorice, Siberian Ginseng Tincture; *Immune Travel Support:* Olive & Artemisia Formula;

Immunity & Allergies: Immune Heal Pack, Juniper & Eyebright Formula; *Kidney & Bladder Health:* Dandelion & Marshmallow Formula, Nettle Leaf Tea; *Kidney Cleanses:* 28 Day Kidney Cleanse, One Day Kidney Cleanse; *Lazy Bowel:* Barberry Capsules, Chamomile & Cascara Capsules, Organic Linseed Seeds, Organic Psyllium Husks; *Liver Cleanses:* 28 Day Liver Cleanse, One Day Liver Cleanse; *Lungs & Breathing:* Breathe & Clear Herbal Tea, Mullein & Eucalyptus Formula; *Menstrual Help:* Agnus Castus & Raspberry Formula (Premenstrual), Agnus Castus Tincture, Crampbark Tincture, Menstruation Heal Pack, Parsley & Cornsilk Herb Tea, Squaw Vine & Fennel Formula (Monthly Cycle); *Muscles, Joints & Tendons:* Angelica & Meadowsweet Formula, Body Ease Herbal Tea, Castor Oil Pack Kit, Deep Tissue Oil; *Nervous System Health & Support:* Nerve Heal Pack; *Night Support:* Evening Peace Herbal Tea; *Prostate Support:* Saw Palmetto & Damiana Formula; *Single Tinctures:* Artichoke, Black Cohosh, Black Walnut, Burdock, Cayenne, Chamomile, Cleavers, Dandeion, Fennel, Fenugreek, Gingko, Gotu Kola, Lemon Balm, Lobelia, Milk Thistle, Nettle, Olive, Pau d'arco, Saw Palmetto, Schisandra, Skullcap, St. John's Wort, Valerian, Wild Yam, Yellow Dock; *Skin Support:* Cleavers & Burdock Formula, Skin Guard Water; *Soothing & Nurturing the Bowel:*

Chamomile Flowers Tea, Gentian & Liquorice Formula, Marigold & Crampbark Formula, Slippery Elm & Marshmallow Powder; *Useful Tonics for both Sexes:* **American Ginseng & Astragalus Formula, Milk Thistle & Dandelion Formula;** *Uterine Cleansing:* **Marshmallow & Squaw Vine Pessaries**

HERBS OF GRACE ™ ⊘ *i*
Miscellaneous: **Colloidal Silver Spray**

HOLISTIX ™❶
Anti-Fungal Foot Cream

HOLLAND AND BARRETT RETAIL LTD *i*
Cough Syrup: Chesty

ID AROMATICS
Therapeutic Creams: Bug off Cream, Cooling Gel, Gym & Tonic, Healing Gel, Pain Reliever, Wild Yam Cream

ITS ELIXIR UK LIMITED ™ ⊘ *i* 👁
Bump oil; Post bump oil; Scar oil

J.L. BRAGG ☺ ⊘ *i*
Bragg's Medicinal Charcoal Biscuits & Tablets

LANES HEALTH ⊘ *i*
Aqua Ban: Tablets; *Duel Lax:* Extra Strong Tablets; *Olbas:* Olbas Inhaler Stick, Olbas Oil, Olbas Oil for Children, Olbas Original Pastilles

MASTERFOODS ⊘
Aquadrops: Lemon

NATURE'S AID ⊘ *i*
5HTP Complex 100mg; Almond Oil; Aloe Vera Juice Double Strength; Alpha Lipoic Acid & Acetyl-L-Carnitine 250mg; Black Cohosh Complex w Sage; Boldo Complex w Dandelion; Celery Seed Complex w Devils Claw; Coconut Oil; Comfrey Oil; Echinacea Complex w Elderberry; Ginger, Turmeric & Boswellia; Gingko Biloba 3000mg; Glucosamine Hydrochloride 750mg; Green Food Complex & Wheat Grass; Green Tea 1000mg; Hair, Skin & Nails Formula; Passiflora, Lemon Balm & Avena Sativa; Pomegranate Juice (double strength) 500ml; Raspberry Leaf 750mg; Rosehip 750mg; Sage Leaf 500mg; Sasparilla Complex w Burdock; Saw Palmetto Complex For Men; Senna Complex w Liquorice; Senna Extract 875mg; Slippery Elm Complex w Peppermint; Spirulina Blue/Green Algae 500mg; St. Johns Wort 333mg; Valerian Complex w Passiflora; Zinc Lozenge (peppermint)

NEAL'S YARD REMEDIES ⊘ *i* 👁 ⚶ 1998
Aromastream Refill Pads; Australian Bush Flower Remedies; Bach Flower Remedies; Bentonite Clay; Dead Sea Salts; Emulsifying Wax; Green Clay; Herbal Tea Blends; Herbal Tinctures (Blends); Herbal Tinctures (Single Tinctures); Herbs (Dried); Homeopathic Kits (Pillules) but not Apis, Cantharis or Sepia Remedies; Viridian Products (except Glucosamine Chondroitin Complex); *Aromatherapy for:* Breathing Easy; *Oils:* Avocado; *Remedies to Roll for:* Energy, Night Time, Relaxation, Study, Travel; *Tinctures:* Chinese Herbal, Homeopathic

OPTIMAH HEALTH & NUTRITION
⊘ ✦ ⚹ 1995
Echinacea Throat Spray Mint Flavour;
Maxicol; Maxicol Capsules; XS Acid
Aloe Vera Digestive Aid Tablets

ORCHID HEALTHCARE LIMITED ™
Isovon

PHARMA NORD ⊘
Melatonin

POTTER'S HERBAL MEDICINE ✦
Cleansing tablets; Elixir of Echinacea;
Indian Brandee; Nodoff; Out of Sorts;
Skin Clear Tablets; Slippery Elm; Tabritis
Tablets; Vegetable Cough Remover

PURE GAISHA ™☺❶✦
Calming Wheat Bags

QUINESSENCE AROMATHERAPY
☺⊘✦👁
Essential Oil Synergies: Anti-Pollen,
Antiseptic, Anti-Virus, Breathe Ease,
Joint Mobility, Menopause, Muscle
Ease, Pre-Menstrual, Restful Sleep,
Sinus, Stress

SCENT BY NATURE ☺⊘✦⚹ 1986
Ainsworths Flower Remedies: Bach
Rescue Remedy, Single Bach Flower
Remedies; *Green Clay:* Fine Powdered,
Ready-to-Use, w Organic Lemon
Supplement

SCOTTISH HERBAL SUPPLIES ™❶⊘✦
Clays; Herbal Alcoholic Tinctures;
Vegetable/Herbal Ointments

SHANTI PRODUCTS ⊘✦
Hair Lice Lotion

TAYLOR JACKSON
HEALTH PRODUCTS ☺❶⊘✦
M-folia for Psoriasis & Eczema: Bath Oil,
Body Lotion, Body Wash, Conditioner,
Cream, Herbal Extract, Mild Tablets,
Ointment, Scalp Oil, Shampoo, Super
Tablets

THE ESSENTIAL OIL COMPANY ⊘✦👁
Thermotherapy - Microwaveable
Heated Gifts: Cherry Stone Pillow, Hot-
Pak Rectangular Wheat Soother

THE HEMP COMPANY LTD ✦👁
BPA Safe Solutions Body Piercing
Aftercare

THE HUMANE RESEARCH TRUST ⊘✦
Assisi & Berwitz Homeopathic Remedy
Creams: Anal Itching, Arnica, Athletes
Foot, Cuts & Sores, Dry Skin Cream,
Healing, Itching Eczema, Wart; *Berwitz*
Homeopathic Remedies for People:
Burn Cream, Echinacea Cream, First Aid
Cream, Psoriasis Cream, Rheumatism
Cream, Tea Tree Cream, Tennis Elbow
Cream, Varicose Vein Cream

THE ORGANIC HERB
TRADING COMPANY ⊘
Organic Medicinal Tinctures: All except
Propolis

TREE-HARVEST ⊘✦
Gemmotherapy Remedies: All; *Spagyric*
Remedies: All

WELEDA ⊘ ✦ ⚲ 1985

Rhinodoron Nasal Spray; *Aches & Pains:* Arnica Lotion, Copper Ointment, Massage Balm with Arnica, Massage Balm with Calendula, Skin Tone Lotion; *Coughs & Colds:* Cough Elixir, Rhinodoron Nasal Spray; *Eye Care:* Larch Resin Lotion; *Oral Hygiene:* Medicinal Gargle; *Skin Complaints:* Calendula Lotion, Combudoron Lotion, Combudoron Spray; *Stress & Strain:* Avena Sativa Comp Drops; *Tummy Troubles:* Chamomilla 3X Drops, Chamomilla 3X Granules, Melissa Comp Drops

WELLFOODS LTD ⊘ ✦

Linda Kearns Cake - The wholly natural approach to relieving the symptoms of the menopause: Cherry, Cranberry, Date & Walnut, Original, Tropical

WHOLISTIC RESEARCH COMPANY

Colon Cleanse Herbal Programme; Liver, Kidney, Colon Detox Herbal Programme

SUPPLEMENTS

A. VOGEL

Aesculus Forte Tablets; Anti Ageing Complex; Detox Box; Helix Slim Tablets; Kelp Tablets; Linoforce; Menosan Tablets; Milk Thistle Tablets; Nature-C; Pomegranste Spirulina Complex; Silecea Capsules; Silecea Liquid

ALL SEASONS HEALTH ™

Chlorella Powder; Chlorella Tablets; Spirulina Powder; Spirulina Tablets

ALOE PURA ✦

Aloe Liquid Fibre Juice; Aloe Vera Colon Cleanse; Aloe Vera Digestive Aid; Aloe Vera Juice Maximum Strength; Cranberry Flavoured Aloe Vera Juice; Organic Aloe Vera Juice; Pineapple and Papaya Flavoured Aloe Vera Juice; Wildberry Flavoured Aloe Vera Juice

AQUASOURCE ™⊘ ✦

Bifidus Complex & Klamath Lake Algae 90 Vegetable Capsules; Cell Power – Instant Nutrition; CoQ10 Complex w Chromium Polynicotinate & Algae 30 Vegetable Capsules; Digestive Enzymes & Klamath Lake Algae 60 Vegetable Capsules; Green Energy — Algae & Hawaiian Spirulina & Alfalfa 75 & 300 Vegetable Capsules; Klamath Lake Algae 60 & 120 Vegetable Capsules; Klamath Lake Algae Powder 50g & 150g; Klamath Lake Algae Suspended in Organic Apple Juice 60ml; Lactobacillus Acidophilus & Klamath Lake Algae 90 Capsules; Lighten-Up! Advanced Meal Replacement with Algae - Vanilla Flavour; Start Easy Pack (Klamath Lake Algae 50 Vegetable Capsules, Digestive Enzymes & Klamath Lake Algae 60 Vegetable Capsules, Lactobacillus Acidophilus & Klamath Lake Algae 50 Vegetable Capsules, Bifidus

Complex & Klamath Lake Algae 50 Vegetable Capsules); Sun Power – Instant Nutrition; Super Antioxidant with Pycnogenol 60 Vegetable Capsules

AZIZ CHAIR ™
Black Seed Oil

BEAUTY NATURALS *i*
Eye Bright Vision Support Formula; Nails & Skin Nutrient Formula

BENECOL
Mini Drink: Dairy Free

BIO-HEALTH LTD ⊘ *i*
'Pure-fil: Kelp & Vitamins; *Pure-fil:* Agnus Castus, Anti-Oxidant Herbs, B Complex (High Potency & Yeast-free), Bio-Caps Multivitamin & Mineral, Bio-E, Black Cohosh, Buchu Leaf, Buffered C Crystals, Capiscum Fruit, Celery Seed, Chamomile Flowers, Cinnamon Bark, Co-Enzyme Q10, Cramp Bark, Cranesbill Root, Damiana Herb, Dandelion Leaf, Devil's Claw, Echinacea Root, Extra Calcium with Magnesium Zinc and Vitamin D, Extra Iron, Extra Magnesium, Extra Mineral Complex, Extra Selenium, Extra Zinc, Fenugreek Seed, Feverfew Leaf, Ginger Root, Gingko Leaf, Glucosamine HCL, Golden Seal, Hawthorn Berry, Hop Strobile, Iceland Moss, Korean Ginseng, Liquorice Root, Melilot Herb, Melissa Leaf, Milk Thistle, Misteltoe Herb, Nettle Root, Passiflora Herb, Prickly Ash Bark, Primula Root, Psyllium Husk,

Raspberry Leaf, Red Clover Flowers, Rutin & Buckwheat, Sage Leaf, Senna Leaf, Skullcap Herb, Slippery Elm, St John's Wort, Turmeric Rhizome, Valerian Root, Vitamin B&C, Vitamin C – 500mg (Buffered), Vitamin C – 500mg with Bioflavonoids, Whole Garlic, Wild Yam Root, Willow Bark, Wormwood Herb

BIONA
Pressed Multi-Vital Juice

BRUNEL HEALTHCARE ⊘ *i* ⅄ 1992
Vertese Capsules: Evening Primrose Oil, Flaxseed, Glucosamine & Flaxseed, High Strength Coenzyme Q10, Natural Vitamin E, Omega Oils 3, 6 & 9, Omega Oils 3, 6 & 9 Plus CoQ10 & Ginseng, Omega Oils 3, 6 & 9 Plus Pomegranate

CEDAR HEALTH LTD
Bio-Strath Elixir Tablets; *Innovia:* Lestrin; *Ortis:* Ginseng, Ortisan Tablets, Vital Iron Plus; *Ortis Pure Plan:* Apple, Prune, Tablets; *Padma 28:* Padma; *Serra Pamies:* Keravit, Pil-Food

COUNTRY LIFE
2 Methyl 13-C™™ "Fruit Punch"; 4 Thought®® The Ultimate Brain Formula; 5-HTP Trytophan; 7-KetoTrim™™; Acerola C with Bioflavonoids; Acetyl L- Carnitine 500 mg with B-6 (Veg. Caps); Action B-100; Action B-50; Action Max®® XXXTREME™™; Active B-12 (Dibencozide 3,000 mcg); Active Lipoic Acid; Basic-B; Beyond Food®®; Biotin; Brewer's Yeast; Buffer-C; Buffered

Vitamin C with RH; Burn N Trim™™; Calcium Ascorbate Crystals; Calcium Citrate; Calcium with Boron; Calcium-Magnesium with Vitamin D Complex; Cal-Mag; Cal-Mag (Mini Tabs); Cal-Mag Complex; Cal-Mag Potassium; Cal-Mag-Zinc; Cal-Snack (Calcium with Magnesium Wafer); Cap C-500; Caralluma Extract; Carb Phaser; Chewable Adult Multi with Antioxidants; Chewable Vitamin E Wafer; Choline; Chromium; Chromium Picolinate; Circulation Factors®®; Circu-Pressure®®; Citrus Bioflavonoid Complex; Citrus Bioflavonoid/Rutin Complex; Coenzyme Active B-6 50 mg; Coenzyme B-Complex; Daily Fiberx; Daily Total One™™ Iron-Free; Dairy-Zyme; DHEA; DHEA 25 mg Complex For Women; DHEA 50 mg Complex For Men; Diet Power®®; DMAE; E Vitamin & Selenium; Enhances QM-1™™ Iron-Free; Essential Amino Stack; Essential Creatine Monohydrate; Essential Glutamine; Essential Life; Essential Liquid Carnitine; Ester-C®® w/Bioflavonoids; Flush-Free Niacin; Folic Acid; GABA Relaxer; Genaslim™™; Ginseng Supreme Complex; GlucoLean™™ (Ephedra Free); Glycemic Factors™™; Glycine 500 mg with B-6; Go Less™™; Grape Seed Extract; Green Edge II™™ Powder Vegan Formula; Green Tea Extract; GTF Chromium; Herbal Mood Boost; Hi-B-100; Homocysteine Shield®®; Inositol Powder; Iron 25 mg; Iron Aid™™; Iron-Free Multi-Mineral Complex; L-Arginine 500mg with B-6 (Veg. Caps); L-

Carnitine 500 mg with B-6 (Veg. Caps); Lean Results™™ "Ephedra Free Weight Loss"; Lecithin Granules; L-Glutamine 1,000 mg with B-6; L-Glutamine 500 mg with B-6 (Veg. Caps); Lipoic Acid; Liquid Goji & Acai; Liver Support Factors®®; L-Lysine 1000 mg with B-6; L-Lysine 500 mg with B-6; L-Lysine 500 mg with B-6 (Veg Caps); L-Methionine 500 mg with B-6; L-Phenylalanine 500 mg with B-6 (Veg Caps); L-Theanine (Veg Caps); L-Tyrosine 500 mg with B-6 (Veg Caps); Lumatol AC™™; Mag/Potassium/Aspartate; Magnesium; Magnesium 300 mg with Silica; Malic Relief Formula; Max For Men®®; Max-Growth P. M.™™; Maxi Baby-C®® (Liquid); Maxi B-Caps w/Taurine; Maxi C-Complex; Maxi Pre-Natal®®; Maxine®® For Women; Maxine®® For Women Iron-Free; Maxine's Intima Roses & Chocolate; Maxine's Menopause Formula; Maxi-Zinc; Maxi-Zyme®® Extra Strength; Melatonin; Memory Formula; Menopause Support; Metabolizer (Lipotropic); Milk Thistle Extract; MSM; Multi-Mineral Complex; N, N-Dimethylglycine 125 mg (Sublingual); Nerve & Osteo Support; Niacin; Niacinamide; Norwegian Kelp; Nutri Chol-less®®; Olive Leaf Extract; Omega Fiber™™ Powder; Omega Vegetarian™™ 3-6-9 (Liquid); PABA; Pantothenic Acid; Papaya 22 mg Chewable; Potassium; Pregnenolone; Prosta-Max For Men; Pro-Vaso NO2™™; Psyllium Seed Husk; Pycnogenol®®; Resveratrol Plus; R-

Lipoic Acid; Rutin; Saw Palmetto & Pygeum Extract; Selenium; Seniority; Sleep Tight Factors®®; Sour Gummy Dolphin Pals; Stress "M"®®; Super 10 Antioxidant; Superior B-12 Sublingual Berry Flavored Lozenges; Superior Multiple™™; Superior Vitamin C; Tall Tree Children's Chewable; Tall Tree Children's Chewable Wafer; Taurine 500 mg with B-6; Taurine 500 mg with B-6 (Veg Caps); The Maximized®® Masculine Formulation; Thyro-Max; Triple Strength Bromelain; Ultimate Fat Metabolizer®®; Vanadyl Sulfate; Vegetarian Support™™; Vitamin B-1 100 mg; Vitamin A 10,000 units Dry; Vitamin B-12 1,000 mcg; Vitamin B-12 with Folic Acid; Vitamin C Complex; Vitamin C Crystals; Vitamin C Wafer; Vitamin C with RH; Vitamin E; Vitamin E Complex (Liquid); Vitamin K; Water Factors™™; Yohimbe Extract; Yohimbe Power; Zinc; Zinc Lozenges; *Herbal Extracts Liquid Pharmacy™™:* Black Walnut/Wormwood, Children's Echinacea Complex, Echinacea Superior, Echinacea/Goldenseal, Milk Thistle Extract, Yohimbe Extract, Yohimbe Wild African Bark

CUBANA PRODUCE LTD ™
Spirel C (180 tablets); Spirel G (180 tablets); *100% Cuban Spirulina Platensis:* **Spirel Powder 100g and 500g, Spirel Spirulina (100 Vege capsules), Spirel Spirulina (180 tablets)**

DEVA NUTRITION ™☺ ✔
Calcium Plus; CLA; Coenzyme Q10; Flax Seed Oil Capsules; Iron Free Vegan Multivitamin One Daily; Omega-3 DHA; Sublingual B-12; Vegan Borage Oil; Vegan Chia Seed Oil; Vegan Evening Primrose Oil capsules; Vegan Glucosamine HCL; Vegan Glucosamine MSM/CMO; Vegan Hair Nails and Skin; Vegan Multivitamin; Vegan Prenatal Multivitamin; Vegan Vitamin D; *Vegan Herbal Line:* **Brain Support, Colon Cleanse, Gingko Biloba, Kava Kava, Liver Support, Saw Palmetto, St John's Wort, Valerian**

DIPL - KFM (FH) WOLFGANG SCHILLER ☺
Oleador: Arganööl "Classic", Arganööl "Light", Arganööl "Pur"

EMERGEN-C
Electro Mix Lemon Lime; Essentially All Advanced Multi-Vitamin; Sleep Health Night-Time Vitamin C; Super Gram 2 Vitamin C; Super Gram 3 Enhanced Vitamin C; Tangerine Ora-Pops Vitamin C; *Multi-Vitamin:* Kids Multi-Vitamin Strawberry, Multi-Vitamin Strawberry; *Speciality Health:* Bone Health Mixed Berry, Heart Health Black Cherry, MSM Lite 5 Calories; *Super Energy Booster: 1,000mg Vitamin C:* Acai Berry, Cranberry, Lemon Lime, Lite 5 Calories, Pink Lemonade, Raspberry, Super Orange, Tangerine, Tropical

FOREVER LIVING PRODUCTS
Aloe Berry Nectar; Aloe Bits 'n Peaches; Aloe Blossom Tea; Aloe Vera Gel; B12 Plus; Gingko Plus; Lycium Plus

FOREVER YOUNG INTERNATIONAL LIMITED
Prebio 7V

G & G VITAMINS
Acidophilus; Aloe Vera; Atriplex; B Complex; B Complex with Vitamin C; Betacarotene; Betaine; Bifido; Biotin; C plus Minerals; C with Bioflavonoids; Cal Mag Kit; Calcium Ascorbate; Calcium Citrate; Calcium Gluconate; Cal-M; Cal-M Capsules; Cat's Claw; Chewable C (Raspberry & Cherry Flavour); Choline & Inositol; Choline Bitartrate; Chromium; Chromium GTF; Co Q10; Cranberry Extract; Craze-Away; Dolomite; Echinacea; Energy Plus Protein; EssentialFood; Eyebright & L-Lutein; Fibre Detox; Fibre Flora; Fizz C (Orange Flavour); Folic Acid; Fruit Fortress; Garlic; GC70; Ginkgo Biloba; Good Morning Protein Plus; GUK; Herbal energy Formula; Inositol; Iron Amino Acid Chelated; L-Arginine; Lecithin Granules; Lemon Balm & Ginkgo Biloba; Lipoic Acid & Acetyle Carnitine; Magnesium Ascorbate; Magnesium Carbonate; Magnesium Citrate; Magnolia; Manganese Amino Acid Chelated; MSM; MSM Pure Powder; MSM with Vitamin C; Multiminerals with Amino Acid Chelated; Multiminerals with Chelate Factors; Natural E 400 (Capsules not Softgels);

Organic Devil's Claw; Organic Goldenseal; Organic Guarana; Organic Milk Thistle; Organic Peppermint; Organic Saw Palmetto; Organic Siberian Ginseng; Organic St John's Wort; Organic Valerian; PABA (Para Amino Benzoic Acid); Papain; Potassium; Practitioner's Acidophilus; Practitioner's Bifidus; Pro-Bifidus; Pro-Dophilus; Psyllium Husks; Pure C Powder (Ascorbic Acid); Pycnogenol; Rutin; Salt Capsules; Saw Palmetto with Zinc; Seagreens Food; Selenium; Selenium & A, C, E and EPO; Siberian Ginseng; SlimaSleep; SlimaWake; Spirulina; St Johns Wort; Sublingual B Complex; Sublingual B12 (Cyanocobalamin); Sublingual CoQ10; Sublingual Vitamin C & Bioflavonoids; Tropical C; Vitamin B1 (Thiamin); Vitamin B12 (Cyanocobalamin); Vitamin B15 Pangamic Acid; Vitamin B2 (Riboflavin); Vitamin B3 (Nicotinamide); Vitamin B3 Niacin (Nicotinic Acid); Vitamin B5 (Pantothenic Acid); Vitamin B6 (Pyridoxine); Vitamin C (with Rosehips, Acerola & Dolomite); Wormwood; Zinc Amino Acid Chelated; Zinc Citrate

GREEN PEOPLE CO. ™ ⊘ ✦
Omega 3 & 6 Sprinkle; *Capsules:* **Seaweed;** *Liquids:* **Hawthorn & Artichoke Formula, Omega 3 & 6 Fuel 3:1**

GREEN VALLEY TRADING CO. ™☺
All products are vegan

GUARANA COMPANY ™
Aççaíí; Brazilian Ginseng (Pfaffia paniculata); Catuaba; Guarana Powder; Maca; Maura Puama; Spirulina Powder; *Drink Powders:* Jungle Detox Plus, Jungle Energy Boost, Jungle Gym, Jungle Love, Jungle Super Energy Boost

HEALTH & PLUS LTD ™⊘ⓘ
Acidophilus; Agnus Castus 500mg; Aloe Vera Juice; Amino L-Arginine; Amino L-Glutamine; Amino L-Lysine; Amino L-Methionine; Amino L-Tyrosine; Artichoke; Ascorbic Acid Powder 250g; B25 Complex; Beta Carotene 15mg; Bilberry with Eyebright; Black Cohosh; Brewer's Yeast; Calcium Ascorbate & Ascorbic Acid Powder 250g; Calcium Ascorbate Powder 250g; Cats Claw; Chelated Iron; Chewable Vit C 500mg; Chromium Picolinate; Cinnamon 500mg; Citri-Trim Plus; Co Enzyme Q10 30mg; Co Enzyme Q10 60mg; Digest Plus; Dolomite & D; Dong Quai; E400; Ester C 1000; Fibre Gum; First Probiotic; Folic Acid; FOS; Ginger Root; Glucosamine & MSM; Glucosamine HCL 1500; Goldenseal; Gotu Kola; Junior B Complex; Junior Multivitamin and Mineral; Kelp 300mg; Konjac Fibre; Konjac Fibre Powder; Korean Ginseng; Lecithin 550mg; Lecithin Granules; Lycopene Plus; Magnesium L-Aspartate; Megadophilus; Milk Thistle; MSM; Multi Probiotic; Mushroom Extract Complex; Octosanol; Optim-Eyes;

Organic Selenium; Phase 2 500mg; Potassium 100mg; Premier Garlic; Psyllium Seed Husk Fibre; Red Clover; Sage; Saw Palmetto & Zinc; Selenium 200mcg; Selenium 50mcg; Sodium Ascorbate Powder; Spirulina; St. John's Wort; TMG Complex; Tribula Plus; Tyro Tan; Whole Grape; Zinc; Zinc Citrate; *Liquiforce Traditional Plant Tinctures:* Agnus Castus, Bilberry, Black Cohosh, Cat's Claw, Chamomille, Dandelion, Devil's Claw, Echinacea, Elderberry, Feverfew, Ginger, Ginkgo Biloba, Goldenseal, Gotu Kola, Hawthorn, Horsechestnut, Horsetail, Marigold, Milk Thistle, Nettle, Red Clover, Sage, Saw Palmetto, Slippery Elm Formula, St. John's Wort, Uva Ursi, Valerian, Wild Yam; *Veganicity:* Agnus Castus 500mg, Agnus Castus Tincture, Artichoke, B25 Complez, Beta Carotene, Bilberry Tincture, Bilberry with Eyebright, Black Cohosh, Black Cohosh Tincture, Brewer's Yeast 300mg, Calcium Extra, Cats Claw Tincture, Chamomille Tincture, Chelated Iron 24mg, Chromium 200µµg, Cinnamon 500mg, Co Enzyme Q10 30mg, Co Enzyme Q10 60mg, Dandelion Tincture, Devil's claw Tincture, Digest-Ase, E400, Echinacea Tincture, Elderberry Tincture, Ester-C 1000, Feverfew Tincture, Folic Acid 400µµg, Ginger Tincture, Ginkgo Biloba Tincture, Glucosamine & MSM, Glucosamine 1500, Glucosamine 750mg,

Goldenseal, Goldenseal Tincture, Gotu Kola Tincture, Hawthorn Tincture, Horsechestnut Tincture, Horsetail Tincture, Kelp 300mg, Konjac Fibre 500mg, Korean Ginseng, Lecithin 550mg, Lycopene Extra 10mg, Marigold Tincture, Megadophilus, Milk Thistle, Milk Thistle Tincture, MSM 1000mg, Multi Probiotic, Multivitamin&Mineral, Mushroom Complex, Nettle Tincture, Optim-Eyes, Palmetto Extra, Phase 2 500mg, Premier Garlic 500mg, Red Clover, Red Clover Tincture, Sage, Sage Tincture, Saw Palmetto Tincture, Selenium 200µµg, Slippery Elm Tincture, Spirulina 500mg, St. John's Wort, St.John's Wort Tincture, Tasty C 500mg, TMG Extra, Tribula Extra, Uva Ursi Tincture, Valerian Tincture, Vitamin B12 100mcg, Whole Grape, Wild Yam Tincture, Zinc 10mg

HEALTH PERCEPTION *ì*
Seredrin; Super Antioxidant; Vegetarian Glucosamine 750mg

HEALTHQUEST LIMITED ™⊘*ì*
Body Shield; Chill Out; Lift; Man; Nutri-Aid; Woman

HEALTHY AND ESSENTIAL ™
Essential Woman; Forti Flax; Omega Man; Omega Twin

HERBS HANDS HEALING LTD ™⊘*ì*
Empty Vegetable Cellulose Capsules; Superfood; *Single Herbs:*

Agnus Castus Berry, Agrimony Herb, American Ginseng root, Angelica Root, Artemisia Herb, Artichoke Leaves, Astragalus Root, Balm of Gilead Buds Glyc, Barberry Root Bark, Bayberry Herb, Bitter Orange Peel, Black Cohosh Root, Black Walnut Hulls, Bladderwrack Seaweed, Blessed Thistle Seed, Blue Cohosh Root, Boneset Herb, Borage Leaves, Boswellia Resin, Buchu Leaves, Bupleurum Root, Burdock Root, Burdock Seed, Californian Poppy Leaves & Flowers, Cascara Sagrada Bark, Catmint Herb, Cayenne Pods, Celery Seed, Chamomile Flowers, Chickweed Herb, Chicory Root, Chinese Liquorice Root, Cinnamon Bark Squills, Cleavers Herb, Cornsilk, Corydalis Tuber, Cramp Bark, Damiana Leaves, Dandelion Root, Devils Claw Root, Dong Quai Root, Echinacea Root, Elderberry Glycerate, Elecampane Root, Eucalyptus Leaves, Eyebright Herb, False Unicorn Root, Fennel Seed, Fenugreek Seed, Figwort Herb, Gentian Root, Geranium Herb, Ginger Root, Gingko Leaf, Goats Rue Herb, Golden Seal Root, Gotu Cola Herb, Gravel Root, Hawthorn Berries, Hawthorn Flower Tops, Hops Strobiles, Horehound (White) flw, lfe, Horse Chestnut Fruit, Bark, Hyssop Herb, Juniper Berries, Lady's Mantle Herb, Lavender Flowers, Limeflowers, Liquorice Root, Lobelia Herb, Marigold Flowers,

Marshmallow Root, Meadowsweet Herb, Milk Thistle Seed, Motherwort Herb, Mugwort Leaves, Mullein flw/lfe, Myrrh Gum Resin, Nettle Root, Nettles Leaves, Oak Bark, Olive Leaves, Oregano Leaves, Oregon Grape Root, Osha Root, Parsley Root, Pasque Flower Herb, Passion Flower Herb, Pau d'Arco Bark, Pennyroyal Herb, Peppermint Leaves, Plantain Leaves, Poke Root, Prickly Ash Bark, Red Clover Flowers, Red Raspberry Leaves, Rehmannia, Rhen Shen Ginseng Root, Rhubarb Root, Rosemary Leaves, Sage Leaves, Sarsaparilla Root, Saw Palmetto Berries, Schisandra Berries, Shativari, Siberian Ginseng Root, Silver Birch Leaves, Skullcap Herb, Solomons Seal, Squaw Vine Tuber, St Johns Wort Herb, Thuja Leaves, Thyme Herb, Triphala Fruits, Tumeric (Yu Jin) Root, Usnea Herb, Uva Ursi Leaves, Valerian Root, Vegetable Glycerine, Vervain Herb, White Willow Bark, Wild Cherry Bark, Wild Lettuce Herb, Wild Oats/ Herb/ Seed, Wild Yam Root, Withania (Ashwaganda) Root, Wood Betony Herb, Yarrow Herb, Yellow Dock Root

HERBS OF GRACE ™⊘ ✦
Bleckman Formulae: **All;** *Blended Herbs:* **All;** *Fluid Extract Blends:* **All;** *Glycerites:* **All;** *Phytobiophysics Flower Formulae:* **All;** *Single Fluid Extracts:* **All;** *Single Herbs:* **All**

HIGH BARN OILS ™
Linseed Flour; Linseed Oil 500ml; Linseed Oil in capsules; Linseeds; Milled Linseed

HIGHER NATURE PLC ™⊘ ✦
Advanced Brain Nutrients; Advanced Nutrition Complex; AEterna Gold Hyaluronic Acid; Alka-Clear (Powder & Capsules); Aloe Gold (Cherry/Cranberry); Aloe Gold (Natural); Alpha; Arginine; Astaxanthin and Blackcurrant; Balance For Nerves; Betaine HCL; Bio Minerals; Boswellia & Devil's Claw; Bromelain; B-Vital; Calcium Ascorbate; Calma-C; Candiclear; Cardio Heart Nutrients; Cat's Claw Concentrate; Cat's Claw Tea Bags; Chlorella; Chromium Polynicotinate 200mcg; Citricidal Liquid; Citrisafe®®; Co-Enzyme Q10; ColoClear Extra; DLPA Complex; Dong Quai & Agnus Castus; Easy 3(powder); Echinacea & Black Elderberry; Energy Breakfast Shake; Fizzy C Effervescent Vitamin C; Folic Acid 400mcg; FOS; FreeCarb; Glutamine Capsules; Glutamine Powder; H Factors; HCA; Herbal SpringClean; High Fibre Vitality Shake; High PC Lecithin Granules; High Stability Colloidal Silver; High Strength Mexican Yam; Immune &; Imunoglukan®®; Lysine 500mg; Lysine-C; Maxi Multi (Iron Free); Mega Potency Ginkgo 6000; Menophase; Milk Thistle & Artichoke; Muira Puama & Damiana

Aphrodisiaca; Mum-2-Be; Neversnore; Nutrition For Healthy Veins; Ocean Kelp; Olive Leaf Extract; Osteofood; Paraclens; Periwinkle extract; Phosphatidyl Serine; PreMenstrual Complex; Probio- Daily; Probio- Easy; Probiogest; Probio-Mints; Red Sterol Complex; Rhodiola & Ashwagandha; Rosehips C 1000; Saw Palmetto & Pygeum Bark; Sea Calcium; Selenium 200mcg; Serotone 5HTP; Sheep's Sorrel Complex; Sher Skin Support Formula; St John's Wort; Sublingual High Potency Vitamin B12 200mcg; Sublingual Zinc; Super Osteofood; Super Strength Cranberry; Super Strength Supergar 8000; Superphyte; Sx; Theanine 100mg; TMG; Ultra C Plus; UltraTrace®® Trace Mineral Drops; Vegetarian Glucosamine Hydrochloride; Visualeyes; X Factors; Zinc; *MSM:* Crystals, Joint & Muscle Body Balm, Tablets; *Natural Medicine Company:* Children's chewable, Daily Probiotic Formula, Healthy Eyes, Liquid Silver, Multivitamin & Mineral Complex For Men, Multivitamin & Mineral Complex For Women, Optimum Pregnancy Nutrients, Skin, Hair and Nails, Snore-free, The Sweet Alternative; *True Food®®:* All Man, B Complex, B6, Beta Carotene, C, Calcium & Magnesium, Easy Iron, GTF Chromium, Magnesium, Maxi Q10, Natural Vitamin E, Selenium, Soyagen®®, Super Potency

Soyagen®®, Supernutrition Plus, Wise Woman, Zinc

HOLISTIX ™❶
Spirulina: **Powder 150g, Powder 250g, Powder 50g, Tablets 150g, Tablets 250g, Tablets 50g, Tablets 50g Refills**

HOLLAND AND BARRETT RETAIL LTD ◢
Aloe Vera Juice Drink; Damiana Leaves Liquid; DGL Chewable Liquorice; Oats Avena; *Chewable Tablets:* Acerola C with Bioflavonoids, All Natural Pineapple Bromelain, Papaya Enzyme Chewable; *Childrens Supplements:* Echinacea for Juniors Liquid Extract; *Liquid Extract:* Cranberry, Ginkgo-Bilboa, Guarana, Japanese Oil of Peppermint, Milk Thistle, Mullein Leaf, Peppermint, Saw Palmetto, Siberian Ginseng, St. Johns Wort, Valerian Root; *Powder:* Brewers Yeast, Creatine, Oil of Peppermint, Pure Vitamin C; *Protein Powders:* Pure Soya Protein Powder; *Slimming:* Diet Aid; *Tablets:* Absorbable Magnesium, Alfalfa, Amino Acid Chelated Manganese, B - 100 (Vitamin B Complex), B - 100 (Vitamin B Complex) Timed Release, B - 50 (Vitamin B Complex), B-1 100mg, B-12, Biotin, Brewers Yeast, C with Rose Hips, C-500mg Buffered, Caprylic Acid, C-Complex with Bioflavonoids, Chelated Boron, Chelated Copper, Chelated Zinc Tablets, Chewable Calcium, Chinese Chlorella, Choline, Chromium Picolinate, Cider Vinegar, Citrus Bioflavonoids, Complete B, DLPA

500mg, Dolomite, Folic Acid, Gotu Kola, Green Barley Grass 500mg, GTF Chromium, Guarana, High Strength Zinc 15mg, Horse Chestnut, Iron & Vitamin C, Iron Tablets with Vitamins & Minerals, L-Glutamine 500mg, Magnesium 250mg, Magnesium Tablets, Natural Amino 1000mg, Niacin B-3, Pantothenic Acid, Potassium Chelated 99mg, Rutin, Selenium, Selenium Seven Day Souper Cabbage Diet, Siberian Ginseng, Silica Complex, Spirulina, Taurine, Timed Release Pantothenic Acid Tablets, Vitamins for the Hair, Zinc Picolinate

INTERNATIONAL PARTNERSHIP LTD (SEAGREENS DIVISION) ™☺⊘
Seagreens- Ascophyllum Fine Granules: **Iodine Plus Capsules;** *Seagreens-Mixed Wrack:* **Food Capsules, Food Granules**

KORDEL'S
Enzogenol VegCaps; Lysine VegCaps; OptiMSM®® 1000mg Tablets; *Advanced Herbals:* Black Cohosh & Isoflavone Veg Caps, Celery Plus Tablets, Cranberry with Uva Ursi & Buchu VegCaps, Dong Quai Plus VegCaps, Ginkgo Plus VegCaps, Milk Thistle Plus VegCaps, St John's Wort with Ginkgo & Ginseng VegCaps; *Advanced Lifestyle:* Advanced Pro-biotic Complex VegCaps, B' at Eze Tablets, Bilberry 5000 & Eyebright Tablets, Horse Chestnut & Butchers Broom Complex Tablets, Junior Time Multivitamins Plus Tablets, Perilla with

Coleus VegCaps, Red Clover Plus Isoflavone Complex Tablets, Saw Palmetto Plus Tablets, Silica 2500 Plus Tablets, Super Calcium Magnesium Bone Formula Tablets, Teenage Multi Tablets, Tribulus Plus Herbal Complex Tablets, Valerian Plus Herbal Complex Tablets, Women's Multi Tablets; *Herbs:* Agnus Castus Tablets, Boswellia VegCaps, Dong Quai Standardised Extract 1000mg Tablets, Griffonia Seed VegCaps, Guarana Ginseng Complex VegCaps, Milk Thistle Standardised Extract 1000mg Tablets, Rhodiola Root Extract VegCaps, Sea Kelp Tablets, Siberian Ginseng 600mg Tablets, St John's Wort Standardised Extract 1000mg Tablets; *Minerals:* Chromium 200ug (from Picolinate) VegCaps, Magnesium Chelate Tablets, Silica Tablets, Zinc (from Amino Acid Chelate) VegCaps; *Multivitamins:* Nutri Time Tablets, Super 75 One a Day Multivitamin & Mineral Formula Tablets, Women's Iron Complete VegCaps; *Vitamins:* Balanced B50 Capsules, Ester C Tablets

KUDOS VITAMINS AND HERBALS ⊘⸙
Acidophilus plus Bifidus; AllerPlex; Calcium Magnesium and Zinc; Cats Claw 900mg; Chromium GTF; Circuplex Formula; ClensoPlex; Co Enzyme Q 10 40mg; Cranberry Complex; Devil's Claw 900mg; Digestive Enzymes; Dong Quai 900mg; Echinacea 900mg; Eye Bright Vision Support Formula; Feverfew 900mg; Ginkgo Biloba 900mg; Hair Nutrient Formula; Korean Ginseng 900mg; LivoPlex; Maca (Lepedium

meyenii) 900mg; MenoPlex; Milk Thistle; Prenatal; Rhodiola Rosea 900mg; Saw Palmetto 900mg plus Zinc; Siberian Ginseng 900mg; Soya Isoflavones 30mg; St John's Wort 900mg; Valerian 900mg; *Free Form:* Amino Acid Complex, L-Carnitine, L-Glutamine, L-Lysine

L'AGE VERT LINXIS ™
Chlorella; Guarana; Odontella tablets; Odontella vegecaps

LIFEPLAN PRODUCTS LTD ™ ⊘ ⚹
5-HTP; Acetyl L Carnitine & Alpha Lipoic Acid; Agnus Castus; Biotin 2.5mg; Boron Triple Source Trace Mineral; Brewer's Yeast; Buffered Vitamin C with Rosehip & Acerola & Citrus Bioflavonoids - 500mg; Calcium & Magnesium - 500mg Powdered Dolomite; Calcium & Magnesium - 800mg Powdered Dolomite; Calcium Pantothenate - 250mg; Caprylic Acid; Chamomile Blend; Chelated Multiminerals; Chewable Vitamin C - 100mg; Chewable Vitamin C High Strength with Acerola & Bioflavonoids - 500mg; COQ10 30mg; Cranberry Extract - 200mg; Damiana Leaf Capsules; Dandelion Root; Devils Claw - 500mg; Digestive Enzymes; Echinacea - 1000mg Time Release; Echinacea - 360mg; EPO 1000mg; Evening Primrose Oil Capsules; Eyebright; Feverfew; Fibre - 440mg; Flaxseed Oil Capsules; Folic Acid; Golden Seal - 420mg; Hair Care

Nutrients; Hawthorn; High Strength Vitamin B6 - 100mg; Horny Goat Weed Formula; Horse Chestnut Formula; L-arginine; Lecithin Granules; L-glutamine; Lutein; Nettle Leaf & Eyebright & Echinacea; Omega Blend Oil; Parsley Piert Powder - 125mg; Prune and Senna; Pycnogenol - Maritime Pine Bark Extract - 30mg; Raspberry Leaf; Red Clover; Rhodiola Rosea; Rutin; Sage; Saw Palmetto; Sea Kelp with Added Calcium - 400mg; Siberian Ginseng High Strength - 600mg; Slippery Elm; Soyplus - Soya Isoflavones with Folic Acid; St. John's Wort Extract - 333mg; Standardised Extract of Ginger - 50mg; Standardised Extract of Milk Thistle - 175mg; Super Multinutrient; Swiss Hayflower; Thiamine 100mg; Triple Source Magnesium; Valerian; Valerian Formula; Valerian Passiflora & Hops; Vitamin B12 - 25mcg; Vitamin B12 1000mcg; Vitamin B12 - 1000mcg; Vitamin B6 - 50mg; Vitamin C & Zinc; White Willow Bark; Women's Multinutrient; Zinc - 10mg; Zinc Amino Acid Chelate; Zinc and Lysine Tablets; *Capsules:* Guarana Powder, Nettle Powder

MCKEITH ☺
24 Hour Detox; Fast Formula Slim; Living Food Energy Powder; Living Food Immune Defence Capsules; Organic Turbo Greens

MELBROSIN UK LIMITED ™
Acidophilus plus Bifidus; AllerPlex; Amino Acid complex; Black cohosh 900mg- high potency; Calcium, Magnesium & Zinc; Cats claw 900mg high potency; Chromium GTF; Circuplex Formula; ClensoPlex; Co-enzyme Q10 40mg; Cranberry complex; Devil's claw; Digestive enzymes; Dong Quai 900mg; Echinacea 900mg; Eye bright (vision support formula); Feverfew 900mg; Gingko Biloba 900mg; Hair Nutrient formula; Korean Ginseng 900mg; L- Carnitine; L-Glutamine; LivoPlex; L-Lysine; Maca 900mg; MenoPlex; Milk Thistle; Pre-natal; Rhodiola Rosea 900mg; Saw Palmeto 900mg plus Zinc; Siberian Ginseng 900mg; Soya Isoflavones 30mg; St John's Wort 900mg; Valerian 900mg; Zinc citrate 20mg; Zinc gluconate 50mg

NATROL ✔
Acai; Activin Grape Seed Extract; Calcium D-Glucarate; Calcium with Magnesium; China Chlorella; Cholesterol Balance Beta Sitosterol; Cinnamon Extract; CitriMax Balance; DHEA 10 mg; DHEA 25 mg; DHEA 50 mg; GarliPure Maximum Allicin caplets; GarliPure Once Daily tablet; Ginkgo Biloba 120 mg tablet; Hot Flashex tablet; Iron Liquid; Lycopene 15 mg tablet; Melatonin 1 mg tablet; Melatonin 1 mg time release tablet; Melatonin 3 mg tablet; Melatonin 3 mg time release tablet; Melatonin 5 mg tablet; Melatonin 5 mg time release tablet; Melatonin Liquid; NADH - 5, 10 & 20 mg; Niacin 500 mg time release tablet; Oat Bran tablet; ProstatExcell tablet; SelenoExcell; Sleep n Restore tablet; Slenderite; St. John's Wort tablet; Stress Complex tablet; Theanine tablet; Vegetarian Hyaluronic Acid MSM & Glucosamine capsule; Water Pill tablet

NATURE COMPLETE LTD ™☺
Chlorella capsules; Organic Chlorella; Organic Chlorella tablets; Organic Spirulina; Organic Spirulina tablets; Spirulina capsules

NATURE'S AID ⊘ ✔
Acetyl-L-Carnitine 250mg; Agnus Castus 1000mg; Aloe Vera 10000mg; Alpha Lipoic Acid 200mg; Bilberry 5000mg; Black Cohosh 500mg; Boldo 200mg; Boswellia 400mg; Brewer's Yeast 300mg; Calcium, Magnesium & Boron; Calcium, Magnesium & Zinc; Chromium Picolinate 200ug; Conc. Garlic Allicin 2000ug; Cranberry 5000mg; Devil's Claw 1000mg; Dong Quai 500mg; Echinacea 500mg; Feverfew 200mg; Folic Acid 400ug; Ginger 500mg; Ginkgo Biloba 6000mg; Korean Ginseng 600mg; Magnesium 150mg Amino Acid Chelate (w Vit B6); Mega Potency Vit B Complex 100 Time Release; Milk Thistle 150mg; Passiflora 300mg; Pycnogenol 30mg; Red Clover 500mg; Rhodiola 500mg; Saw Palmetto 500mg; Sea Kelp 187mg; Siberian

Ginseng 600mg; Soya Isoflavones 50mg; St Johns Wort 500mg; Super Vit B6 (high potency) 100mg; Traditional Herbal Bronchial Balsam (cough mixture); Valerian 500mg; Vit B Complex; Vit B Complex & C High Potency; Vit B6 50mg; Wild Yam 500mg; Zinc Gluconate 4mg elemental; Zinc Picolinate 15mg elemental; *Vit C:* 1000mg Time Release (w citrus bioflavonoids), 200mg Chewable (with rosehips & citrus bioflavonoids), 500mg Chewable (with rosehips & citrus bioflavonoids), Low Acid (w rosehips & bioflavonoids) 1000mg, Sugar Free Chewable (w citrus bioflavonoids) 500mg

NATURE'S OWN LTD ™
Cherry-C; Choline; *A Vitamins:* **Betacarotene (50/100);** *B Vitamins:* **Biotin, Choline, Folic Acid, Niacin (Vitamin B3), P. A. B. A. (Para-Amino-Benzoic Acid), Pantothenic Acid (Vitamin B5), Pyridoxine (Vitamin B6), Riboflavin (Vitamin B2), Thiamin (Vitamin B1), Vitamin B Complex Plus (30/50/90), Vitamin B Complex Plus Vitamin C (30/50), Vitamin B12;** *C Vitamins:* **Ascorbic Acid Powder, Bioflavonoid Complex & C (50/100), Calcium Ascorbate Plus Bioflavonoids (30/50/100), Cherry-C, Vitamin C w Bioflavonoids (30/50/100);** *Cytoplan - Nutritional Support:* **Bromelain - Proteolytic Digestive Enzyme;** *Cytoplan- A Vitamins:* **Beta Carotene;** *Cytoplan- B Vitamins:* **Choline Bitartrate Powder,**

Multi B Extra, Phosphatidyl Choline, Riboflavin (Vitamin B2); *Cytoplan- C Vitamins:* **Calcium Ascorbate Powder, Vitamin C & Bioflavonoids, Vitamin C & Bioflavonoids (Ascorbic Acid), Vitamin C & Bioflavonoids (Calcium Ascorbate), Vitamin C Extra;** *Cytoplan- Colon Cleanse:* **Cytocleanse, Psyllium Husk Powder (340g/142g);** *Cytoplan- E Vitamins:* **Vitamin E;** *Cytoplan- Minerals:* **Iron/Molybdenum, Selenium, Zinc Extra, Zinc Orotate, Zinc/Copper;** *Cytoplan- Multi-Formulations:* **Anti Oxidant Plus CoQ10, Antioxidant plus Q10, Antox, CMB Formula, Cyto Gold 60/120, Cytoplex (Multi Vitamins & Chelated Minerals), Dantox (High B6 MVM plus 3 Amino Acids), Euro Formula (Multi Vitamin/Mineral), Foundation Formula 1, Foundation Formula 2, Karoshil (Solace), Nourish Bar - Orange Carob, Nourish Bar - Orange Carob (Pack of 3), Nourish Bar - Plain, Nourish Bar - Plain (Pack of 3), P5P Extra, Super B Extra, Trace Mineral Complex;** *Cytoplan- Nutritional Support:* **Alfalfa, Aloe Vera Gel - Topical Application, Aloe XL Inner Leaf, Aloe XL Whole Leaf, Castor Oil (cold-pressed), Cyto-Biotic Active, Cyto-Vite, Cyto-Zyme, Evening Primrose Oil (Vegicaps) - GLA 10%, Flaxseed Oil - Vegicaps - Omega 3 0.5ml/500mg, Fos-a-Dophilus, Kelp, Lycopene, Milk Thistle, Probiotic Plus (30/60), Siberian Ginseng;** *Cytoplan-*

Phytofood ™ & Phytomed ™: **Cherry-C, Eye-Cyt, GTF Chromium, Immunovite, Phyto-Flavone, Phytofood™ Calcium, PhytoMins, Phytoshield, Phytox - Phyto-Antioxidant;** *Cytoplan-Minerals:* **Calcium;** *Cytoplan-Nutritional Support:* **Phospholec (Super-Strength Lecithin);** *Dentavital:* **1-3, 1-6 Beta Glucan, Aloe Vera Juice, Bifidophilus Plus, Gold, Immune Plus, Iron, Vit C Extra;** *Digestive Aids:* **Bromelain - Proteolytic Digestive Enzyme, Fos-a-Dophilus, Probiotic Plus (20/30/60), Psyllium Husk Powder;** *E Vitamins:* **Vitamin E150 (30/50), Vitamin E300;** *healthcreation:* **Be Bright, Digest Plus, Friendly Bacteria, Fruits, Roots & Shoots, Lycopene, Max-Immune 1-3, 1-6 Beta Glucan, Timeless;** *Lifestyle:* **Fifties, Senior Citizens, Students, Working Men, Working Women;** *Minerals:* **Calcium (50/30), Calcium Calcified Seaweed, G. T. F. Chromium, Iron / Molybdenum, Magnesium, Manganese, Phytofood ™™ Calcium (30/60), Potassium, Selenium 100mcg Elemental, Selenium 200mcg Elemental (30/50), Trace Mineral Complex, Zinc Orotate 100mg (50/100), Zinc/Copper (30/50);** *Multi-Formulations:* **CMB Formulation, Dolomite 500mg, Euro Gold 30/90, Karoshil, Mins, Multivitamin & Mineral (30/60/100), Opti-Mum, Regenerate;** *Nutritional Support:* **Brewers Yeast (BPC), D-Glucosamine HCl, Evening Primrose Oil 10% GLA - Vegicaps (30/90), Flaxseed Oil - Organic Oil - Vegicaps, Homocysteine - Heart Support, Homocysteine Formula, Kelp Plus - High Iodine Natural Multi Mineral, Organic Garlic (Vegicaps) Powdered Whole Garlic, Pro-Travel, Rutin, Siberian Ginseng - Whole Powdered Root**

NATURE'S AID LIMITED ™
5 - HTP Complex 100mg Tablets; Acetyl - L - Carnitine 250mg Tablets; Acidophilus Complex Capsules; Agnus Castus 100mg Tablets; Aloe Vera 50mg Tablets; Aloe Vera Juice; Alpha Lipoic Acid 200mg Tablets; B Complex & C Tablets; Bilberry 50mg Tablets; Black Cohosh 200mg Tablets; Boldo 50mg Tablets; Boswellia 400mg Capsules; Brewers Yeast 300mg Tablets; Calcium, Magnesium and Boron Tablets; Calcium, Magnesium and Zinc Tablets; Chromium Picolinate 200mg Tablets; Complete Multivitamin and Minerals; Concentrated Garlic Tablets; Cranberry 200mg Tablets; Devils Claw 1000mg Tablets; Dong Quai 500mg Tablets; Echinacea 70mg Tablets; Echinacea Complex Tablets; Feverfew 200mg Tablets; Folic Acid 400mg Tablet; Ginger Root 500mg Tablets; Ginger, Turmeric and Boswellia Tablets; Ginkgo Biloba Tablets; Glucosamine Hcl 750mg Tablets; Green Food Complex with Wheat Grass; Green Tea 1000mg Tablets; Hair, Skin and Nail Tablets; Korean Ginseng 600mg

Tablets; Magnesium 150mg Tablets; Milk Thistle 150 mg Tablets; MSM 1000mg 90 Tablets; Passiflora 300mg Capsules; Passiflora, Lemon Balm and Avena Sativa Tablets; Pomegranate Juice; Pycnogenol 30mg Tablets; Raspberry Leaf 375mg Tablets; Red Clover 500mg Tablets; Rhodiola Root 500mg Tablets; Rosehip 750mg Tablets; Sage Leaf 50mg Tablets; Saw Palmetto 500mg Tablets; Sea Kelp Tablets; Senna 125mg Tablets; Siberian Ginseng 600mg Tablets; Soya Isoflavones Tablets; Spirulina 500mg Tablets; St Johns Wort; Super Vitamin B6 Tablets; Valerian Root 500mg Tablets; Vitamin B Complex Tablets; Vitamin C Chewable 200mg Tablets; Vitamin C Chewable 500mg Tablets; Vitamin C Low Acid 1000mg Tablets; Vitamin C Time Release 1000mg Tablets; Wild Yam 500mg Tablets; Zinc Gluconate Tablets; Zinc Lozenges; Zinc Picolinate Tablets

NATURES REMEDIES ⊘ ✓
Zotrim

NATURKRAFTWERKE ᵀᴹ
Black Cumin Oil Capsules

NEAL'S YARD REMEDIES ⊘ ✓ ☜ ⚕–1998
Aloe Vera Juice; Witch Hazel

NEWAYS INTERNATIONAL UK LTD
Green Qi; Orachel

OPTIMAH HEALTH & NUTRITION ⊘ ✓ ⚕–1995
Aloe Vera 20,000mg Lemon & Lime Flavour Tablets; Bamboo Silica VegCaps; Boldo Herbal Complex Tablets; Calcium Plus Magnesium & Boron Tablets; Cat's Claw Standardised Extract 1000mg Tablets; Creatine Powder; Dolomite Tablets; Dong Quai Standardised Extract 1000mg Tablets; Echinacea 512mg Tablets; Echinacea Alcohol-Free Liquid Extract Fresh Fruit Flavour; Echinacea High Potency Liquid Extract; Echinacea High Potency VegCaps; Echinacea Standardised Extract 750mg Tablets; Folic Acid Complex Tablets; Gentle C Tablets; Ginkgo Biloba Standardised Extract 2000mg Tablets; High Potency Multivitamin & Mineral Tablets; Kelp Tablets; Korean Ginseng 600mg Orange Flavour Tablets; Liquid Evening Primrose Oil Lemon; Liquid Evening Primrose Oil Natural; Milk Thistle Standardised Extract 1000mg Tablets; MSM 1000mg Tablets; Multi B & C Complex Tablets; Multivitamin & Mineral One A Day Tablets; Organic Noni Juice; Original Herbal Complex for Women VegCaps; Peppermint Tablets; Selenium & Vitamins A, C & E Tablets; Siberian Ginseng Tablets; St John's Wort Standardised Extract 2000mg Tablets; Super Strength Aloe Vera Tablets; Vitamin B Complex Tablets; Vitamin B1 100mg Tablets; Vitamin B12 Tablets; Vitamin B5 Tablets; Vitamin B6 100mg Tablets; Vitamin C & Bioflavonoids Tablets; Vitamin C Chewable Tablets; Zinc Gluconate Tablets; *MANUKA*

GOLD: Lecithin Granules; *Thursday Plantation Tea Tree:* Echinafizz Fresh Fruit Flavour

OREGANUM HEALTH LTD. ™☺
Body Benefits: **Organic Evening Primrose Oil, Organic Flax Oil, Organic Hemp Oil, Organic Omega Blend**

PANACEA APS ™
Udo's Choice- Ultimate Oil Blend: **Evening Primrose Oil**

PHARMA NORD ⊘
Bio-Biloba; Bio-C Vitamin; Bio-Carnitine; Bio-Chromium; Bio-Fiber; Bio-Garlic; Bio-Lipoic Acid; Bio-Magnesium; Bio-Methionine; Bio-MSM&Silica; Bio-Pycnogenol; Bio-Trim; Omega 7; Prelox; SelenoPrecise

POTTER'S HERBAL MEDICINE ✓
Life Drops; New Relax; Potters Cleansing Herbs; *Red Kooga:* Energise Sachets, Energise Tablets, Ginseng and Ginkgo Biloba Tablets, Ginseng Capsules, Ginseng Tablets

POWER HEALTH PRODUCTS ⊘ ✓
Alfalfa 500mg; Aloe Vera 10,000 Double Strength; Aloe Vera Juice Drink 99.7%; Alpha Lipoic Acid 200mg; Alpha Lipoic Acid 200mg & L-Carnitine 500mg; B Complex 100% RDA; B12 500ug; B6 100mg; Bilberry 2500mg; Black Cohosh 350mg; Blue Green Algae 200mg; Borage Oil (Starflower Oil) Liquid Cold Pressed; Bromelain 10mg & Papain 100mg; Butterbur Root Powder 100mg; Calcium 400mg; Calcium 400mg, Magnesium 150mg & Vitamin D 2.5µµg; Calcium Pangamate (B15) 50mg; Calcium Pantothenate (B5) 500mg; Cat's Claw 34mg; Chromium Picolinate 200ug; Citrin 500 500mg (250mg HCA); CLA (Conjugated Linoleic Acid) 500mg capsules; Co Enzyme Q10 30mg; Cranberry Juice 1675mg with Vitamin C 100mg Sugar Free; Cranberry Juice Concentrate Drink Mix; Cranberry Juice Double Strength 4500mg; Echinacea 300 Standardised 4% Extract; Ester C 500mg; Folic Acid 400ug; Goji Berry; Green Tea 1000mg; Hi Zinc 2mg Elemental; Iron - Amino Acid Chelate 14mg; Kelp 500mg; Magnesium 300mg; Mega H40; Mega H40 Vegetarian Hard Shell Capsule; Mexican Wild Yam 500mg; Multi Fibre Plus; Multimineral & Zinc; Oral Zinc 25mg (3.5mg Elemental); Phytosterols 400mg; Pomegranate Extract 500mg; Potassium 200mg & Vitamin C 50mg; Power ACE Super Antioxidant; Pregnancy Multivitamin; Rhodiola 500mg; Rutivite; S.O.D. 5000 (Super Oxide Dismutase); Saw Palmetto (4:1 extract) 1000mg & Uva Ursi 100mg; Selenium 100ug & Zinc 2mg; Senna 37.5mg (7.5mg Sennosides); Soya Isoflavones, Kudzu Root & Red Clover; Spirulina 500mg; Super Ginkgo Plus (with Green Buckwheat & Vit E); Vit C 1000mg with Citrus Bioflavonoids; Vit C Powder (drink mix); Vitamin C 500mg Orange with Betacarotene Chewable; Xtra Zinc 15mg Elemental; Olive Leaf 450mg

PRINCIPLE HEALTHCARE

Active Defence Vit C & Zinc; Brain Smart; Echinacea; Energise Tablets; Evening Primrose oil; Garlic 2mg; Gingko Bilboa; Iron 14mg; Korean Ginseng; Leg Vein Health; Magnesium; Peppermint capsules; Pomegranate; Selenium ACE; Skin, Hair & Nails; St Johns Wort; Vitamin B6; Zinc 15mg

PURPLE FLAME AROMATHERAPY ⊘ ✦

T3 Essence Range: All

QUEST VITAMINS ⊘ ✦

Acidophillus Plus2 billion lactic bacteria; Agnus Castus 71mg Extract; Bilberry 60mg Extract; Bio C Complex 500mg vitamin C with bioflavonoids; Black Cohosh 40mg Extract; Boron 3mg; Buffered C 700mg with Bioflavonoids; Cal-Mag Plus multiminerals; Coenzyme Q10 30mg; Cranberry 200mg Extract; Devils Claw 17mg Extract; DL-Phenylalanine 500mg; Echinacea 294mg Extract; Energy Nutrient Complex; Enzyme Digest with Betaine HCl; Folic Acid 400ug; Ginger 250mg Extract; Ginkgo Biloba 150mg Extract; Ginkgo Biloba 40mg Extract; Green Coffee Extract – 200mg Extract; Green Tea 100mg Extract; Heart Nutrient Complex magnesium & Co Q10 with vitamins; Horse Chestnut 250mg Extract; Iron 15mg with vitamins & Minerals; Isoflavones 40mg Extract; Kyolic Garlic 100mg – Aged Garlic Extract; Kyolic Garlic 600mg Extract; Kyolic Garlic Extract 1000mg Extract; Kyolic Liquid – Aged Garlic Extract;

Lactase 200mg; L-Arginine 500mg; L-Cysteine 500mg; L-Glutamine 500mg; L-Lysine 500mg; L-Orthithine 500mg; Lp299v 1 billion Lactobacillus Bacteria; L-Phenylalanine 500mg; L-Tyrosine 500mg; Magnesium 150 mg with vitamin B6; Mega B 100 timed release; Mega B50; Milk Thistle 150mg Extract; Multi B Complex plus 500mg vitamin C; Piperine 10mg Extract providing 10mg piperine; Red Clover 500mg Extract; Rhodiola 250mg Extract; Saw Palmetto 36mg Extract; Selenium 200ug with vitamins C & E; Senna 16.7mg Extract; Siberian Ginseng 35mg Extract; St. Johns Wort 333mg Extract; Super Mega B&C plus 1000mg vitamin C & Herbs; Super Once A Day vegan timed release multivitamins & minerals; Turmeric Plus 263mg Extract; Uva-Ursi 90mg Extract; Valerian 83mg Extract; Vitamin B12 500ug plus uva ursi extract; Vitamin B6 50mg plus parsley leaf extract; Vitamin C 1000mg Timed Release with bioflavonoids; Vitamin C 500mg with bioflavonoids; Zinc 15mg with copper

RAW LIVING ™

Cacao Beans; Cacao Nibs; Camu; Carob Pods; Carob Powder; Goji Berries; Maca Bar; Maca Powder; Magic Mix; Purple Corn; Spirulina Powder; Suma; Sunseeds; Vanilla Pods; Whoosh; Yacon Root; *Hi:* **Hi-5, Hi-Bar, Hi-Crunch, Hi-Lovers, Hi-Trail**

RAWCREATION LTD ™☺

Brazilian Ginseng; Cacao Nibs; Carob Powder; Goji Berries;

Guarana Powder; Mesquite Meal; Organic Maca; Organic Purple Corn Extract; Organic Purple Corn Flour; Raw Organic Hemp Seed Protein Powder; Shelled Hemp Seeds; Suma Powder; Suma Vegicaps; Whole Hemp Seeds

RELIV UK ™⊘ ✦
Reliv Classic 504g

SANBERA GMBH ™☺
Men's Vitality Formula; Men's Wellness Formula; Women's Vitality Formula; Women's Wellness Formula

SANMAR GMBH ™
Aloe anmaris Kapseln; Organic Aloe Ferox Juice

SAVANT DISTRIBUTION LTD™❶⊘✦
Health Elements Spirulina; Health Elements Wheatgrass Powder; Udo's Choice Ultimate Oil Blend; Udo's Choice Ultimate Milled Seed Blend - Organic Omega 3-6-9

SEVEN SEAS ™⊘✦
One-a-Day Multivitamins plus Minerals for Vegetarians & Vegans

SHIFA LIFEHERBS INTERNATIONAL (UK) ™
Shifa Blackseed Oil; Shifa Vegagel Blackseed Oil Capsules

SOLGAR VITAMINS ⊘✦
Acetyl-L-Carnitine Vegicaps; Amino 75

Capsules; Arginine-Ornithine Vegicaps; BCAA Plus Capsules; L-Arginine Vegicaps; Maxi L-Carnitine

SOPHYTO LTD ™
Dermal Brightening Bioactive Therapy; Dermal De-Stress Bioactive Therapy; Dermal Purifying Bioactive Therapy; Purify & Energise Super Bioactives; Restore & Revive Super Bioactive; Tone & Balance Super Bioactives

SUPERNUTRIENTS ™☺⊘✦
Organic barleygrass powder; Organic chlorella powder; Organic maca powder; Organic spirulina powder; Organic wheatgrass powder

SWISS HERBAL CONFECTIONERY
Organic Echinacea Cherry Flavoured Lozenges; Organic Echinacea Strawberry Flavoured Lozenges

THE VEGAN SOCIETY ™☺❶✦
Chewable Supplement: **Veg1**

TORQ UK
Vegan Recovery; Bar: 1 Apricot, 2 Sundried Banana, 3 Raspberry & Apple, 4 Pineapple & Ginger, Mixed Box, Sample Pack; Energy: Natural, Natural Lemon, Natural Lime & Lemon, Natural Orange, Natural Organic, Natural Pink Grapefruit; Energy Gel: All Mixed Boxes, Black Cherry Yoghurt Flavour, Forest Fruits w Guarana, Orange & Banana, Sample Pack, Strawberry

Yoghurt Flavour; *Raw:* Carnitine, Glutamine, HMB, Ribose

TOTAL RAW FOOD LTD ™☺❶
All products are vegan

VEGA NUTRITIONALS ™⊘✔
Active Mature Plus Multivitamin & Mineral; Active Mens Multivitamin & Mineral; Active Womens Multivitamin & Mineral; Black Cohosh Complex; Calcium & Vitamin D Tablets; Iron Citrate (15mg); Vega Calcium Chewable; Zinc Citrate (15mg); *Vega antioxidants:* Dunaliella salina(natural betacarotene) 100mg, Multi Antioxidant complex, Pine Bark Complex 30mg; *Vega minerals:* Calcium (Citrate) 100mg, Calcium & vitamin D high strength, Calcium, Magnesium & Zinc, Chelated Calcium 500mg, Chromium 200mcg & vitamin B3, Colloidal Minerals& Kelp Formula, Iron (Bisglycinate) 50mg non Constipating, Iron(citrate)14mg &vitamin C, Kelp & Greens Formula, Magnesium (Citrate) 100mg, Selenium (methionine) 200mcg Yeast Free, Zinc (citrate) 15 mg &vitamin C, Zinc Citrate 50mg, ZMM High Potency Multi Mineral formula; *Vega multivitamins and minerals:* Active Mature 50& Multivitamins and minerals, Active women's multivitamin and minerals, Anti-Oxidant selenium- ACE formula, Spectrum Multi Vitamin and minerals, ZM3 Multivitamin &

Minerals formula; *Vega omega 6 essential fatty acids:* Evening primrose oil formula, Soya Lecithin plus Starflower Oil (Omega 3&6); *Vega probiotics and digestive aids:* Digestive Enzymes formula, Gastrocalm Formula, Non Dairy Acidophilus plus Bifidus Complex, Psyllium Husk Fibre 450mg; *Vega special care formulas:* Cardiohealth Formula, Energizer Formula, Hair-Skin-Nails formula, Menopause Formula, Opti-care 20:20 Formula, PMS Formula, Pre-Natal Formula, Prostate Formula, Slimaide Formula; *Vega specialised nutritional supplements:* Allermex Formula, Alpha lipoic acid& Acetyl L- carnitine 500 - Complex, Champignon Detox Formula, Co-enzyme Q10 30 mg-phyto- antioxidants, Co-enzyme Q10 30mg Extra High Potency, Cranberry Plus Formula, Garlic (Deodorised) 400mg High Potency, Hematinic Blood co-factors, Maxijoint Formula, Multi Detox Complex, Multigluco Tolerance Factors with Karella, Smokers formula, Vitalize-Regenerative Formula; *Vega Standardised herbs - V caps:* Agnus Castus 300mg High Potency, Aloe Vera 500mg High Potency, Dong Quai 750mg High Potency, Echinacea 750mg High Potency; *Vega Standardised herbs - V caps:* Devil's Claw 300mg High Potency; *Vega standardised herbs- V caps:* Black cohosh herbal extract, Echinacea & ginseng and astragalus

herbal complex, Feverfew 750mg
High Potency, Ginkgo Biloba 750mg
High Potency, Ginseng (Siberian)
1700 Complex, Milk Thistle 200-
Complex, Neem Leaf herbal complex,
Panax Ginseng (Korean) 800 Complex,
Rhodiola herbal extract, St John's
Wort 333-Complex, Valerian 900-
Complex; *Vega Standardised herbs -V
caps:* Cat's Claw 1000mg High
Potency; *Vega vitamin B supplements:*
Biotin (vitamin H) 900mcg, Choline
plus Inositol 250mg/250mg, Co-
enzymes B6 (P-5-P)10mg, Folic Acid(
vitamin B9) 400mcg, P.A.B.A Para
Aminobenzoic Acid 300mg, Vitamin
B Complex formula, Vitamin B1
100mg (Thiamine), Vitamin B12
1000mcg, Vitamin B2 40mg
(Riboflavin), Vitamin B3 No Flush
(Nicotinamide), Vitamin B5 200mg
(Calcium Pantothenate), Vitamin B6
plus p-5-p 100mg, Vitamin B6 plus
p-5-p 50mg; *Vega vitamin C
supplements:* Ester-C Formula,
Vitamin B & C Complex, Vitamin C
1000mg - high strength, Vitamin C
1000mg (Calcium Ascorbate)- non
acidic, Vitamin C 1000mg Slow
Release, Vitamin C 1500mg- super
strength, Vitamin C(calcium
ascorbate) 500mg - non acidic, Zinc
C Formula; *Vega vitamin E
supplements:* Natural Vitamin E(D-
Alpha tocopherol) 400iu 335mg dry,
Vitamin E 200iu 134mg dry plus
Selenium Yeast Free

WASSEN INTERNATIONAL ⊘ 𝒾
Coenzyme Q10 & Magnesium;
Coenzyme Q10 & Vitamin E;
Confiance; Magnesium-B; Selene-Activ;
Efamol: Pure Evening Primrose Liquid

WHOLISTIC RESEARCH COMPANY
Cascara Compound; Colon Detox Herbs
and Herbal Drops; Organic Wheatgrass
Powder; Spirulina Tablets

YAOH ™☺❶⊘ 𝒾
Hemp Protein Powder 454g

NOTES

■ **Alternative healthcare** includes herbalists, homoeopaths (but see **homoeopathy**, below), acupuncturists etc. and the use of herbal remedies available from health/wholefood shops and chemists.

■ **Beta-carotene and vitamin D$_2$:** see FOOD NOTES, page 152.

■ **Capsules** may be made from gelatine but animal-free alternatives are increasingly being used.

■ **Contraceptives** may have been tested on animals or contain animal-derived ingredients:

■ **Condoms** have usually been processed with the use of casein (a milk protein), but the Vegan Society sell some that do not use casein.

■ **Oral contraceptives** may contain lactose (milk sugar) and / or magnesium stearate (possibly animal-derived).

■ **Drugs** may or may not contain animal-derived ingredients but will have been tested on animals at some stage in production. The website *www.medicines.org.uk* lists the ingredients of all UK medicines.

■ **Homoeopathic remedies** are derived from plant, mineral or animal substances. Tablets may contain lactose, although sucrose may be used instead. Other animal-derived ingredients are used in homoeopathic products, including snake venom, bee venom and bee pollen. However many homoeopaths have a good working knowledge of veganism and should be able to help locate animal-free alternatives if these exist.

■ **Prescriptions:** In order for a medicinal product to be allowed onto the UK market it must have marketing authorization, also known as a product licence. However doctors can lawfully prescribe unlicensed drugs. Theoretically this means that if an animal-free product is available a GP can prescribe it. However doing so increases the doctor's personal liability should anything go wrong and many doctors are therefore reluctant to prescribe unlicensed alternatives. If a GP is unwilling to ascertain the animal-free status of a product, the patient may have to undertake his/her own research. Pharmacists are useful sources of information.

■ **The Vegan Society** has an information sheet that lists healthcare professionals who are either vegan or have experience of treating vegan patients. Most of those listed are alternative health-care practitioners. Always check that you are happy with the practitioner's level of qualification. Contact the Vegan Society office for more details.

Please note that we do NOT advise you to stop taking medication or prescribed drugs without consulting your GP.

Unfortunately, most drugs have been tested on animals, but here is a list of those that do not contain animal ingredients. Please note, however, that pharmaceutical companies regularly change the contents of their products and so it is best to check with the company if you want to be sure that they are still free from animal ingredients. If you are struggling to get information from pharmaceutical companies then your local pharmacist should be able to contact the company for you.

OVER-THE-COUNTER MEDICATIONS

Painkillers:

Bayer
- Aspro Clear
- Aspro Clear Maximum Strength
- Co-Codamol Effervescent
- Paracodol Tablets

Co-op (confirmed 22.05.08)
- Paracetamol Caplets
- Paracetamol Extra Strength
- Ibuprofen 200mg tablets
- Co-codamol 8/500mg tablets
- Extra Power Caplets
- Co-Codamol Tablets
- Chewable Vitamin C tablets

GlaxoSmithKline
- Panadol Actifast
- Panadol Extra Soluble
- Panadol Night
- Panadol Soluble
- Solpadeine Headache Soluble
- Solpadeine Plus Soluble
- Solpadeine Plus Tablets

Colds and Flu Relief

Bayer
- Askit Powders

GlaxoSmithKline
- Beechams Flu-Plus Hot Berry Fruits
- Beechams Flu-Plus Hot Lemon
- Beechams Cold and Flu Hot Blackcurrant
- Beechams Cold and Flu Hot Lemon
- Beechams Max Strength Throat Lozenges
- Day Nurse Liquid – new formulation
- Night Nurse Liquid

Coldsore Treatment

GlaxoSmithKline
- Zovirax Coldsore Cream

Cough Medicines:

Potters
- Cough Remover product no 17327.
- Catarrh Mixture
- Chest Mixture

GlaxoSmithKline
- Veno's Dry Cough
- Veno's Expectorant
- Veno's for Kids

Hayfever Treatment

GlaxoSmithKline
• Piriton Syrup

Indigestion and Constipation

Bayer
• Alka Seltzer: Original and XS

GlaxoSmithKline
• Andrews Salts
• Eno
• Milk of Magnesia Liquid
• Setlers Antacid
• Tums

Nicotine Replacement

GlaxoSmithKline
• NiQuitin CQ Lozenges
• NiQuitin CQ Gum

Stomach Ulcer Treatment

GlaxoSmithKline
• Zantac Tablets

Travel Sickness

GlaxoSmithKline
• Joy Rides

Cystitis

Bayer
• Canesten Oasis
• Cystopurin

PRESCRIPTION MEDICATIONS

GlaxoSmithKline
Otomize Ear Spray

Roche Products
• Cellcept Injection
(generic name mycophenolate mofetil)
• Cellcept Oral Suspension
(generic name mycophenolate mofetil)
• Cymevene Injection
(generic name ganciclovir)
• Genticin Eye/Ear Drop
(generic name gentamicin)
• Genticin Injection
(generic name gentamicin)
• Gentisone Ear Drops
(generic name gentamicin/hydrocortisone)
• Hypnovel Injection
(generic name midazolam)
• Kytril Injection
(generic name granisetron)
• Pegasys Injection
(generic name pegylated interferon alfa-2)
• Rivotril Injection
(generic name clonazepam)
• Rocephin Injection
(generic name ceftriaxone)
• Tamiflu Oral Suspension
(generic name oseltamivir)

Rosemont Pharma
Rosemont Pharma state that all their
medicines are suitable for vegans
except for:
• Folicare, Folic Acid 0.4mg/5ml Oral
  Solution,
• Lexpec, Folic Acid 2.5mg/5ml Oral
  Solution,

- Uriben, Nalidixic Acid 300mg/5ml Oral Suspension,
- Paracetamol 500mg/5ml Oral Suspension (19.10.07)

PRESCRIBED CONTRACEPTIVES

Pfizer
- Femulen (oral contraceptive)

Janssen-Cilag
- Evra (contraceptive patch)

Bayer
- Noristerat (contraceptive injection)

Bayer
- Merina (Intrauterine Device)

HORMONE REPLACEMENT THERAPY

Novartis
- Estraderm MX patches

■ **Vitamin K** is routinely injected into newborn babies to protect against rare but serious haemorrhage (including brain haemorrhage). In the past the injection was vegan but now includes a carrier made from cow bile, making it unsuitable for vegans. However there is at least one oral version available on a named-patient basis. This means that it must be prescribed and ordered through a doctor. If you wish to use this product, make sure you allow time for it to be sourced and prescribed. If your doctor is unaware of this, your local or hospital pharmacist should be able to help. We must stress that we cannot give medical advice but can only pass on information about the availability of the product. Please feel free to contact the Vegan Society office if you have any queries.

■ If you know in advance that you are going to have medical treatment, contact the hospital or health professionals well ahead of time to let them know that you are vegan.

BABY, INFANT & CHILDCARE

FOOD & DRINK

BABYNAT
Apple & Banana Muesli; Apple & Raspberry Cereal; Baby Rice; Banana Porridge; *Fruit Compotes:* Apple & Apricot Stage II, Apple & Banana Stage II, Apple & Blueberry, Apple & Vanilla/Banana & Plum Dual, Apple Peach/Apple Strawberry Doubles, Banana, Apple & Apricot, Pear and Raspberry, Summer Pudding; *Goodies Fruit Competes:* Apple & Berries Puree, Banana & Mango Puree

BICKIEPEGS ☺◎⌀ ✔
Teething Biscuits for Babies

COW & GATE
Baby Balance Desserts Jars, Stages 1, 2 and 3: Baby Fruit Cocktail, Exotic Fruit Combo, Fruity Muesli, Juicy Fruit Crumble, Juicy Pear & Banana, Mango Surprise, Plum and Apricot Compote, Summer Fruit Salad; *Baby Balance Savoury Jars, Stage 1 (+4 months):* A Taste of Apple, A Taste of Carrot, A Taste of Pear, A Taste of Pumpkin, Sweet Potato Bake, Yummy Baby Veg Risotto; *Baby Balance Savoury Jars, Stage 2 (+ 7 months):* Baby Bean Feast; *Baby Balance Savoury Jars, Stage 3 (+ 10 months):* Mild Mexican Bean Pot, Simply Scrummy Lentil Bake; *Cereals, Stage 1:* Apple & Banana Burst, Pure Baby Rice, Totally Oaty Porridge; *Cereals, Stage 2:* Apple & Blueberry

Sunburst, Multigrain Porridge, Tropical Sunrise; *Cereals, Stage 3:* Fruity Crunch; *Cereals, Stage 4:* Fruity, Sun, Moon & Stars, Hoop-a-Loops, My First Muesli; *Frutapura Pots:* Apple & Apricot, Apple & Banana, Apple & Pear, Apple, Apricot & Strawberry, Apple, Orange & Banana, Banana, Peach & Strawberry, Fruit Cocktail, Pear, Pear & Pineapple, Plum & Apple; *Frutapura Pouches:* Apple & Banana, Exotic Fruit, Fruit Cocktail

HEINZ ™◎
Nurture Soya infant formula

HIPP ORGANIC BABY FOODS ◎ ✔ ☼
Dried Stage 1: Apple, Orange & Banana, Baby Rice, Banana Porridge, Hipp-a-bisc, Mashed Potato with Rosemary; *Stage 1 - Baby Menu:* Mixed Vegetable Medley, Tender Carrots & Potatoes; *Stage 1 - Desserts:* Apple & Blueberry Dessert, Apple & Pear Pudding, Apple & Plum Pudding, Banana & Peach Dessert, Banana & Rice Pudding, Fruit Pots Apple & Pear, Fruit Pots Apple and Strawberry, Mango & Banana Melba, Red Fruit & Apple Compote, William Christ Pears; *Stage 1- Desserts:* Fruit Pots Apple with Banana & Peach, Purley Fruits Apple & Banana, Purley Fruits Apple Strawberry & Blueberry; *Stage 1- First Tastes:* Apple & Banana, Apple Puree, Carrots & Sweetcorn, Pumpkin and Rice; *Stage 2- Desserts:* Tropical Fruit Salad

MOOD FOOD COMPANY ™◎
"Vegan Friendly Foods" category on the online shop.

ORGANIX BRANDS PLC ⊘ ✿
Baby Sweetcorn Rings; Jumbo Carrot
Sticks; *Biscuits:* ABC's, Animal Biscuits,
Gingerbread Men

PETER RABBIT ORGANICS ⊘ ✿
Organic Puree: Apple, Peach & Apricot

**TRUUULY SCRUMPTIOUS ORGANIC
BABY FOOD** ⊘ ✿
Apple, Banana & Mango; Butternut
Squash & Carrot; Carrot, Parsnip &
Swede; No Added Salt Vegetable Stock;
Potato, Courgette & Pea; Sweet Potato
& Parsnip; *Alfie's Deli Brand:* Coconut
Rice Pudding, Pasta & 5 Vegetable
Sauce, Vegetable & Butter Bean
Medley, Vegetable Lentil Casserole

HEALTH CARE

A. VOGEL
Echinacea Junior

BEAMING BABY ™
Organic Facial Cleansing Wipes;
Organic Lavender Nappy Cream;
Organic Lavender Baby Lotion;
Organic Lavender Baby Oil; Organic
Lavender Bubble Bath

BIO-HEALTH LTD ⊘ ✦
Pure-fil: Junior Bio-Caps Multivitamin &
Mineral

FAITH PRODUCTS LIMITED
™ ✦ ☻ ⅔← 1988
Baby Shampoo & Body Wash

HERBS HANDS HEALING LTD ™⊘ ✦
Herbal Formula: Little One's Cough
Syrup

HIGHER NATURE PLC ™⊘ ✦
Dinochews; Herbal Aloe Gold Ear
Drops

NATURE'S OWN LTD ™
Cytoplan- Multi-Formulations:
Childrens Multex, Nourish Drink
Children's Formula; *Multi-
Formulations:* Children's Multivitamin
& Mineral

TOMS OF MAINE ⊘ ✦
Natural Moisturising Body Wash:
Lavender

NAPPIES

BIO-D ™☺⊘ ✦ ☻ ⅔← 1988
Nappy Fresh

TOILETRIES ETC

AKAMUTI
Baby Bottom Butter; Bedtime Baby Bath
Milk; Organic Baby Flower Wash;
Organic Baby Soap; *Baby Oil:* Peach &
Chamomile, Sunshine

AROMA COMFORTS ™☺◌
Baby's Bottom Butter

BABYBOO ORGANICS LTD ™☺◌✿
Babyboo products: **Citrus bodywash, Lavender foaming cleanser, Lavender lotion, Lavender shampoo, Strawberry bodywash**

BEAMING BABY ™
Organic Baby Wipes; Organic Bathtime Bubble Bath; Organic Bathtime Shampoo & Bodywash; Organic Nappy Cream; Organic Skincare Baby Lotion

BURT'S BEES ◌◀☻
Baby Bee: Apricot Baby Oil, Dusting Powder, Shampoo & Wash

CAWARRA COSMETICS LTD ™
Sanctum: **Baby Bath Wash, Baby Conditioner, Baby Moisturiser, Baby Powder, Baby Shampoo**

ENERGIZER PERSONAL CARE ™
Wet Ones: **Little Bottoms- toilet training wipes, Sticky Fingers- hand wipes**

ESSENTIAL CARE
Gentle Wash & Shampoo for Baby; Organic Baby Massage Oil; Organic Baby Repair Lotion; Organic Calming Spritz; Organic Labour Oil; Organic Soothing Salve

ESSENTIALLY YOURS LTD ™☺◌◀☻
My Baby: **Baby Lotion, Bubble Bath, Hair & Body Shampoo, LYB Body Lotion, Massage Oil, Nappy Cream;** *My Baby Range:* **Bubble Bath, Hair&body wash, Massage oil, Nappy cream**

FAITH PRODUCTS LIMITED
™◀☻⅍1988
Baby Body Lotion; Baby Shampoo; Baby tushie cleanse; Nappy cream

FLORAROMA LTD ™
Little Me- Mmmm Moisture Babies: **Bath Soak, Body Cream, Body Wash, Hair Wash;** *Little Me- Shhh Sleepy Head:* **Body Cream, Hair and Body Wash;** *Little Me- Yipeee Playtime:* **Bath Bubbles, Body Cream, Soothing Baby Oil;** *Little Me-Shhh Sleepy Head:* **Bath Milk**

GREEN PEOPLE CO. ™◌◀
Baby Lotion Mum+Baby moisturiser; Baby Wash Lavender; *Organic Babies:* **Baby Wash - Chamomile;** *Organic Children:* **Bath & Shower Gel, Citrus & Aloe Vera Bath & Shower, Citrus & Aloe Vera Shampoo, Conditioner, Shampoo, Spearmint & Aloe Vera Toothpaste, Toothpaste — Mandarin, Top to Toe Lotion**

GREEN VALLEY TRADING CO. ™☺
All products are vegan

HEALTHQUEST LIMITED ™◌◀
Earth Friendly Baby: **Eco Baby Wipes,**

Natural Lavender Cleansing Bar, Natural Unscented Massage Oil (100ml), Organic Chamomile Bubble Bath (370ml), Organic Chamomile Shampoo & Bodywash, Organic Lavender Bubble Bath (370 ml), Organic Lavender Shampoo & Bodywash, Organic Mandarin Bubble Bath (370ml), Organic Mandarin Shampoo & Bodywash, Organic Massage Oil; *Earth Friendly Kids:* Gentle Kids Wipes, Minty Lavender Body Lotion, Minty Lavender Bubblebath, Minty Lavender Handwash, Minty Lavender Shampoo & Bodywash, Zingy Citrus Body Lotion, Zingy Citrus Bubblebath, Zingy Citrus Handwash, Zingy Citrus Shampoo & Bodywash

JASON NATURAL PRODUCTS *i* 👁
Kids Only!™™ Extra Gentle Conditioner; Kids Only™™ Extra Gentle Shampoo; *Earth's Best®®:* 2-in-1 Shampoo & Body Wash, Baby Oil, Diaper Relief Ointment, Everyday Lotion, Extra Rich Therapy Crème, Hair Detangler, Mineral Based Sunblock SPF30+, Toddler Toothpaste

KOBASHI ™☺🚫 *i* 👁⚕1976
Luxury Lotions: **Baby Lotion**

KOOCHIE KOO ™
aromababy: **Aromawipes, Baby Bath Gel, Baby Massage Oil, Moisturising Nappy Change Cream, Mother & Child Massage Oil, Natural Floral**

Water, Natural Powder, Organic Massage Oil, Pure Baby Moisture Lotion, Pure Baby Wash, Pure Hair Cleanse

LAVERANA ™ *i*
Baby & Kinder: **Shampoo;** *Lavera Baby & Kinder Neutral:* **Hair & Body Shampoo, Lotion, Oil Bath, Skin Oil;** *Lavera Basis Sensitiv:* **Kid's Tooth Gel Strawberry-Raspberry**

NATURALLY GIFTED ™
Lavender Baby Soap

NATURE'S GATE
Baby Soothing Shampoo; *Organics:* Baby Oil, Gentle Baby Wash, Naturally Soft Baby Lotion, Soothing Diaper Rash Cream

NEAL'S YARD REMEDIES 🚫 *i* 👁⚕1998
Baby Massage Oil; Baby Soap; Pure Baby Oil

NOTHING NASTY *i*
Bonbon Baby Oil

ORGANIC SOAP COMPANY ™🚫✹
Baby

PURE GAISHA ™☺❶ *i*
Kids Only Body Lotion; Kids Only Lip Balm; Kids Only Shower Gel; Kids Only Solid Perfume; Soothing Baby Balm - For Bubs; Soothing Baby Wash - For Bubs

RAW GAIA ™☺ ✔
Floral Water Spray For Her Babies;
Massage Oil For Her Babies

SIMPLE ✔
Baby: Body Wash, Extra Soft Wipes,
Moisturising All-In-One Wash,
Moisturising Bath, Moisturising Oil Gel,
Moisturising Shampoo, Pure Talc,
Soothing Lotion, Zinc & Castor Oil
Barrier Cream

SOLARAY NUTRITIONAL SUPPLEMENTS
Baby Bath Shampoo; Baby Bath Soap;
Baby Body Lotion

THE HIGHLAND SOAP COMPANY ™⊘
Body Wash: **Mandarin Baby Body**
Wash

TOMS OF MAINE ⊘ ✔
Natural Anticavity Fluoride Toothpaste
for Children: Silly Strawberry; *Natural*
Fluoride-Free Toothpaste for Children:
Silly Strawberry; *Natural Moisturising*
Body Wash: Unscented

TÖÖPFER GMBH ™
Calendula Hautsalbe / Baby
Calendula Ointment; Calendula
Lotion / Baby Body Lotion;
Calendula Waschgel / Baby Washgel
with Calendula

VERDESATIVA S.R.L. ™☺
Shampoo Bimbi

WELEDA ⊘ ✔ ⅋ 1985
Children's Tooth Gel; *Baby Calendula*
Range: Bath, Oil, Soap

NOTES

■ **Animal-free children's shoes** can be difficult to find. Jinga have a children's range of vegan shoes. Green Shoes can supply made-to-order vegan shoes including shoes for children. Some high-street chains may be willing to provide information about the materials used in their shoes. For more general information on finding vegan shoes see the FOOTWEAR & CLOTHING NOTES (page 325)

■ **Baby wipes** may contain lanolin, which is derived from wool and the skin of slaughtered animals.

■ **Farley's Soya Infant Formula** is the only known animal-free complete infant formula available in the UK.

■ **Information on real nappies** can be obtained from the Real Nappy Campaign which is the organiser of Real Nappy Week. For further details or for nearby stockists call the Real Nappy Helpline on 0845 850 0606 or search online at www.realnappycampaign.com.

■ **Vitamin K** is routinely injected into newborn babies to protect against rare but serious haemorrhage (including brain haemorrhage). In the past, the injection was vegan but at the time of going to press it now includes a carrier made from cow bile, making it unsuitable for vegans. There is, however, at least one oral version available on a named-patient basis. This means that it must be prescribed and ordered through a doctor. Please contact the Vegan Society office for more details.

■ **Vegan pregnancy and parenting advice:** The Vegan Society produces a range of information on raising vegan children, including the book *Raising your Vegan Infant – With Confidence* by State Registered Dietitian, Sandra Hood – visit www.vegansociety.com/shop or call 0121 523 1730 for details. See 'SUGGESTED READING' (page 66) for further resources.

■ **Vegan families list:** The Vegan Society has a list of vegan families in the UK who have vegan children and are happy to be contacted for advice and support. Please contact the Vegan Society office for more details.

FOOTWEAR & CLOTHING

BELTS, WALLETS , BAGS ETC

BOURGEOIS BOHEME ™☺
Mens Wallets (various); Womens Bags (various); Womens Purses (various); *Hultquist:* Jewellery (various)

FEEL GOOD HANDBAGS ☺
Handbags: All Products are Vegan

FREERANGERS ™☺✓
Celtic Bag; *Accessories:* **Alex Belt, Aragon Belt, Bow Bag, Buckle Bag, Coin Purse, Conker II Rucksack, Credit Card Holder, Full Wallet, Galadriel Belt, Guitar Strap, Half Wallet, Lucy Bag, Molly Bag, Palm Pilot Case, Prairie Belt, Purse, Sporran, Strider Belt, Watch Strap, Wave Bag, Zoe Bag**

GREEN SHOES ⊘✓
Range of Products Suitable for Vegans

MISS BELLASIS ☺❶✓
Knickers: Carmen, Celestine, Vivian; *Ribbon Collection:* Annie, Hesther, Laurel, Marguerite, Peggy, Velvet; *Satin Collection:* Anis, Catherine, Celestine, Judy, Kitty, Lily, Lina, Lise, Mary, Mary - Collar, Mary - Cuffs, Mima, Rosalie, Roslyn, Tae, Tansy, Violette; *Sequin Collection:* Dorita, Florrie, Margo; *Vintage Trims, Limited Editions:* Bella, Charlotte, Emily, Eve, Irma

VEGAN STORE ™☺❶⊘✓
Business Belt; Faux Leather Wallet; Lorica Watch Strap

VEGANLINE ™☺❶
Microfibre belts & guitar straps cut to order; PVC Wallets made in the UK

VEGETARIAN SHOES ☺❶
Belts: All; *Insoles:* All; *Shoe Laces:* All; *Wallets:* All

VEGETARIAN SHOES AND BAGS ™☺
Bags - All designs; Belts and accessories - All designs

CLOTHING

ADEENA LTD ™⊘
Non Silk Vegan Satin Ties- various colours

BOURGEOIS BOHEME ™☺
Mobile/Mini Ipod Muffs; Scarves (various)

PENNANGALAN ™
B10 Corset Lift Boots

VEGAN STORE ™☺❶⊘✓
Fleece Gloves

VEGETARIAN SHOES ☺❶
Gloves: All; *Jackets:* All; *Leather Look Jeans:* All

FOOTWEAR - FORMAL

NOHARM ™☺
Mens: **Hidden-lace Shoe, Lace-up Ankle Boot, Lace-up Shoe, Slip-on Shoe**

PENNANGALAN ™
Dot Frieda Shoe; Megan Victim Boots

VEGETARIAN SHOES AND BAGS ™☺
Shoes - All designs

FOOTWEAR - GENERAL

ACORN PRODUCTS CO, LLC ™✎
Adult Sox: **Double Duty Knee High, Double Duty Sox, High versa 2-Way Tread, Reg Ptec Sandal Sock, Rei 2-Way Fleece Sock, Versa 2-Way Mid, Versa 2-Way Sox, Versa 2-Way Tread, Versa 2-Way W/Cuff;** *Classic:* **Baxter Moc, Chinchilla Bootie, Chinchilla Collar, Chinchilla Mule, Cozy Bootie, Nex Tex Clog, Nex Tex Moc, Ocelot Thong;** *Classic Comfort:* **Berber Cozy Bootie Womens, Nex Tex Moc Mn, Tech Travel Moc Mens, Tech Travel Moc WM;** *Kids:* **Easy Bootie, Easy Bootie- 2 styles, Kids Mule, Monster Moc, Spa Terry Bootie, Tex Easy Bootie;** *Kids Sox:* **Double Duty Sox Kids, Versa Kid Sox;** *Kids' Sox:* **Rei Kids Sock**

W/Tread, Rei Versa Kid Sock; *Kids Spa:* **Kids Spa Mule, Kids's Spa Moc, Quilted Terry Mule K;** *Shoes:* **Ergo Bootie WM, Strata Moc MN, Via Moc WM;** *Spa:* **Eco Mule Womens, New Spa Slide, New Spa Thong, Quilted Eco Scuff, Quilted Terry Scuff, Sensoria Ballet- Women's, Sensoria Scuff, Sensoria Slide, Sensoria Thong, Spa Bella- Women's, Spa Quilt Scuff- Women's, Spa Slide Mn, Spa Slip-On WM, Spa Wrap, Sporty Spa Moc- Women's, Sporty Spa Slide, Sporty Spa Slide- Women's, Sporty Spa Thong, Wide Spa Slip-On;** *Studio:* **Caftan Mule, Caftan Thong, Dahlia Mule- Women's, Dahlia Thong- Women's, Serendipity, Sophie-women's, Sporty Spa Thong- Women's**

ALTERNATIVE STORES ™☺❶
All products are vegan

EARTH FOOTWEAR ™
Malibu; *Men's Vegan Line:* **Auburn, Classic, Delta, Eastside, Energetic-K, Lazer-K, Logan-K, Malibu, Navigator 2, Nova, Oak, Pilot-K, Rocket-K, Sausalito, Wayside, Yosemite;** *Men's Vegan Line 2008:* **Brighton, Brion, Cabo-K, Coast, Energetic-K, Gulf, Launch-K, Lazer-K, Logan-K, Oak, Rocket-K, Sausalito, Tova, Wayside, Yosemite-K;** *Vegan Casuals:* **Aspen, Breeze, Breeze 2, Delight, Duet, Dune, Eden, Forest, Gidget, Intrigue, Jasmine, Jubilee, Kharma, Kharma 2, Magnetism 2, Melissa 2, Miami,**

Mirage, Navigator & Navigator 2, Newport, Nova, Oasis, Orion 2, Samea, Shirley, Solar, Tofu, Woodland; *Women's Vegan Line:* Allure, Ava, Charisma, Classy, Dakota, Dharma, Energetic, Flight, Flora, Freedom, Harvest, Hippie, Ipanema, Juniper, Lazer, Lodge, Logan, Midway, Pilot, Pirouette 2, Reflect, Rocket, Tranquil, Yosemite; *Women's vegan line 2008:* Alluro, Cabo, Cabo strap, Dakota, Dharmo, Energetic, Flight- microfiber, Flight-twistech, Harvest, Inhale, Juniper, Launch, Lazer- microfiber, Lazer-twistech, Lodge, Logan, Magnetism 2 -bamboo, Magnetism 2-microfiber, Melissa 2, Midway, Oasis, Reflect, Rocket, Solar- salestream, Solar-twistech, Sunset, Tranquil 2, Wish, Yosemite - Nylon strap, Yosemite -E-Strap

EARTH&WEAR LIMITED ™
No Sweat: **Canvas Baseball Boots, Hemp Baseball Boots**

ETHICAL WARES ☺❶✔
All Products are Vegan

FREERANGERS ™☺✔
Denim Kalahari sandals; Ladies Bramble boot; Sparkle sandal; *Ladies:* **Alder Shoe, Ash Sandal, Asym Shoe, Beech Shoe, Birch Shoe, Brook Sandal, Clover Shoe, Criss Cross Sandal, Drifter Shoe, Ebony Shoe, Fern Shoe, Fig Sandal, Gemini Sandal, Heather Clog, Jess Boot,**

Kate Shoes, Laurel Shoe, Lily Shoe, Lucy Shoe, Mary Jane Shoe, Meg Mule, Posy Sandal, Shamrock Shoe, Shell Mule, Snowflake Mule, Venezia Sandal; *Mens:* **Ben Boot, Bracken Shoe, Crag Shoe, Dale Mule, Dene Mule, Drifter Shoe, Elm Sandal, Glen Boot, Heather Clog, Maple Shoe, Pine Shoe**

GEORGETTE BVBA ™☺✔
All shoes are vegan

GREEN SHOES ⊘✔
Mens: Range of Shoes Boots and Sandals Suitable for Vegans; *Womens:* Range of Shoes Boots and Sandals Suitable for Vegans

JINGANDO ™☺
All products are vegan

NATURAL SHOE STORE
Clog: Boston; *Sandal:* Arizona, Gizeh, Madrid, Milano

PENNANGALAN ™
2 Strap Winkle Picker; 3 Strap Smegg Frieda Platform Boots; 3 Strat Fetish Smegg Boots with platform; 3 Strat Fetish Smegg Boots(without platform); 3-Strap High Raider; 4-Strap Winkle Picker Shoes; 4-Strap Winkle Picker Shoes With Bat Buckles; Alex L8 Magic 8-Strap Thigh-High Boots; Alex L8 Victim 8-Strap Thigh-High Boots; Alex Lift Thigh-High Boots; Alex Magic Thigh-High Boots; Alex

Victim Thigh-High Boots; Andy 3-Strap Commando Boots; Anna Frieda Sandal; Anna Magic Sandal; April Lift; April Magic Boots; April Victim Boots; B10 Corset Magic Boots; B10 Corset Ramp Boots; B10 Linda Lift Boots; B6 Elevator Boots; Bucket Musketeer Boots; Calf D-Ring Boots; Carolyn D-Ring Victim Boots; Charlie Commando Boots; Charlie Elevator Boots; Chelsea Boots; Chong Lift Mary Jane; Chow Flare Shoe; Court Shoes With Platform; Cuban Chelsea Beat Boots; Dawn Boots; Dawn Boots With Bat Buckles; Dawn Boots with Coffin Buckles; Dawn Boots With Skull Buckles; Dot Victim Shoe; Easy Plate Panels for Libby 16 Plate Boots; Eva Cloud Sandal; Fang Flare Shoes; Fang Lift Shoes; Fang Ramp Shoes; Fang Victim Shoes; Front D-Ring Thigh Boots; Front D-Ring Thigh Boots With Platform; Gibson Toe-Stitch Shoes; Gibson Winkle Picker; Gladiator Biker Plate Boots; Gloria Boots; Granny Stiletto; Gulliver Shoes; Jason 10 Strap Winkle Picker Boots; Jason 10-Strap Boots With Bat Buckles; Jean O-Ring Magic Boots; Jean O-Ring Victim Boots; Jodi Cloud Granny Boots; Jodi Flare Boots; Jodi Frieda Platform Boots; Jodi Lift Boots; Jodi Magic Platform Boots; Jodi Ramp Boots; Jodi Victim Platform Boots; Kim Victim Stretch Fit Thigh Boots; Kim Victim Thigh Boots; L2 Raider Commando Boots; L3 Magic Boots; L5 Flare Boots; L5 Frieda; L5 Gloria

Boots; L5 Magic Platform Boots; L5 Victim Boots; L8 Alex Lift 8-Strap Thigh High; Lara Croft Tomb Raider Boots; Libby 16 Plate Commando Boots; Libby 16 Plate Elevator Boots; Libby 16 Plate Magic Boots; Libby 16 Plate Victim Boots; Libby Commando Boots; Libby Easy Plate Lift Boots; Libby Elevator Boots; Libby Lift Boots; Libby Magic Boots; Libby Plate Ramp Boots; Libby Ramp Boots; Libby Victim Platform Boots; Linda Cloud Granny Boots; Linda Commando Boots; Linda D-Ring Victim Boots; Linda Flame Flare Boots; Linda Flare Boots; Linda Frieda; Linda Lift Boots; Linda Magic; Linda Ramp Boots; Linda Victim Boots; Low Bucket Musketeer Boots; Lush Lift Sandal; Mad Fish Big Flame Boots; Mad Fish Big Flap Boots; Mad Fish Big Shark Boots; Mad Fish Big Zipper Boots; Mad Fish Flame - Black Shoes; Mad Fish Flap - Black Shoes; Megan Lift Boots; Megan Magic Boots; Megan Ramp Boots; Mesh-Sides Ankle Boots; Minx Boots; Minx Boots With Bat Buckles; Minx Boots With Skull Buckles; Minx Coffin Boots; Minx Cowboy Boots; Minx Pentagram Boots; Mitch Lift Boots; Mitch Ramp Boots; Molly Lift Boots; Molly Ramp Boots; Mule Magic; Nan Trish Victorian Granny Boots; Outside D-Ring Inside Zip Thigh High Boots; Padded Libby Lift; Padded Libby Victim; Pirate Twin Plate Straps-Pennangalan; Plain Court Shoes; Platform D-Ring Boots; Po Flare Platform Shoe; Po Magic Platform Shoe; Poko Flare Cross-Strap Shoe; Polly Flare Boots; Polly Magic Boots; Polly Victim; Saloon Calf Boots; Set of 6 Smegg Straps; Shirley D-Ring Platform Boots, Black Zip; Shirley Eyelet Platform Boots, Black Zip; Simply Commando Boots; Simply Elevator; Simply Frieda; Simply Lift Boots; Simply Magic Platform Boots; Simply Victim Boots; SIS Platform Boots, Silver Zip; Ski-Hook Thigh High Boots; Ski-Hook Thigh High Boots With Platform; Smegg Commando Boots; Smegg Elevator Boots; Smegg Lift Boots; Smegg Magic Platform Boots; Smegg Ramp Boots; Smegg Victim Platform Boots; Spirit Bat Boots; Spirit Boots; Spirit Coffin Boots; Steel Single Plate Straps-Pennangalan; Storm B-10 Magic Boots; Storm B-10 Victim Boots; Storm Commando Boots; Storm Elevator Boots; Storm(L5) Lift Boots; Thigh-High Commando Zip Boots; Tina Kat Platform Boots; Transmuters Boots With Zip; Turbo Magic Boots; UV Single Plate Straps- Pennangalan; Velda Boots With Magic Heel; Wang Cloud Shoe; Wang Lift Shoe; Zac Elevator Boots; Zac Lift Boots; Zac Magic Boots; Zac Plate Elevator Boots; Zac Plate Lift Boots; Zac Plate Magic Boots; Zac Plate Victim Boots; Zac Victim Boots; Zak Commando Boots; Zak Plate Commando Boots; Zip Thigh High Boots; Zip Thigh High Boots With Platform

RAGAZZI VEGAN ™☺◌
Vegan shoes- all products are vegan

THE ESSENTIAL OIL COMPANY ◌🕯👁
*Thermotherapy - Microwaveable
Heated Gifts:* Slippies Microwave
Slippers

VEGAN STORE ™☺❶◌🕯
Mens Footwear: **Atlanta Shoe, Bean
Shoe, Eagle Pass Boot, Fitter Flop,
President Slipper, Savage Boot
Black, Sonic Sneaker, Trekker
Sandal, Washington Gibson, Yukon
Boot, Yukon High Leg Boot, Yukon
Zip Up Boot;** *Womens Boots:* **Berlin,
Berlin Zip, Buckle, Lace, Milano Boot
Black, Polar, Polar Ankle, Polar Star,
Polar Stitch, Savage Boot Black,
Slouch, Tula, Tula Ankle, Tula Faux
Fur, Twister, Yukon, Zip Up;** *Womens
Footwear:* **Baci Sandal, Ballerina
Pump, Ballerina Strap Pump, Bella
Loafer, Betty Shoe, Buckle Pump,
Cetim Sandal, Charm Toe Post,
Chunky Mule, Coite Loafer, Coite
Mule, Comfort Sandal, Debra
Sandal, Fitter Flop, Flower Toe Post,
Hamptons Sandal, Honey Sandal,
Jupiter Sandal, Kate Shoe, Love 100
Sandal, Miami Sandal, Nancy
Sandal, Olivia Cross Strap Sandal,
Olivia Sandal, Oxygen Sandal,
Palma Pump, Paula Shoe Black,
Romiclog, Sahana Sandal, Sally
Pump, Santa Monica Sandal, Savana
Toe Post, Skinny Trekker, Sonic
Sneaker, Sophisto Sandal, Sorrento
Sandal, Star Sandal, Strappy Mule,**

**Susy Sandal, Sweetie Sandal,
Tallulah Mule, Tiger Trainer, Trip
Sandal, Twist Sandal, Venice Sandal,
Wheat Sandal, Zizi Mule, Zizi Shoe**

VEGANLINE ™☺❶
**Canvas: Various, including
Unswoosher Hemp Sneakers &
Camouflage Boots; Microfibre boots
and shoes including Bouncing
Boots; Sandals: Various women's
sandals including Denim & Strappy
Sandals; Women's Synthetics:
Various including Sanutex Winter
Boots**

VEGETARIAN SHOES ☺❶
Boots and Shoes: All - Over 150 Styles;
Shoe Care: Black Polish, Clear Dubbin

VEGETARIAN SHOES AND BAGS ™☺
Shoes - All designs

FOOTWEAR - SPORTS

NEW BALANCE
Mens Running - Cushioning: All; *Mens
Running - Lightweight:* All; *Mens
Running - Supportive Cushioning:* All;
Mens Running - Trail: MR921BY; *Mens
Running -Trail:* M783BK, M783GO,
MR873EU; *Mens Training:* MX1009WN;
Mens Walking: MW859BK; *Womens
Running - Cushioning:* All; *Womens
Running - Lightweight:* All; *Womens
Running - Supportive Cushioning:* All;
Womens Running - Trail: W783BB,

W783GC, WR873EU; *Womens Training:*
WX1009BL, WX505NF; *Womens
Walking:* MW859BK

VEGETARIAN SHOES AND BAGS ™☺
Shoes - All designs

WATERPROOFERS, POLISHES & CLEANERS

VINDOTCO UK LTD ™☺⊘ ✦
Really Works: **White Shoe
Trainer/Tennis/Golf Shoe Restorer**

NOTES

■ **Footwear:** The number of mail order and internet companies offering quality animal-free footwear has increased over recent years. If you would like our current list of companies that provide footwear please contact the Vegan Society office for our clothing and footwear fact sheet. Entirely vegan shoe shops are rare; Vegetarian Shoes has a shop in Brighton and Bourgeois Bohème has a shop in London. Cheap non-leather shoes are stocked by many high-street shops, and although the use of synthetic adhesives is commonplace it may be difficult to obtain guarantees.

Be aware that 'Nubuck' is leather. Non-leather, animal-free materials include Lorica, Pleather, Chlorenol, Hydrolite, Durabuck, Vegetan, PVC, Birkibuc and Cork Leather.

■ **Running and training shoes:**
Many sports footwear companies stock models made entirely of non-animal materials but may be unable or unwilling to guarantee that the adhesives used are non-animal. New Balance indicate on their website which of their running shoes are suitable for vegans.

HOME
& OFFICE

AIR FRESHENERS

ESSENTIALLY NATURAL ™
Lavender Pillows; Sliding Door Oil Burner

HOLISTIX ™❶
Festive: **Festive Spray**

NATURAL ECO-TRADING LTD ™☺✔ ☞
Earth Friendly Products: **Uni-Fresh (Cinnamon), Uni-Fresh (Citrus), Uni-Fresh (Lavender), Uni-Fresh (Parsley), Uni-Fresh (Vanilla)**

NATURAL HOUSE PRODUCTS LIMITED ™☺✔
Room Aroma Citrus Fusion; Room Aroma Mediterranean; Room Aroma Orange Blossom; Room Aroma Tropical

NATURAL SENSE ™
Room Fragrance

NOTHING NASTY ✔
Room Spray: Relaxing, Sensual, Uplifting

POTIONS AND POSSIBILITIES ⊘✔
Room Spray: Atmosphere Spray For Computer Room, English Garden, English Lavender, English Rose

PURPLE FLAME AROMATHERAPY ⊘✔
Pure Resin Pearls: All

QUINESSENCE AROMATHERAPY
☺⊘✔☞
Mood Enhancers: Arabian Nights, Autumn Meadows, Celestial Dream, Elemental Forest, Fantasia, Forbidden Fruit, Illuminessence, Moonflower, Secret Garden, Tranquilla, Wild Passion

TISSERAND AROMATHERAPY PRODUCTS ™☺
At home: **Bitter orange and Jasmine fresh linen mist;** *Lavender Products:* **Lavender bed linen mist;** *Pre-mix 100% pure essential oil blends exclusively for vaporisation:* **Energy, Menthol clear, Sleep tight;** *Vaporising units:* **Aroma-stream, Aroma-stream replacement cartridge, Personal vaporiser**

BLEACHES

ASTONISH ✔☞
Bathroom Range: Active Bleach - Tablets

SONETT OHG ™
Bleaching Complex

BRUSHES

ASTONISH ✔☞
Furniture Care Range: Dust Buster (+ Optional Extension Handle)

CANDLES AND INCENSE

ABSOLUTELY PURE ⊘
Travel Candle

ESSENTIALLY NATURAL ™
Sisal Insense Sticks; *Eco Soy Wax
candles:* **Frankincense Essential Oil,
Geranium & Ylang Ylang, Lavender,
Lavender & Bergamot, Lavender &
Chamomille, Lavender & Citronella,
Lavender & Eucalyptus, Lavender &
Geranium, Lavender & Ylang Ylang,
Lover's Lavender, Orange &
Lemongrass, Patchouli & Geranium,
Peppermint & Cinammon, Stay
Awake!**

FIGS & ROUGE ™☺
Candles: **Jasmine, Jasmine and
Sweet Geranium, Rose**

GREEN VALLEY TRADING CO. ™☺
All products are vegan

HOWAD LTD T/A INCOGNITO ™❶⊘✍
Incense Sticks

KOBASHI ™☺⊘✍👁✂1976
Misc: **Burner-Vapourisers**

LIZ EARLE ✍👁
Vital Oils Candles

NEAL'S YARD REMEDIES ⊘✍👁✂1998
Night Lights (White); Tall White China
Burners

NO COWS ☺❶ *Soya Wax Candles:* Tea
Lights (set of 6), Votive Candles

POTIONS AND POSSIBILITIES ⊘✍
Scented Candles: English Garden,
English Lavender, English Rose

PURPLE FLAME AROMATHERAPY ⊘✍
Aromatherapy Candles: All

SCENT BY NATURE ☺⊘✍✂1986
Incense & Resin: Pure Tree Resins

SHEARER CANDLES ⊘✍
Candles: All except church candles
marked as containing 10% beeswax.

SIMPLY SOAPS ™❶⊘✍👁✂2003
India; Love; Mesopotamia; Om

SKINCARE CAFE LTD ™☺
**Lemongrass candle; Ylang ylang
candle**

SUPERCOOK
Candles: All

**TISSERAND AROMATHERAPY
PRODUCTS** ™☺
Candles: **Citrus, Exotic Spice**

TREE-HARVEST ⊘✍
Incense: All; *Pure Plant Wax Candles:*
Pillar Candles, Scented Dinner Candles,
Scented Glass Pot Candles, Taper
Candles, Tea Lights, Unscented Dinner
Candles, with Essential Oils

CARPET PRODUCTS

ASTONISH 🎧 👁
Floor & Carpet Range: Carpet & Upholstery Shampoo, Instant Carpet & Upholstery Shampoo, Machine Carpet Shampoo

CLEANERS - GENERAL

ASTONISH 🎧 👁
Clean it Bam Multi Purpose Degreaser; Travelmate Germ Clear; *Bathroom Range:* Acrylic Cleaner, Bathroom Cleaner, Cream Cleaner - Orange Fresh, Cream Cleaner - Original, Cream Cleaner - w Bleach, Enamel Cleaner, Glass & Tile Cleaner, Shower Self Cleaner; *Germ Killers:* Anti Bacterial Cleanser, Mould & Mildew Remover; *Glass, Ceramic, Tile & Household Range:* Household Antibacterial Paste Cleaner, Orange Household Paste Cleaner, Window Cleaner; *Kitchen & Cookware Range:* Ceramic Hob Cleaner, Kitchen Cleaner, Oven & Cookware Cleaning Paste, Oxy Plus, Oxy Plus Gel, Stainless Steel Cleaner, Stainless Steel Cream Cleaner; *Special Cleaners:* Orange Power Multi-Surface, Silver Cleaner

AURO
Plant Soap Concentrate

BIO-D ™☺🚫🎧 👁🌿1988
Bathroom+ Shower Cleanser; Glass & Mirror Cleaner; Multi-Surface Cleaner; Ready- to- use Multi Purpose Cleaner; Ready-to-use Bathroom Cleaner

CELLANDE MIDLANDS 🚫🎧
Glass & Plastic Cleaner for Computers Spectacles etc

DRI-PAK LTD ☺🚫🎧🌿2000
Liquid Soda Crystal Spray; *Clean and Natural Cleaning Products:* Bicarbonate of Soda, Citric Acid, Household Borax, Limescale Remover Spray, White Vinegar

FOREVER LIVING PRODUCTS
Aloe MPD Detergent

GREEN PEOPLE CO. ™🚫🎧
Organic Multi-Surface Cleaner

HERBS HANDS HEALING LTD ™🚫🎧
Home & Kitchen Cleaner

JUNGLESALE LIMITED ™
Neem Bathroom Cleaner; Neem Household Cleaner

NATURAL ECO-TRADING LTD ™☺🎧👁
Earth Friendly Products: **Creamy Cleanser, Earth Enzymes, Everyday Stain & Odor Remover, Floor Kleener, Fruit & Vegetable Wash, Furniture Polish, Orange Mate Concentrate, Orange Mate RTU, Parsley Plus RTU, Shower Kleener,**

Toilet Bowl Cleaner, Window Kleener, Window Kleener (Lavender)

NATURAL HOUSE PRODUCTS LIMITED ™☺ ✔
Bathroom Spa; Nursery Spa; Salad Spa Fruit and Vegetable Wash; Surface Spa Multi-Surface Cleaner; Window Spa Glass and Mirror Cleaner

ORANGE BURST LIMITED ™☺
Pierre d'Argent

OSMO UK ⊘ ✔
Gard Clean Green Growth Remover; Liquid Wax Cleaner

SODASAN ™
All Purpose Cleaner; Bath and Shower Cleaner; Glass Cleaner; Lime Remover; Orange Universal Cleaner; Scouring Cream; Scouring Powder; Toilet Bowl Cleaner; Vinegar Cleaner

SOLARAY NUTRITIONAL SUPPLEMENTS
Earthaware All-Purpose Household Cleanser; Liquid Sparkle Spray Cleaner

SONETT OHG ™
All Purpose Cleanser; Bathroom Cleaner; Grease Dissolver; Scouring Liquid; Scouring Powder; Window Cleaner

THE CRUELTY FREE SHOP ™☺❶
All products are vegan

VINDOTCO UK LTD ™☺⊘ ✔
Really Works: De-Greaser Deodoriser, Super Concentrated Cleaner, Wild Apple Concentrated Cleaner

CLEANERS - INDUSTRIAL

VINDOTCO UK LTD ™☺⊘ ✔
Really Works: Graffiti Remover

DISHWASHER PRODUCTS

AQUADOS LTD ™☺
Dishwasher Powder: Aquados Pro Dishwash, Simply Dishwash Active, Simply Dishwash Citrus

ASTONISH ✔ ◉
Dishwashing Range: 2 in 1 Dishwasher Tablets, Limescale Appliance Remover, Rinse Aid, Super Concentrate Dishwasher Liquid

BIO-D ™☺⊘ ✔ ◉⅄ 1988
Dishwasher Powder; Dishwasher Rinse Aid

FAITH PRODUCTS LIMITED
™ ✔ ◉⅄ 1988
Dishwasher Gel 1 Ltr / 5 Ltr; Rinse Aid 500ml / 5 Ltr

SODASAN ™
Auto Dish Tabs; Automatic Dishwashing Powder

SONETT OHG ™
Dishwasher Detergent; Tablets For Dishwashers

DISINFECTANTS

ASTONISH 🌢 👁
Germ Killers: Antiseptic Disinfectant, Germ Clear Disinfectant

BIO-D ™☺🚫🌢👁✄ 1988
Natural Disinfectant

CAURNIE SOAPERIE ☺🚫🌢✄ 1976
DES Disinfectant

GAMA HEALTHCARE LIMITED ™☺🌢
Clinell: **Disinfectant Spray, Instant Hand Sanitiser, Universal Sanitising Wipes**

SONETT OHG ™
Surface Disinfectant

FABRIC CONDITIONERS

BIO-D ™☺🚫🌢👁✄ 1988
Fabric Conditioner

SONETT OHG ™
Fabric Softener

FLOOR PRODUCTS

ASTONISH 🌢 👁
Floor & Carpet Range: No Rinse Floor Cleaner, Non Slip Floor Polish, Wood Floor Cleaner

AURO
Floorcare

OSMO UK 🚫🌢
Wash & Care Floor Cleaner

FURNITURE & OTHER POLISHES

ASTONISH 🌢 👁
Furniture Care Range: Orange Oil Furniture Polish; *Special Cleaners:* Brass & Copper Cleaner

BIO-D ™☺🚫🌢👁✄ 1988
General Purpose Polish

GENERAL

FREERANGERS ™☺🌢
Accessories: **Pencil Case & Pencils**

NEVER TOO BUSY TO BE BEAUTIFUL ™🌢
Cocktail: **Clothes Scenter;** *Dear John:* **Clothes Scenter**

TISSERAND AROMATHERAPY PRODUCTS ™☺
Aroma Bowl and Warming Dish

HOME FURNISHINGS

ESSENTIALLY NATURAL ™
Lavender Neck Rescue; Luxury Comfort Cushion; Luxury Comfort Tube; Luxury Lavender Keyboard Rest; Wooden Soap Dish

NATURAL INSULATION
Roof Insulation: Isonat, Isovlas, Warmcel

NO COWS ☺❶
Organic Cotton Bath Sheet; Organic Cotton Bath Towel; Organic Cotton Bathrobe; Organic Cotton Flannel; Organic Cotton Hand Towel; Organic Cotton Towel Bale

THE ESSENTIAL OIL COMPANY ⊘ ✔ ◉
Thermotherapy - Microwaveable Heated Gifts: Beddy-Bear Bed Warmer, Henry Warmheart Teddy Bear, Hot-Bunny Bed Warmer

TISSERAND AROMATHERAPY PRODUCTS ™☺
Lavender Products: **Lavender Head Cooling Cushion, Lavender Wheat Cushion**

INSECT REPELLENTS

HOWAD LTD T/A INCOGNITO ™❶⊘✔
Anti-Mosquito Camouflage

PAINT BRUSHES - DIY

OSMO UK ⊘ ✔
Quality Brushes & Polishing Pad

PAINT, VARNISHES, WOODSTAINS,ETC

AURO
Thinner and Brush Cleaner; Wallpaper Adhesive; *Airfresh Paint:* White; *Chalk Paint:* White; *Coloured Natural Resin Wall Paint:* Matt - See Colour Chart; *Fillers:* Multi Filler, Wood Filler; *Gloss:* Coloured - See Colour Chart; *Lacquer:* Clear Gloss, Clear Matt; *Matt Silk:* Coloured - See Colour Chart; *Natural Resin Oil Professional Wall Paint:* Semi Matt - See Colour Chart, Semi Matt - White; *Natural Resin Wall Paint:* Matt - White; *Primers:* Hard Primer, Natural Metal Primer, Priming Oil, Special Primer, Wood Primer; *Radiator Paint:* White - Matt Finish; *Topcoats:* White Topcoat - Gloss, White Topcoat - Matt Silk, Woodstain Topcoat; *Undercoats:* White Undercoat

B&Q
Colours Range - Emulsions for Walls:
All; *Colours Range - Trim Paints for
Wood and Metal:* All Gloss and Satin

ECOS PAINTS ☺🚫 ✦
*Ecos Garden Spectrum Shed & Fence
Treatment:* All; *Exterior Woodstains:* All;
Interior Woodstain Varnishes: All;
Odourless Solvent-Free Organic Paints:
All

NUTSHELL NATURAL PAINTS
Wallpaper Paste; *Emulsion:* Super 2.5
litres, Super 5 litres

OSMO UK 🚫 ✦
Brush Cleaner & Thinner; Door Oil;
Paint-Remover; Top Oil; Wood Filler;
Wood Protector; Wood Reviver; *Exterior
Country Colour:* All; *Exterior One Coat
Only:* All; *Exterior Wood:* Clear Oil
Wood Finish, Fence & Garden Stain,
Wood Oils, Wood Stain & Preservation,
WR Base Coat; *Interior Hardwax Oil:*
For Floors, Special Floor Finish, White
Foundation; *Interior Wood Wax Finish:*
Clear Extra Thin, Opaque, Transparent;
Opaque Gloss Exterior Wood Stain: All

VINDOTCO UK LTD ™☺🚫 ✦
Really Works: **Adhesive Remover**

PHOTOGRAPHIC PAPERS

EPSON
HP Everyday Photo Paper in Semi Gloss;
Tri-fold Brochure Paper in Matte; *Digital
Photo Papers:* All

HP
Digital Photograph Paper: Everyday
Photo Paper Semi Gloss, Tri-fold
Brochure Paper Matte

TOILET PRODUCTS

ASTONISH ✦ 👁
Bathroom Range: Toilet Bowl Cleaner

BIO-D ™☺🚫 ✦ 👁⚘1988
Toilet Cleaner

HERBS HANDS HEALING LTD ™🚫 ✦
Bathroom Deep Cleaner

NEAL'S YARD REMEDIES 🚫 ✦ 👁⚘1998
Aromastone

SONETT OHG ™
Toilet Cleaner

WASHING POWDERS, STARCH ETC

AKAMUTI
Soapnuts

AQUADOS LTD ™☺
Simply Pure; *Washing Powder:*
Aquados Pro Bio, Aquados Pro Non Bio, Simply Active - Biological, Simply Sensitive - Non Biological

ASTONISH ◖ ☻
Travelmate Stain Clear; *Fabric & Laundry Range:* 2 in 1 Liquid Laundry Detergent, Colour Boosters, Crease Clear Starch, Fabric Freshener, Large Lint Remover, Limescale Prevention, Oxy Plus, Stain Bar, Stain Remover, Whites Booster

BIO-D ™☺⊘ ◖ ☻⅍1988
Dishwasher Powder; Laundry Liquid; Washing Powder

DRI-PAK LTD ☺⊘ ◖ ⅍2000
Soda Crystals; *Aqua Softna:* Limescale Preventer Laundry Powder, Limescale Preventer Laundry Tablets, Washing Machine Descaler; *Clean and Natural Cleaning Products:* Pure Liquid Soap (for laundry)

FAITH PRODUCTS LIMITED
™◖ ☻⅍1988
Laundry Liquid 1 Ltr / 5 Ltr

KITCHEN GARDEN
Detergent Free Laundry Disks

NATURAL ECO-TRADING LTD ™☺◖ ☻
Earth Friendly Products: **Baby Laundry Soap, Delicate Wash, ECOS Free & Clear, Ecos Laundry Powder, ECOS Lavender, ECOS Lemongrass, ECOS Magnolia & Lilies, Oxo Brite, Spray Starch, Zainz Laundry Pre-Wash**

NATURAL HOUSE PRODUCTS LIMITED ™☺◖
Organic Soap Flakes

SODASAN ™
Bleaching Additive; Clear Rinse; Comfort-Sensitiv Laundry Detergent; Compact Laundry Detergent; Liquid Laundry Detergent; Liquid Spot Remover Soap; Regenerating Salt; Soap Flakes; Soft Soap; Spot Remover Soap; Water Softener; Wool Detergent

SONETT OHG ™
Industrial Washing Booster; Industrial Washing Powder; Laundry Rinse/Decalcifier; Olive Washing Liquid; Starch Spray and Ironing Aid; Washing Liquid; Washing Liquid - Colour; Washing Powder

VINDOTCO UK LTD ™☺⊘ ◖
Really Works: **Oxygen Stain Remover, Pre Wash Dirt & Stain Remover**

WASHING-UP PRODUCTS

ASTONISH *✔ ☞*
Dishwashing Range: Tea Coffee & Stain Remover; *Kitchen & Cookware Range:* Pan Rack & Fryer Tablets, Scouring Pads

BIO-D ™☺◯ *✔ ☞⅄*1988
Washing Up Liquid

CAURNIE SOAPERIE ☺◯ *✔ ⅄*1976
Washup Liquid

FAITH PRODUCTS LIMITED
™*✔ ☞⅄*1988
Washing Up Liquid 1 Ltr / 5 Ltr

NATURAL ECO-TRADING LTD ™☺*✔ ☞*
Earth Friendly Products: **Dishmate Almond, Dishmate Apricot, Dishmate Grapefruit, Dishmate Lavender, Dishmate Pear, Wave, Wave Powder - Sachets, Wavejet**

NATURAL HOUSE PRODUCTS LIMITED ™☺*✔*
Organic Washing-up Liquid

SODASAN ™
Washing Up Liquid

SONETT OHG ™
Washing Up Liquid

VINDOTCO UK LTD ™☺◯*✔*
Really Works: **Sink & Drain Cleaner**

NOTES

■ **Adhesives** may be processed from hide, bones, fish or dairy products such as casein. Non-animal adhesives are based on starch, cellulose, natural rubbers, or inorganic substances based on silicone. The trend is towards using cheaper, synthetic materials.

■ **Banknotes** are produced from cotton fibre and linen rag, without the use of gelatine.

■ **Beds and mattresses** generally contain synthetic materials, such as acrylic, viscose, polyester, polypropylene, nylon or acetate. However, wool or other types of animal hair may be used in some mattresses.

■ **Pillows and duvets** are increasingly being made from cotton and polyester but some may be stuffed with feathers.

■ **Ceramics, glass, pottery:** Bone china goods contain around 50% bone ash. Porcelain, *plain* sanitary items (toilets, cisterns, sinks, etc) and *plain* earthenware glazed mugs (the glazes used are inorganic pigments made from minerals) appear to be animal-free. However, if a motif is added, it may be fixed with animal-derived glues. Glass consists of silica (in the form of sand), sodium oxide, calcium oxide, magnesium oxide and aluminium oxide, and appears to be animal-free.

■ **Envelope adhesives** are usually animal-free.

■ **Fabric dyes** for home use are usually synthetic and are often tested on animals. 'Natural' dyes may contain animal substances, such as cochineal / carmine.

■ **Floor coverings** made from PVC may be manufactured using possibly animal-derived stearates as stabilisers and stearic acid as a lubricant during certain production processes.

■ **Furniture** may contain synthetic or plant-based fibres (e.g. nylon, acrylic, polyester, cotton, hemp) or animal-derived materials, including leather, suede, wool, animal hair (especially horse) or feathers.

■ **Incense sticks** may contain gelatine or another animal substance as a binder.

■ **Match heads** may contain gelatine, which is used as a binder.

■ **Paint** may contain casein or shellac and the ingredients may have been animal-tested.

■ **Paper** is usually sized (enhances the resistance of paper to liquid penetration and provides surface strength, stiffness and a glaze to the finished sheet) with starch derived from maize, wheat, potatoes or rice, but gelatine is still used for high-grade paper products.

■ **Casein** is sometimes used as a binder in high quality food board and art papers. Some very specialist grades may contain chitin / chitosan.

■ **Postage stamps:** the gum on British stamps is animal-free, consisting of polyvinyl alcohol (petroleum based) and dextrin (from starch).

■ **Rubber:** Natural rubber is made from latex (sap obtained from rubber trees) combined with other materials, including the following which could be animal-derived: carbon black (E153), glycerol (E422), salts of fatty acids (E470), stearic acid (E570), calcium stearate (E572). Synthetic rubbers are made from oil and a combination of chemicals.

■ **Rubber gloves** may involve the use of milk casein as a processing aid in the latex.

■ **Water filters** contain charcoal, usually vegetable-based.

ANIMAL CARE

FOOD & FOOD SUPPLEMENTS

HIGHER NATURE PLC ™⊘ *i*
Almost Human® SuperDog MSM;
Almost Human® SuperDog
Ultimate Nutrition; Almost Human®
SuperPet Organic 3:6:9 Oil

**INTERNATIONAL PARTNERSHIP LTD
(SEAGREENS DIVISION)** ™⊙⊘
Seagreens- Mixed Granules: **Equine
Granules, Pet Granules**

SIMPLE SYSTEM LTD ™
Blue Bag Grass Pellets; Eclipse
Recovery; Endurocomplete; Green
Gold; Instant Linseed; Just Grass;
Justamint; Luciebix; Luciecobs;
Lucienuts; Luciestalks; Lunar Eclipse;
Metaslim; Organic Cider vinegar;
Partial Eclipse; Purabeet; PuraMint
Pellets; Pure Garlic Flakes; Pure
Garlic Powder; Pure Ocean
Seaweed; Pure organic Salt Bucket;
Red Bag Grass Pellets; RuffStuff;
Sundried Lucerne Bales; Timothy
Cobs; Total Eclipse; Traditional
Brewers Yeast

VEGEPET
Vegecat; Vegecat Kibble Mix; Vegecat
pH; Vegedog; Vegekit pH

YARRAH ORGANIC PET FOOD ™⊘✿
Multi Dog Biscuits; Organic
Vegetarian Dog Food; Vegetarian
Chunks With Vegetables;
Vegetarian Dog Biscuits; Vegetarian
Duo Snacks

HEALTH & CARE PRODUCTS

FOREVER LIVING PRODUCTS
Veterinary Aloe Spray

JR LIGGETT ☺ *i* 👁
Foaming Face & Body Wash: Lemon &
Lime, Unscented, Western Slope, White
Sage; *Shampoo:* My Dog Fergie's
Shampoo

JUNGLESALE LIMITED ™
Neem Horse Shampoo; Neem Pet
Shampoo; Pet Insect Spray; Stable
Cleaner

MASON'S PRODUCTS ☺⊘ *i* ⊰1976
Dog Oil for Massaging (For Dogs Horses
& Humans)

NATURAL ECO-TRADING LTD
™☺ *i* 👁
Earth Friendly Products: **Natumate**

RED STAR NATURAL LIQUID SOAPS
™☺⊘ *i* 👁⊰1980
Natural Hard Bar Dog Shampoo 125g:
**Minty Muttley, Mud Puppy, Sexy
Rexy;** *Natural Hard Bar Horse Shampoo
125g:* **Pony Polish;** *Natural Liquid Dog
Shampoo 500ml:* **Minty Muttley, Mud**

Puppy, Sexy Rexy; *Natural Liquid Horse Shampoo 1000ml:* **Pony Polish**

SCENT BY NATURE ☺ ⊘ ✦ ⚘ 1986
Bioforce Flower Remedies: Flower Remedies for Animals

SOLARAY NUTRITIONAL SUPPLEMENTS
Organimals: Grooming Spray For Dogs, Shampoo For Dogs

THE HUMANE RESEARCH TRUST ⊘ ✦
Tea Tree Coat Conditioner for Dogs & Cats; *Assisi Homeopathic Remedies for Pets:* Euphrasia Eye Drops, Five Flower Remedy, Sore Paws Ointment, Verbascum Ear Drops; *Natural Drops:* Ear, Eye; *Natural Grooming Lotions:* Cats, Dogs, Small Animals; *Shampoos:* Aromatic for Dogs, Tea Tree for Dogs & Cats

NOTES

The inclusion of an 'Animal Care' section should not be construed as indicating support for the pet industry or ownership of pet (companion) animals. Pets exist solely for human gain — in the case of the pet trade: financial; in the case of pet owners: pleasure — and their freedom is necessarily restricted. In the quest for the 'perfect' pet, breeds of animals including dogs, cats, birds and fish have, through genetic manipulation, been created with 'aesthetically-pleasing' deformities. Many animal-free shoppers find pet ownership incompatible with their animal rights philosophy and those who find themselves caring for animals often do so because tens of thousands of domestic animals are unwanted and would otherwise be destroyed.

For our fact sheet on feeding your cat or dog a vegan diet, see www.vegansociety.com or contact the Vegan Society office for a copy.

GARDEN & LEISURE

ARTS & CRAFTS

DALER-ROWNEY LTD ⊘ ✔

Artist Oil Colours: All except Ivory Black & Blue Black; *Artists' Brushes:* Cryla, Dalon, Series 260 270 & 280; *Cryla:* All except Ivory Black; *Designer's Gouache:* All except Neutral Grey 2, Paynes Grey, Lamp Black, Cool Grey 1,2,3 & Warm Grey 1,2,3; *F.W. Artist Inks:* All; *Georgian Oil Colours:* All except Ivory Black, Prussian Green & Coeruleum Hue; *Painting Surfaces & Equipment:* All except Saunders Waterford, Langton & Bockingford Papers, Canvas Panels & Rabbit Skin Size; *Pearlescent Liquid Acrylic Inks:* All; *Rowney Block Printing Colours (Water Based & Oil Based):* All; *System 3 Colours:* All except Raw Sienna

WINSOR & NEWTON ⊘ ✔

Artisan Water Mixable Oil Colour: All except Ivory Black; *Artists' Acrylic Colour:* All except Ivory Black, Payne's Grey; *Artists' Oil Colour:* All except Blue Black, Carmine, Ivory Black; *Artists' Soft Pastels:* All; *Artists' Oilbar:* All except Ivory Black, Payne's Gray; *Artists' Pigment (Dry Ground):* All except Ivory Black, Carmine; *Brushes:* Artisan Water Mixable Oil Colour Brushes, Cotman, Galeria, Monarch, Special Value Brushes: Synthetic, University; *Calligraphy Inks:* All; *Cotman Water Colour:* All except Viridian Hue, Raw Umber, Ivory Black; *Designers Gouache:* All except Ivory Black, Raw Sienna, Winsor Green, Spectrum Yellow, Intense Blue, Sky Blue, Purple Lake, Prussian Blue, Linden Green, Grenadine, Flame Red, Burnt Umber, Bengal Rose, Primary Blue, Lamp Black, Spectrum Violet; *Galeria Flow Formula Acrylic Colour:* All except Ivory Black, Payne's Grey; *Griffin Alkyd Fast Drying Oil Colour:* All except Ivory Black; *Poster Paint:* All; *Water Colour Mediums:* All except Ox Gall, Lifting Preparation; *Water Colour Papers:* Bockingford; *Winton Oil Colour:* All except Ivory Black, Raw Umber

CLEANERS - OUTDOOR

ASTONISH ✔ ☞

Car Care Range: All Weather Screen Wash, Anti Fog Glass Clear, Back to Black, Black Shine Restorer, Carpet & Upholstery Trigger (Car), Crystal Clear Wash & Wax 2 in 1, Engine Degreaser, Engine Degreaser Trigger, Fabric Deodoriser Trigger (Car), Fabric Fresh, Glass Clear, Ice Guard, Interior Cleaner, Mini Duster, Pre-Wash Car Treatment, Tar and Insect Remover, Travel Mate Range, Travelmate Glass Clear, Vinyl Trim & Dashboard Cleaner, Wash & Wax, Watermate, Wheel Cleaner

VINDOTCO UK LTD ™☺⊘ ✔

Really Works: **Block Paving Cleaner & Restorer**

GARDENING & COMPOST PRODUCTS

FERTILE FIBRE ™
Vegrow Organic: **Growbag, Multipurpose Compost, Potting Compost, Seed Compost, Special Mix range**

INTERNATIONAL PARTNERSHIP LTD (SEAGREENS DIVISION) ™☺⊘
Seagreens: **Agricultural Granules, Ascophyllum Granules, Garden Granules, Nutri granules**

TAMAR ORGANICS ⊘
Seaweed Extract Liquid Feed; *Fertiliser:* Cumulus 5-5-5, Cumulus K, Cumulus NK, Rock Phosphate, Seaweed Meal

GLUES, STICKY TAPE, ETC

VEGAN STORE ™☺❶⊘⚭
Weldbond: **Multi Purpose Glue**

SMOKING PRODUCTS

RIZLA ☺
Filter Tips; *Papers:* King Size Blue, King Size Red, King Size Slim Blue, King Size Slim Silver, Regular Blue, Regular Green, Regular Red, Regular Silver

SWEDISH MATCH
All Snus Products

NOTES

■ **Musical instruments:** All modern guitar strings are made from metal or nylon. Guitar picks are now made of plastic. The heads of most modern percussion instruments are non-animal 'skin'. World or traditional percussion instruments may be made with animal skins. Some Remo heads are animal-free.

■ **Photographic film and papers** used in traditional photography contain gelatine. However, digital cameras are now as affordable as traditional cameras and several types of paper available for printing digital photographs are animal-free.

■ **Tattoo inks** may contain animal derived ingredients. The Vegan Society has some information on tattoo inks that are free of animal products. Contact the Vegan Society office for more details.

■ **Tennis balls** may contain wool.

■ **Vegan-organic (veganic) or stockfree gardening** is becoming more and more popular; see USEFUL ADDRESSES page 59 for details of the Vegan Organic Network.

■ **Video cassette / audio tapes and CDs / DVDs** appear to be animal-free.

SUPERMARKETS

FOOD

BREADS, ROLLS, PIZZA BASES ETC
Champion: Goldenfries; *Crazy Crocadile:*
Banana Milkshake Mix; *Romano:* Ciabatta
Classic, Ciabatta Rolls; *Stone Mill:* Seed
Top Granary Rolls; *Village Bakery:* White
Floured Baps, Wholemeal Rolls Topped
with Bran & Oats

BREAKFAST FOODS
Harvest Morn: Fruit and Fibre

CAKES & CAKE MIXES
Village Bakery: Ginger Parkins, Sultana
Scones

CONFECTIONERY & SWEET SNACKS
Dominion: Mint imperials; *Stone mill:*
Apple Pie, Fruit loaf

COOKING AIDS - SWEET
Be Light: Sweetener Granules

DESSERTS
Village Bakery: Rhubarb Pie

'ICE CREAMS', SORBETS ETC
Macey's: Ice lollies

PICKLES, SAUCES, VINEGARS ETC
Bramwells: Chunky apple sauce,
Cranberry sauce; *Colway:* Extra hot
summer ketchup; *Newlands:* Piccalilli;
Specially selected: Apple and pear sauce,
Country Mix Sauce, Lightly salted hand
cooked chips, Three apple sauce;

Worldwide Cook in Sauces: Black Bean,
Sweet and Sour

SAVOURIES - CANNED/BOTTLED
Organic: Baked Beans

SAVOURIES - CHILLED/FRESH
The Little Salad Bar: Mediterranean

SAVOURIES - FROZEN
Champion: Battered Onion Rings, Roast
potatoes, Steak cut chips, Three way
cook oven chips; *Four seasons:* Beer
battered onion rings, Cajun natural
battered onion rings

SNACKS - SAVOURY
Snackrite: Dry Roast Peanuts; *Specially
selected:* Sea salt and black pepper
hand cooked chips

SOUPS
Soupreme: Minestrone chilled soup,
Tomato and red pepper fresh soup

SPREADS - SWEET
Grandessa: Apricot Conserve, Blackcurrant
Conserve, Blood Orange Contemporary
Marmalades, Fine cut lime marmalade,
Mandarin Contemporay Marmalades,
Pink Grapefruit Contemporay
Marmalades, Raspberry Conserve,
Sicilian lemon contemporay marmalade,
Strawberry Conserve, Strawberry High
Fruit Spread, Thick Cut Grapefruit
Marmalade, Thick Cut Orange
Marmalade, Thin Cut Lime Marmalade;
Ouventure: Rhubarb Conserve with
Vanilla Flavouring

DRINK

ALCOPOPS
Tamova: Purpleberry Vodka Mixer

SOFT
Clear Sensation: Red Apple Flavoured Still Water; *Del rivo:* Apple/raspberry drink, Blackcurrant nector vit-juice drink, GC Tropical Juice Drink, Orange juice drink; *Hyberry:* Blackcurrant High Juice, Tropical High Juice; *Moreton Hills:* Cranberry & Raspberry Sparkling Flavoured Water, Peach Flavoured Sparkling Spring Water; *Solesta Burst Pouch Packs:* Apple, Blackcurrant, Orange; *Sunsqueeze:* Strawberry Aqua Shots; *Topstar:* Iron Brew, Iron Brew Diet; *Westdales:* American Ginger Ale, Diet Tonic Water

SPIRITS & APÉRITIFS
Highland Earl: Whisky; *St Amandus:* Liebfraumilch

FOOD

BISCUITS

Bourbon Creams; Fruit Shortcake Biscuits; Ginger Nuts; Morning Coffee Biscuits; Oatmeal biscuits; Rich Tea Biscuits

BREADS, ROLLS, PIZZA BASES ETC

10 Flour Tortillas; 6 Flour Tortillas; Bakers Gold Tinned Open Top White Thick 800g; Bakers Gold Tinned Open Top Wholemeal Thick 800g; Big loaf medium white 800g; Big loaf Thick white 800g; Chapatis; Crumpets; Danish soft & light thick cut white bread 400g; Fruit Malt Loaf; Garlic and Rosemerry focaccia mix; Hovis Medium Sliced Wheatgerm Bread; Malted bread 800g; Medium sliced brown bread 800g; Medium sliced white bread 800g; Medium Wholemeal sliced bread 800g; Multigrain loaf bread mix; Pain Rustique Twin Pack; Pan bread medium brown 800g; Pan bread white medium 800g; Part baked white baguettes; Pizza base mix; Sandwich Baguette Granary; Scottish batch sliced white bread 800g; Stonebaked garlic bread; Stonebaked garlic pizza bread; Thick sliced white bread 800g; Traditional French Baguette; White loaf bread mix; White Muffins; *Bakers Gold Thick Sliced Loaf:* Wholemeal; *Big Loaf:* Medium White, Thick White; *Bread Mixes:* Garlic & Rosemary Foccacia, Multigrain Loaf, Pizza Base, White Loaf; *Brown Bread:* Granary Malted, Smartprice Medium Sliced; *Extra Special:* Black Pepper Ladder Bread; *Fresh For a Week Medium Sliced Bread:* White, Wholemeal; *Good For You Bagels:* Cinnamon & Raisin, Onion, Plain, Sesame Seed; *Pitta Bread:* Smartprice; *Pitta Breads:* Garlic, White, Wholemeal; *Smartprice:* 12 White finger rolls, 12 White rolls; *White Bread:* Extra Thick Sliced, Medium Sliced (Square Cut), Organic Sliced, Scottish Batch Sliced, Smartprice Medium Sliced, Smartprice Thick Sliced, Thick Sliced (Square Cut), Wholesome Medium, Wholesome Thick; *Wholemeal Bread:* Medium Sliced (Square Cut), Organic Sliced, Thick Sliced (Square Cut)

BREAKFAST FOODS

55% fruit muesli 500g; Apricot Wheats; Bran Flakes; Cinnamon apple oats sensations; Cornflakes; Cranberry wheats; Frosted flakes 500g; High bran; Organic Bran Flakes; Organic Corn Flakes; Ready Oats; Simply porridge 10x27g; Sultana Bran; *Muesli:* Good For You Fruit, Wholewheat; *Smartprice:* Bran Flakes, Corn Flakes, Crispy Rice Cereal

'BURGERS', 'SAUSAGES', 'MEAT' SLICES ETC

Apple and Herb Stuffing Mix; Apricot and orange stuffing mix; Cranberries in port stuffing mix; Meat Free Savoury Mince; Parsley lemon and thyme stuffing mix; Sage and onion stuffing mix

CAKES & CAKE MIXES
Assorted Jam Tarts; Chocolate sponge mix; Fairy cake mix; Muffin mix; Ready to roll icing; Ready to roll white icing; *Cake Mixes:* American Style Banana Muffin, American Style Blueberry Muffin, American Style Double Choc Chunk Muffin, Chocolate Sponge, Fairy Cakes; *Smartprice:* 6 Apple Pies, 6 Raspberry Flavour Tarts

CONFECTIONERY & SWEET SNACKS
Barley Sugar; Blackcurrant drops; Lemon bon bons; Lemon drops; Peppermint chewing gum; Sherbert fruit cocktails; Spearmint chewing gum; *Smartprice:* Lollipops, Mint Humbugs, Mintbugs

COOKING AIDS - SAVOURY
Stuffing Mix: Apple & Herb, Apricot & Orange, Parsley Lemon & Thyme, Sage & Onion, Smartprice Sage & Onion

COOKING AIDS - SWEET
Crumble Topping; Golden marzipan; White marzipan; *Dessert Sauce:* Extra Special Raspberry & Drambuie; *Extra Special Dessert Sauce:* Orange & Cointreau; *Mincemeat:* Almond and Amaretto, Pecan Walnut and Brandy; *Ready to Roll Icing:* Standard, White; *Smartprice:* Golden marzipan

CRACKERS, CRISPBREADS ETC
Asda Breadsticks; Black Pepper Bread Sticks; Blackpepper Breadsticks; Breadsticks; Butter Puffs; Cracker selection; Cream Crackers; Melba toast; Rye crispbread; Spicy Ready to Eat Pappadums; Water biscuits; *Ready to Eat Pappadums:* Plain

DESSERTS
6 Brandy Snap Baskets; Raspberry Topping; *Vegetarian Jelly Crystals:* Lemon, Orange, Strawberry

DIPS & DRESSINGS
Chargrilled Red pepper Houmous; Creamy French Dressing; Fresh Houmous; Fresh Salsa Dip; Houmous; Sun dried tomato pasta salad; Tomato,Pepper and chipotle chilli salsa; *Chilled:* Salsa Dip; *Dressings:* French; *Good for you:* Pitta and houmous snack pack; *Good for You Dressings:* Oil Free Vinaigrette, Tomato & Herb; *Houmous:* Fresh; *Salsa:* Bean

GRAVIES & STOCKS
10 vegetable stock cubes; Onion Gravy; Onion Gravy Granules; Vegetarian Gravy Granules

'ICE CREAMS', SORBETS ETC
Lollies: Kids Rocket, Orange Juice; *No Added Sugar Lollies:* Blackcurrant Flavoured, Kids, Lemon Flavoured, Orange Flavoured

PASTRY
36 Vol Au Vents; Shortcrust Mix; Smartprice Shortcrust Mix; Puff

PICKLES, SAUCES, VINEGARS ETC
Apple Sauce; Baby Gherkins in Sweet & Sour Vinegar; Balsamic mustard;

Barbecue ketchup; Blackbean cooking sauce; Brown Sauce; Brown sauce squeezy; Cashew nut stirfry sauce; Chop suey sauce; Chow mein sauce; Cider Vinegar; Coarse grain mustard; Cranberry and onion glaze; Cranberry sauce; Crinkle Cut Beetroot; Dijon mustard smooth and hot; Distilled Malt Vinegar; English mustard; French Mustard Mild & Distinctive; French Mustard Mild and Distinctive; Garlic and rosemerry glaze; Garlic Mustard; Goan curry sauce; Green thai curry sauce cooking sauce; Hamburger Relish; Hot & Spicy Chilli Pickled Onions; Jalfrezi cooking sauce; Kung pao style fry sauce; Lemon and ginger glaze; Lemon and ginger stir fry sauce; Madras cooking sauce; Malt Vinegar; Medium curry paste; Mild curry paste; Mint jelly; Mint sauce; Mixed pickle; Mustard piccalilli; Onion chuntey; Onion Chutney; Piccalilli; Pimento stuffed olives; Red cabbage; Red thai curry cooking sauce; Redcurrant Jelly; Rogan josh cooking sauce; Sichaun stir fry sauce; Sliced black olives; Smartprice Malt Vinegar; Soy and garlic stir fry sauce; Spiced fruit chutney; Spicy tomato pasta sauce; Squeezy american mustard; Sweet and sour cooking sauce; Sweet and sour with extra pineapple cooking sauce; Sweet chilli sauce fry sauce; Sweet harvest pickle; Sweet piccalilli; Sweetcorn relish; Tangy Sandwich Spread; Teriyaki stir fry sauce; Tikka Flavoured Pickled Onions; Tomato and herb cooking sauce; Tomato chutney; Whole black olives; Whole

green olives; Wholegrain Balsamic Mustard; Yellow thai sauce; *Beetroot:* Baby in Sweet Vinegar, Crinkle Cut in Sweet Vinegar, Sliced in Malt Vinegar; *Condiments:* Bramley Apple Sauce, Cranberry Sauce, Extra Special Cumberland Sauce, Extra Special Fresh Mint Jelly, Mint Sauce; *Cooking Sauces:* Black Bean, Goan Curry, Good for You Sweet & Sour, Mediterranean Tomato, Rogan Josh, Sweet & Sour, Sweet & Sour w Extra Pineapple, Vindaloo; *Curry Paste:* Medium, Mild; *Deli:* Mini Gherkins; *Extra Special:* Mango Chutney; *Glazes:* Cranberry & Onion, Garlic & Rosemary, Lemon & Ginger; *Good for you:* Sweet and sour cooking sauce, Sweet and sour sauce, Sweet and sour stir fry sauce; *Mustard:* Coarse Grain Hot & Crunchy, Dijon Smooth & Hot, English; *Organic Cooking Sauces:* Sweet & Sour, Tomato & Herb; *Packet Casserole Sauce Mixes for Cooking:* Beef in Ale, Sausage; *Pasta Sauces:* Fresh Napoletana, Napoletana, Original Bolognese, Smartprice Bolognese, Spicy Tomato, Sundried Tomato, Tomato & Chunky Vegetable, Tomato & Garlic, Tomato & Mushroom; *Piccalilli:* Sweet; *Pickle:* Brinjal, Extra Special Lime, Mixed; *Sauces:* Barbecue, Barbeque Ketchup, Brown, Smartprice Tomato Ketchup, Smartprice Tomato Ketchup Squeezy, Squeezy Brown, Sticky BBQ, Texan Style BBQ, Tomato Ketchup, Tomato Ketchup Squeezy, Yellow Bean & Cashew Nut; *Smartprice:* Sliced Beetroot in Malt Vinegar, Tomato ketchup, Tomato sauce Squeezy; *Stir*

Fry Sauces: Garlic & Chilli, Reduced Fat Sweet & Sour; *Vinegar:* Red Wine, White Wine

PIES & PASTIES
Smartprice: 2 Apple Pies

SAVOURIES - CANNED/BOTTLED
Baked Beans in Tomato Sauce; Bombay Potato; Mixed Bean Salad; Mixed beans in tomato sauce; Reduced sugar and salt Baked beans in tomato sauce; Tomato & Chilli Pizza Topper; Vegetable Balti; Vegetarian spaghetti bolognese; *Deli:* Pease Pudding; *Healthy Choice:* Chick Pea Dahl; *Smartprice:* Baked Beans, Baked Beans in Tomato Sauce, Spaghetti, Spaghetti in Tomato Sauce, Spaghetti Loops, Spaghetti loops in tomato sauce, Vegetable Curry; *Spaghetti:* Loops In Tomato Sauce

SAVOURIES - CHILLED/FRESH
Aloo Potato; Beetroot Salad; Cous Cous with vegatables; Italian style pasta salad; Marinated Corn on the Cob Chunks; Marinated mixed olives; Mini Onion Bhajis; Mixed Bean salad; Mixed Vegetable & Mushroom; Onion Bhajis; Organic Golden Vegetable Rice; Potato Wedges w Olive Oil & Rock Salt; Potato Wedges w Parsley & Oil; Thai Curry Kit Prepack; Tomato Pakora; Vegetable Bhajis; Vegetable Pakora; Vegetable Rice Salad; Vegetable Samosas; Vegetable Spring Rolls; *Aloo:* Mushroom; *Bhajis:* 12 Mini Onion, 6 Onion, Mini Onion, Mini Vegetable; *Extra Special:* Ratatouille; *Good for You:*

Mediterranean Cous Cous, Pasta & Sundried Tomato Salad, Roasted Red Pepper Arrabiata, Spanish Style Potatoes, Spiced Rice Salad, Sun Dried Tomato Pasta Salad, Tex Mex Rice, Vegetable Balti & Pilau Rice, Vegetables w Balsamic Dressing; *Pakora:* Achari, Broccoli, Mixed Vegetable, Onion; *Spring Rolls:* Mini Vegetable

SAVOURIES - DRIED
Fajita Dinner Kit; Tomato and basil pasta in sauce; *Instant Noodle Snacks:* Good for You Chicken Chow Mein Flavour, Good for You Mediterranean Tomato Flavour, Paprika Chicken Flavour, Smartprice Beef & Tomato Flavour, Smartprice Chicken & Mushroom Flavour, Smartprice Spicy Curry Flavour, Spicy Curry Flavour; *Instant Pasta Break Snacks:* Tomato & Herb; *Smartprice:* Instant mash potato

SAVOURIES - FROZEN
Garlic & Rosemary Roast Potatoes; Garlic Mushrooms; Hot & Spicy Onion Rings; Micro Chips; Nut Cutlet; Onion Bhaji & Vegetable Samosa Pack; Onion bhajis; Oriental Vegetable Sir Fry; Potato Croquettes; Potato Waffles; Vegetable Samosas; *3 Way Cook Chips:* Straight Cut; *Frying Chips:* Crinkle Cut, Smartprice Straight Cut, Steak Cut; *Good for You:* Potato Wedges, Roast Potatoes, Straight Cut Oven Chips; *Oven Chips:* American Fries, Good For You Straight Cut, Steak Cut, Straight Cut

SNACKS - SAVOURY

Barbecue beef Flavour instant noodles; Dry Roasted Peanuts; Mediterranaen style tomato cous cous; Paprika chicken flavour instant noodles; Poppadums; Ready Salted Crisps; Spicy curry flavour noodle snack; Tomato and herb pasta break; Vegatable Samosa; *Bhajis:* 12 mini onion bhaji, 12 Onion bhaji; *Extra Special:* Handcooked Crisps w Seasalt; *Smartprice:* Lightly Salted Tortilla Chips, Ready Salted Crisps; *Tortilla Chips:* Lightly Salted Round, Regular

SOUPS

Vegetable; *Good for you:* Roasted red pepper and bean soup, Spicy lentil and vegetable soup

SOYA AND OTHER 'MILKS'

Soya; Soya sweetened with Apple juice; Soya unsweetened

SPICES

Barbecue style wedge and veg seasoning; Cajun seasoning; Chicken seasoning; Garlic and herb seasoning; Garlic bread seasoning; Italian seasoning; Pilau rice seasoning; Southern fried style wedge and veg seasoning; Steak seasoning

SPREADS - SAVOURY

Yeast Extract; *Extra Special:* Tapenade Roasted Red Pepper & Tomato

SPREADS - SWEET

Apricot jam; Blackcurrant Jam; Bramble Jelly; Continental apricot conserve; Continental blackcurrant conserve; Continental raspberry conserve; Fine cut lime shred marmalade; Fine cut orange shred marmalade; Ginger preserve; Pink grapefruit marmalade; Raspberry jam; Seedless raspberry jam; Shredless orange marmalade; Strawberry jam; *Extra special:* Apricot jam, Blackberry jam, Blackcurrant Jam, Dark thick cut marmalade, Fruits of the forest jam, Kiwi and gooseberry, Raspberry jam, Strawberry jam, Three fruit marmalade; *Jam:* Apricot, Blackcurrant, Organic Strawberry, Seedless Raspberry, Smartprice Mixed Fruit, Smartprice Strawberry, Strawberry; *Jelly:* Bramble; *Marmalade:* Extra Special Pink Grapefruit, Fine Cut Lime Shred, Fine Cut Orange (25% Less Sugar), Fine Cut Orange Shred, Organic Orange, Shredless Orange, Smartprice Orange, Thick Cut Orange; *Preserve:* Ginger; *Reduced sugar:* Apricot jam, Blackcurrant Jam, Raspberry jam; *Smartprice:* Mixed fruit jam, Strawberry jam

DRINK

BEERS

Lager: Belgian, French, German, Shandi

'HOT'

Drinking Chocolate; Fairtrade Drinking Chocholate

SOFT

Apple, Pear and Blackberry juice drink (No added sugar); Bitter Lemon; Blue Charge Energy Drink; Blue Charge Energy Drink Diet; Blue Charge Energy Drink Diet Cranberry; Cranberry and Blueberry juice drink with Echhinacea; Cranberry Drink; Cranberry juice drink; Diet Iron Brew; Diet Lemonade; Dry Ginger Ale; Ginger Ale; Grape Apple & Raspberry; Iron Brew; Just Cola; Just Cola with Vanilla; Just Diet Cola; Just Diet Cola with Citrus; Kids Lemonade; Kids Sugar Free Totally Bubbly Orangeade; Lemonade; Lemonade juice drink; Orange & Grapefruit; Pear and Blackcurrant juice drink; Soda Water; Traditional Style Cream Soda; *Cordial:* Blackcurrant, Elderflower & Lemon, Peppermint; *Flavoured Spring Water:* Cranberry with Natural Extracts of Ginger & Lemongrass, Tangerine & Lime w Natural Extracts of Guarana & Ginseng; *Flavoured Spring Water Drink - Still:* Cranberry, Mango & Guava, Raspberry w Green Tea Extract, Sicilian Lemon; *Flavoured Water:* Grapefruit & Mandarin, Strawberry & Vanilla; *Fruit Crush:* Berry (No Added Sugar), Citrus, Summer, Tropical; *Fruit Juice Drink:* Cranberry & Raspberry; *High Juice:* Apple Squash, Blackcurrant, Cranberry & Apple, Florida Orange, Summerfruits Squash, Tropical Squash, White Grape & Peach Squash; *Indian Tonic Water:* Low Calorie, Standard, Twist Lemon Flavour; *Juice Drink (w Added Vitamins ACE & Calcium):* Orange, Tropical; *Kids Chilled No Added Sugar Juice Drink:*

Apple Pear & Blackberry, Orange Pineapple & Banana; *Kids No Added Sugar Juice Drink:* Apple & Blackcurrant, Cherry Berry, Orange; *Kids Sugar Free Totally Bubbly:* Appleade, Cherryade, Lemonade, Limeade; *Low Calorie:* Bitter Lemon, Ginger Ale; *Low Calorie Indian Tonic Water:* Twist Lemon Flavour, Twist Lime Flavour; *No Added Sugar Crush:* Apple & Blackcurrant, Citrus Berries, Orange & Pineapple; *No Added Sugar Flavoured Spring Water:* Apple & Mango, Blackberry & Elderflower, Calm Lemon & Vanilla, Lemon & Lime; *No Added Sugar Fruit & Barley Juice Drink:* Orange, Peach & Apricot; *No Added Sugar Fruit Juice Drink:* Cranberry; *No Added Sugar High Juice:* Apple & Blackcurrant Squash, Apple & Strawberry Squash; *No Added Sugar Juice Drink:* Apple & Blackcurrant & Barley, Pink Grapefruit & Barley, Summerfruits (Added Vits ACE & Calcium); *No Added Sugar Squash:* Apple, Apple & Blackcurrant, Blackcurrant, Forest Fruits, Lemon & Lime, Orange, Orange & Pineapple, Smartprice Apple & Blackcurrant, Strawberry, Strawberry Fruit; *Smartprice:* Tonic Water; *Smoothies:* Orange Mango & Banana, Pineapple Banana & Pear, Strawberry Banana & Guava; *Spring Water Drink:* Peach Flavour (No Added Sugar); *Squash:* Apple & Blackcurrant, Lemon & Lime, Lime Cordial, Orange & Pineapple, Orange (10% Fruit); *Traditional Style:* Dandelion & Burdock, Diet Lemonade, Ginger Beer, Lager Shandy, Lemonade

SPIRITS & APÉRITIFS

Apple & guava; Blended scotch whisky; Bourbon (Old Sam); Brandy; Coconut rum; Cognac; Dandelion & Burdock; Dark rum; French Brandy; Gin; Islay malt whisky; Napoleon French Brandy; Old kilkenny Irish whiskey; Peach Schnapps; Raspberry & vanilla; Scotch whiskey 8yrs; Single highland malt whisky; Sparkling perry; Speyside malt whisky; Tropical twist; Vodka; Vodka (43% best); Whisky; White rum; *Fortified British Wine:* Medium, Rich Cream; *Fortified Wine:* Finest reserve port; *Smartprice:* Whisky

WINES - RED

Californain red; Californain reserve zinfadel; Californain zinfadel; Chanti; Chateauneuf de pape; Cotes de rhone; Cotes de rhone villages; Marvelli extra dry; Marvelli rosso; Minervois; Montepulciano d'abruzzo; Red wine; Sicilain red; Syrah; Valpolicella; *Argentinian:* Malbec, Malbec Reserve, Red Select Blend, Red Wine; *Bulgarian:* Cabernet suavignon; *French:* Beaujolais, Chateauneuf Du Pape Red Wine, Claret, Cotes Du Rhone Villages, Minervois, Reserve Claret; *Italian:* Chianti; *South African Cape:* Merlot, Pinotage, Red; *USA Californian:* Red Wine, Reserve Zinfandel, Sweet Red, Zinfandel

WINES - ROSÉ

Californain rose; Rose d'anjou; *Australian:* Medium Rose; *USA Califorian:* Rose

WINES - SPARKLING

Californian reserve chardonnay; Californian white wine; Cava Mas miralda; Cava Medium dry mas miralda; Cava rosada mas miralda; Champagne rose; Muscadet; Orvieto abbocatto; Sancerre vielles vignes; Vintage Champagne; Viognier

WINES - WHITE

Californian chardonnay; Chateauneuf de pape blanc; Chilean white; English wine; Frascati; Marvelli Bianco; Pinot grigio doc; Soave; Vin de pays chardonnay; *Australian:* White Wine; *Chilean:* Chardonnay, Reserve Sauvignon Blanc; *French:* Chenin Blanc Demi-Sec, Muscadet, Vin de Pays Chardonnay; *Hungarian:* Chardonnay, Dry chardonnay, Medium chardonnay; *Italian:* Frascati, Frascati Selezione, Orvieto Abbocatto, Soave, Soave Classico; *Organic:* White wine; *South African Cape:* Chardonnay, Chenin Blanc, Created for Curry White (Semillon/Chardonnay), Reserve Sauvignon Blanc, Sauvignon Blanc, White; *USA Californian:* Chardonnay, Reserve Chardonnay, White Wine

FOOD

BISCUITS
Bourbon Creams; Fruit Shortcake; Ginger Nuts; Morning Coffee; Nice; Oatens; Rich Tea; Rich Tea Finger; Shortcake

BREADS, ROLLS, PIZZA BASES ETC
Baps; Bun Crown; Ciabatta; Ciabatta Rolls; Currant Buns; Finger Rolls; Grande Mange Blanc Rolls; Kibbled Seed Loaf; Luxury White Batched Rolls; Malted Grain Rolls; Nettle Bread; Olive Ciabatta; Olive Pave; Petit Parisienne; Rustique Elat Rolls; Soft White Rolls; Spiced Fruit Buns; Split Rolls; Sub Rolls; Teacakes; Tomato Foccacia; White Bread; Wholemeal Rolls; *Part-Baked:* Brown Loaf, French Flute, Vienna Stick, White Loaf; *Pitta Bread:* Garlic & Coriander, White; *Take & Bake:* Homecrust Sandwich Loaf, Small White Baguette, White Petit Pain, Wholemeal Loaf, Wholemeal Petit Pain

CAKES & CAKE MIXES
White Iced Buns

COOKING AIDS - SAVOURY
Sage & Onion Stuffing Mix

DIPS & DRESSINGS
Dijon Mustard; English Mustard

PICKLES, SAUCES, VINEGARS ETC
Brown Sauce; Cranberry Sauce; Mint Sauce; Redcurrant Jelly; Sweet & Sour Sauce; Tomato Ketchup; *Cooking Sauces:* Rogan Josh; *Pasta Sauce:* Napoletana, Original, w Mushrooms, w Peppers; *Pickled:* Baby Beetroot; *Vinegar:* Cider, Red Wine, White Wine

SAVOURIES - CANNED/BOTTLED
Beans in Tomato Sauce; *Budgens & HP:* Healthy Beans in Tomato Sauce

SAVOURIES - CHILLED/FRESH
Beansprout & Vegetable Stir Fry; Bombay Potato; Family Stir Fry; H&S Wedges; Mushroom Dopiaza; Mushroom Stir Fry; Roast Potatoes w R&T; Sticky Rice; Vegetable Jalfrezi; Vegetable Samosas; Vegetable Spring Rolls

SAVOURIES - FROZEN
Hot & Spicy Wedges; Oven/Fry Frozen Chips

SEASONAL FOODS
Christmas Puddings; Hot Cross Buns

SNACKS - SAVOURY
Crisps: Ready Salted; *Nuts:* Jumbo Salted Peanuts, Salted Peanuts; *Nuts - Roasted & Salted:* Cashews, Pistachios

SPREADS - SWEET
Mincemeat; *Conserves & Jams:* Apricot, Blackcurrant, Bramble, Raspberry, Strawberrry; *Jellies:* Lemon, Lime; *Orange Marmalade:* Fine, Shredless, Thick

DRINK

SOFT
American Cola; American Diet Cola; American Ginger Ale; Apple & Blackcurrant; Cream Soda; Diet Lemonade; Diet Tonic; Lemonade; Pink Lemonade; Shandy; Soda Water; Tonic Water w a Twist of Lemon; Traditional Diet Lemonade; Traditional Lemonade; *Juices - Ambient:* Cranberry, English Apple, Pineapple, Pink Grapefruit, Pure Orange; *Juices - Chilled:* Cloudy Apple; *No Added Sugar:* Apple & Blackcurrant, Cherryade, Lemon, Orange Lemon & Pineapple, Orangeade, Whole Orange

SPIRITS & APÉRITIFS
Cognac; Gin; Port Wine; Prince Royal Brandy; Vodka

WINES - WHITE
Bordeaux Blanc Sec; Bordeaux Sauvignon Blanc

FOOD

BISCUITS

Digestives; Ginger Snaps; Oatcakes; Orange Zest Bar; Reduced Fat Digestive; Reduced Fat Rich Tea; Rich Tea; Rich Tea Fingers; *Organic:* Digestive

BREADS, ROLLS, PIZZA BASES ETC

Bagels: Caramelised Onion and Poppy Seed, Cinnamon and Raisin, Multi-Seed, Plain, Sesame; *Bread Rolls:* Ciabatta, Crusty White Morning, Green Olive, Malted Grain, Panini, Soft White, Soft White Split, Soft Wholemeal; *Breads:* Baker's Multigrain, Baker's White, Bloomer Multiseed, Brown Batch Loaf, Ciabatta, Half Ciabatta, Highbran, Kvi Brown Loaf, Peperonata Ciabatta, Plain White Loaf (Scottish Batch), Premium White Medium, Premium White Thick, Premium Wholemeal Loaf, Premium Wholemeal Thick Sliced Loaf, Ready to Bake Half Baguettes, Sandwich White Medium Sliced Loaf, Seed Roll Crown, Seeded Batch Loaf Unsliced, Soft Granary Loaf, Soft White Seeded, Stoneground Cob, Two in One Loaf, Two in One Muffins, Two in One Soft Farmhouse Loaf, Wheatgerm, White Batch Loaf, Wholemeal Medium Sliced; *Bruschettine:* Cracked Black Pepper, Green Olive, Lightly Salted; *Count On Us:* Country Grain Thick Sliced, Granary Thick Sliced, Soft Grain Bloomer; *Farmhouse:* Crusty Granary, Crusty White, Soft Golden Wholemeal, Soft Oatmeal, Soft White; *In Store Bakery:* 3 Seed Baguette, 3 Seed Roll, 5 Seed Golden Wholemeal Crusty Cob, Bagel, Baked Tartine Slices, Bakers Choice Roll, Black & Green Olive Pave, Brown Farmhouse, Brown Roll, Countrygrain Crusty Loaf, Crusty Ciabatta, Crusty White Bloomer 400g; 800g, Granary Farmhouse, Green Olive Ciabatta Roll, Multi-seed Bagel, Rustique Baguette, Rustique Roll, Sesame Seed Pretzel, White Crusty Loaf 400g; 800g, White Farmhouse Loaf, Wholemeal Crusty Loaf 400g; 800g, Wholemeal Farmhouse; *Organic:* Ciabatta, Multigrain Loaf, Multiseed Loaf, Organic Poppy and Sunflower Seen Roll Ring, Stoneground Cob, White Loaf, Wholemeal Batch Loaf, Wholemeal Loaf; *Pitta Breads:* Mini White, Mini Wholemeal, Two in One pockets, White, Wholemeal; *Sweet Breads:* Chocolate Baklava Selection, Whisky Fruit Loaf; *Tortilla:* Tortilla Wraps, Wholemeal Tortilla Wraps

BREAKFAST FOODS

Wheat Bisks; *Count On Us:* Fruit and Nut Muesli, Multi Fruit and Flake, Tropical Fruit and Bran Multi Flakes; *Granola:* Crunchy Sultana; *Muesli:* Exotic Fruit and Nut Wholegrain, Fruit & Nut, Luxury Fruit & Nut 500g; 1kg, Luxury Fruit and Nut Wholegrain, Swiss Style Wholegrain, Unsweetened Fruit & Bran 500g; 1Kg

CHOCOLATE

Santa Domingo Dark Chocolate Coated Cherries; Single Origin Ecudor Dark Chocolate; Single Origin Sao Tome Dark Chocolate

CONFECTIONERY & SWEET SNACKS

Caramalised Hazelnut and Peanut Bar; Caramalised Sesame and Sunflower Seed Bar; Coconut Ice; Cool Mint Chewing Gum; Peanut Brittle; Rhubarb and Custard; Sherbet Lemons; Sugar Free Coolmint Chewing Gum; Sugar Free Menthol Airplus Chewing Gum; Sugar Free Very Berry Chewing Gum; Vanilla Dusted Pumpkin Seeds

COOKING AIDS - SWEET

Mincemeat: Classic, Connoiseur

DESSERTS

Compote: Exotic Fruit; *Dessert Sauce:* Raspberry; *Eat Well:* Raspberry Jelly, Summer Fruit Puddings; *Frozen:* Blackberry and Blackcurrant Sorbet

DIPS & DRESSINGS

Avocado, Mint and Lime Dressing; Balsamic & Blueberry Dressing; Classic French Dressing; Fire Roasted Pepper Salsa Dip; Greek Olive Oil Dressing with Mint and Lemon Juice; Houmous; Reduced Fat French Dressing; Reduced Fat Houmous; Spicy Red Pepper Houmous; *Count On Us:* Balsamic Vinegar, Olive and Herb Dressing, White Wine Vinaigrette Dressing; *Dressing:* Classic French, Sunblush Tomato & Roasted Onion; *Eat Well:* Roasted Red Pepper, Tomato & Chilli Dressing, Tomato Salsa; *Organic:* Houmous

MARGARINES, FATS, OILS ETC

Sunflower Spread

PICKLES, SAUCES, VINEGARS ETC

Chunky Fajita Marinade; Cranberry and Raspberry Juice Drink; Cranberry Sauce with American Cranberries; Crinkle Cut Beetroot in a Sweet Vinegar; Cucumber Relish; Dijon Mustard with Chablis; English Mint Sauce with Fresh Mint; English Vineyard Mustard; Olive Stir Through; Original Recipe Crinkle Cut Pickled Beetroot 280g; 705g; Piccalilli; Ploughmans Pickle; Red Cabbage in Malt Vinegar; Scottish Mint Jelly; Super Berry Smoothie; Tewksbury Mustard Pot; Tropical Island Blend Smoothie; Wholegrain Mustard; *Chutney:* English Bramble, Festive Fruit, Spicy Mango, Sweet Mango; *Count On Us:* Lightly Salted Baked Potato Crisps; *Eat Well:* Neopolitan Tomato Sauce, Tomato and Chargrilled Veg Sauce; *Marinade:* Hot and Smokey Spice Rub, Mediterranean Style Herb Rub, Moroccan Style Spice Rub, Sticky Barbecue, Sweet and Sour, Tangy Citrus & Dill Herb Rub, Tequila, Peri Peri & Lime; *Mustard:* Hot English; *Pasta Sauce:* Sweet Cherry Tomato and Roquette, Tomato & Aubergine, Tomato & Basil 330g; 530g, Tomato & Herb 330g; 530g, Tomato & Mushroom, Tomato & Roasted Garlic, Tomato & Roasted Vegetable; *Relish:* Peri Peri, Tomato; *Sauce:* BBQ, Bramley Apple

Sauce with Vintage Cider, Brown; *Stir Fry Sauce:* Sweet and Sour, Sweet Chilli and Ginger; *Stir Through Pasta Sauces:* Roasted Italian Vegetable

SAVOURIES - CANNED/BOTTLED
Greek Olives with Orange & Peppers; *Count On Us:* Vegetable Casserole

SAVOURIES - CHILLED/FRESH
Baby Leaf Stir Fry; Falafel; Indian Selection with Tomato & Chilli Dip; Indian Style Spiced Rice; Italian Style Lentils, Pasta & Pinenuts; Marinated Artichokes; Med Veg Pasta with Red Pepper Sauce; Morroccan Chickpea & Cannelini Bean w Saffron; Olive Stuffed with Almonds; Orza Pasta with Slow Roasted Pasta; Roasted Red & Yellow Peppers; Rosemary Potatoes; Savoury Vegetable Rice; *Chips:* Organic, Oven; *Eat Well:* Vegetarian Vegetable Chilli; *Global Meal Solutions:* Aloo Gobi Sag; *Olives:* Kalamata & Green, Mixed Marinated, Pitted Baby Kalamata, Pitted Green, Queen Green, Whole Kalamata; *One Pan:* Couscous, Peppers, Tomato & Courgette with Spiced Coriander Harissa Dressing; *Roasting Veg:* Oven Roasted Ratatouille w Thyme & Olive Oil Dressing, Squash & Potato Bake w Sage Dressing; *Salads:* 3 Bean with Mint Vinaigrette, Couscous and Roasted Vegetables, Crunchy Salad Bowl 100g; 170g, Giant Couscous & Wheatberries with Roasted Butternut Squash, Med Vegetables & Pasta Salad, Rice, Lentil & Roast Aubergine Salad, Rice, Lentil & Roast Aubergine with a Garlic Dressing,

Santini Tomato Salad with Classic French Dressing, Santini Tomatoes & Avocado Salad & Balsamic Dressing, Sweet Buffet Salad; *Stir Fry:* Mushroom, Pea Shoot and Vegetable, Rainbow, Vegetable & Beansprout; *With Sauce:* Green Bean Selection w Provencale Sauce

SAVOURIES - FROZEN
Crispy Wedges; Curly Fries; *Chips:* Chunky, Count On Us Chunky - 4 pack, Crinkle Cut, Gastropub; *Count On Us:* Chunky Chips; *Fries:* American Style Coated; *Frozen:* Catering Fries

SEASONAL FOODS
Cherries in Kirsch; Christmas Spiced and Oven Roasted Nuts and Dried Fruit; Peaches/ apricots in Brandy; Pickled Pears in Champagne Vinegar; Redcurrant Sauce with Cabernet Sauvignon; Wild Cranberry Sauce; *Christmas:* Cranberry & Ruby Port Sauce, Mustard with Ale, Strawberry & Champagne Conserve

SNACKS - SAVOURY
Beef & Onion Rings; Bombay Mix; Crunchy Twists BBQ Bacon; Dry Roasted Peanuts 150g; Herb Flavoured Roasted Mixed Nuts; Indian Bombay Mix Can; Kalamate Olives with Chilli; Lightly Salted Totilla with Black Pepper; Luxury Dried Fruit Mix; Maple Cured Bacon Flavoured Twists 150g; Marinated Greek Olive Selection; Mini Poppadums; New Lightly Salted Reduced Fat Crinkles 55g; 150g; New Reduced Fat Crinkles Salt &

Vinegar 150g; Oriental Spring Onion 150g; Oven Roasted Large Peanuts and Cashews with Cracked Black Pepper and Sea Salt; Rice and Oat Bran Cakes; Salt & Vinegar Chiplets 50g; Salt & Vinegar Potato Thins; Salt & Vinegar Twists 40g; Small Queen Green Olives with Lemon and Garlic; Speciality Italian Nut Selection with Sun Dried Tomatoes and Herbs; Spicy Bbq; Spicy Chilli Tortilla; Spicy Chipolte Bbq Twists; Stuffed Greek Olives; *Count On Us:* Poppadums; *Crisps:* Apples, Beetroot - Lightly Salted, Carrot - Lightly Salted, Chilli and Lime Salsa Flavour, Hand Cooked 150g, Hand Cooked Sea Salt and Balsamic Vinegar, Highland Burgundy Red Lightly Salted Handcooked, Lightly Salted Handcooked, No Salt Handcooked 150g, Sea Salt and Crushed Black Pepper Handcooked; *Eat Well:* Oven Roasted Nut, Dried Fruit and Seed Selection; *Food To Go:* Crinkle Crisps Ready Salted, Crinkle Crisps Salt and Vinegar Flavour, Lightly Salted Handcooked Crisps, Sea Salt & Crushed Black Pepper Handcooked Crisps, Sea Salt And Balsamic Vinegar Handcooked Crisps; *Global Meal Solutions:* Frites, Indian Starter Selection Pack, Mini Onion Bhajis and Vegetable Pakoras, Thai Sticky Rice, Vegetable Curry; *Organic:* Mini Black Pepper Oatcakes; *Pretzels:* Giant Lightly Salted, Lightly Salted, Salt & Pepper

SOUPS

Carrot & Clementine; Italian Broth & Pasta; Minestrone; Tomato & Basil; Winter Vegetable; *Food To Go:* Tomato & Basil

SPREADS - SWEET

Conserve: Apricot, Blackcurrant, Blueberry, Hedgerow, Raspberry, Red Cherry, Rhubarb & Ginger, Strawberry; *Marmalade:* Bitter Sweet Orange and Cranberry, Course Cut Seville Orange, Lemon and Lime, Medium Cut Blood Orange, Medium Cut Mandarin, Medium Cut Ruby Red Grapefruit, Medium Cut Seville Orange, No Peel Orange, Orange & Whisky

DRINK

SOFT

Apple & Blackcurrant Still Water 1l; Blueberry Juice Drink; Blueberry, Strawberry and Blackberry Smoothie; Cloudy Lemonade; Cola 2l; Cranberry Juice Drink; Elderflower Flavoured Sparkling Water; Fiery Ginger Beer; Fruit Infusions: Peach, Lime and Ginger; Lemon & Lime Carbonate 2l; Lemon and Lime Still Flavoured Water; Lemonade 1l; Lemonade Mixer 500ml; Mango Madness Smoothie; Non Alcoholic Mulled Punch; Passionfruit and Alphonso Mango High Juice Cordial; Pomegranate and Raspberry Juice Drink; Pomegranate, Blueberry and Cranberry Smoothie; Redcurrant, Raspberry and Camomile Fruit Infusion; Simply Sunshine Smoothie; Sparkling Alphonso Mango and Passionfruit;

Sparkling Florida Orange; Tonic Water Mixer 500ml; *Count On Us:* Blackcurrant High Juice, Cranberry and Raspberry Juice Drink, Orange High Juice, Pomegranate and Blueberry Juice Drink, Strawberry and Raspberry Smoothie; *Diet:* Cola 2l, Lemon and Lime Carbonate 2l, Lemonade 2l, Sparkling Florida Orange; *Eat Well:* Apple Juice w Sparkling Spring Water, Orange Juice w Sparkling Spring Water; *Food To Go:* Blackberry and Echinacea, Blackcurrant Still Fruity Water, Cola 500ml, Cranberry and Raspberry Sparkling Water, Diet Cola 500ml, Diet Sparkling Alphonso Mango and Passionfruit Carbonate, Diet Sparkling Florida Orange, Diet Sparkling Sicilian Lemon Mexican Lime, Mango & Lime Fruity Water, Peach and Raspberry Sparkling Water Drink, Pomegranate and Raspberry Juice Drink, Raspberry Still Fruity Water, Ruby Orange and Mandarin Still Water, Simply Foods Sparkling Orange and Lemon Energizing Drink, Sparkling Berry Energising Berry Drink, Sparkling Florida Orange, Sparkling Lemon And Lime Energy Drink; *High Juice:* Blackcurrant, Cranberry & Raspberry, Florida Orange, Florida Pink Grapefruit, Lemon & Lime, Summer Fruits; *Mixer:* American Ginger Ale 500 ml, Bitter Lemon 500 ml; *Multipack:* American Ginger Ale Mixer Cans; *Multipack - Mixer Cans:* American Ginger Ale, Diet tonic & Lemon, Tonic; *Sparkling Spring Water Drink 1l:* Cranberry & Raspberry; *Sparkling Water:* Blueberry &

Pomegranate 1l; *Sparkling Water (with A Twist):* Lemon, Raspberry; *Speciality:* Elderflower Cordial, Raspberry Cordial, Sparkling Elderflower Presse; *Spring Water Drink 1l:* Lemon & Lime Sparkling, Lemon & Lime Still, Orange Still, Strawberry Still

HOME & OFFICE

FABRIC CONDITIONERS
Citrus Fabric Conditioner; Fresh Meadow Fabric Conditioner; Ocean Meadow Fabric Conditioner

WASHING POWDERS, STARCH ETC
Eco Concentrated Laundry Liquid; Eco Delicate Laundry Liquid; Eco Laundry Powder; Eco Laundry Tablets

WASHING-UP PRODUCTS
Eco Washing Up Liquid

FOOD

BREADS, ROLLS, PIZZA BASES ETC

Hot Cross Buns; *Baked Goods:* Crumpets, Italian Heat and Serve Ciabatta, Italian Heat and Serve Ciabatta Rolls, Kids Mini Bagels, Kids Mini Pittas, Mini White Pitta, Teacakes, White Hot Cross Buns, White Pitta, Wholemeal Muffins, Wholemeal Pitta; *Basics:* Medium Sliced White Bread, Muffins, White Pitta, White Rolls; *Bread:* Medium White Stays for up to 7 Days, Medium Wholemeal Stays for up to 7 Days, Scottish Square Medium, Thick White Stays Fresh for up to 7 Days, Thick Wholemeal Stays Fresh for up to 7 Days, White Medium Sliced, White Medium Sliced A Soft Tasty White Bread, White Thick Sliced, White Thick Sliced A Soft Tasty White Bread, Whole and White Medium Sliced, Wholemeal Medium Sliced, Wholemeal Medium Sliced Packed Full of Wholegrain Goodness, Wholemeal Thick Sliced, Wholemeal Thick Sliced Packed Full of Wholegrain Goodness; *Bread Mixes:* Mixed Grain Speciality, Sunflower Speciality Brown Bread; *Free From:* Breadcrumbs; *Free From - Bread Mixes:* Bread Mix; *Rolls:* White Floury Batch Rolls, Whole and White Floury Batch Rolls, Wholemeal Floury Batch Rolls; *So Organic:* Ciabatta, Malt Loaf, Plain Bagels, Stoneground Wholemeal Thick Sliced Bread, White Thick Sliced Bread, Wholemeal Pitta; *Taste the Difference:* Bruschettina Selection, Heat and Serve Ciabatta, Heat and Serve Mixed Olived Ciabatta Rolls, Slowfermented Heat and Serve Ciabatta Plain, Slowfermented Heat and Serve Ciabatta with Slow Roasted Aegean Tomatoes, Slowfermented Piegata, Soft White Batch Thickley Sliced, Soft Wholemeal Multiseeded Batch Thickly Sliced, Soft Wholemeal Oat Topped Batch Thickly Sliced

BREAKFAST FOODS

Be Good to Yourself: Muesli; *Breakfast Cereals:* Fruit and Nut Muesli, Fruit Muesli, Golden Syrup Easy Oats, High Fibre Bran, Instant Hot Oat Cereal, Malties, Organic Bran Flakes, Whole Grain Apricot Wheats, Whole Grain Blueberry Wheats, Whole Grain Cranberry Wheats, Whole Grain Mini Wheats, Whole Grain Raisin Wheats, Wholewheat Biscuits, Wholewheat Muesli; *Free From:* Fruit and Nut Muesli, Golden Porridge; *So Organic:* Strawberry Crisp Cereal

CAKES & CAKE MIXES

Free From: Apple and Blackcurrant Pies, Cherry Bakewell Tarts, Chocolate Chip Cookies, Cranberry and Blueberry Bars, Real Fruit Jam Tarts

CHOCOLATE

Chocolate Selection, Mint Crisps, Rice Crackle Soya Choc Bar, Tangerine Flavour Soya Choc Bar

CONFECTIONERY & SWEET SNACKS

Confectionery: Cinema Style Sweet Popcorn, Citrus Slices with Soft Centers and Natural Fruit Juices, Cough Candy, Fizzy Strawberry Laces, Mint Imperials, Rhubarb and Custard, Sherbet Cocktails, Sherbet Filled Wafer Sweets, Sherbet Pips, Strawberry Laces, Strawberry Pencils; *Free From:* Soya Choc Bar; *Free From - Biscuits:* Rich Tea Biscuits, Shortcake, Stem Ginger Cookies

COOKING AIDS - SWEET

Mincemeat

DESSERTS

Summer Fruit Jelly Terrine; *Basics:* Apple Pie; *Compotes and Coulis:* Forest Fruit Compote, Scottish Raspberry Coulis; *Free From:* Vanilla Custard; *Taste the Difference:* Mandarin and Pineapple Jellies, Scottish Raspberry and Pink Champagne Compote, Tropical Fruit Jelly

DIPS & DRESSINGS

Basics: French Dressing; *Be Good to Yourself - Dressings:* French Vinaigrette, Lime Lemon Grass and Chilli, Raspberry, Red Pepper, Sweet Balsamic and Garlic; *Cooking Sauces:* Thai Chilli Dipping; *Dressings:* French, Mango and Chilli; *So Organic - Dressings:* Balsamic, Garlic and Herb Dressing; *Taste the Difference - Dressings:* French Dressing with Chardonnay, Lemongrass Lime Leaf and Galangal, Raspberry and Rioja, Sweetflamed Pepper and Piri Piri

GRAVIES & STOCKS

Gravy Granules for Vegetarian Dishes

'ICE CREAMS', SORBETS ETC

Iced and Frozen Desserts: Lemon Sorbet, Mango Sorbet, Raspberry and Blueberry Sorbet

MARGARINES, FATS, OILS ETC

So Organic: Olive Spread

PICKLES, SAUCES, VINEGARS ETC

Artichoke Antipasto; Green Gordal and Black Kalkidis Olives in a Lemon Zest and Red Chilli Pepper Dressing; Mixed Mushroom Antipasto; Mixed Pepper Antipasto; Peranzana Olives in a Vinaigrette Dressing; Piccalilli; Sundried Tomato Antipasto; Sweet Piccalilli; *Basics:* Mint Sauce, Onion Chutney; *Be Good to Yourself - Cooking Sauces:* Balti Cooking, Chilli Con Carne, Italian Tomato and Herb, Mediterranean Vegetables Stir In, Plum and Ginger, Szechuan Tomato; *Chutneys:* Jalapeno Relish, Onion Relish, Sweetcorn Relish, Tomato and Chilli Relish, Tomato Relish; *Cooking Sauces:* Cantonese Black Bean Stir Fry, Chinese Sweet and Sour, Hot Mixed Pepper, Indian Jalfrezi, Indonesian Satay, Italian Sundried Tomato and Balsamic Vinegar Stir In, Madras, Mushroom, Onion and Garlic, Oriental Black Bean, Oriental Lemon and Ginger, Siciliana, Stir Fry Ginger and Shiitake, Stir Fry Hoi Sin, Sweet and Sour Stir Fry, Szechuan Sweet and Sour, Thai Green Curry, Thai Red Curry Paste, Tomato and Basil, Tomato and Chilli,

Tomato and Garlic, Tomato and Herb; *So Organic:* Mint Sauce; *Table Sauce:* Bramley Apple, Brown, Cranberyy Sauce, French Dark Mustard, French Dijon, Fresh Mint, Mango and Chilli Marinade, Mint, Mint Jelly, Redcurrant Jelly, Smooth Bramley Apple, Sticky Barbeque Marinade, Tomato Ketchup, Tomato Ketchup Reduced Sugar and Salt, Wholegrain Mustard; *Taste the Difference:* Cranberry Sauce, Dressed Picholene Olives, Nocellara Del Belice Olives; *Taste the Difference - Chutneys:* Balsamic Fruit, Caramelised Red Onion, Caramelised Red Pepper, Mango Plum and Ginger, Spicy Onion; *Taste the Difference - Cooking Sauces:* Mediterranean Vegetable, Sugo Pomodoro; *Taste the Difference - Dressings:* Lemon and Piri Piri Marinade; *Taste the Difference - Table Sauce:* Smokey Barbeque and Brown Ale Marinade, Sweetflamed Pepper Marinade

SAVOURIES - CANNED/BOTTLED
Mixed Bean Salad in Water; Mixed Beans in a Mild Chilli Sauce; Ratatouille Provencale; *Baked Beans:* In Tomato Sauce, Reduced Sugar Reduced Salt in Tomato Sauce; *Basics:* Baked Beans in Tomato Sauce, Spaghetti in Tomato Sauce; *Meat Free:* Vegetable Chilli in a Rich Spicy Sauce with Red Kidney beans; *Pasta:* Meatfree Spaghetti Bolognese in a Rich Sauce with Chopped Tomatoes; *So Organic:* Baked Beans in Tomato Sauce, Spaghetti in Tomato Sauce

SAVOURIES - CHILLED/FRESH
Couchilli Olives with Pine Nuts; Dressed Queen Green Olives; Felafal; Stuffed Vine Leaves; *Taste the Difference:* Mixed Olives Dressed Kalamata and Green Olives

SAVOURIES - DRIED
Basics: Beef and Tomato Flavour Noodles; *Basics - Instant Noodles:* Chicken and Mushroom Flavour Snack, Chicken Curry Flavour, Chicken Flavour; *Free From:* Sage and Onion Stuffing Mix; *Instant Noodles:* Chicken Curry Flavour, Chicken Flavour, Vegetable Flavour; *So Organic:* Sage and Onion Stuffing Mix; *Taste the Difference:* Apricot and Flaked Almond Stuffing Mix, Cranberry Orange and Roasted Chestnut Stuffing Mix, Sage Roasted Onion and Lemon Stuffing Mix

SAVOURIES - FROZEN
Basics: Chips; *Be Good to Yourself:* Oven Chips; *Chips and Potato Products:* American Style Oven Chips, Chunky Cut Chips, Crinkle Cut Chips, Jacket Wedges, Straight Cut Chips; *Taste the Difference - Chips and Potato Products:* Extra Chunky Chips

SNACKS - SAVOURY
Marinated Black Pelion Olives with Chilli and Garlic Dressing; Marinated Kalamate Olives; Marinated Queen Olives; *Basics:* Tortilla Chips; *Be Good to Yourself:* Rosemary and Sea Salt Pitta Chips; *Crisps:* Salt Your Own Crisps; *Naturals:* Prawn Cocktail Flavour,

Ready Salted; *Snacks:* Baked Snack Selection, Hot Mango Flavour Bites, Lightly Salted Tortilla Chips, Mini Poppadoms, Multi Seedin Jumbo Pretzels, Potato Squares, Ready Salted Potato Triangles, Salt and Vinegar Crunchy Sticks, Salted Pretzels, Sea Salt Popcorn, Sun Dried Tomato and Red Pepper Bites; *Taste the Difference:* Black Pepper and Sea Salt Parsnip Crisps, Lightly Salted Charlotte Potato Crisps, Lightly Salted Sweet Potato and Plantain Crisps, Root Vegetable Crisps, Sea Salt and West Country Cider Vinegar Crisps, Sea Salt Crisps

SOUPS

Extra Thick Vegetable Soup; *Basics:* Vegetable; *Instant Soups:* Minestrone Soup in a Cup; *Packet Soups:* French Onion Soup Simmer and Serve; *So Organic:* Leek and Potato, Lentils and Mixed Pepper, Tomato and Basil, Tuscan Bean, Winter Vegetable; *So Organic - Chilled Soups:* Tomato and Basil

SOYA AND OTHER 'MILKS'

Sweetened; Unsweetened; *Free From:* Rice Drink, Soya Drink Sweetened, Soya Drink Unsweetened

SPREADS - SWEET

Basics: Medium Cut Orange, Mixed Fruit Jam; *Conserves:* Apricot Conserve, Blackcurrant, Ginger Preserve, Raspberry, Red Cherry, Strawberry; *Jams:* Apricot, Blackcurrant, Bramble Jelly, Damson, Raspberry, Reduced Sugar Apricot, Reduced Sugar

Blackcurrant, Reduced Sugar Morello Cherry, Reduced Sugar Raspberry, Reduced Sugar Strawberry, Strawberry, Strawberry with No Bits; *Marmalades:* Extra Thick Cut Orange, Fine Cut Orange, Fine Cut Orange Shred Jelly, Medium Cut Orange, Reduced Sugar Fine Cut Orange, Reduced Sugar Thick Cut Orange, Shredless Orange Jelly, Thick Cut Orange, Thick Cut Orange and Ginger; *So Organic - Marmalades:* Fine Cut, Thick Cut Seville Orange Marmalade

DRINK

SOFT

Classic Cola; Cloudy Lemonade; Cola; Diet Cloudy Lemonade; Diet Cream Soda; Diet Dandelion and Burdock; Diet Ginger Beer; Diet Orange Mango and Peach; Diet Pineapple and Grapefruit; Lemonade; No Added Sugar Fizzy Cherry; No Added Sugar Fizzy Limeade; No Added Sugar Fizzy Orange; No Added Sugar Orange; *Basics - Juice Drinks:* Orange, Orange with Sweetener; *Be Good to Yourself:* Cranberry and Apple No Added Sugar Juice Drink, Cranberry and Raspberry No Added Sugar Juice Drink, Cranberry No Added Sugar Juice Drink; *Be Good to Yourself - Squash:* Blackcurrant High Juice with No Added Sugar, Orange High Juice with No Added Sugar, Pink Grapefruit High Juice with No Added Sugar, Tropical High Juice with No

Added Sugar; *Energy Drink:* Blue Bolt, Diet Blue Bolt Stimualtion Drink; *Flavoured Water:* Kids Grape Apple and Raspberry Juicy Water, Kids Juicy Water Apple, Kids Juicy Water Orange and Banana; *Juice Drink:* Apple and Pear, Apple and Raspberry, Cranberry, Cranberry and Raspberry, Fruit Cocktail, Lime and Mint Mojito, No Added Sugar Apple, No Added Sugar Apple and Blackcurrant, No Added Sugar Apple and Strawberry, No Added Sugar Orange, No Added Sugar Tropical, Organic Cranberry, Organic Tropical, Pineapple Mango and Passion Fruit, Pomegranate, Pomegranate and Blueberry, Still Lemonade; *Mixers:* American Ginger Ale, Bitter Lemon, Bitter Shandy, Diet American Ginger, Diet Bitter Lemon, Diet Indian Tonic Water, Diet Indian Tonic Water with Lemon, Diet Indian Tonic Water with Lime, Dry Ginger Ale, Ginger Beer, Indian Tonic Water, Indian Tonic Water with Lemon, Indian Tonic Water with Lime, Lemon Squash, Lime Cordial, Soda Water; *So Organic:* Cranberry Juice Drink; *Sparkling Spring Water Drink:* With a Hint of Apple and Pomegranate No Added Sugar, with a Hint of Elderflower No Added Sugar, with a Hint of Lemon and Lime No Added Sugar, with a Hint of Orange and Mango No Added Sugar, with a Hint of Peach No Added Sugar, with a Hint of Strawberry and Kiwi No Added Sugar; *Squash:* Apple and Blackcurrant, Apple and Blackcurrant Squash, Apple and Blackcurrant with Sweetener, Blackcurrant, Hi Juice Apple, Hi Juice Apple and Blackcurrant, Hi Juice Blackcurrant, Hi Juice Cranberry Cherry and Apple Squash, Hi Juice Lemon, Hi Juice Orange, Hi Juice Pink Grapefruit, Hi Juice Summer Fruit, Hi Juice Tropical, No Added Sugar Apple, No Added Sugar Apple and Blackcurrant, No Added Sugar Blackcurrant, No Added Sugar Lemon, No Added Sugar Lemon and Lime, No Added Sugar Orange, No Added Sugar Orange and Mango, No Added Sugar Orange Lemon and Pineapple, No Added Sugar Summer Fruits, No Added Sugar Tropical, Orange, Orange Lemon and Pineapple

FOOD

BISCUITS
Bourbon Creams; Fruit Shortcake; Ginger Nuts; Mini Gingerbread Shapes; Morning Coffee; Reduced Fat Rich Tea; Rich Tea Biscuits; Rich Tea Fingers; Shortcake

BREADS, ROLLS, PIZZA BASES ETC
Brown Bread; Crumpets; Long Life white Bread; Long Life Wholemeal Bread; Mini Pitta Bread; Part Bake Organic White Bloomer; Part Bake Organic White Bread; Part Bake Organic Wholemeal Bread; Part Bake White Farmhouse; Part Bake White Sandwich Tin; Part Bake White Split Tin; Pizza Base Mix; Plain Breadsticks; Ring of Roll; Scottish Plain Batch Bread; White Bread; White Finger Rolls; White Hot Dog Rolls; White Muffins; White Pitta Bread; Wholemeal Baps; Wholemeal Pitta Bread; *Best Ever:* Mult Seeded Deli Rolls, Multi Seeded Deli Rolls, Multiseeded Farmhouse Loaf, Oatmeal Deli Rolls; *Instore Bakery:* Baguette A L'Ancienne, Batched Crusty Rolls, Brown Batched Crusty Rolls, Brown Rustic Style Rolls, Ciabatta Rolls, Cross cut Batards, French Rolls, Grand Rustic Style Loaf, Harvester Ploughmans Roll, Malted Harvester Bread, Onion & Herb Ciabatta, Organic Brown Bloomer, Organic Malted Wheat Bloomer, Organic Petit Pain, Organic White Bloomer, Organic Wholemeal Tin Bread, Panini Rolls, Petite Parisienne, Poppy Seed Roll, Premium French Stick, Sunflower Seed Bread Rolls (Triangular), Sunflower Seed Roll, Tiger Bread, Tiger Rolls, Tomato & Basil Rustic Style Rolls, Whit Farmhouse Bread, White Bloomer, White Ploughmans Rolls, White Rustic Style Rolls, White Tin Bread, Wholemeal Tin Bread; *Makes Sense:* Garlic Baguette; *Simply Value:* Malt Loaf, Pitta Bread; *So Good:* Olive Ciabatta Loaf; *Value:* White Bread

BREAKFAST FOODS
Breakfast Bran; GI Fruit Muesli; Instant Hot Oat Cereal; Oat Sachets Original; Wheat Biscuits; *Healthy Choice:* Cranberry Wheats, Malted Wheats; *Simply Value:* Wheat Biscuits

CAKES & CAKE MIXES
Crumble Mix; Shortcrust Pastry Mix

CONFECTIONERY & SWEET SNACKS
Apple Laces; Candy Watches and Necklaces; Flying Saucers; Stawberry Fizzy Laces; Stawberry Laces; Sugared Almonds

COOKING AIDS - SWEET
Granulated Sweetener; Mincemeat; Red Glace Cherries

CRACKERS, CRISPBREADS ETC
Cream Crackers; Sesame Breadsticks; Water Biscuits

DESSERTS
Apple Pie; Apple Strudel; Rich Fruit Christmas Pudding; Woodland Fruit

Strudel; *Christmas Range:* Rich Fruit Christmas Pudding

DIPS & DRESSINGS
Country Vegetable; French Dressing; Houmous; Lemon & Coriander Houmous; Reduced Fat Houmous; Roasted Red Pepper Houmous; Salsa; *Best Ever:* Balsamic Dressing, Chilli & Red Pepper Houmous; *Healthy Choice:* French Dressing, Reduced Fat French Dressing

GRAVIES & STOCKS
Simply Value: Gravy Granules

'ICE CREAMS', SORBETS ETC
Cherryade Flavour Water Ice Lolly; Cola Flavour Water Ice Lolly; Lemon Sherbet Flavour Water Ice Lolly; Lemonade Flavour Water Ice Lolly; Mango Sorbet; Pear Drop Flavour Water Ice Lollies; Rhubarb and Custard Flavour Water Ice Lollies; Rocket Lollies

PICKLES, SAUCES, VINEGARS ETC
Apple Sauce; Arrabbiata Sauce; Black Bean and Garlic Stir Fry; Black Bean and Garlic Stir Fry Sauce; Bramley Apple Sauce; Chilli Medium Sauce; Chunky Vegetable Pasta Sauce; Cranberry Sauce; Garlic and Onion Pasta Sauce; Green Thai Sauce; Hoisin Stir Fry Sauce; Hot Caramelised Red Onion Chutney; Madras Sauce; Mint Sauce; Mixed Pickle; Mushroom Pasta Sauce; Mustard Piccalilli; Napolentans Sauce; Pepper Pasta Sauce; Rogan Josh Sauce; Spicy Szechuan Stir Fry Sauce; Sweet and Sour Sauce; Sweet Pickle; Szechaun Stir Fry Sauce; Tomato and Herb Pasta Sauce; *Best Ever:* Apple and Mint Jelly, Cranberry Sauce with Port, Sweet tomato & Chilli Chutney; *Healthy Choice:* Pasta Sauce, Sweet and Sour Sauce; *Instore Bakery:* White Crusly Seeded Bloomer; *Simply Value:* Brown Sauce, Pasta Sauce, Tomato Ketchup; *So Good:* Orchard Fruit Chutney

SAVOURIES - CANNED/BOTTLED
Baked Beans in Tomato Sauce; Chilli Beans; *Economy:* Mushy Peas; *Good Intentions:* Baked Beans; *Simply Value:* Baked Bean in Tomato Sauce, Spaghetti in Tomato Sauce

SAVOURIES - CHILLED/FRESH
American Fries 3-Way Cook; *Deli:* Cocktail Mix, Croutons, Greek Country Mixed Olives with Herbs, Italian Style Antipasti, Lemon Stuffed Olives with Lemon Zest, Marinated Pitted Black & Green Olives with Garlic, Meditarranean Pasta Salad, Mini Onion Bhaji, Mixed Greek Olives with Cumin and Chilli, Mixed Mediterranean Peppers, Mushroom Antipasti, Pease Pudding, Pimento Stuffed Olived with Italian Marinade, Pitted Black and Green Olives with Herbs de Provance, Pitted Green Olives with Chilli, Whole Queen Olives with Herbs; *Healthy Choice:* Mediterranean Style Pasta Salad, Tomato & Basil Couscous; *Indian:* Bombay Potato, Mini Indian Selection, Onion Bhajis; *Party:* Mini Aloo Tikki, Mini Onion Bhaji, Mini Spinach Pakora, Mini Vegetable Samosa

SAVOURIES - DRIED
Apple and Herb Stuffing Mix; Instant Mash Potato Mix; Parsley Thyme & Lemon Stuffing Mix; Parsley, Thyme & Lemon; Sage & Onion Stuffing Mix

SAVOURIES - FROZEN
8 Vegetable Spring Rolls; Crinkle Cut Chips 3-Way Cook; Mini Indian Selection; Potato Waffles; Roast Potatoes; Steak Cut Chip 3-Way Cook; *Simply Value:* Deep Fry Straight Cut Chips

SNACKS - SAVOURY
Lightly Salted Tortilla Chips; Ready to Salt Crisps; *Best Ever:* Lightly Salted Handcooked Crisps, Sea Salt & Balsamic Vinegar Handcooked Crisps, Sea Salted handcooked Crisps, Sweet Chilli Handcooked Crisps; *Simply Value:* Ready Salted Crisps

SOUPS
Tomato & Basil

SPREADS - SWEET
Fine Cut Orange Marmalade; Medium Cut Orange Marmalade; Orange Shred Marmalade; Pure Fruit Blackcurrant Jam; Pure Fruit Raspberry Jam; Pure Fruit Seedless Raspberry Jam; Pure Fruit Strawberry Jam; Redcurrant Jelly; Thick Cut Orange Marmalade; Pure Fruit apricot Jam; *Best Ever:* 3 Fruit Marmalade, Apricot Conserve, Blackcurrant Conserve, Fine Cut Marmalade, Raspberry Conserve, Red Cherry Conserve, Strawberry Conserve;

Simply Value: Medium Cut Orange Marmalade, Mixed Fruit Jam

DRINK

BEERS
Bavarian Wheat Beer; *Best Ever:* Bavarian Beer

CIDERS & PERRIES
Oak Conditioned Cider, Single Orchard Cider; *So Good:* Oak Conditioned Cider

SOFT
A Hint of Cranberry; A Hint of Grapefruit; A Hint of Lemon and Lime; A Hint of Peach; American Ginger Ale; Apple & Blackcurrant Squash; Apple & Blackcurrant Squash No Added Sugar; Apple and Blackcurrant Flavoured Still Spring Water; Apple and Blackcurrant Still Juice Drink; Apple Juice Drink with Sweeteners; Bitter Lemon; Blackcurrant Juice Drink with Sweeteners; Cherryade No Added Sugar; Cloudy Diet Lemonade; Cloudy Lemonade; Cola; Cranberry Juice Drink; Cream Soda; Dandelion & Burdock; Diet Cola; Diet Lemonade; Ginger Beer; Hi Juice Orange Drink; Hi-Juice Blackcurrant Drink; Hi-Juice Citrus Drink; Hi-Juice Raspberry Cranberry & Blueberry Drink; Hi-Juice Summer Fruits Drink; Indian Tonic Water; Lemon Squash No Added Sugar; Lemonade; Limeade No Added Sugar; Low Calorie Bitter Cranberry; Low Calorie Bitter Lemon; Low Calorie

Indian Tonic Water; Low Calorie Indian Tonic Water & Lemon; Orange and Peach Still Juice Drink; Orange and Pineapple Squash; Orange and Pineapple Squash No Added Sugar; Orange and Raspberry Squash No Added Sugar; Orange Juice Drink with Sweeteners; Orangeade No Added Sugar; Shandy; Simply Value Orange Drink; Soda Water; Still Spring Water with a Splash of Apple & Cranberry; Still Spring Water with a Splash of Lemon & Lime; Still Spring Water with a Splash of Peach & Raspberry; Summer Fruits Squash No Added Sugar; Tropical Flavoured Still Spring Water; Tropical Fruit Juice Drink; Tropical Fruit Squash No Added Sugar; Whole Orange Squash; Whole Orange Squash No Added Sugar; Lemon Squash; *Healthy Choice:* No Added Sugar Cranberry Juice Drink, No Added Sugar Orange Juice Drink; *Simply Value:* Apple and Blackcurrant Drink, Cola, Lemonade

SPIRITS & APÉRITIFS

French Brandy; Gin; Navigators LBV Port; Prince Charlie 8 Year Old Whisky; Prince Charlie Whisky; Vodka; White rum

WINES - RED

Beaujolais; Beaujolais Rouge; Sa Limited Release Shiraz; Vin De Pay Du comte Tolosan; Vin De Pays De L'Herault Red

WINES - ROSÉ

Rose d'Anjou AC 2005; Vin De Pays Comte Tolosan

WINES - WHITE

Argentine Chardonnay 2005; Argentine White; Chilean Sauvignon Blanc; Chilean/Semillon Chardonnay 2005; Domaine Sainte Agathe Oak Aged Chardonnay; French Dry White Wine; Muscadet AC 2004; Muscadet AC 2005; Vin De Pays Du Comte Tolosan; Vina Cana Rioja Blanco

FOOD

BISCUITS
Spar ginger nuts; Spar morning coffee biscuits; Spar rich tea fingers

BREADS, ROLLS, PIZZA BASES ETC
Spar brown rolls; Spar brown rolls-scotland; Spar Med standard loaf; Spar part-baked twin white baguettes; Spar part-baked white crusty rolls; Spar scottish batch bread; Spar thick standard loaf; Spar white pitta bread; Spar white rolls; Spar white rolls-scotland

CAKES & CAKE MIXES
Spar apple pies

CONFECTIONERY & SWEET SNACKS
Spar american hardgums; Spar Candy shack flying saucers; Spar mint imperials

COOKING AIDS - SAVOURY
Spar tomato puree

COOKING AIDS - SWEET
Glace cherries

CRACKERS, CRISPBREADS ETC
Spar cream crackers

PICKLES, SAUCES, VINEGARS ETC
Spar concentrated mint sauce; Spar Distilled vinegar; Spar malt vinegar; Spar Peanut butter crunchy; Spar Peanut butter smooth; Spar tomato ketchup

SAVOURIES - DRIED
Spar basmatti rice; Spar conchigile; Spar Fusilli; Spar lasagne; Spar pudding rice; Spar rigati(penne); Spar spaghetti

SAVOURIES - FROZEN
Spar American fries chips; Spar crinkle cut chips; Spar southern fried potato wedges; Spar Steakhouse chips; Spar value frying chips

SNACKS - SAVOURY
Spar large dry salted peanuts; Spar large salted peanuts; Spar Luxury Mixed nuts; Spar Mixed fruit; Spar onion bhajis; Spar pappadums; Spar salted cashews; Spar salted pistachios; Spar spicy crackers; Spar vegetable spring rolls

SPREADS - SWEET
Spar Medium orange marmalade

DRINK

BEERS
Spar lager; Spar premium lagar

CHAMPAGNE
Spar Cava rosado brut

LOW & NON-ALCOHOLIC
Spar lambrusco bianco

SOFT
Spar blue bear energy drink light; Spar blue bear energy drink reg; Spar cherryade; Spar lemonade; Spar orangeade

SPIRITS & APÉRITIFS
Spar Brandy; Spar canadian whiskey;
Spar COD whiskey; Spar cola; Spar
imperial vodka; Spar iron brew; Spar
london gin; Spar white rum; *Spar
finest:* Scotch whisky; *Spar saver:* Cola,
Lemonade

WINES - RED
Spar Australian shiraz cabernet; Spar
californain Red; Spar claret

WINES - ROSÉ
Spar Rose d'anjou

WINES - SPARKLING
Spar cava Brut

WINES - WHITE
Spar australian chardonnay semillon;
Spar chablis; Spar chilean chardonnay;
Spar Igt Pinot Grigio Veneto; Spar
Muscadet AC; Spar soave; Spar
Valpolicella; Spar VDP French Country
White

HOME & OFFICE

BLEACHES
Spar thick bleach original

WASHING POWDERS, STARCH ETC
Spar spring fresh fabric conditioner

FOOD

BISCUITS
Digestive biscuits; Morning Coffee; Morning coffee biscuits; *Crackers:* Water Biscuits - High Baked

BREADS, ROLLS, PIZZA BASES ETC
12 Crumpets; 2 soda farl; 4 fruited Teacakes; 4 pancakes; 4 Paninis; 4 plain muffins; 4 Potato Breads; 4 Potato Cakes; 5 Jam filled mini iced buns; 6 Fruited Teacakes; 6 Plain pitta breads; 6 reduced fat hot cross buns; 6 sultana scones; 8 Burger Buns; 8 Crumpets; Brown Loaf; Choco snaps; Ciabatta; Danish white bread-medium slice; Easter 6 hot cross buns; Everyday Medium sliced white bread; Fairtrade fruit mince pies; Fruit Loaf; Grand; Grand batard; Long life white baguette; Long life white petit pain; Longer life white bread-Medium; Mini gingerbread men; Naturally healthy - Wholemeal bread Med/Thick; Naturally healthy 4 large malted baps; Naturally healthy 6 wholemeal pitta breads; Naturally healthy 6 wholemeal rolls; Onion baton; Parisien white baguette; Pizza Base Mix; Scotch pancakes; Scottish square white bread-Medium; Truly irresistible 4 seeded batch rolls; Truly irresistible caramelised apple danish; Truly irresistible ciabatta; Truly Irresistible French White Baguette; Truly irresistible golden wholemeal seeded batch loaf; Truly irresistible irish brown batch loaf;

Truly irresistible mixed olive rolls; Truly irresistible Multigrain rustique; Truly irresistible oat topped batch rolls; Truly irresistible oatmeal batch loaf; Truly irresistible raisin & rosemary ring; Truly irresistible tomato tear and share bread; Truly irresistible white farmhouse batch loaf; Truly irresistible wholemeal seeded batch loaf; White bread thick; White demi baguette; *Baps:* 4 Large Malted, 4 Large White, 6 Burger Buns w Sesame Seeds, 6 Sliced Burger Buns w Sesame Seeds, 8 Burger Buns w Sesame Seeds; *International:* 4 Ready to Eat Poppadums; *Loaves:* Bakers Choice Medium White, Bakers Choice Medium White N. Ireland, Brown - Medium Sliced, Danish Medium, Danish Thick, Everyday White, Everyday Wholemeal Medium, Gold Malted Grain - Thick Sliced, Gold White Thick, Gold Wholemeal - Thick Sliced, Long Life White Medium, Longer Life White - Thick Sliced, Medium Sliced Wholmeal, Thick Sliced Wholemeal, White, White - Extra Thick Sliced, White Extra Thick N. Ireland, White Sliced, Wholemeal - Medium Sliced; *Naan Breads:* 2 Spicy Garlic, Garlic & Coriander, Meal Solutions Plain, Plain; *Pitta Bread:* 6 Garlic, 6 Plain, Healthy Living 6 Wholemeal; *Ready to Bake:* 2 Baguettes, 6 Petit Pain; *Rolls:* 12 Morning, 4 Premium White, 4 Wholemeal Deli Style, 6 Finger, 6 Morning, 6 White, 6 Wholemeal, 8 White, Bakers Choice White, Scottish White; *White Part Baked:* 2 Baguettes, Petit Pain

BREAKFAST FOODS

Bran Flakes; Choco Hoops; Corn flakes; Crisp rice; Crunchy oat cereal; Crunchy rice & wheat flakes; Everyday Frosted Flakes; Everyday Muesli; Fairtrade muselli; Frosted flakes; Fruit & fibre; Fruit & Nut Muesli; Golden nut cornflakes; Golden puffs; Healthy living porridge oats with wheatbran; High fibre bran; Instant Hot Oat Cereal; Instant hot oats; Malt crunchie cereal; Maple & Pecan Crisp; Maple and pecan crisp; Mixed Fruit Muesli; Mixed fruit muselli; No added sugar swiss muselli; Perfect choice; Strawberry crisp; Sultana Bran; Swiss muselli; Whole wheat biscuits; Wholewheat Biscuits

CAKES & CAKE MIXES

Crumble Mix; Fairy Cake Mix; Luxury Sponge Cake Mix; Rock Cake Mix; Scone Mix; Shortcrust Pastry Mix

CONFECTIONERY & SWEET SNACKS

American Hard Gums; Assorted fruit flavoured lollies; Assorted Fruit Flavour Lollies; Co-op streaky crispies; Dry roasted peanuts; Fizzy strawberry lances; Flying saucers; Fruit drops; Fruit jellies; Fruit Sherbet Mix; Mint imperials; Orange & Lemon Slices; Roasted salted cashews; Roasted salted peanuts; Rose & Lemon Flavour Turkish Delight

COOKING AIDS - SAVOURY

Barbecue style seasoning; Dumpling mix; Golden Breadcrumbs; Shortcrust pastry mix; *Stuffing Mixes:* Parsley & Thyme, Sage & Onion

COOKING AIDS - SWEET

Cut Mixed Peel; Fairtrade demerara sugar; Glace Cherries; Granulated Sweetener; Lemon Juice; Mincemeat; Ready To Roll Icing; Ready to Roll White Icing; *Baking:* Yu-Lade, Yu-Lade - Ginger; *Fruit Fillings:* Apple, Apple & Blackberry, Blackcurrant, Red Cherry; *Marzipan:* Golden, White

CRACKERS, CRISPBREADS ETC

Cream crackers; Italian plain breadsticks; Melba toast

DESSERTS

Custard powder; Rich fruit christmas pudding; Triple pack instant custard mix; Truly irresistable christmas pudding; Yu-lade; *Frozen:* Everyday Twin Apple Pies

DIPS & DRESSINGS

Salsa; Spiced Tomato & Onion; *Bag Salads:* Chardonnay Flavour Salad Dressing, French Dressing, Mint Drizzle, Pasta Salad, Spiced Orange Salad Dressing, Truly Irresistible Mango & Chilli Dressing; *Dressings:* French, Very Low Fat Vinaigrette; *Dressings - Low Cal:* Virtually Fat Free Vinaigrette; *Mustard:* Dijon, French

'ICE CREAMS', SORBETS ETC

10 Orange Juice Lollies; 10 Rocket Lollies; 10 sour lollipops; 6 Assorted push up fruit lollies; Assorted fruit lollies; *Sugar Free Mini-Pops:* Orangeade

PICKLES, SAUCES, VINEGARS ETC

Apple Sauce; Apricot jam; Barbecue relish; Black bean cook in sauce; Blackcurrant Jam; Chow mein stir fry sauce; Chunky vegatable pasta sauce; Crunchy peanut butter; Dijon mustard; English mint sauce; English mustard; Fairtrade Bramley Apple Sauce w Kentish Cider; Fairtrade Bramley apple sauce with kentish cider; Fairtrade Cranberry Sauce w Port; Fairtrade cranberry sauce with port; French Mustard; Healthy living tomato and herb pasta sauce; Hot and spicy pasta sauce; Jalfezi cook in sauce; Mint jelly; Mint sauce; Orange and ginger jam; Premium apricot soft set concerve; Premium Blackcurrant soft set conserve; Premium Raspberry soft set conserve; Premium red cherry soft set conserve; Reduced fat salad cream; Rogan josh cook in sauce; Sandwich pickle; Sandwich spread; Smooth peanut butter; Sweet and sour cook in sauce; Sweet picalilli; Tomato and herb pasta sauce; Truly irresistible apple sauce; Truly irresistible english mustard; Truly irresistible mint sauce; Truly irresistible sun-dried tomato and basil pasta sauce; Truly rresistible sweet red pepper and balsamic; Truly rresistible cranberry sauce; Wholegrain mustard; *Brown Sauce:* Brown Sauce, Everyday, Squeezy Bottle; *Chutneys:* Mango Chutney; *Clear Pickled Onions:* Silverskin, Standard, Strong; *Cook In Sauce:* Black Bean, Healthy Living Sweet & Sour, Jalfrezi, Rogan Josh, Sweet & Sour; *Fresh Pasta Sauces:* Organic Tomato & Basil; *Gherkins:* Baby in Vinegar, Pickled; *Pasta Sauces:* Arrabbiata, Garlic & Onion, Healthy Living, Hot & Spicy, Mushroom, Napoletana, Organic Tomato & Basil, Spicy Red Pepper, Sun-Dried Tomato & Basil, Sundried Tomato Vodka & Chilli, Tomato & Herb, w Mushrooms; *Pickled Beetroot:* Baby, Sliced, Sweet Crinkle Cut; *Pickled Onions:* Sweet; *Pickles:* Sandwich, Sweet; *Red Cabbage:* Sweet Pickled; *Relish:* Barbeque, Hamburger, Onion, Sweetcorn; *Tomato Ketchup:* Everyday, Squeezy, Standard; *Vinegar:* Distilled Malt, Malt

SAVOURIES - CANNED/BOTTLED

Baked Beans in Tomato Sauce; Everyday baked beans; Organic Baked beans in tomato sauce; Ratatouille Provencale; Reduced salt Baked beans in tomato sauce; *Baked Beans:* In Reduced Sugar & Salt Tomato Sauce, In Tomato Sauce, Organic in Tomato Sauce; *Spaghetti:* Everyday, In Reduced Sugar & Salt Tomato Sauce, In Tomato Sauce, Organic in Tomato Sauce, Rings In Tomato Sauce

SAVOURIES - CHILLED/FRESH

12 Indian selection; 4 Vegetable spring rolls; 6 Onion bhajis; Arrabbiata pasta sauce; Beetroot Salad; Chinese stir fry with mushrooms and coriander; Classic salad with green herb dressing; Family vegatable stir fry; Gourmet pasta salad; Houmous; Italian pasta salad; Mixed vegetable stir fry; Moroccan cous cous; Mushroom stir fry; Organic tomato &

basil pasta sauce; Premium Moroccan Style Couscous; Ready to Roast Potatoes; Reduced red pepper houmous; Sichaun stir fry; Simply stuffed mushrooms; Sweet and sour stir fry; Sweetcorn with chilli oil herb dressing; Truly irresistible Babyleaf salad with blackberry and mint dressing and seed sprinkles; Vegetable kebab kit with herb dressing; *Deli:* Bombay Potato, Croutons, Hot & Spicy Potato Wedges, Mammoth Green Olives (52%) (stone in) in a Lemon Marinade, Mini Onion Bhaji, Mini Vegetable Samosa, Mini Vegetable Spring Roll, Mixed Leaf Salad, Moroccan Style Cous Cous, Mushroom Provencale, Onion Bhaji, Pilau Rice, Potato Wedges, Stuffed Olives, Vegetable Samosa, Vegetable Spring Rolls; *Ethnic Snacks:* Onion Bhajis, Party Mini Bhaji Selection w Dip, Vegetable Samosas; *Meal Solutions - Indian:* Aloo Saag, Bombay Potatoes, Fragrant Pilau Rice, Peshwari Rice, Pilau Rice; *Meal Solutions - Snacks:* 6 Mini Spring Rolls; *Potato Wedges:* Garlic & Herb, Party Pack; *Ready Meals - Oriental:* Vegetable Spring Rolls 4; *Snack Salads:* Gourmet Pasta Salad, Premium Moroccan Style Cous Cous; *Stir Fry:* Black Bean, Mixed Vegetable, Sichuan, Sweet & Sour, Szeuchan; *Truly irresistible:* Baby beetroot in a sweet chilli marmalade, Mango and chilli salad dressing, Power stir fry; *Variety Salads:* Beetroot, Pasta & Pepper, Pasta & Tomato, Three Bean

SAVOURIES - DRIED

Everyday spaghetti; Everyday vegetable soup; Instant mashed potato; Microwavable mediterranean rice; Sage and onion stuffing mix; Spaghetti rings in tomato sauce; *Savoury Rice:* Barbecue Flavour, Biryani, Chicken Flavour, Curry, Mixed Vegetable, Mushroom, Pilau

SAVOURIES - FROZEN

12 mini vegetable spring rolls; Breaded Vegetable Rings; Golden Vegetable Rice; Italian Style Vegetable Stir Fry; Mini Spring Roll Selection; Oriental Style Mixed Vegetable Stir Fry; Oven Crunchies; *Fry Chips:* Everyday Straight Cut, Steak Cut; *Frying Chips:* Crinkle Cut, Steak Cut; *Microwave Chips:* Crinkle Cut; *Onion Rings:* Breaded; *Oven Chips:* American Style 3-way Cook, Crinkle Cut, Crinkle Cut 3-way Cook, Everyday, Healthy Living Reduced Fat, Steak Cut 3-way Cook, Straight Cut, Straight Cut 3-way Cook; *Potato Products:* Hash Browns, Hot & Spicy Wedges, Party Mini Rostis, Plain Cut Wedges, Roast Potatoes, Waffles, Wedges; *Potatoes:* Crispy, Roast

SEASONAL FOODS

6 Deep Filled Mince Pies; *Nuts:* Xmas Roasted & Salted Pistachios; *Xmas Puddings:* Premium, Rich Fruit

SNACKS - SAVOURY

Bombay Mix; Chilli Tortilla Chips; Dry roasted peanuts; Fairtrade salted peanuts; Fruit and nut mix; Mini breadsticks; Mini Poppadums; Oatcakes; Ready Salted Potato Rings; Roasted and salted cashews; Roasted and salted jumbo peanuts; Roasted salted pistachios in shells; Truly irresistible black olive and basil twists; *Nuts:* Assorted Mixed Nuts & Raisins, Mixed Nuts & Raisins, Mixed Nuts & Raisins - 2003, Roasted Salted Cashews, Roasted Salted Mixed, Roasted Salted Peanuts & Cashew Nuts; *Peanuts:* Large Roasted Salted, Large Salted, Roasted Salted; *Potato Crisps:* Organic Ready Salted, Smoky Bacon Flavour (Single Bag within Multi), Trad Ready Salted, Trad Salt & Vinegar; *Ready Salted:* Crunchy Sticks

SOUPS

Broth & Soup Mix; Organic Vegetable; Potato & Leek; Thick Vegetable; *Packet:* Calorie Counter Cup Soup Minestrone

SOYA AND OTHER 'MILKS'

Organic Unsweetened Soya Drink; UHT Sweetened Soya Drink; *Soya Drink:* Organic Sweetened, Unsweetened

SPICES

Cajun Style Seasoning; Chinese Style Seasoning; Mediterranean Style Seasoning; Mexican Style Seasoning; Thai Style Seasoning; *Curry Powder:* Hot, Mild

SPREADS - SAVOURY

Truly irresistitible coarsegrain mustard; Truly irresistible dijon mustard; Yeast Extract; *Peanut Butter:* Crunchy, Smooth

SPREADS - SWEET

Bramble Jelly; Ginger Conserve; Truly irresisitible thick cut fresh fruit three fruits marmalade; Truly irresistible fine cut fresh fruit seville orange marmalade; *Jam:* Apricot, Blackcurrant, Damson, Everyday Mixed Fruit, Orange & Ginger, Plum, Raspberry, Raspberry Seedless, Strawberry; *Marmalade:* 3 Fruits, Coarse Cut Orange, Everyday Thin Cut Orange, Fine Cut Orange, Orange Jelly - Thin Cut, Orange Shredless, Sweet Orange, Thick Cut Orange, Thin Cut Lemon; *Premium Soft Set Conserve:* Apricot, Blackcurrant, Raspberry, Red Cherry, Strawberry

DRINK

ALCOPOPS

Glitz Black Ice: Vodka Blend; *Glitz Ice:* Orange, Vodka Blend - Blueberry, Vodka Blend - Crystal; *Glitz Imperial:* Black, Blackcurrant, Lemon, Orange, Watermelon

BEERS

Belguim premium lager; Best Bitter; Czech premium lager; Delaney's irish country cream; Fairtrade organic ale; French Premium Lager; Mild; Organic ale; Premium lager; Spanish premium lager; Strong premium ale; Summer breeze; Summer Breeze Ale; Super strength lager; Traditional Bitter; Wheat beer; *Lagers:* Belgian Premium, French Premium, Premium, Spanish Premium, Superstrength

CIDERS & PERRIES
Strong dry cider; Tillington Hill Premium Reserve Dry Cider

'HOT'
Camomille Infusion; Drinking Chocolate; Fairtrade Mulled Wine Sachet; Green Tea; Peppermint Infusion; Truly Irresistible Fairtrade Drinking Chocolate

LOW & NON-ALCOHOLIC
Lemonade Shandy

SOFT
Apple & Raspberry from Concentrate Drink; Apple and mixed berry juice drink; Apple,strawberry and redcurrant squash; Bitter Lemon; Blackcurrant cordail; Citrus juice drink; Cloudy Lemonade; Cranberry juice drink; Diet cola; Diet lemonade; Everyday cola; Fairtrade mango and orange smoothie; Fairtrade orange and pink guava smoothie; Ginger ale; Lime cordial; Mixed fruit flavour squash; No added Limeade; No added sugar caffeine free cola; No added sugar cherryade; No added sugar limeade; No added sugar orangeade; No added sugar raspberryade; No added sugar Still apple and blackcurrant flavour juice drink; No added sugar strawberryade; Orange,lemon and pineapple squash; Sparkling cranberry juice drink with spring water; Sparkling lemonade shandy; Tropical fruit flavour juice drink; Tropical fruit juice drink; *American Dry Ginger Ale:* Low Calorie, Standard;

Bitter Lemon: Low Calorie, Standard; *Carbonates:* Cloudy Lemonade, Cola Flavour Drink, Cream Soda, Dandelion & Burdock, Everyday Lemonade, Ginger Beer, Orangeade, Soda Water, Sparkling Apple Juice, Sparkling Apple Juice from Concentrate, Standard Lemonade; *Cola:* Everyday, Standard; *Cordials:* Apple & Blackcurrant Flavour Drink, Blackcurrant Flavour, Lime w Sugar & Sweeteners, Mixed Fruit Flavour Drink, Whole Lemon Flavour Drink, Whole Orange Flavour Drink; *Crush:* Pink Grapefruit; *Diet Carbonates:* Cloudy Lemonade, Cola, Lemonade; *Everyday:* Low Calorie Orange Drink, Orange Lemon & Pineapple Flavour Drink; *Everyday No Added Sugar:* Orange Lemon & Pineapple Flavour Drink; *High Juice:* Apple, Apple Squash, Blackcurrant, Orange, Pineapple & Grapefruit, Tropical Fruit; *Indian Tonic Water:* Low Calorie, Standard, w a Twist of Lemon, w a Twist of Lime, w Lemon; *Juice:* Apple, Tomato; *Juice Drink:* Citrus, Cranberry, Sparkling Cranberry w Spring Water; *Juice Drinks:* Apple & Blackcurrant, Apple & Mixed Berry, Cranberry, Fairtrade Orange From Concentrate, Tropical; *No Added Sugar:* Orange Drink, Orange Drink w Sweeteners, Strawberryade, Summer Fruits Flavour Fruit & Barley Drink; *No Added Sugar Barley Water:* Pink Grapefruit; *No Added Sugar Carbonates:* Caffeine Free Cola, Cherryade w Sweeteners, Cola, Cola w Sweeteners, Lemonade w Sweeteners, Limeade w Sweeteners, Orange &

Peach Fruit Juice Drink, Raspberryade, Strawberryade w Sweeteners; *No Added Sugar Cordials:* Apple & Blackcurrant Flavour Drink, Apple Flavour Drink, Lemon & Lime, Strawberry, Whole Orange Flavour Drink; *No Added Sugar Diet Carbonates:* Cherryade, Lemonade, Limeade, Orangeade; *No Added Sugar Diet Crush:* Apple, Grapefruit, Lemon & Lime, Orange, Pineapple & Grapefruit; *No Added Sugar Fruit & Barley Drink:* Peach & Apricot Flavour, Pink Grapefruit Flavour; *No Added Sugar Juice Drink:* Orange & Peach Still, Tropical, Tropical w Sweeteners; *No Added Sugar Juice Drinks:* Apple & Strawberry, Apple & Strawberry w Sweeteners, Blackcurrant, Blackcurrant w Sweeteners; *No Added Sugar One Shot Bottles:* Apple & Blackcurrant Fruit Juice Drink, Apple & Blackcurrant Still Juice Drink; *Orange Juice:* Everyday Pure, Fair Trade (Smooth), Freshly Squeezed, Pure Florida from Concentrate w Juicy Bits, Pure from Concentrate; *Pure Juice:* Orange & Pineapple, Pineapple; *Pure Juice from Concentrate:* Apple, Florida Pink Grapefruit, Grapefruit, Pineapple; *Sparkling Spring Water:* Elderflower & Lime; *Sparkling Spring Water Drink:* Apple & Blackberry, Lemon & Lime, Orange & Cranberry, Peach, Raspberry

SPIRITS & APÉÉRITIFS

Napoleon Brandy; Premium Fair Trade White Rum; Premium London Dry Gin; Premium Scotch Whisky; Premium Triple Distilled Vodka; Scotch Whisky; *Delaney's:* Irish Cream, Irish Whiskey

WINES - FRUIT

Ginger; Green Ginger

WINES - RED

Australian Red Wine; Cape Boo Bridge Shiraz; Cape Shiraz Reserve; Chilean Cabernet Sauvignon; Chilean Cabernet Sauvignon Reserve; Chilean Merlot; Corbières Rouge; Côôtes du Rhone; Cyprus Island Vines Red Wine; Cyprus Mountain Vines Cabernet Sauvignon; Cyprus Mountain Vines Semillon; Elephant Trail Shiraz Pinotage; Jacaranda Hill Shiraz; Long Slim Chilean Cabernet Merlot; Rioja Cuvee Nathalie; Romanian Prairie Merlot 2000; Swirling Skirts Argentinian Bonarda Shiraz Famatina Valley; Underworld Shiraz Viognier; Vin de Pays d'Oc Cabernet Sauvignon 2003; Vin de Pays d'Oc Fruity Red Wine; Vin de Pays d'Oc Merlot; Vin de Pays d'Oc Shiraz 2003; Vin de Table Red; *Fair Trade:* Cape Affinity Red, Cape Cabernet Sauvignon, Shiraz Reserve; *Laid Back Ruby:* Ruby Cabernet, Ruby Cabernet 2002, Ruby Cabernet 2003; *Organic:* Tierra Sana Tempranillo

WINES - ROSÉ

Cape Ha-de-da Rose; Vin de Pays d'Oc Shiraz Roséé 2003; Vin de Pays d'Oc Syrah Roséé 2001; *Fair Trade:* Chilean Merlot Roséé 2004

WINES - SPARKLING
Bucks Fizz; Tempranillo Sparkling Red
Wine 2003; Tempranillo Sparkling Red
Wine 2004

WINES - WHITE
Australian Orange Sauvignon Blance
Reserve 2000; Australian White Wine;
California Chardonnay Colombard The
Big Chill; California Chardonnay
Colombard The Big Chill 2003;
California Starlight Coast Chardonnay;
California Starlight Coast Zinfandel;
Cape Chardonnay Reserve - Seal Bay;
Cape Oak Aged Chenin Blanc; Cape
White; Catalan Chardonnay Jaume
Serra - Barrel Fermented; Chilean
Chardonnay; Chilean Chardonnay
Reserve; Corbièères; Elephant River
Colombard Cardonnay; Hungarian
Chardonnay 3 litre; Hungarian White;
Lambrusco Bianco; Long Slim Chilean
Chardonnay Semillon; Reserve Côôtes
du Rhone Blanc 2003; Sicilian White;
South Australian Chardonnay; Vin de
pays d'oc Cotes des Gascogne 2003;
Vin de Pays d'Oc Chardonnay 2003;
Vin de Pays du Jardin de la France
Sauvignon Blanc 2003; *Fair Trade:* Cape
Chenin Blanc 2003, Cape Chenin Blanc
2004, Cape Unity White; *Organic:* Cape
Soleil Chardonnay, French Vin de Pays
d'Oc Chardonnay Sauvignon Blanc

TOILETRIES & COSMETICS

BATH & SHOWER
Liquid Shower-Premium: Body Wash -
Refreshing

FOOD

BISCUITS

Celery seed Biscuits; Cream cracker; Fruit Shortcake; Ginger Nuts; High Bake; Morning coffee biscuits; Oatcakes with cracked black pepper; Rich Tea Biscuit; Rich Tea Finger; Rye & Sesame biscuits; Traditional breadsticks; *Patisserie:* Gromit Biscuit

BREADS, ROLLS, PIZZA BASES ETC

Brown Pitta Bread; Brown Rolls; Brown Thin Sliced Bread; Cinnamon and Raisin Bagels; Crusty Wholemeal Farmhouse; Daktyla; Farmhouse Batch Crusty White; Farmhouse Batch Malted and Seeded; Farmhouse Batch Multigrain; Farmhouse Batch Soft White; Farmhouse Batch Wholemeal; Farmhouse Batch Wholemeal and Seeded; Focac Rosemary; Fruited Teacakes; Giant Pretzels; Granary; Granary Rolls; Hot Cross Buns; Italian Ciabatta; Italian Style Panini; Longer Life White Medium Sliced Bread; Longer Life Wholemeal Medium Sliced Bread; Mediter Ciaba; Mixed Sliced Bloomer; Organic Bagels; Organic Wholegrain Farmhouse; Organic Wholegrain Tin; Organic Wholemeal Tin; Pane Rustico; Pitta Bread 6; Poppadums; Sea salt & Cracked Black Pepper Pretzels; Seeded Batch Loaf; Soft White Bread Medium Sliced; Soft White Bread Thick Sliced; Stoneground Wholemeal Bread Medium Sliced; Tuscan Unsalted Bread; Walnut Bread; White and Wholegain Bread Medium Sliced; White and Wholegrain Bread Thick Sliced; White Batch; White Burger Buns; White Crusty Rolls; White Floured Baps; White Giant Baps; White Granary Rolls; White Medium Sliced Bread; White Picnic Pitta Bread; White Pitta Bread; White Rolls; White Sliced Bloomer; White Thick Sliced Bread; White Tin; Wholegrain Farmhouse; Wholegrain Long Tin; Wholegrain Muffins; Wholemeal and Seeds Bread Thick Sliced; Wholemeal and Seeds Thick Sliced; Wholemeal Baps; Wholemeal Batch; Wholemeal Medium Sliced Bread; Wholemeal Pitta Bread; Wholemeal Rolls; Wholemeal Soft Sandwich; White Finger Rolls; *Frozen Products:* Half Baguettes, Petits Pains; *Unwrapped Bakery:* Baguette, Boule, Crusty Rolls, Flute, French Roll, Granary Pave, Granary Tin, Herb Knot, Malt Tin, Mised Olive Rustic, Organic Baguette, Organic Brown Bread, Organic Malt Long Tin, Organic White Bread, Organic White Farmhouse, Organic White Large Tin, Pain Au Levain, Pain Cirque, Petit Mange Blanc, Petit Pain, Petit Parisienne, Plain Bagels, Poppy Knot, Poppy Knot Seeded Roll, Pretzel, Round Crusty Roll, Rustic Wholemeal Roll, Seeded Bloomer, Stone Baked Baguette, Walnut Roll, White Bloomer, White Farmhouse, White Granary, White Granary Knot, White Long Split Tin, White Sandwich, White Sourdough Bread, White Tin, Wholemeal roll

BREAKFAST FOODS

Apricot and Fig Muesli; Blueberry & Cranberry Crisp; Cranberry and Blueberry Muesli; Cranberry Muesli; Fruit & seed Muesli; Fruit and Nut Muesli; Fruit Muesli; Fruit Seed and Nut Muesli; Malted Wheats; Maple & Nut Muesli; Maple & Pecan Crisp; Muesli; Muesli Base; Tropical Muesli; Wholegrain Apricot Wheats; Wholegrain Cranberry Wheats; Wholewheat Biscuits; *Orchard:* Fruit Muesli; *Perfect Balance:* Malted Flakes Cereal

CHOCOLATE

After Dinner Mints; Plain Chocolate; Swiss Dark Chocolate

CONFECTIONERY & SWEET SNACKS

Chocolate brazil nuts; Clear Mints; Mint imperials; Mint thins

COOKING AIDS - SWEET

Chinese Stem Ginger in Syrup; Rhubarb chunks in light syrup; *Marzipan:* Golden, White; *Topping:* Blueberry & Blackcurrant, Morello Charry and Kirsch, Orange & Passion Fruit, Raspberry

DESSERTS

Summer Pudding; Winter Pudding; *Patisserie:* Apple and Blackberry Pie, Apple Pie, Family Apple and Blackberry Pie, Family Apple Pie

DIPS & DRESSINGS

Fresh Salsa; Guacomole Supreme; Homous Mini Pots; Houmous; Organic Houmous; Reduced Fat Houmous; Roasted Red Pepper Houmous; Roasted Red Pepper Stir Through Sauce; Salsa Supreme; Slow Roasted Tomato Houmous

'ICE CREAMS', SORBETS ETC

Fruit Juice Lollies; Orange Juice Lollies; Rocket Lollies

PICKLES, SAUCES, VINEGARS ETC

Apple Sauce; Dark Soy sauce; Dijon mustard; Dill & Mustard Sauce; English mustard; French Dressing; French Mustard; Hot & Spicy Mango Chutney; Japanese Soy Sauce; Light Soy sauce; Mango Chutney; Mint Jelly; Mint sauce; Plum & Ginger sauce; Red Onion Chutney; Roasted Mediterranean Vegetable Stir Through Sauce; Salsa Relish; Spicy Peach Chutney; Sticky Barbecue Marinade; Sun Dried Tomato Stir Through Sauce; Teryki Sauce; Tewkes mustard; Thai Marinade; Tomato & Chilli Marinade; Tomato & Mixed Mushroom Pasta Sauce; Tomato & Onion Relish; Tomato and Basil Cooking Sauce; Tomato and Chilli Pasta Sauce; Wholegrain mustard

SAVOURIES - CHILLED/FRESH

Beetroot Salad; Cous Cous and Roast Vegetable Salsa; Falafel; Marinated Artichokes; Mini Vegetable Spring Rolls; Moroccan Cous Cous Salad; Olive Oil

Mash; Pasta and Roast Vegetable Salad; Rice and Mango Salad; Spinach & Carrot Pilau; Tomato and Garlic Pizza with Chilli Oil; *Food Court:* Bombay Potatoes, Carrot Orange & Beetroot salad, Cherry Tomato Salad, Chickpea & Bean Salad, Chilli Stuffed Kalkid, Couscous & Roasted Vegetable Salad, Couscous Roast Veg, Italian Antipasti, Masala Dal, Mediterranean Pasta Salad, Mediterranean Vegetable, Mediterranean vegetable salad, Moroccan Couscous salad, Pasta Roast Veg, Peperoni Rossi, Rice Lentil & Mushroom salad, Sambhar, Seasonal Potato Salad, Spiced Potato Salad, Spicy Mexican Bean, Spinach & Carrot pilau, Stuffed Kalkid, Tabbouleh Salad, Tarragon Bean, Vegetable Spring Roll

SAVOURIES - FROZEN
American Fries; Crinkle Oven Chips; Curly Fries; Fry Chips; Potato Rosti; Potato Skins with Sea Salt and Cracked Black Pepper; Spicey Wedges; Steak Cut Oven Chips; Straight Cut Oven Chips; Straight Cut Oven or Fry Chips

SNACKS - SAVOURY
Hand cooked potato crisps: Sea salt; Lemon & Thyme; Low fat crinkle cut; Natural Roasted Cashew Nuts; Natural Roasted Peanuts; Organic Crisps; Potato Hoops; Potato sticks; Ratatoullie; Ready salted crisps; Roasted & Salted Nut mix; Roasted salted Cashew; Roasted salted large peanuts; Salt & vinegar crisps; *Crisps:* Onion Rings, Salt & Vinegar Twirls

SOUPS
Aubergine & Red Pepper Soup; Chunky Minestrone; Chunky Three Bean; Italian Bean Soup; Pumpkin & Coconut Soup; Thai Coconut & Chilli Soup; Tomato & Basil; Tuscan Bean

SOYA AND OTHER 'MILKS'
Organic soya

SPICES
Curry powder; Italian Seasoning; Mixed Herbs; Mixed Spice

SPREADS - SAVOURY
Organic Peanut Butter; Smooth Peanut Butter; Wholenut Peanut Butter

SPREADS - SWEET
Ginger Conserve; Maple Syrup No1; Maple Syrup No2; Soft set Raspberry Conserve continental; *Jam:* Reduced Sugar Apricot, Reduced Sugar Berries & Cherries, Reduced Sugar Blackcurrant, Reduced Sugar Raspberry, Reduced Sugar Strawberry, Soft set Apricot Conserve continental, Soft set Blackcurrant Conserve continental, Soft set Morello Cherry conserve; *Marmalade:* Fresh Fruit 3 Fruits, Fresh Fruit Grapefruit, Fresh Fruit Lemon, No Peel Orange, Orange & Ginger, Reduced sugar Orange, Seville Orange, Star Ruby Grapefruit; *Organic Marmalade:* Seville Orange

DRINK

CHAMPAGNE
Fleury Pèère et Fils Brut NV
Champagne, France; G. H. Mumm
Demi Sec NV Champagne, France;
Mumm Cordon Rouge NV Champagne,
France; Waitrose Blanc de Blancs NV
Champagne, France; Waitrose Brut NV
Champagne, France; Waitrose Brut
Special Reserve 1996 Vintage
Champagne, France; Waitrose Brut
Special Reserve 1999 Vintage
Champagne, France

'HOT'
Cocoa; Drinking chocolate

SOFT
Alphonso mango & Passion Fruit
smoothie; Blueberry Juice Drink; Pink
lemonade Crush; Pomegranate Juice
Drink; Still Lemonade; Tropical Crush

WINES - RED
Angove's Stonegate Limited Release
Petit Verdot 2005/06 S Australia;
Araldica Albera Barbera d'Asti
Superiore 2005 Piemonte, Italy;
Bouchard Pèère et Fils 2004/05 Savigny-
lèès-Beaun, Burgundy, France; Brown
Brothers Tarrango 2006 Victoria,
Australia; Canaletto Primitivo 2004/05
Puglia, Italy; Casanova di Neri Tenuta
Nuova 2002 Brunello di Montalcino,
Toscana, Italy; Cave de Bully Cuvéée
des Vignerons 2006 Beaujolais,
Burgundy, France; Cave de Saint-
Déésirat Cuvéée Prestige 2004 Saint-
Joseph, Rhôone, France; Cave des
Clairmonts 2005 Crozes-Hermitage,
Rhôone, France; Chapoutier, Organic
Côôtes du Rhôone 2005/06 France;
Chââteau de Chéénas 2006 Moulin-àà-
Vent, Burgundy, France; Chââteau
Maris Vieilles Vignes 2004/05 Minervois
Cru La Livinièère , South of France;
Chateau Musar 2000 Bekaa Valley;
Chââteau Saint-Maurice 2004 Côôtes
du Rhôone, France; Crozes-Hermitage
2004/05 Alain Graillot, Rhôone, France;
Cuvéée Chasseur 2006 Vin de Pays de
l'Héérault, Languedoc, South of France;
Deakin Estate Merlot 2004 Victoria,
Australia; Diemersfontein Pinotage
2007 Wellington, South Africa;
Domaine Albert Mann Grand P Pinot
Noir 2004 Alsace, France; Domaine de
la Perrièère 2005/06 Corbièères, South
of France; Domaine de la Vougeraie Les
Petits Noizons 2005 Pommard,
Burgundy, France; Domaine Heresztyn
Vieilles Vignes 2004 Gevrey-
Chambertin, Burgundy, France;
Domaine Pascal Maillard 2005 Chorey-
lèès-Beaune, Burgundy, France;
Duckhorn Vineyards Merlot 2004 Napa
Valley California, USA; Eva's Vineyard
Chenin Blanc / Pinot Grigio /
Kiráályleáányka 2005 Neszméély
Region, Hungary; Finca Flichman Shiraz
Oak Aged Reserva 2006 Mendoza,
Argentina; Fruits of France Grenache
2006 Vin de Pays d'Oc, South of
France; Gracia Merlot / Mourvèèdre
Reserva Superior 2004 Maipo Valley,

Chile; Henschke Henry's Seven Shiraz / Grenache / Mourvèèdre / Viognier 2004 Barossa Valley, S Australia; Herrick Shiraz 2006 Vin de Pays d'Oc, South of France; Jean-Luc Colombo 2006 Crozes Hermitage, Rhôône, France; La Chasse du Pape Shiraz 2006 Vin de Pays d'Oc, South of France; La Rectorie 2006 Côôtes du Ventoux, Rhôône, France; La Vieille Ferme Red 2005 Côôtes du Ventoux, Rhôône, France; Mas Collet Celler de Capççanes 2003 Montsant, Spain; Monasterio de Santa Ana Monastrell 2005 Jumilla, Spain; Mont Gras Cabernet Sauvignon / Syrah Reserva 2005 Colchagua Valley, Chile; Montes Alpha Syrah 2006 Apalta Vineyard, Colchagua Valley, Chile; Peter Lehmann Clancy's 2004 Barossa Valley, Australia; Peter Lehmann Shiraz 2004/05 Barossa Valley, S Australia; Querciabella Classico 2004 Chianti, Toscana, Italy; Ravelli Rosso 2006, Italy; Rutherglen Estates Durif 2005 Victoria, Australia; St Hallett Gamekeeper's Reserve 2006 Barossa Valley, S Australia; Terra Viva Merlot del Veneto 2006 Veneto, Italy; Yalumba Handpicked TGV 2005/06 Barossa Valley, S Australia; Yalumba Organic Shiraz 2006 S Australia; Yalumba 'The Octavius' Old Vine Barossa Shiraz 2000 S Australia

WINES - SPARKLING

Blason de Bourgogne Créémant de Bourgogne Roséé NV, France; Freixenet Cava Rosado Brut NV, Spain; Louis Bouillot La Perle 2004 Créémant de Bourgogne France; Prosecco La Marca NV, Italy; Simonsig Brut Roséé 2005 South Africa; Waitrose Cava Brut NV, Spain

WINES - WHITE

Blason de Bourgogne 2006 Saint-Vééran, Burgundy, France; Cape Grace Semillon / Chenin Blanc 2007 South Africa; Cape Mentelle Semillon / Sauvignon Blanc 2007 Margaret River, W Australia; Cardeto Orvieto Classico Secco 2006 Umbria, Italy; Catena Chardonnay 2006 Mendoza, Argentina; Cave de Buxy Les Coèères 2005/06 Montagny Premier Cru, Burgundy, France; Cave de Lugny Chardonnay 2006 Mââcon-Villages, Burgundy, France; Cave de Turckheim Gewüürztraminer 2006 Alsace, France; Cave des Vignerons de Chablis 2006 Petit Chablis, Burgundy, France; Domaine Fèèvre 2004 Chablis Grand Cru Côôte Bouguerots, Burgundy, France; Domaine Fèèvre 2004 Chablis Grand Cru Les Preuses, Burgundy, France; Domaine Fèèvre 2004 Chablis Grand Cru Vaudesir, Burgundy, France; Douglas Green Chardonnay 2007 Western Cape, South Africa; Fiano di Avellino dei Feudi di San Gregorio 2006 Campania, Italy; Finca Las Higueras Pinot Gris 2006/07 Lurton, Mendoza, Argentina; Henschke Louis Semillon 2005/06 Eden Valley, S Australia; Jackson Estate Sauvignon Blanc 2006/07 Marlborough, New Zealand; Joseph Drouhin 2005 Puligny-Montrachet Premier Cru Les Folatieres,

Burgundy, France; Joseph Drouhin 2006 Rully Premier Cru, Burgundy, France; La Chasse du Pape Chardonnay / Viognier 2005/06 Vin de Pays d'Oc, South of France; La Grille Classic Barrel Fermented Chenin Blanc 2006 Anjou, France; Nepenthe Riesling 2006 Adelaide Hills, S Australia; Palacio de Bornos Verdejo 2006 Rueda, Spain; Ravelli Bianco delle Venezie 2005/06 Veneto, Italy; Rustenberg Chardonnay 2005 Stellenbosch, South Africa; Stoneleigh Sauvignon Blanc 2007 Marlborough, New Zealand; The Naked Grape Sauvignon Blanc 2006 Vin de Pays des Charentes, France; Vincent Girardin Le Limozin 2004/05 Meursault, Burgundy, France; Waitrose Italian Organic Bianco Moncaro 2006 Marche, Italy; Wither Hills Sauvignon Blanc 2007 Marlborough, New Zealand; Yalumba Organic Viognier 2006/07 S

SUPERMARKETS NOTES

NOT LISTED?

The absence of a supermarket may be due to one of two reasons: the supermarket informed us that they do not, or no longer provide a vegan list (Iceland, Tesco and Lidl) or the supermarket did not respond to our repeated requests for information (Morrisons).

As with all manufacturers and retailers, they are most likely to improve their vegan customer service if they receive requests from many individual vegans; once they realise the size of the vegan market they are more likely to act as they will perceive it to be in their interest.

Iceland:

Iceland Foods Ltd
Second Avenue
Deeside Industrial Park
Deeside
Flintshire
CH5 2NW
Telephone: 01244 842842

You can email them using their online form at www.iceland.co.uk/feedback.

Lidl:

Lidl UK GmbH
19 Worple Road
Wimbledon
SW19 4JS
Telephone: 0870 444 1234

Morrisons:

Customer Service Dept
Wm Morrison Supermarkets plc
Hilmore House
Gain Lane
Bradford
BD3 7DL
Telephone: 0845 611 6111

Tesco

Tesco Customer Service
PO Box 73
Baird Avenue
Dryburgh Industrial Estate
Dundee
DD1 9NF
Telephone: 0845 7225533

THE HELPFUL

Some of the more enlightened supermarkets now take the step of marking their vegan own brand products. Although there is no substitute for The Vegan Society's own trademark, this is a very welcome development and shows an increased recognition of the importance of vegans as a group of customers.

Sainsbury's and the Co-op have good vegan labelling policies on their own brand products.

WHAT'S MISSING?

The listings we have received from the supermarkets have focused on the foods that they produce. The absence of own brand toiletries, cosmetics and household products in the listings does not mean that vegan products in these ranges do not exist. If enough people requested such information then it is likely that supermarkets could be persuaded to extend their vegan lists beyond their food ranges.

UP-TO-DATE?

Supermarkets regularly change their suppliers, or product lines. If you have a query about a particular product, you may wish to contact the company directly. See COMPANY CONTACTS, page 396.

When updates are made to lists, they will be available at www.animalfreeshopper.com

HUMANE COSMETICS STANDARD

The following supermarkets are approved by BUAV to use their Humane Cosmetics Standard on their own brand toiletries and cosmetics: the Co-op, Marks & Spencer. BUAV's humane standards only guarantee no animal testing, they don't guarantee no animal ingredients.

For more information on the Humane Cosmetics Standard, see ANIMAL TESTING CRITERIA, page 48.

CIWF COMPASSIONATE SUPERMARKET OF THE YEAR AWARDS

Every two years, Compassion in World Farming (CIWF) holds an awards ceremony for compassionate supermarkets. The winners in 2007/08 were as follows:

Compassionate Supermarket of the Year – Marks & Spencer

Most Improved Compassionate Supermarket – Sainsbury's

For more information, contact Compassion in World Farming (see USEFUL ADDRESSES, page 59)

COMPANY CONTACT DETAILS

- **A. Vogel** enquiries@bioforce.co.uk 01294 277 344
- **A'Beckett's Vineyard** www.abecketts.co.uk 01380 816669
- **Absolute Aromas** www.absolute-aromas.com 01420 540400
- **Absolutely Pure** www.absolutelypure.com 0870 760 6915
- **Acorn Products Co, LLC** www.acorn.com (207) 786-3526
- **Adeena Ltd** www.adeena.co.uk 08707 605 49321
- **Ahimsa Cosmetics** www.ahimsacosmetics.co.uk 07902 849763
- **Ainsworths** www.ainsworths.com 0207 935 5330
- **Ajitas Vege Chips** www.ajitas.com 61 7 55 250670
- **Akamuti** www.akamuti.co.uk 0845 458 9242
- **Alara Wholefoods Ltd** www.alara.co.uk 020 7387 9303
- **Aldi Stores Ltd** www.aldi-stores.co.uk 01827 710832
- **Alicer** www.alicer.com 32 4 362 9822
- **All Seasons Health** www.allseasonshealth.com 01329 230991
- **Allied Bakeries** www.alliedbakeries.co.uk 01628 764300
- **Allinson** www.allinsonbread.com
- **Alnavit GmbH** www.alnavit.de/ 06257 9322 088
- **Aloe Dent** www.optimah.com
- **Aloe Pura** www.optimah.com
- **Alpro UK Ltd** www.alprosoya.co.uk 01536 720 605
- **Alternative Stores** www.alternativestores.com 0191 236 1043
- **Alvin Connor Limited** www.alvinconnor.com 0151 448 0368
- **Amanda Trading Ltd T/A African Delights** www.africandelights.co.uk 020 8400 4842
- **AmaZene** www.amaZene.com 01279 239 222
- **Ambrosian Vegetarian Foods** www.synergynet.co.uk/ambrosian/our_range.htm 01283 225 055
- **Amisa** www.windmillorganics.com
- **Anglesey Natural Foods** www.quinova.co.uk 01248 422011
- **Anheuser-Busch** www.budweiser.co.uk
- **Anila's Authentic Sauces Ltd** www.anilassauces.com 020 8577 6162
- **Animal Aid Society** www.animalaid.org.uk 01732 364546
- **Ann Elise Skincare** www.anneliseskincare.co.uk 01304 368298
- **Annemarie Borlind** www.borlind.com
- **Aqua Natural** www.aquanatural.co.uk 01933 441818
- **Aquados Ltd** www.simplywashing.com 01924 894513
- **AquaSource** www.aquasourcealgae.com 01392 822155

- **Archers** www.archers.com
- **Arcim Hypogeen b.v.** www.hypogeen.nl 00 31 356 945 297
- **Aroma Comforts** 31 Hackney Grove, London, E8 3NR 0208 985 5956
- **Aroma Crystal Therapy** www.aromacrystal.com
- **Aromafoods** www.aromafoods.org.uk 0800 0744 876
- **Artisan Biscuits** www.artisanbiscuits.co.uk 01335 342 373
- **Asda** www.asda.com 0113 243 5435
- **Aspall** www.aspall.co.uk 01728 860 510
- **Astonish** www.astonishcleaners.com 0113 236 0036
- **Auro** www.auroorganic.co.uk 01452 772020
- **Australian Nougat Company** www.ausnougat.com.au 07548 853132
- **Aveda** www.aveda.co.uk
- **Aziz Chair** www.oleador.com 0049 160 366 8954
- **B&Q** www.diy.com 0845 609 6688
- **Babyboo Organics Ltd** www.babyboo-organics.co.uk 0870 850 1311
- **Babycakes Direct** www.babycakesdirect.co.uk 07951 215121
- **Babynat** www.babynat.co.uk
- **Bacheldre Watermill Organic Flowers** www.bacheldremill.co.uk 01588 620 489
- **Barefoot Botanicals** www.barefoot-botanicals.com 0870 220 2273
- **Baron Wine Cellars, Ltd T/A Tishbi Estate Winery** www.tishbi.com, www.tishbi.eu 972-4-6380434/5
- **Barry M Cosmetics** www.barrym.com 020 8349 2992
- **Baxters** www.baxters.co.uk 01343 820393
- **Beaming Baby** www.beamingbaby.com 0800 0345 672
- **Beanie's Health Foods** www.beanieshealthfoods.co.uk 01489 574 593
- **Beauty Naturals** www.beautynaturals.com 0845 094 0402
- **Beauty Without Cruelty** www.bwcv.com 01473 612641
- **Belvoir Fruit Farms** www.belvoircordials.co.uk 01476 870 286
- **Bendicks of Mayfair** www.bendicks.co.uk 01962 844800
- **Benecol** www.benecol.co.uk
- **Bertolli** www.bertolli.com
- **Betty Crocker** www.bettycrocker.com 1-800-446-1898
- **Bickiepegs** www.bickiepegs.co.uk 01224 790626
- **Bio-D** www.biodegradable.biz 01482 229950
- **Biofair** www.windmillorganics.com
- **Biofun bvba** www.biofun.be 0032 50 2898 07
- **Bio-Health Ltd** www.bio-health.co.uk 01634 290115
- **Biona** www.windmillorganics.com 020 8547 2775
- **Bio-Oil** www.bio-oil.info
- **Bisto** www.aahnight.co.uk 0800 234 6328

- **Black Opal International Australia** www.blackopalinc.com/index.html
- **Black Sheep Brewery Plc** www.blacksheepbrewery.com 01765 689227
- **Blackfriars Bakery** www.blackfriarsbakery.co.uk 0116 262 2836
- **Blue Dragon** www.bluedragon.com
- **Blue Lotus Products Ltd** www.bluelotusproducts.co.uk 0116 299 8122
- **B'Nice** www.bnice.be 00 (32) 1461 1306
- **Bodylove** www.cherrybliss.com
- **Boots Company Plc** www.boots-plc.com 0115 950 6111 / 0115 968 7035
- **Bourgeois Boheme** www.bboheme.com 0208 878 8388
- **Brackencraft** www.bsoaps.com
- **Braham & Murray Ltd** www.goodwebsite.co.uk 01271 858 377/ 0207 727 7785
- **Brakspear's** www.brakspear-beers.co.uk/ 01993 890 800
- **British Sugar plc** www.britishsugar.co.uk 020 7589 6363
- **Britvic** www.britvic.co.uk 0800 032 1767
- **Bronnley & Co Ltd** www.bronnley.co.uk 01280 702291
- **Broughton Pastures** www.BroughtonPastures.co.uk 01442 823 993
- **Brunel Healthcare** www.bruhealth.co.uk
- **Budgens Stores** www.budgens.co.uk 020 8422 9511
- **Budweiser** www.budweiser.com 020 8332 2302
- **Buitoni** www.buitoni.co.uk
- **Burton's Foods Ltd** www.burtonsfoods.com 0151 488 4536
- **Burt's Bees** www.forever-natural.com 01628 898410
- **Bute Island Foods Ltd** www.buteisland.com 01700 505357
- **Cadbury Trebor Bassett** www.cadbury.co.uk 0121 451 4444
- **Calder Valley Soap** www.uksoaps.net 01422 362202
- **Caledonian Brewing Co** www.caledonian-brewery.co.uk 0131 337 1286
- **Caledonian Curry Co.** www.caledoniancurry.co.uk 01863 766025
  Mobile: 0787 67 62 395
- **Capitelli Oils** www.capitelli-oils.co.uk
- **Carlsberg UK Ltd** www.carlsberguk.co.uk 01604 668866
- **Carmel Winery** www.carmelwines.co.il 020 8902 3002
- **Carrie's Cookies** carrie@soyummy.co.uk 01803 867080
- **Cauldron Foods Ltd** www.cauldronfoods.co.uk 0845 7413 666
- **Caurnie Soaperie** www.caurnie.com 0141 776 1218
- **Cawarra Cosmetics Ltd** www.sanctumaustralia.com 00 61 2 6680 3266
- **Cebra Ethical Chic** www.cebraonline.com 0117 385 1420
- **Cedar Health Ltd** www.cedarhealth.co.uk 0161 483 1235
- **Cellande Midlands** www.cellande.co.uk 0121 472 2903
- **Celtic Chocolates Ltd** info@celticchocolates.eu 00353-405 57077
- **Chegworth Valley Juices** www.chegworthvalley.com 01622 859 272

- **Chimans** sallyagarwal@yahoo.co.uk 01271 883864
- **Chocolala Limited** www.chocolala.co.uk 01422 844779
- **Clearspring** www.clearspring.co.uk 020 8749 1781
- **Clive's Pies** www.clivespies.co.uk 01364 642279
- **Colmans** www.colmans.co.uk 020 7822 5252
- **Colman's** www.colmans.co.uk
- **Constellation Wines** www.cbrands.eu.com 01483 690 000
- **Cooplands** www.cooplands.co.uk 01302 818000
- **Country Life** www.country-life.com
- **Cow & Gate** www.cowandgate.co.uk 08457 623 623
- **Cropton Brewery** www.croptonbrewery.co.uk 01751 417310
- **Cubana Produce LTD** www.spirel.co.uk 0207 427 5145
- **Cuisine de France** www.cuisinedefrance.ie 00353 1405 7200
- **D & D Chocolates** www.d-dchocolates.com 02476 370909
- **Daivita** www.mantra-care.com +386 5993 7683
- **Daler-Rowney Ltd** www.daler-rowney.com 01344 461 000
- **Daloon Foods** www.daloon.com
- **Daniel Field** www.danielfield.com 0800 077 8270
- **Daniel Field Laboratory Ltd** www.freefromproducts.com 07838 249071
- **Dark Secrets Chocolate** darksecretschoc@yahoo.co.uk 01273 476966
- **Dees Caribbean Imports** deesimports@hotmail.com 0208 5398484
- **Dendron Ltd** 42 Caxton Way, Watford Business Park, Watford, Hertfordshire, WD1 8QZ
- **Desert Essence** www.desertessence.com 020 8614 1411
- **Deva Nutrition** www.devanutrition.com (+001) 888 517 7620
- **Dietary Needs Direct** www.dietaryneedsdirect.co.uk 01527 570444
- **Diomed Developments Ltd** www.4headaches.co.uk
- **Dipak Foods Ltd** 13 Willowbrook Workshops, Syston Street West, Leicester, Leicestershire, LE1 2JU 0116 2511300
- **Dipl - Kfm (FH) Wolfgang Schiller** www.oleandor.com 00 49 511 470 3860
- **Discovery Foods** www.discoveryfoods.co.uk 01494 464460
- **Divine Chocolate** www.divinechocolate.com 020 7378 6550
- **Dixie Diners Club** www.dixiediner.com
- **Dm-drogerie markt GmbH & Co KG** www.dm-drogeriemarkt.de
- **Dolma** www.dolma-perfumes.co.uk 0115 963 4237
- **Dolmio** www.dolmio.co.uk 0800 952 1234
- **Dome** www.domecosmetics.com 020 8746 1900
- **Doves Farm Foods Ltd** www.dovesfarm.co.uk 01488 684880
- **Dr Hauschka** www.drhauschka.co.uk 01386 791 022
- **Dragonfly Foods** www.beany.co.uk 01364 642700

- **Dri-Pak Ltd** www.dripak.co.uk 0115 932 5165
- **Droyt Products** www.droyts.com 01257 417251
- **Dunkerton's Cider Company** www.dunkertons.co.uk 01544 388653
- **Durex** www.durex.com
- **Earth Footwear** www.earth.us and www.earthvegan.us 781-893-7474
- **Earth&Wear Limited** www.earthandwear.com 0845 257 5725/01745 571 881
- **Earthpure** www.earthpure.co.uk 01994 241 484
- **Earth's Beauty** www.earthsbeauty.com
- **Eat Me LTD** www.eatmeonline.com 0788 680 87 73
- **Ecco Bella** www.eccobella.com
- **Eco Lips, Inc** www.ecolips.com 00 1 319 364 2477
- **Ecos Paints** www.ecosorganicpaints.com 01524 852371
- **Ecosoapia** www.ecosoapia.com info@21stcenturyhealth.co.uk 0207 289 2121
- **EJs Conscious Chocolate** www.consciouschocolate.co.uk
  07949 171245 / 01892 546146
- **Ella Drinks** www.bouvrage.com 01786 834342
- **Emergen-C** www.emergenc.com 1-800-854-0249
- **Emiliana Organico** www.emiliana.cl
- **Energizer Personal Care** www.wetones.co.uk 01494 5333 00
- **Epson** www.epson.co.uk 08702 416900
- **Essential Care** www.essential-care.co.uk 01638 716593
- **Essential Trading Co-Operative Ltd** www.essential-trading.coop 0117 9583550
- **Essentially Natural** www.e-nat.co.uk 08000 664916
- **Essentially Yours Ltd** www.essentially-yours.co.uk 01372 463 322
- **Ethical Wares** www.ethicalwares.com 01570 471155
- **Eveolution Beauty Limited** www.shopeveolution.co.uk 01698 860046
- **Everards Brewery** www.everards.co.uk 0116 201 4100
- **Faith Products Limited** www.faithinnature.co.uk 0161 724 4016
- **Fantasy Ice Creams Ltd** www.fantasyicecream.co.uk
- **Fauser Vitaquellwerk KG** www.vitaquell.de 0049 40 572020
- **FaysNZ Ltd** www.fays.net 00 64 210310 939
- **Feel Good Handbags** www.feelgoodhandbags.co.uk 01695 580713
- **Fentimans Ltd** www.fentimans.com 01434 609847
- **Fertile Fibre** www.fertilefibre.co.uk/ 01432 853111
- **Fetzer Vineyards** www.fetzer.com
- **Figs & Rouge** product.nick@googlemail.com 01244 344321
- **First Foods Ltd** www.first-foods.com 01494 431355
- **First Quality Foods** www.firstqualityfoods.co.uk 08707 771910
- **Five Star Foodies** www.fivestarfoodies.com 00 1 513 272 6555
- **Floraroma Ltd** sandrine@brandarchitekts.com 020 8614 4700

- **Floris** www.florislondon.com 01884 242626
- **Fonseca** www.fonseca.pt
- **Forever Living Products** www.aloevera.co.uk 01327 830855
- **Forever Young International Limited** forever-young@lineone.net
  0208 648 6777
- **Freedom Brewery Ltd** www.freedomlager.com 01283 840721
- **Freerangers** www.freerangers.co.uk 01207 565957
- **Fry Group Foods** www.frys-special.com +27 31 700 3022/3
- **Full of Beans** tempeh@globalnet.co.uk 01273 472627
- **Fullers** www.fullers.co.uk 020 8996 2000
- **Funk Bubble** www.funkbubble.co.uk 07775 898 889
- **G & G Vitamins** www.gandgvitamins.com 01342 312 811
- **G. Costa & Co** www.gcosta.co.uk 01622 717777
- **Gama Healthcare Limited** www.gamahealthcare.com 08452 011 644
- **Geeta's Foods Limited** www.geetasfoods.com 0208 450 2255
- **General Dietary** www.generaldietary.com 020 8336 2323
- **Geo Organics** www.venturefoods.co.uk 01743 289 133
- **George Bateman & Son** mjcullimore@bateman.co.uk 01754 880317
- **Georgette bvba** www.georgette.be 0032 3289 9639
- **Gerber Juice Company** www.gerberfoods.com 01278 441600
- **Gilchesters Organics Ltd** www.gilchesters.com 01661 886119
- **Gluten Free Foods Ltd** www.glutenfree-foods.co.uk 020 8953 4444
- **Glyde Health PTY LTD** www.glydehealth.com 0061 2 9415 8933
- **Gobblin Wholefoods** Unit 5, Station Rd Ind Est·, Elmswell, Bury St. Edmund,
  Suffolk, IP30·9HR 01359 241841
- **Golden Wonder** www.goldenwonder.com 01724 281222
- **Goodlife Foods** www.goodlife.co.uk 01925 837810
- **GR Wright & Sons Ltd** www.wrightsflour.co.uk 0208 344 6900
- **Granose** www.hain-celestial.co.uk
- **Granovita UK Ltd** www.granovita.co.uk 01933 273717
- **Green People Co.** www.greenpeople.co.uk 01403 740350
- **Green Shoes** www.greenshoes.co.uk 01364 644 036
- **Green Valley Trading Co.** www.gvtc.co.uk or www.veganhealthandbeauty.com
  01283 769898
- **Green Wych** dawnireland.mysite.orange.co.uk (01803) 315012
- **Greencity Wholefoods** www.greencity.co.uk 0141 554 7633
- **Green's** www.kerrygroup.com
- **Grolsch** www.grolsch.co.uk 01283 513358
- **Guarana Company** www.guaranaco.com 01273 621406
- **Gwynt Y Ddraig Cider** www.gwyntcider.com 01443 209 852

- **Hall & Woodhouse Ltd** www.hall-woodhouse.co.uk
- **Halls** www.cadburyschweppes.com
- **Handmade Flapjack Company Ltd** www.handmade-flapjack.co.uk 024 7658 8350
- **Happy And Healthy Foods** info@happyandhealthyfoods.com +61242360529
- **Harbourne Vineyard** www.harbournevineyard.co.uk
- **Harlow Lubricants** www.harlube.co.uk 0208 203 9493
- **Health + Plus Ltd** www.healthplus.co.uk 01323 872277
- **Health Perception** www.health-perception.co.uk 01252 861 454
- **Healthpol** www.healthpol.co.uk 020 8360 0386
- **Healthquest Limited** www.healthquest.co.uk 0845 310 4411
- **Healthy and Essential** www.healthyandessential.com 08700 536000
- **Healthy Herbs** www.healthy-herbs.org 01565 755022
- **Hedgecraft** www.hedgecraft.co.uk
- **Heineken** www.heineken.com +31 (0)20 523 92 39
- **Heinz** www.heinz.co.uk 0208 573 7757
- **Hellmanns** www.hellmanns.co.uk 0800 435562
- **Hemp Garden** www.hempgarden.co.uk 01424 434370
- **Hendersons** www.hendersons-relish.co.uk 0114 272 5909
- **Herbs Hands Healing Ltd** www.herbshandshealing.co.uk 0845 3453727
- **Herbs of Grace** www.herbsofgrace.co.uk 01638 712123
- **Herbsgo Limited T/A Clive Foot** www.clivefoot.com 0114 2668100
- **High Barn Oils** www.highbarnoils.co.uk 01403 730326
- **Higher Nature Plc** www.highernature.co.uk 01435 883484
- **Hipp Organic Baby Foods** www.hipp.co.uk 0845 050 1351
- **Holistix** www.holistixherbs.co.uk 0151 734 1940
- **Holland and Barrett Retail Ltd** www.hollandandbarrett.com 02476244400
- **Holsten** www.holsten.de
- **Honesty Cosmetics Ltd** www.honestycosmetics.co.uk 01629 814888
- **Hotel Chocolat** www.hotelchocolat.co.uk 0870 442 8282
- **House of Dorchester** www.hodchoc.com 01420 84181
- **Hovis** www.hovisbakery.co.uk
- **Howad Ltd T/A Incognito** www.lessmosquito.com 0207 221 0667
- **Howden Soap Co.** www.howdensoap.co.uk 01430 434643
- **HP** www.hp.com
- **Hula Hoops** www.hulahoops.com
- **Humdinger Ltd** www.humdinger-foods.co.uk 01482 625790
- **Hypogeen** www.hypofit.com 0031356945297
- **I Am Natural** www.iamnatural.co.uk 07737 764 660/01903 815597
- **Ice Guard** www.optimah.com

- **ID Aromatics** www.idaromatics.co.uk 0113 242 4983
- **Il Mangiar sano S.p.A.** www.ilmangiarsano.com. 0039 0423 420099
- **Inbev** www.inbev.com 0870 24 111 24
- **Inika** www.inika.com.au +51 2 4268 5342
- **Innginni Limited (Ohsobo)** www.ohsobo.com 01923 842884 / 07967 810275
- **Innocent Oils** www.innocentoils.com 01473 622816
- **International Partnership Ltd (Seagreens Division)** www.seagreens.com 084506 400403
- **Its Elixir UK Limited** www.itselixir.com 01228 818 885
- **J&D Black Ltd** www.jdblack.co.uk 01252 344010
- **J.L. Bragg** www.charcoal.uk.com 01473 748345
- **Jason Natural Products** www.jason-natural.com 0800 626 697
- **Jeremy's Soups** jeremys.soups@tiscali.co.uk 017683 53311
- **Jethros** www.jethros.co.uk 01273 417 405
- **Jif** www.unilever.co.uk 020 7822 5252
- **Jingando** www.jingashop.com 0208 8771630
- **Johnnie Walker** www.johnniewalker.com
- **Jordans** www.jordans-cereals.co.uk 01767 318222
- **JR Liggett** www.jrliggett.com
- **Juice Beauty** www.juicebeauty.com
- **Junglesale Limited** www.junglesale.com 0871 2501271
- **Jus-Rol** www.jusrol.co.uk 0800 125 577
- **Just Wholefoods** www.justw.demon.co.uk 01285 651 910
- **K Creations** www.k-creations.co.uk 02380 559 943
- **Kallo Foods** www.kallofoods.com 01428 685100
- **Kelloggs** www.kelloggs.co.uk 0161 869 2000
- **Kerry Foods Ltd** www.puredairyfree.co.uk 01924 284 800
- **Kettle Chips** www.kettlefoods.co.uk
- **Kingfisher Natural Toothpaste** www.kingfishertoothpaste.com 01603 630484
- **Kingsmill** www.lovekingsmill.com 0800 197 0110
- **Kinnerton Ltd** www.kinnerton.com 020 7284 9500
- **Kitchen Garden** www.kitchen-garden.co.uk (01926)851415
- **Kitchen Garden Preserves** www.kitchengardenpreserves.co.uk 01453 759612
- **Knobbly Carrot Food Company** www.theknobblycarrot.co.uk 01570 422 064
- **Knorr** www.knorr.com
- **Kobashi** www.kobashi.com 01392 217628
- **Koochie Koo** www.koochiekoo.com 01277 224070
- **Kordel's** www.kordels.com
- **KP** www.kpnuts.com 08080 576887
- **Kudos Vitamins and Herbals** www.kudosvitamins.com 0800 389 5476

- **L'Age Vert Linxis** www.agevert.com 0033 344 09 02 74
- **Lanes Health** www.laneshealth.com 01452 524012
- **Larabar** www.larabar.com
- **Laverana** www.lavera.co.uk 00 49 51 0393 91-0/ 01557 870 203
- **Leeora Vegetarian Food** www.leeoras.co.uk 01206 330 334
- **Lifefood Czech Republic s.r.o.** www.lifefood.eu +420 606 656 656
- **Lifeplan Products Ltd** www.lifeplan.co.uk 01455 556281
- **Limney** www.davenportvineyards.co.uk 01892 852 380
- **Linda McCartney** www.lindamccartneyfoods.co.uk 0800 626 697
- **Lindt & Sprungli** www.lindt.com 020 8602 4100
- **Little Satsuma** www.littlesatsuma.com 07730 659002
- **Little Valley Brewery Ltd** www.littlevalleybrewery.co.uk 01422 883888
- **Live Native** www.livenative.com 01470 521704 / 07912 978608
- **Liz Earle** www.lizearle.com 01983 813 999
- **Longcroft Soap Company** www.longcroftsoap.co.uk 01324 411587
- **Love Foods** www.lovefoods.co.uk 0870 046 7010
- **Love the Planet** www.lovetheplanet.co.uk 01224 733955
- **Luscombe Organic Drinks** www.luscombe.co.uk 01364 64 30 36
- **Lush** www.lush.co.uk 01202 667830
- **LVF Mineral Makeup** www.lvfmineralmakeup.co.uk 07788446641
- **Lyme Bay Winery** www.lymebaywinery.co.uk 01297 551355
- **Lyme Regis Fine Foods Ltd** www.lymeregisfoods.com 01428 722 900
- **MacSween of Edinburgh** www.macsween.co.uk 0131 440 2555
- **Majestic Wine Warehouse Ltd** www.majestic.co.uk 01923 298 200
- **Majik Blankit Skin Care** www.majikblankit.co.uk 01424 421 907
- **Malagasy** www.malagasy.co.uk 0845 094 3827
- **Mandala Aroma Ltd** www.mandala-aroma.com 01254 831 629
- **Manic Panic** www.manicpanic.com
- **Marigold** www.marigoldhealthfoods.com 0207 388 4515
- **Marks & Spencer** www.marksandspencer.com 0845 302 1234
- **Marmite** www.marmite.co.uk
- **Mars** www.mars.com
- **Mason's Products** www.dogoil.co.uk 01706 379817
- **Masterfoods** www.masterfoods.co.uk
- **Maxim Marketing Company** www.maximmarketing.co.uk 020 8689 0773
- **McCain** www.mccain.co.uk 01723 584141
- **McCoys** www.unitedbiscuits.com
- **McKeith** www.gillianmckeith.info
- **McVities** www.unitedbiscuits.com
- **Mediterranean Foods (London) Ltd** www.mediterraneanfoods.uk.com
  020 89 688444

- **Meinklang** www.vintageroots.co.uk 0800 980 4992
- **Melbrosin UK Limited** www.kudosvitamins.com 01256 773299
- **Meridian Foods** www.meridianfoods.co.uk 01490 413 151
- **Merrydown** www.merrydown.co.uk 01737 735007
- **MH Foods Ltd** www.mhfoods.net 01322 337711
- **Michelob** www.michelob.com
- **Miss Bellasis** www.missbellasis.com 07776 081 846
- **MJ Health(NZ) Ltd** www.doctorwendy.net 0064 63531948
- **Montagne Jeunesse** www.montagnejeunesse.com 01639 861550
- **Montezumas Chocolates** www.montezumas.co.uk 0845 450 6304
- **Mood Food Company** www.moodfoodcompany.co.uk
- **Mood Foods Limited** www.cacaomagic.co.uk / www.moodfoods.biz
  01223 700424
- **Moom UK** www.moom-uk.com 08452345668
- **Mooncup Ltd.** www.mooncup.co.uk 01273 355020
- **Morrocco Method** www.morroccomethod.com 805 534 1600
- **Mothers Pride** www.premierfoods.co.uk 01727 815850
- **Mrs Crimble's** www.stilettofoods.com 08451 300869
- **Mulu Chocolate Ltd** www.muluchocolate.co.uk 0208 402 5809? 01702 527 158
- **Munchy Seeds** www.munchyseeds.co.uk 01728 833004
- **Natasha's Living Food** www.natashaslivingfood.ie +353 (0)1 6174 807
- **Natracare** www.natracare.com 0117 9823492
- **Natrol** www.natrol.co.uk
- **Natura Organics** www.naturaorganics.com 01273 808380
- **Natural by Nature Oils** www.naturalbynature.co.uk 01582 840848
- **Natural Eco-Trading Ltd** www.greenbrands.co.uk 01892 616871
- **Natural House Products Limited** www.natural-house.co.uk 0115 960 4038
- **Natural Insulation** www.naturalinsulations.co.uk 01920 821069
- **Natural Sense** www.naturalsenseproducts.co.uk 01424 716461
- **Natural Shoe Store** www.birkenstock.co.uk 020 7602 2866
- **Naturally Gifted** www.naturally-gifted.co.uk 0208 715 1245
- **Naturally ME Inc** www.naturalfeast.com 207 737 2237
- **Nature Complete Ltd** www.naturecomplete.com 020 8539 5585
- **Natureís Aid** www.naturesaid.co.uk 01772 686231
- **Natureís Own Ltd** www.natures-own.co.uk 01684 310022 / 310099
- **Nature's Aid Limited** www.naturesaid.co.uk 01772 686231
- **Nature's Gate** www.natures-gate.com
- **Nature's Path Foods INC** www.naturespath.com 1-888-808-9505
- **Natures Remedies** naturesremedies.uk.com 01494 727 888
- **Naturgreen** www.naturgreenfood.com

- **NaturKraftWerke** www.naturkraftwerke.com 0041 44 9722777
- **Neal's Yard Remedies** www.nealsyardremedies.com 01747 834 634
- **Nestlé** www.nestle.co.uk 01904 604 604
- **Never Too Busy To Be Beautiful** www.bnevertoobusytobebeautiful.com 01202 667830
- **New Balance** www.newbalance.co.uk 01925 423000
- **New Seasons** www.newseasons.co.uk 01235 821110
- **New York Bagel Co. LtdStarburst** www.newyorkbagel.co.uk 01709 580840
- **Neways International UK Ltd** www.neways.co.uk 01480 861764
- **Nielsen-Massey Vanillas Inc.** www.nielsenmassey.com
- **Nimble** www.nimblebread.co.uk 08707 288888
- **No Cows** www.nocows.com 07747 605271
- **NOHARM** www.noharm.co.uk 01733 564077
- **Nothing But Goodness Limited** www.nothingbutgoodness.com 0203 087 3683
- **Nothing Nasty** www.nothingnasty.com 01600 861 816
- **Nutshell Natural Paints** www.nutshellpaints.com 01392 421 535
- **Oatly** www.oatly.com
- **Odysea** www.odysea.com 0207 796 1166
- **Optimah Health & Nutrition** www.optimah.com
- **Orange Burst Limited** www.pierredargent.com 0845 650 2266
- **Orchid Healthcare Limited** www.orchidhealth.co.uk 020 8961 0085
- **Oreganum Health Ltd.** www.body-benefits.co.uk 0845 838 2232
- **Organatural** organatural@pc2web.co.uk 01749 677884
- **Organic Botanics** www.organicbotanics.com 01273 60 98 99
- **Organic Soap Company** www.organicsoap.net 020 8488 2469
- **Organico** www.organico.co.uk 0118 9 238 766
- **Organix Brands Plc** www.babyorganix.co.uk 0800 393511
- **Orgran** www.orgran.com
- **Oshadhi** www.oshadhi.co.uk 01223 242242
- **OSMO UK** www.osmouk.com 01296 481 220
- **Panacea ApS** www.panacea.dk +45 48 27 7110
- **Pasante Health Care** www.pasante.com 01903 753844
- **Pasta King (UK) Ltd** www.pastaking.co.uk 0800 458 78 98
- **Pataks Foods** www.pataks.co.uk 01942 267000
- **Patchwork Traditional Food Company** www.patchwork-pate.co.uk 01824 705832
- **Patisserie Organic** www.patisserieorganic.co.uk 02074 821922
- **Paul Penders Co** www.paulpenders.com/
- **Paul's Tofu** www.soyfoods.co.uk 01664 560572
- **Pennangalan** www.pennangalan.co.uk 017 53 67 80 76

- **Pennard Organic Wines & Cider** www.pennardorganicwines.co.uk 01749 860393
- **Pernod Ricard** www.pernod-ricard.com
- **Pertwood Organic Cereal Company** www.pertwood.co.uk 01985 217770
- **Peter Lehmann** www.peterlehmannwines.com
- **Peter Rabbit Organics** www.peterrabbitorganics.com 020 7637 5505
- **Pharma Nord** kfennell@pharmanord.com 01670 519989
- **Phileas Fogg** www.phileasfogg.com 01207 580999
- **Pinks Boutique** www.pinksboutique.com 01332 204804
- **Pitfield Brewery** www.pitfieldbeershop.co.uk 0845 833 1492
- **Pitrok Ltd** www.pitrok.co.uk 020 8563 1120
- **Plamil Foods Ltd** www.plamilfoods.co.uk 01303 850588
- **Polar Sun Products Ltd** www.polarsunproducts.com +372 60 13 701
- **Porter Foods Co Ltd** www.porter-foods.co.uk 01279 501711
- **Pot Noodle** www.potnoodle.co.uk 0800 032 3251
- **Potions and Possibilities** www.potions.co.uk 01394 386 161
- **Potter's Herbal Medicine** www.pottersherbal.co.uk 01942 219 960
- **Power Health Products** www.power-health.co.uk 01759 302595
- **Premier Foods** www.premierfoods.co.uk 0151 522 4000 or 01785 280215
- **Premier Lifestyles Ltd** www.yoconut.com 0191 2400 800
- **Principle Healthcare** www.principlehealthcare.co.uk 01756 792600
- **Probios** www.probios.it
- **Puraty Ltd** www.puraty.com 0560 235 2055
- **Pure Gaisha** www.puregaisha.com
- **Pure Health Limited** www.eastwestherbshop.com 01582 380000
- **Purely Wicked Shakes Limited** www.purelywicked.co.uk 0786 335 1169
- **Purple Flame Aromatherapy** www.purpleflame.co.uk 01676 542 542
- **PZ Cussons UK Ltd** www.originalsource.co.uk 0161 491 8000
- **QianNa Agricultural Products Ind & Trading Co. Ltd** www.qiannafoods.com 00 86 22 26889240
- **Quaker Oats Ltd** www.quakeroats.com 020 8574 2388
- **Quality Sea Veg** www.seaveg.co.uk/ 01438 213194
- **Quest Vitamins** www.questvitamins.co.uk 0121 359 0056
- **Quinessence Aromatherapy** www.quinessence.com 01530 835918
- **Quintessential Soaps** www.quintessentialsoap.co.uk 01453 766 931
- **Quinua Real Brasil Ltda** www.quinuareal.com.br 0055 11 3063 4007
- **R & R Tofu** www.clearspottofu.co.uk 01653 690235
- **R J Foods Limited** www.rjfoods-flapjack.com 01202 481471
- **Ragazzi Vegan** www.ragazzivegan.com 626-810-5151
- **Rakusen's** www.rakusens.co.uk 01132 784821
- **Rare Natural Care, Inc.** www.rarenatural.com 001 310 839 2696

- **Raw Gaia** www.rawgaia.com 01273 311 476
- **Raw Living** www.rawliving.co.uk 0844 561 7448
- **Rawcreation Ltd** www.detoxyourworld.com 08700 113 119
- **Real Organic Foods** www.realorganic.co.uk 01491 615 280
- **Realeat** www.hain-celestial.co.uk
- **Rebecca's Cakes** www.thevegancakegirl.co.uk/ 0781 328 2587
- **Red Bull** www.redbull.co.uk 020 7434 0100
- **Red Star Natural Liquid Soaps** www.redstarnaturalliquidsoaps.co.uk
  01384 873748
- **Redbush Tea Co** www.redbushtea.com 0845 601 2658
- **Redwood Wholefood Company** www.redwoodfoods.co.uk 01536 400557
- **Reliv UK** www.reliv.com/UK/EN/home.html 01527 559811
- **Ren** www.renskincare.com 020 7724 2900
- **Renbow** www.renbow.co.uk 0870 366 5410
- **Renk's Industrial LTDA** rafaelduarte@renks.com.br
- **Rice Dream** www.tastethedream.eu
- **Ritter Sport** www.ritter-sport.de +49 7157-97-210
- **Rizla** www.rizla.co.uk/
- **RJ's** www.rjslicorice.co.nz
- **Roar Chocolate** www.roarchocolate.co.uk 01273 677524
- **Robert Cain & Company Limited** www.cainsbeers.com 0151 709 8734
- **Rocks Organic Cordials** www.rocksorganic.com 0118 934 2344
- **Rococo Chocolates** www.rococochocolates.com 020 7352 5857
- **Rosie's Gourmet Products (UK) Limited** www.rosiesproducts.co.uk
  020 8202 7557
- **Rubicon Drinks Ltd.** www.rubiconexotic.com +44 (0)20 8900 9944
- **Ryvita** info@ryvita.co.uk
- **Saaf International Limited** www.saafpureskincare.com 0113 2265849
- **Sacla** www.sacla.co.uk 01494 687900
- **Safe 2Eat Ltd** www.safetoeat.com 01663 744452
- **Sainsbury's Supermarkets Ltd** www.sainsburys.co.uk 020 7695 8602
  or 0800 636 262
- **Samuel Smith** christian@samuelsmiths.biz 01937 832225
- **Sanbera GmbH** www.sanbera.com 0041 44 389 84 17
- **Sanchi** www.sanchi.co.uk 020 8450 9419
- **Sanitarium Health Food Co** www.sanitarium.com.au
- **Sanmar GmbH** www.sanmar.ch 0041 76376 6316
- **Sant'Or** www.santorwines.gr 0030 269 309 1104
- **Sauces of Choice** enquiries@saucesofchoice.co.uk 01935 431 924
- **Sauflon Pharmaceuticals** www.sauflon.co.uk 0208 322 4200
- **Savant Distribution Ltd** www.savant-health.com 0113 3885235

- **Savvy Cosmetics** www.urthminerals.com 250 217 7864
- **Scent By Nature** www.scentbynature.net 01493 369 678
- **Science In Sport** www.scienceinsport.com 01254 246 060
- **Scottish Herbal Supplies** keithandmo@tiscali.co.uk 01770 820314
- **Seabrook Potato Crisps Ltd** www.seabrookcrisps.com 01274 546405
- **Seasoned Pioneers** www.seasonedpioneers.co.uk 0800 0682348
- **Sedlescombe Organic Vineyard** www.englishorganicwine.co.uk 01580 830715
- **Seeds of Change** www.seedsofchange.co.uk 0800 952 0000
- **Seven Seas** www.sseas.com 01482 375234
- **Shanti Products** www.shantiproducts.co.uk 01233 733 061
- **Sharwoods** www.sharwoods.com 08700 742 796
- **Shea By Nature** www.africanblacksoaponline.co.uk 07716 853180
- **SheaCare** www.sheacare.co.uk 08708 034 527
- **Shearer Candles** www.shearer-candles.com 0141 445 1066
- **ShellBelles** www.shellbelles.co.uk 01992 621815
- **Sheppy's Cider** www.sheppyscider.com 01823 461 233
- **Shifa Lifeherbs International (UK)** www.shifalife.com 01223 243368
- **Simple** www.simpleskincare.co.nz 0121 712 6523
- **Simple System LTD** www.simplesystem.co.uk 01371 870753
- **Simply Nature** www.simply-nature.co.uk 01580 201687
- **Simply Organic** www.simplyorganic.co.uk 01443 237 222
- **Simply Soaps** www.simplysoaps.com 01603 720869
- **Sjaak's Organic Chocolates** sjaaks.com 707-775-2434
- **Skin Blossom Limited** www.skinblossom.co.uk 020 8332 7622
- **Skincare Cafe Ltd** www.skincarecafe.com 0870 44 327 44
- **Skinvac** www.skinvac.com
- **Skol** 0845 7820 820
- **Smart Beauty** www.smartcolour.info 0870 608 9990
- **Smilde** www.smildefood.uk.com 01892 669616
- **Smithfield Wine** www.smithfieldwine.com 0161 273 6070
- **Sodasan** www.sodasan.com 00 49 4956 40720
- **Solano Trading** 11 Summerhill, Frome, Somerset, BA11 1LT 01373 473809
- **Solaray Nutritional Supplements** www.solaray.co.uk 01273 693 022
- **Solgar Vitamins** www.solgar.com 01442 890355
- **Soma Organic** www.somajuice.com 0870 950 7662
- **Somerfield** www.somerfield.co.uk 0117 935 9359
- **Somerset Cider Brandy Company & Burrow Hill Cider** www.ciderbrandy.co.uk 01460 240782
- **Sonett OHG** www.sonett.eu 00 49 7555 92950
- **Sophyto Ltd** www.sophytoorganics.co.uk/ 0800-680-0671
- **Source Foods** www.miso.co.uk

- **SPAR** www.spar-int.com www.spar.co.uk +31 20 626 6749
- **SpaRitual** www.sparitual.co.uk 0161 768 2868
- **Special Effects Hair Dyes** www.specialeffectshairdye.co.uk
- **Spectrum Brewery** www.spectrumbrewery.co.uk 07949 254383
- **Spiral Foods** www.spiralfoods.com.au
- **Splash English Wines** www.splashwines.co.uk 01484 323814
- **Stella McCartney** www.stellamccartney.com
- **Suki Pure Skin Care** www.sukipure.com 1.413.584.7854
- **Suma Wholefoods** www.suma.coop 0845 458 2290
- **Sun Zapper** www.sunzapper.com
- **Sunblest** www.alliedbakeries.com
- **Supercook** www.supercook.co.uk 01977 687 300
- **Superdrug** www.superdrug.com 020 8684 7000
- **Supernutrients** www.supernutrients.co.uk 01225 830517
- **Swedish Glace** www.fayrefield.com 1270 589311
- **Swedish Match** www.swedishsnus.com
- **Sweetbird** www.beyondthebean.com
- **Swiss Herbal Confectionery** www.optimah.com
- **Swizzels Matlow Ltd** www.swizzels-matlow.com
- **Taifun** www.taifun-tofu.com
- **Tamar Organics** www.tamarorganics.co.uk 01579 371087
- **Tanjero** www.tanjero.co.uk 01142 562977
- **Taoasis GmbH Aroma-Kosmetik & Verlag** www.taoasis.de 49 5261 9383 0
- **Tara Smith Limited** www.gingerlilycosmetics.co.uk 0115 9587681
- **Tawas Crystal UK** www.tawascrystal.co.uk 0141 944 3260
- **Taylor Jackson Health Products** www.taylor-jackson.com 0871 874 0464
- **The Booja-Booja Company Ltd** www.boojabooja.com 01508 558888
- **The Chocolate Alchemist** www.thechocolatealchemist.co.uk 01798 860 995
- **The Co-operative** www.co-op.co.uk 0161 8275688
- **The Cruelty Free Shop** www.crueltyfreeshop.com.au 61-2-9799-4776
- **The Deodorant Stone (UK) Ltd** www.deodorant-stone.co.uk 01559 384856
- **The Durham Brewery Ltd** www.durham-brewery.co.uk 0191 377 1991
- **The English Provender Co.** www.englishprovender.com
- **The Essential Oil Company** www.eoco.org.uk 01256 332737
- **The Famous Chocolate House 1657** www.chocolatehouse1657.co.uk 01539 740702
- **The Food Doctor LTD** www.thefooddoctor.com 0800 093 5877
- **The Hemp Company Ltd** www.tattooaftercare.co.uk 01244 315486
- **The Hibiscus Drinks Company Limited** www.hibiscusdrinks.com 01604 581717
- **The Highland Soap Company** www.highlandsoaps.com 01397 713 919

- **The Hop Back Brewery** www.hopback.co.uk 01725 510 986
- **The Humane Research Trust** www.humaneresearch.org.uk 0161 439 8041
- **The Innis & Gunn Brewing Company** www.innisandgunn.com 0131 337 4420
- **The Natural Skincare Company LTD** www.thenaturalskincarecompany.co.uk
  01403 790913
- **The Natural Spa Company Limited** www.thenaturalspacompany.co.uk
- **The Organic Herb Trading Company** www.organicherbtrading.com
  01823 401205
- **The Organic Spirits Company** www.junipergreen.org www.uk5.org
  01483 894 650
- **The Perfumers Guild** www.perfumersguild.com 01923 260502
- **The Raw Chocolate Company Limited** www.therawchocolatecompany.com
  01273 493 331
- **The Vegan Society** www.vegansociety.com 0121 523 1730
- **Thomas Lowndes & Co** www.thomaslowndes.com 01403 270007
- **Thorntons** www.thorntons.co.uk 0800 454537
- **Tints of Nature** www.tintsofnature.co.uk 01590 613490
- **Tiny Deol (Curry Slim)** www.tinydeol.com 0116 238 67 56
- **Tisserand Aromatherapy Products** www.tisserand.com 01273 325666
- **Tofutti** www.trianobrands.co.uk 020 8861 4443
- **Toms of Maine** www.tomsofmaine.com 001 207 985 2944
- **TOPAS Klaus Gaiser GmbH** www.wheaty.de +40 7473 25515
- **T pfer GmbH** www.toepfer-gmbh.de +49 8374 9340
- **Torq Uk** www.torqfitness.co.uk 0845 128 4312
- **Total Raw Food Ltd** www.totalrawfood.com 0700 340 1233
- **Traditional Scottish Ales** www.traditionalscottishales.com 01786 817000
- **Traidcraft Plc** www.traidcraft.co.uk 0191 491 0591
- **Treasured Earth Skincare** www.treasuredearth.com.au 00615 9391 4860
- **Tree-Harvest** www.tree-harvest.com 01531 635 284
- **Trialia Foods Australia** www.trialiafoods.com.au 0061 3 9701 1666
- **Trinity Lifecare(Holdings) Limited** www.dentaplex.co.uk
- **Tropical Wholefoods** www.tropicalwholefoods.com 0191 548 0050
- **TrueLove Organics Limited** www.trueloveorganics.com 0208 534 1909
- **Truthful Co. Ltd (Purely Skincare)** www.purelyskincare.co.uk 01204 531 281
- **Truuuly Scrumptious Organic Baby Food** www.bathorganicbabyfood.co.uk
  01761 239 300
- **Turtle Island Foods** www.tofurky.com
- **Tyrrells Potato Chips** www.tyrrellspotatochips.co.uk 01568 720244
- **Ultra Glow Cosmetics** www.ultraglowshop.co.uk 01473 612641
- **Uncle Benís** www.unclebens.co.uk

- **Unilever** www.unilever.com 020 7822 5252
- **United Biscuits Ltd** www.unitedbiscuits.co.uk 01494 463388
- **Urtekram** www.urtekram.dk +45 9854 2288
- **Vega Nutritionals** www.vegavitamins.co.uk 08452 267 300
- **Vegan Perfection** www.veganperfection.com.au (00) +61 39398 6302
- **Vegan Store** www.veganstore.co.uk 01273 302979
- **Veganline** www.veganline.com 020 8286 9947
- **VegeFarm Corp** www.vegefarm.com.tw 00-886-3-3279090
- **Vegepet** www.vegepet.com
- **Vegetalia Limited** www.vegetalia.co.uk 01959 523941 / 07810 882802
- **Vegetarian Shoes** www.vegetarian-shoes.co.uk 01273 685685
- **Vegetarian Shoes And Bags** www.vegetarianshoesandbags.com 00 1 818 307 5994
- **Vegetarians Choice** 171 Merley Lane, Wimborne, Dorset, BH21 3AG 01202 889900
- **Veggies Catering Campaign** www.veggies.org.uk 0845 458 9595
- **Veg-Out** www.veg-out-sussex.com 01323 449341
- **Venture Foods Uk Ltd** www.venturefoods.com/ www.seriouslyorganic.co.uk 01743 289133
- **VERDESATIVA S.r.l.** www.verdesativa.com +39 06 912 510 87
- **Vicco** www.worldsend.co.uk 0845 094 1635
- **Victoria Manor Spa Retreat T/A Livinia Natural Skincare** www.liviniaskincare.com.au
- **Vimto** www.vimto.co.uk 01925 222222
- **Vinceremos Organic Wines** www.vinceremos.co.uk 01132 440002
- **Vindotco UK Ltd** www.reallyworks.co.uk 01652 652444
- **Vintage Roots** www.vintageroots.co.uk 0118 976 1999
- **Visionary Soap Company** www.visionarysoap.co.uk 01424 460 022
- **Viva!** www.viva.org.uk 0117 944 1000
- **Waitrose** www.waitrose.com 01344 424680
- **Walkers Snack Foods Ltd** walkers.corpex.com/cr15p5/index.htm 0800 274 777
- **Warburtons** www.warburtons.co.uk 01204 556600
- **Wassen International** www.wassen.com 01372 379828
- **Weetabix Ltd** www.weetabix.co.uk 01536 722181
- **Weleda** www.weleda.co.uk
- **Wellfoods Ltd** www.bake-it.com 01226 381712
- **Wells & Young's** www.charleswells.co.uk 0500 00 33 08
- **Westerham Brewaery Co Ltd** www.westerhambrewery.co.uk 01732 864427
- **Westler Foods Ltd** www.westlerfoods.com 0800 027 6336
- **Weston & Sons Ltd** www.westons-cider.co.uk 01531 660233

- **White Wave** www.hain-celestial.co.uk
- **Whitworths Ltd** www.whitworths.co.uk 01933 653000
- **Wholebake Ltd** www.wholebake.co.uk 01490 412297
- **Wholistic Research Company** www.wholisticresearch.com 0845 430 3100
- **Wicken Fen** www.wickenfen.co.uk 01361 883150
- **William Grant & Sons** uk.glenfiddich.com/
- **William Santus & Co. Ltd** www.uncle-joes.com 01942 243 464
- **Winning Ways Fine Foods Limited** deborah@winning-ways.co.uk 01799 599999
- **Winsor & Newton** www.winsornewton.com 020 8424 3200
- **Wojnar's Wiener Leckerbissen** www.wojnar.at +43 1 815 85 05 11
- **Wrigley Co Ltd** www.wrigley.com 01752 701107
- **Wychwood Brewery** www.wychwood.co.uk 01993 890 800
- **X35 Energy Ltd** www.x35energy.com 0116 268 12 82
- **Yagga SRL** www.yagga.co.uk
- **Yaoh** www.yaoh.co.uk 01179 239053
- **Yarrah Organic Pet Food** www.yarrah.com 0031 341 439850
- **Zedzfoods** www.zedzfoods.co.uk 01691 648029

INDEX

Y

Z

Membership / Renewal

THE
Vegan
SOCIETY

○ I wish to become a member and support the work of the Vegan Society.

○ I wish to renew my membership. Membership No. (if known)

....

Name:....................................Address:..................................

....Postcode:..........................

Tel:....................................email:..................................

Date of Birth: (for security purposes) ..../........./........

Occupation:..

A copy of the Society's rules (Memo & Articles of Association) can be viewed on our website or at our office. Alternatively you may buy a copy for £5.

○ Please tick this box if you are a dietary Vegan.
This entitles you to voting rights in the Society's elections if aged 18+.

○ Please treat my membership subscription as Gift Aid. I have paid UK income or capital gains tax equal to the amount the Society reclaims.

○ My income is less than £8000 per year and I qualify for the low income discount of 33%.*

○ I wish to enrol other members of my household for an additional £7 each.**

Please give full names of additional members and specify if dietary vegan and / or under 18. (If more than six additional members please attach separate sheet.)

contiued overleaf

Individual **£21**	
* Less **£7** low-income deduction (if applicable)	
** Add **£7** per additional household member	
Life **£350**	
Memo & Articles of Association **£5**	
Overseas: Europe &**£5** / Rest of World &**£7**	
Donation	
Total:	

How to pay

Payment must be made by credit card, sterling International money order or sterling cheque drawn on a British bank.

- **Cheque / PO** payable to *The Vegan Society*   ● **Credit / Debit card** (below)
- **Direct Debit** ◯ Please send me a form ● **Website:** www.vegansociety.com

☐☐☐☐☐☐☐☐☐☐☐☐☐☐☐☐☐☐☐☐☐

Please debit my Visa / Mastercard / Visa Delta / Connect / Switch / Solo card number

Name on card:..Signature:...................................

Today's date........../........../.........Start date:........./..........Expiry date........../..........

Switch Issue No.:.................

Please return to: **Membership Dept.**
The Vegan Society ┃ **Donald Watson House** ┃ **21 Hylton Street**
Hockley ┃ **Birmingham B18 6HJ** ┃ **UK.**
Tel: **0845 45 88244** ┃ Fax: **0121 523 1749**
Visit: **www.vegansociety.com** email: **membership@vegansociety.com**

This form may be photocopied